# NOBEL PRIZE LIBRARY

———

*EUCKEN*

*FRANCE*

*GALSWORTHY*

# Nobel Prize Library

PUBLISHED UNDER THE SPONSORSHIP OF THE
NOBEL FOUNDATION & THE SWEDISH ACADEMY

*Rudolf Eucken*

*Anatole France*

*John Galsworthy*

ALEXIS GREGORY, *New York*, AND
CRM PUBLISHING, *Del Mar, California*

# CONTENTS

———

# Rudolf Eucken

## 1908

---

"In recognition of his earnest search for truth, his penetrating power of thought, his wide range of vision, and the warmth and strength of presentation with which in his numerous works he has vindicated and developed an idealistic philosophy of life"

---

*Illustrated by* MAURICE FRANTZ POINTEAU

# PRESENTATION ADDRESS

## By *HARALD HJÄRNE*

DIRECTOR OF THE SWEDISH ACADEMY

---

ALFRED NOBEL was a man of action who, during his successful business career in the competing markets of many countries and in the international trade centers, had developed an awareness of the inner contradictions and dangers of modern developments. Mankind still seemed to him to need help, and therefore he thought that the best investment for his own fortune would be to use its interest to support those of whom the future would reveal that—in the words of his will—"mankind profited most from them."

The ambiguity of all human work and its tools or weapons challenged him to a personal deed in behalf of human progress. He knew the enormous usefulness of his own technical inventions for military purposes; therefore, he wanted to support any promising efforts toward international peace. How could his worldly mind have overlooked that all our civilization is full of strife, that it invites abuse as well as proper use, and that it can be turned toward evil as well as good?

His chief interest, however, was the intellectual sphere, despite its inherent contradictions. It appeared to him, the cosmopolitan familiar with the languages and civilizations of France and England, as a complex of arts and sciences, of exact natural science and humanistic belles-lettres. The former he sought to stimulate by supporting discoveries and inventions for the benefit of mankind. Turning to literature with the same philanthropic concern, he established a prize for what he called "excellence in works of an idealistic tendency."

Alfred Nobel was deeply influenced by the outlook of Victor Rydberg's poetry and philosophy. He knew what ideals mean to the human mind, to the will that creates and maintains civilization, cultivates and reaps its fruits, and through the struggle and darkness of life breaks a path toward a new dawn of light and peace. Wherever such ideals are manifested in their infinite variety and strengthen the willingness of men to serve each other—whether in the poet's inspiration, the philosopher's attempt to solve the riddle of life, the historian's biographies, or the work of any scholar or writer that looks toward those ideals as models in his freedom and independence—there one finds the literature that Alfred Nobel had in mind. This literature makes use of whatever art and science can offer, and from it mankind "profits the most" precisely because it mirrors the ideal truth without any regard for the useful. The creations and forms of this literature are as manifold as the ideals, and they are forever new and free.

The Swedish Academy has therefore felt that it acted with the sanction of Alfred Nobel when it decided this year to award the Literature Prize founded by Nobel to one of the most prominent thinkers of our age, Professor Rudolf Eucken, "in recognition of his earnest search for truth, his penetrating power of thought, his wide range of vision, and the warmth and strength of presentation with which in his numerous works he has vindicated and developed an idealistic philosophy of life."

For over thirty years Professor Eucken has been publishing profound contributions in several areas of philosophy. His activity as a writer has yielded increasingly many and important books as his basic philosophy has become both more coherent and more comprehensive. Particularly in recent years he has published the works that afford us the most thorough introduction to his thought; moreover, the wider public has received from him uncommonly lucid and powerful expositions of his attempts to resolve the most urgent problems of contemporary civilization. Thus he is in the midst of giving the final shape to his mature thought, and everywhere one can see new ideas which we hope he will be able to develop fully in the near future.

I cannot here give a detailed account of Eucken's long and versatile career as a philosopher, because time is short and the subject difficult for one with little knowledge of most of his special fields. I can only make some generalizations and dwell in particular on the historical foundations of his Weltanschauung and his views on the meaning of historical processes. Professor Eucken considers history a decisive influence on his philosophy, and it was philological and historical studies that led him toward philosophy. Ever since his early days the actual life of man and society has meant much more to him than the abstractions of mere thought analysis. Unfortunately we shall have to omit many interesting ramifications of his thought in order to get a clear picture at least of its main results.

The confident and rising idealism today in the intellectual life not only of Germany but everywhere on the higher and freer levels of civilized life is very different from those proud constructions which bore that name and which went bankrupt half a century ago with Hegel's magnificent system. It was an attempt to derive the inexhaustible wealth of life and the world from abstract categories and concepts by means of a daring dialectic, and to force all human research, all civilization, under the yoke of a complete system of thought. But closer analysis revealed this attempt to be beyond the competence of the philosophical search for truth, and in fact it accelerated the change to an equally dogmatic materialism.

We Swedes know that even at the zenith of dialectic absolutism Boström directed his logical criticisms toward its basic attitudes. By going back to earlier views both here and abroad, he developed a different outlook which has had its adherents in this country up to the present. There is an indisputable resemblance between his views and those developed by Professor Eucken in his writings. This is not surprising, for they both represent a basic type that since the earliest days of civilization—notwithstanding temporary eclipses—has preserved its vitality in the face of pantheistic abstractions as well as materialistic fear of thought. But this characteristic agreement in their basic views does not exclude independent and personal development; on the contrary it rather promotes it, and no branch of philosophy has produced so many marked profiles as realistic idealism. Socrates and Plato were led by this idealism to hold that philosophy is a search for truth rather than a fixed dogma, and this tireless search, by whatever means, has characterized philosophy throughout the ages. Thus Eucken and Boström reached their common goal by quite different means.

Since his youth Eucken has carefully observed the busy and steady philosophical attempts to reassess external and inner experience and to gain firm ground again after the collapse of the bold philosophical systems. Philosophy turned in different directions with varying expectations and success. Sometimes the motto was "Back to Kant," and the great metaphysical iconoclast served as a model for thorough studies of the limits of human knowledge, or else one listened hesitantly to his declaration of an eternal realm of reason based on unassailable moral postulates. Again there were attempts to give philosophy a safe position by tying it to the victorious advances of modern science or, more successfully, by independently questioning its presuppositions and methods. There were attempts to discover the secrets of the human soul in its manifestations, whether by observation or experiment, and there was hope that such research would lead toward the discovery of the proper relation of physical and psychological existence.

Eucken has been familiar with all these schools, but his main field has been historical and critical research on the emergence and development of main streams of thought in connection with the evolution and change of general culture. Like so many pioneers in his field, he has always been convinced that there can be no true progress without a proper regard for tradition and that there is more to the annals of philosophy than a kaleidoscope of systems rising and falling with equal suddenness. As Eucken has often emphasized, there can be no continuity in philosophy unless it grows like the other sciences and continually treats and develops the same problems, lest every mind should believe that he could start all over from the beginning only to be replaced by someone else in the same manner.

Apart from collections of monographs and essays in this field, Eucken as early as 1878 published the first comprehensive results of his method. In *Grundbegriffe der Gegenwart* (Basic Concepts of Modern Thought) he discusses the origin, formulation, and development of common modern concepts since the days of ancient philosophy and scholasticism. Such terms are "subjective and objective," "experience and evolution," "monism and dualism," "mechanistic and organic," "law and individuality," "personality and character," "theoretical and practical," "immanence and transcendence." But he is not interested merely in a definition of terms; he wants to describe the leading goals and attitudes of a period by elucidating, in his own words, "concepts as a mirror of their time." With each dissection the object becomes more clearly delineated. In the fourth edition, which appeared this year, the scope of the book has widened; it has become a thorough critique of the conflicts in modern civilization; accordingly, the title of the book has been changed to *Geistige Strömungen der Gegenwart* (*Main Currents of Modern Thought*, 1908). Indeed, the author has developed his own basic ideas in it, and it is a rewarding labor to study them in their wealth and complexity.

A thinker who considers the perennial questions of human civilization from this point of view will soon learn that he cannot solve them either by ignoring their close interrelation or by limiting himself to epistemological questions. Undoubtedly these problems constantly impinge upon each other; they cover the whole of human existence, influence individuals that are particularly susceptible to their importance, and thereby exercise a reforming power over entire communities and ages. The attempt to trace them in their vital and seminal role amounts to giving a comprehensive survey of human intellectual history. At the same time such a project is more conducive to arousing and widening philosophical interest than a mere analysis of conflicting dogmas, schools, and sects. Eucken undertook such a task in *Die Lebensanschauungen der grossen Denker: Eine Entwicklungsgeschichte des Lebensproblems der Menschheit von Plato bis zur Gegenwart* (*The Problem of Human Life as Viewed by the Great Thinkers from Plato to the Present Time,* 1890). This work, revised and expanded through seven editions, bears witness not only to the depth and scope of Eucken's research but to his mastery of marshaling his thoughts and to the maturity of his style.

Eucken has developed his own philosophy in several works such as *Der Kampf um einen geistigen Lebensinhalt: Neue Grundlegung einer Weltanschauung* (The Struggle for a Spiritual Content of Life: New Principles of a Philosophy, 1896) and *Grundlinien einer neuen Lebensanschauung* (*Life's Basis and Life's Ideal: The Fundamentals of a New Philosophy of Life,* 1907) as well as the more popular *Der Sinn und Wert des Lebens* (*The Meaning and Value of Life,* 1908) and *Einführung in eine Philosophie des Geisteslebens* (Introduction to a Philosophy of the Mind, 1908). The last-mentioned work in particular is a masterly and lucid exposition of his views.

In recent years Eucken has also turned his attention to religious questions, in *Der Wahrheitsgehalt der Religion* (*The Truth of Religion,* 1901) and *Hauptprobleme der Religionsphilosophie der Gegenwart* (Main Problems of Contemporary Philosophy of Religion, 1907), the latter based on three lectures delivered during a theological summer institute at the University of Jena. This year he has developed his ideas about the philosophy of history at some length in a treatise that forms part of the great encyclopaedic work *Die Kultur der Gegenwart* (Contemporary Civilization). According to hints in recent works he is now planning a thorough re-examination of ethical problems.

His deep insights into history and his significant attempts to relate his own thoughts on the forces of life to the evidence of history place Eucken far above the superficial attitudes that exaggerate and misinterpret the inner meaning of history. These attitudes, at the cost of an unprejudiced love of truth, have become all too common in this century of history.

Furthermore, Eucken sees a threat to civilization in the caricature of historicism, which partly intends to drag all firm goals and higher aims into the whirlpool of a misunderstood relativity and partly supports the frequent attempts to limit and paralyze the human will by fitting all human developments and achievements into a supposed naturalistic and fatalistic causal nexus. But in contrast to Nietzsche, for instance, he does not believe in the right or ability of the overweening individual to maintain his own will to power in the face of the obligations to the eternal majesty of moral laws. It is not the individual or the superman in his separate existence, but the strong character formed in the consciousness of free harmony with the intellectual forces of the cosmos, and therefore profoundly independent, that in Eucken's view is called upon to liberate us from the superficial compulsion of nature and the never completely inescapable pressure of the historical chain of cause and effect.

In history as well as in his personal existence man has life of a higher nature, a life originating not in nature but existing in itself and through itself, a life of the mind, which is in reality beyond time but which is revealed to us only in temporal manifestations. All true development presupposes some basis of existence. To the extent to which man comes to participate in the intellectual life, he acquires a power that is eternal and above the vicissitudes of time. This eternal life is a realm of truth, for truths with a limited existence are unthinkable. At the same time it is an infinite whole of living power, far above the world as it appears to us but exercising its influence in the world for us and through us. It is not an abstract castle in the air to which we can escape on the wings of a mystical and supposedly logical imagination, but as a wholly living power it confronts our entire personality with an either–or, a choice of the will that makes the evolution of man and mankind a ceaseless struggle between the higher and the lower life.

History is the mirror of mankind's victories and defeats in this struggle, the vicissitudes of which have been due to the self-determination of the free personality. Hence no philosophy of history can predict the future of this struggle. Even the civilization handed to us as a heritage does not survive by itself but demands our persistent and personal struggle for the true and genuine life of the mind. Nothing else can justify and support our endeavors for morality and art and our political and social work.

"Utilitarianism," Eucken says, "whichever form it assumes, is irreconcilably opposed to true intellectual culture. Any intellectual activity degenerates unless it is treated for its own sake." Although a great admirer and lover of art, Eucken has turned with equal severity against the aestheticism which is preached so loudly in our days and which "infects only reflective and pleasure-loving hedonists." "No art that values itself and its task can afford to condemn morality. A creative artist of the highest order has hardly ever been a follower of an aesthetic view of life." Our Runeberg is a poet after his heart, for such an outlook "with its indifference to moral values and its arrogant exclusiveness is quite foreign to him." And only those nations, whether great or small, that have created and maintained a civilization full of genuine intellectual life have a contribution to make to mankind. A contribution may be made only by those nations whose future consists not in a vain endeavor to use material force and weapons to "transform quantity into quality," but in the ever-growing revelation of eternal life within the limits of temporal existence.

Eucken does not reject a metaphysics that tries to express conceptually those things that are accessible to us in the infinite realm of truth and life. But he has not constructed an everlasting system, nor did he want to do so. His philosophy, which he himself calls a philosophy of action, operates primarily with the forces of human evolution and is therefore more dynamic than static. We may regard him as a *Kulturphilosoph* who fully meets the standards and needs of our age.

Professor Eucken—The lofty and scholarly idealism of your Weltanschauung, which has found such vigorous expression in your many and widely read works, has justified the Swedish Academy in awarding to you the Nobel Prize for Literature for this year.

The Academy greets you with sincere and respectful admiration and hopes that your future works, too, will bear ample fruit for the benefit of culture and humanity.

There was no formal Acceptance Speech by Eucken.

# ETHICS AND
# MODERN THOUGHT
## A THEORY OF THEIR RELATIONS

### By RUDOLF EUCKEN

*Translated by* Margaret von Seydewitz

---

## CONTENTS

# I

## The Ethical Problem in the Present Time

In former times, nothing seemed more plausible and more certain than morality. It was a tower of strength, where men sought refuge in the midst of all the doubts and conflicts of life. This was especially the case during the Age of Enlightenment. Men were beginning to believe less absolutely in the religion handed down to them, but they clung all the more to morality. Metaphysical speculation and theoretical endeavours to reveal the innermost essence of things encountered growing oppositon, yet morality was welcomed as something superior to all complications, and valuable to all. It was held to be the pivot of Archimedes, which gives stability to the whole of life.

In our days morality has ceased to be a matter of such unquestionable certainty, and has been drawn into the wave of disintegration which is passing over our minds. Formerly the scientific definition and accurate conception of morality were matters of contention; but it is now the fundamental idea of morality that is questioned. Many of our contemporaries are of opinion that the revelations of modern science and the claims of modern life have destroyed the foundations of morality and made it untenable in the old sense. Morality in the old sense demands dissociation of our aspirations from our own personal interest, and devotion to something that is esteemed higher; whenever an action that appears good is seen to proceed from selfish motives, it can no longer claim any moral value. There is a widespread tendency in modern life, to question the possibility of such detachment from the *Ego,* and to acknowledge the coercion exercised over man by his instinct of self-preservation. Emancipation from this restraint is not even considered desirable, for constant strife and competition seem necessary to life and progress, and a softening of this strife would inevitably reduce the energy of life.

Morality further demands independence and spontaneity of action. An action performed under the pressure of external coercion or mechanical habit, loses immediately its moral character. Now such independence and spontaneity are not possible apart from some kind of free choice, yet this would contradict the law of causality, which in the present age is generally considered to rule the whole of reality. In man's soul, the supremacy of this law of causality is strengthened by our growing insight into the power of heredity and of social environment. Yet morality in the old sense stands and falls with man's power of spontaneous and independent decision.

It is difficult also for morality to retain in modern life the position and estimation it formerly enjoyed. It used to be invested with unique significance, and placed high above all other manifestations of the inner life. This conviction found its strongest expression at times of great historical import. We all remember the words of Jesus: "What shall it profit a man, if he shall gain the whole world, and lose his own soul?" The same conviction is expressed in philosophical language by the greatest antique philosopher and the greatest modern philosopher: Plato and Kant. Plato says: "All the gold on the earth and under the earth is less precious than virtue." Kant says: "If righteousness should perish, it would not be worth while for men to inhabit the earth."

But this conviction of the absolute supremacy of the moral task requires an inner gradation of life, for which modern conditions offer no scope. For modern life subordinates all aspiration and endeavour to the aim of enhancing the process of life. Every action is valued as a means to this end; and morality could only hold its own as an instrument of human welfare. But such degradation of morality would mean annihilation of morality. The present time is not entirely dominated by such a movement against morality, only a few currents of thought are so absolute in their negation of ethical claims. But these currents could never have attained the strength and expansion they undoubtedly exhibit, if in our day morality were more securely established and more distinctly formulated. It is the want of union in moral ideals (never before so strongly marked) which gives added power to the enemies of morality.

There are to-day no less than four kinds of morality, often crossing and opposing each other, which claim men's allegiance. These are:

Religious Morality,

The Morality of Reason or of immanent idealism,

The Morality of Work,

Social Morality.

Religious Morality and the Morality of Reason have come down to us from past ages, and grow out of an inner world of thought. The Morality of Work and Social Morality are specific results of the present time, growing out of work in a visible world of realities. The two older forms of morality form an antithesis to the two newer forms, as will hereafter be seen.

The most effectual kind of morality is still the religious one—for us, the morality associated with Christianity, the religion of ethical redemption. Christianity, which is founded on a holy will superior to the world, exalts moral action far above arbitrary human choice and human aim. It completely severs moral action from all natural inclination, dissociates it from all external performance, and gives it a purely spiritual character. It supplies a most powerful impulse to action, by connecting man's destiny with his attitude to his moral obligations. The awakening and ennobling power inherent in Christianity was not confined to individuals, but was embodied in a large section of the human race, creating a spiritual atmosphere which still acts powerfully on individual souls, even if they themselves are not conscious of it. Religious morality still continues to influence us in this way. All other kinds of morality could not be as effectual as they are, were they not constantly supplemented and deepened by religious morality.

And yet we cannot ignore the fact that in our day the supremacy of religious morality is often contested. The world of religion no longer encompasses man as a matter of course, and this also weakens its moral influence. At the same time many objections are raised against the nature and demands of religious morality. Owing to the closer connection between man's endeavour and his environment and to the accentuation of the struggle for existence, this kind of morality appears too mild, too soft, too subjective, and there is often a desire for a sterner and more virile kind. Religious ethics do not seem to have sufficient latitude to transform the whole of life. We can therefore understand the widespread desire for something which can sufficiently supplement religious ethics.

At all periods of higher civilisation, religious morality has been supplemented and completed by the morality of reason, which was developed above all by the philosophers, from the Stoics down to Kant and Fichte. Here morality does not proceed from a superior and divine will, but from man's own reasonable nature. This nature seems to demand recognition of a universal law, and voluntary submission to it; only then does man bring his own being to perfection. The morality arising herefrom is strong and manly; it incites man to a proud independence of spirit, and exalts him far above everyday life. To this morality of reason we owe the scientific development of the moral world of thought, and the distinct formulation of conceptions like Duty and Conscience. By means of such conceptions, the morality of reason also influences our own time, without however taking the lead, as it did during the Age of Enlightenment. The idea of reason as the sure foundation of our spiritual life is no longer universally accepted, and has little influence on the man of to-day. He is too fully conscious of his subordination to the world of sense, of which he is a member, to be able to enfranchise himself completely from it, and to assert his own superior power. The rationalistic conception of life reckons with strong, self-centred personalities, who, as we know, do not abound in our time.

Morality could not be in close touch with the movements and problems of the present day, if—either as religious or as rational morality—it were inseparable from belief in an invisible world. But the latest development of life supplies morality with valuable motives derived from the visible world, and even creates new specific forms of morality. On the one hand, the impulse comes from modern work; on the other hand, from modern society. In both cases, we have forces that were always at work, but that gain considerable significance from the conditions of modern life.

All really earnest work is directed towards some object which it seeks to penetrate; it impels us to value the object for its own sake, and to treat it according to its own requirements. Man is thus exalted above his own personal opinion and inclination. Only in modern times has work reached its full development as a factor of education and of moral culture. For work has now become more and more independent of separate individuals; it is becoming a concern common to all mankind, and it forms its own great complexes. Such a complex is modern science. It is no longer dependent on individuals, but has formed a fabric of its own. In accordance with the development it has attained, science dictates to individuals the channels and methods of their work, presents problems to be solved, and indicates the means of their solution. The individual works in vain, if he detaches himself from the movement of the whole. His enrolment in the movement of the whole imparts to life a distinctly ethical character. For the individual must subordinate himself completely to the demands of the whole; he must repress everything bearing upon his own will and desire; he must feel that his own efforts are part of the great sum of human endeavour, the promotion of which must be his highest satisfaction. Single workers come and go, but through the work of generations the proud edifice of science is ever growing. As Bacon says: *"Multi pertransibunt et augebitur scientia."* (Many will pass by, and science will grow.)

What applies to science is equally true of the other provinces of life. In modern times, mighty complexes are everywhere springing up, which encompass individuals with their superior power. We see this above all in technical and industrial work, but also in state organisation, in education with its schools and so forth. All these finally unite in the comprehensive conception of civilisation and culture, —in the idea of man's supremacy over the world by means of his work.

It is evident that a strong moral force is here engendered. Without this ethical factor, without a constant enrolment and subordination, modern civilisation could never have reached its present development. Yet we cannot deny that this morality of work has inner limitations. The technical side of work does indeed repress and even destroy all individual will; but it is an open question in what temper the work is done, whether from love to the work or from petty and selfish motives. It is quite possible for a petty and narrow frame of mind to be accompanied by the greatest technical skill. Further work spurs on towards achievement, and the worker is judged by what he achieves. What becomes of his inner life, of his whole personality, is a matter of indifference. Here we are only parts of a structure, and are nothing at all in ourselves. This must become so more and more in proportion as work is specialised, and vitalises an ever smaller part of the individual's powers. Moreover the union of men which in this direction takes place, is only confined to their common work. However closely connected they may be through their work, their individual principles and convictions can be very different, if not absolutely hostile. It is, in our day, above all, the social problem, which divides men into hostile factions. In one special direction—that of work—there is an ethical development of life; but we cannot base on it an inner entity of right and humanity. The morality thus developed is cold and impersonal; it lacks inner warmth, and cannot appeal to the whole personality.

In this respect, social morality is infinitely superior to the morality of work. For social morality proceeds from the immediate relation of man to man. Here also, something old and familiar acquires a new form and stronger influence. It was an old conviction that man could only develop in connection with his fellow-men, towards whom his activity was mainly directed. But what has re-cast the idea of society in a new mould, is the modern doctrine that men are not united by their common relation to an invisible world—ruled either by a Divine Being or by an all-pervading Reason—but by their actual living together in the realm of experience. This modern doctrine points out that individuals not only meet during the course of their life, but that they are interdependent from the very beginning,—that union and life with others is a fundamental necessity for every human being. In developing this idea, modern sociology shows, by means of innumerable statistics, how the nature and welfare of the individual depends upon the condition of the whole. It tries to prove that all progress—even for the individual—is inseparable from the amelioration of the community at large; such amelioration therefore becomes the main object of endeavour. Modern sociology at the same time advocates the idea of a common responsibility, a solidarity of all human life and action. Strong motives are thus offered to the individual to direct his activity, beyond his own personal interest, towards the welfare of all, and to find in work for the welfare of others—in "altruistic" action—the highest value of life.

The "social" ethics thus developed are further enhanced by the growing conviction that the traditional form of life in the community is capable—nay needful—of fundamental changes. Formerly the structure of society was above all aristocratic in character. The conduct of life was in the hands of a small minority. They alone acquired full development of all their powers and full possession of earthly goods, which the rest could only enjoy in part and through the agency of the favoured few. This division of mankind appeared to be too firmly established by the divine will or by a mysterious destiny for human endeavour to try and alter it. The modern man, in the consciousness of his power, by no means considers these things incapable of change. For him, it is a sublime task to suppress such distinctions, and to let "all that bears human features" (Fichte) participate in the work and enjoyment of life.

We can here discuss neither the possibility of solving this problem in all its bearings, nor the complications resulting therefrom. But we cannot deny the strong ethical stimulus of such a movement. It has resulted in an eager desire to strengthen the weak, to raise aspiring spirits, to oppose injustice, to eradicate suffering as far as possible, and to increase the enjoyment of life. In all this, there is much warmth and vigour, a strong feeling of responsibility, and recognition of the rights of others. No other ethical force so strongly influences the men of to-day, as the social idea; we see this in legislation, in education, in every relation of man to man. This idea counteracts egoism, and produces such a wealth of humane action, as was hardly ever witnessed at any period of the world's history.

But even here, in spite of so much that is admirable, inner limitations are evident. Life and morality are concentrated on activity for others. But this activity is more for man's external welfare than for that of his soul,—more for the conditions of life than for life itself. Inner problems find too often only a secondary consideration and the personality as a whole is apt to be neglected. This morality of social activity believes in the existence of goodwill and its growth by means of external activity, and takes human virtue for granted. But it has nothing to offer that could allay the inner conflicts, or could overcome the dark, wild, and passionate element in man's soul. Nor does this kind of morality sufficiently realise what complications and passions are inseparable from life in the community: the strife for power and supremacy, the vanity and unreality which arise and rapidly spread among its members. Social morality shows a very optimistic conception of

man, which is often contradicted by experience. However great therefore the merits of social morality may be in one special direction, it takes up the problem too superficially, and offers no firm foundation for morality, which it presupposes rather than creates.

Morality to-day thus appears to be accompanied by much confusion and many complications. There is no lack of separate developments, but these cross and oppose each other. What one kind of morality takes to be its chief source of strength, appears to another to be mere weakness. The inner and spiritual character of the older forms is condemned by the younger forms as a subjective illusion, while the unremitting activity of the latter seems to their opponents to be an exclusive concentration on external work. Life as a whole has become uncertain to us in its deepest aspects; and we are no longer satisfied with the moral impulses coming from the life around us. We hesitate between absolutely different kinds of morality, which can only fully develop their individual characteristics by injuring one another; this must inevitably weaken the influence of morality on the whole of life. At the same time, movements hostile to morality encounter less opposition, and gain ground in spite of their inherent superficiality. Morality, once an undoubted possession of mankind, has thus come to be a difficult problem; instead of ruling over man from the height of its superiority, it seems now to depend on his opinion and choice.

The condition of things resulting herefrom is becoming more and more unendurable. If morality is weakened, then life is robbed of a strong impulse, an ennobling power, and a dominant aim; it is in danger of inner insignificance and disintegration. The salt of life is then lacking, which alone can keep it fresh and healthy, and with all its outer brilliancy, it is threatened with inner decay. If we are to resist this danger with all our might, then science must help to overcome the uncertainty and want of concentration so characteristic of our time, and to gain full recognition of morality as a whole. To do this, it is above all necessary to find some point of view whence we can successfully combat this disintegration.

We shall therefore have to consider first of all how such a point of view may be attained.

## II

## The Ethical Principle

The intricate situation of to-day necessarily incites us to reflection. We must consider our life as a whole; we must ask ourselves whether human existence comprises various kinds and gradations of life, and whether a task thus arises which embraces all man's endeavour. There can be no doubt that human life is not confined to one single plane,—that all variety of endeavour does not easily unite to form a definite entity, but that heterogeneous elements meet and mingle in man.

Man at first appears to be part of nature, of the world of sense, subject to its laws and impulses. Dim and unreasonable instincts pervade man's soul with compelling force. Our conceptions grow out of sense impressions, and form at first the purely mechanical concatenation which we term "association," while all our efforts are directed towards individual self-preservation. In all this, man is entirely within the limitations of nature. Yet though this natural life at first predominates, it does not represent the whole of our life. We become aware of new features, which we characterise as "spiritual." We see how man grows independent of his environment, and strives to subdue

it from without and within. By thought he frees himself from the shackles of his environment, and asserts himself against the whole world; at the same time he is driven back to the world, and feels impelled to fathom it and to make it his own by personal experience. His actions do not always remain a mere part of nature's concatenations. He can detach himself from all cohesion. In unbridled egoism he can subordinate every event and action to his own well-being; or he can absorb into himself all that at first existed beside him and apart from him, and that often appeared hostile, and can thus manifest boundless love and sympathy. His natural instinct of self-preservation will then appear too small and insignificant; he can even come to feel its narrow restrictions as intolerable.

If we pass from the individual to the whole of mankind, we see in civilisation and culture a new form of life opposed to mere nature. For man is no longer swayed and ruled by what assails him from without, but he confronts it with new aims and ideals. He judges and weighs; he approves and rejects; he forms new complexes, like those of state organisation and of science. In all this, man is the representative of a new and specific kind of life; he manifests an independence unknown to nature.

This new life differs from nature and from what may be attained on the basis of nature, not only in single characteristics, but in all its manifestations and even in its fundamental essence. Nature forms a tissue of separate elements, which come into reciprocal action but lack all inner cohesion. Great complexes are thus formed, but no combination amounts to real cohesion: there is no inner whole, and no life proceeding from such an inner entity.

All life grows out of contact with the environment; therefore intellectual participation is indissolubly bound to the world of sense. In this life of nature, the intellect can create no conceptions independent of sense impressions, and action cannot free itself from the power of natural impulse. All inner values can here be nothing more than an accessory and reminiscence of what reaches us from without.

We see something essentially different, wherever spiritual life develops. Here life is not decomposed into a multitude of separate particles, but inner cohesions are formed, which embrace and dominate all achievement of individual beings. This is especially the case when human thought aspires towards Truth. Every individual has his own sum of conceptions and his own special associations; but he does not possess a truth of his own. All search for truth is based on the conviction that something must be acquired which is common to all men, and which embraces and governs them all. Aspiration thus extends far beyond separate individuals. We have here not a disconnected mass of assertion and dogma; all is gathered into a well ordered cohesion, and all separate efforts result in progression to the whole. Every kind of intellectual endeavour presents a similar situation. Thus the Good and the Beautiful are not values confined to single individuals; every man striving after them, only contributes towards the sum of common endeavour, and what he wins for himself is at the same time a gain for all. Aspiration is not confined to a limited number of separate results, but the manifestation of a great whole is sought for: a comprehensive realm of the good and the beautiful.

Once the mind is thus concentrated on the whole, greater spiritual independence inevitably ensues. For it is necessary to rise above the sense impression and constantly to assert the autonomy of the soul, if aspiration from the whole and to the whole is to be successfully developed. From being a mere accessory, the soul now becomes in all respects a source of independent life. In science ideas gain a significance of their own, apart from the impressions of sense; they develop their own laws, and react with transforming power on what they have absorbed, as we see in the case of mathematics. Our own mind supplies the forms in which we shape our world. Feeling also frees itself from sense impressions. Sense enjoyment no longer suffices for man's happiness. His relation to other human beings does not remain confined to external contact; pity and love can embrace the whole of mankind, as is proved by the great religions. We can no longer doubt man's capacity of aspiring to values far beyond external possessions; and his inner life, the development of his own individual personality may become a matter of paramount importance to him.

But this inner life, with all its distinct manifestations, can cope successfully with the outer world and its forcible inroads, only by developing an inner realm which it extends to an independent world of its own. This does in reality take place. What was at first beside us and apart from us, can be transferred to the soul without merging into it. The antithesis between internal and external values, which at first seemed to disintegrate life, can be overcome, if spiritual endeavour absorbs the object and brings it into reciprocal action with spiritual forces. Where spiritual development is at its highest, life does not fluctuate between the subjective and objective, but unites both in itself, brings them into reciprocal action, and develops one by means of the other. Such a triumph over antitheses is to be seen most clearly in the province of art. Art is not merely capable of copying external objects as exactly as possible, or of rendering with the greatest possible truth the feeling of the individual: really great art must embrace both factors and blend them to a perfect unity. This is how a real work of art is created, which then gives to life an inner expansion and a new reality.

As in art, so also in the other provinces human life. In the mutual relation of man to man, the spiritual phase by no means does away with all distinctions, but it exalts us above them, and embraces them all from a higher point of view. Individuals are not to be merged in a hazy and colourless whole, but in rising towards a higher life an inner communion becomes possible, within which even what is alien becomes to a certain extent our own. This enables men to understand each other, to put themselves in the place of one another, to find themselves in others. Man acquires in such communion a vaster self, which is not dependent on one tiny atom, but has a whole world of its own.

If scientific research is not to degenerate into barren scepticism, it must also overcome the antithesis of the subjective and the objective. To do this, it assimilates external objects by means of thought, and strives to embrace at the same time both the inner man and the outer world, developing one by means of the other.

We observe everywhere this tendency to subject everything to the operation of spiritual forces—to create and develop an inner world. Here all problems are confined to life itself, which is no longer concerned with extraneous matters, but with itself alone. In this inner world, life develops in its own way; it finds its aims and ideals in itself, in its own perfection, in its complete triumph over the antitheses it embraces.

How are we to interpret this new life and its origin? It cannot have proceeded from that nature inferior to man, from which it differs even in its most elementary fundamental forms. It cannot be a creation of man alone, in whom—as experience proves—it is far too weak, too much alloyed with lower and sensual elements, for a new gradation of life to originate in him. Nothing therefore remains but to recognise in this inward tendency a movement of the universe—a movement in which man is privileged to participate, but which he could never engender from out of his own nature. The recognition of such a movement completely changes the aspect of reality. The universe now seems to embrace two planes, and to be rising—at least as far as humanity is concerned—from one plane to the other. A new light is cast on reality, which ceases to be a collection of separate and non-cohesive elements, and becomes capable of comprehensive operation and of self-concentration. We realise that what at first appeared to be the whole of reality was only its outer aspect, which is supplemented by the new depth revealed to us. It is only the development of these depths that gives life its real significance; values come into existence which lie beyond the natural instinct of self-preservation—such values as the good, the true, and the beautiful.

Let us now see how this order of things strikes and influences man. The new phase of life at first appears—in man—only in a few individual operations, while his life and aspiration are still mainly determined by nature and natural self-preservation. A certain spirituality does indeed appear wherever there is human life, yet only as something subordinate, as an accessory to another kind of life, but without the autonomy necessary to a comprehensive and self-centred whole, which could develop its own specific character. If man is to participate in the movement of the universe and bring the spiritual into full operation in himself, this autonomy of the spiritual life is of paramount importance. It can only develop where a movement reaches man from the universe, embraces him, and determines his further course. But, at the same time, man must recognise and seize this impulse, thus taking possession of this new life. We have seen that what used to be considered of secondary importance, is now of paramount value. This requires a reversion of the original order of things, a readjustment of the values of life. We have not to realise any new achievement within a given sphere of activity, or to further develop existing conditions; we have to acquire an essentially new life.

The requirements thus formulated lead to a system of ethics. Its fundamental doctrine is man's power to rise by free action to the higher plane of cosmic life, and to develop it with all the strength of his soul. We have shown that the new object of our endeavour is not something unfamiliar that suddenly invades our consciousness. For it is the working within us of some spiritual force, that exalts us above the animal world to the status of human beings. But the spiritual life undergoes an essential change, as soon as it acquires autonomy within us. As long as it was held to be of secondary importance, it was chiefly appreciated as a means towards human ends: spiritual forces were to give us more power over external realities, and fuller enjoyment of life, but we did not penetrate into the life of the spirit and there find a new world. If we do this in accordance with the transformation of life we have been considering, great results will soon appear. In science and art, as well as in law and morality, our efforts will be accompanied by such strength, devotion, and gladness as we never before experienced. We shall operate with the laws and powers inherent in the things themselves; we shall become indifferent to outer profit and success, and shall find full satisfaction in the manifestation of genuine spiritual life, in spite of the trials and difficulties it may offer. If the spiritual life can thus grow towards perfection, undisturbed by human aims, it will manifest all its values in

rich and pure abundance; it will reveal a new world, and will open up a new depth of reality. We thus take possession of a world which exalts us far above all petty human considerations, yet which is not alien and unfamiliar to us, but is essentially our own life and being.

With autonomy, the spiritual life also gains more unity. As at first manifested in human life, it is divided into a variety of separate branches—such as art, science, law, technical knowledge—which lack all inner cohesion and mutual understanding. If the autonomy of the spiritual life reveals a new phase of reality, it must also form a comprehensive whole, of which all the separate provinces are but the various manifestations. They themselves now appear in a new light, and every province must determine its position and significance in the whole, and must submit to the operation of the forces proceeding from the whole. This will give more depth and more soul to the activity in each separate province, while all will seek to come into closer touch and to supplement one another.

All this implies a great task for man. He is an imperfect and unfinished being, full of contradictions. He has to seek and achieve genuine life; he must penetrate from the sphere of effects to that of their causes; he must recognise the great cosmic movement as a personal concern of his own, and must thus give meaning and value to his life and aspiration.

We have here a matter of vast import. Not only must the new world be recognised and taken possession of by the individual, but a new order of things, valid for all humanity, must be created and triumphantly asserted against an entirely different order of things. Instead of the mere juxtaposition which the world of sense at first presents to us, we must establish inner cohesion in society and history. The efforts of all humanity must supplement the visible world, to which we remain bound, by an invisible one, and must make of this invisible world the chief seat of human life. While time is forever flowing onward, permanent truths and values of life must be found, which can sustain from within all aspiration and endeavour. We human beings must realise a higher life within given natural conditions; and to do this, we have first to create and establish a new order of things within our own sphere of existence. This transforms our life into a never ending task, but also imparts to it an incomparable greatness. While thus striving forward, the individual must first of all submerge himself in the new world as a whole, until he finds there his true life, his real and higher self. A complete negation of the little *Ego* and emancipation from it are requisite. This does not mean that the individual is to disappear and be absorbed by the infinite. The infinite becomes a living present at this special point, and the individual must take possession of it and assert it. He must also promote the forward movement of life, and must enrich reality by the culture of a spiritual individuality, very different from the one nature has given him. This spiritual individuality can only develop on the basis of the spiritual life, from which it takes its aims and standards; and it must always be in harmony with the movement of the whole.

It is evident that all these factors have laid the foundations for a system of ethics. As we have seen, life as a whole challenges man to a great change, to a decision, an action, but also to unremitting work for the establishment of a new order of things. That which gives us human beings our pre-eminence and constitutes our innermost essence is not to be gained without our own efforts, and pervades our life as a continuous task. We may call the morality arising thence the Ethics of the Spiritual Life, for the centre

of life and its ruling motive lie in man's relation to a superior spiritual life, which is at the root of his own being and yet has to be acquired by his own action and effort. Morality represents the principles underlying this great change. Morality grasps the question as a whole. Morality elucidates the fact that all the variety of work is dominated by strife for a spiritual self, a strife which can only be successful if the original situation is reversed.

We must now try to determine more closely what form these ethics are to take, and whether they are able to overcome the objections which confront every kind of morality.

## III

## A Defence of the Ethical Principle

Before we proceed further in the direction indicated, we must see whether our own convictions are capable of overcoming the opposition and impediments to morality, presented by widespread currents of contemporary thought. Were we unable to overcome them, then all further advance would be stamped by inner uncertainty.

The first objection was, that all human action must tend to the preservation and advancement of the performer, so that action apart from self-interest, as required by morality, is impossible. We are told that man cannot be inspired and moved to action by any aim outside his own personality, and that even where this appears to be the case, closer examination reveals some hidden motive of self-interest. This was the doctrine of Spinoza and is now a widespread conviction. There is undoubtedly some truth in the fundamental idea, but it is by no means certain that this truth is rightly applied. It is true that all endeavour must start from the life and being of a man and reflect back on him. Something absolutely alien would necessarily leave us cold and indifferent; by his action man must in some way grow and gain and assert his own inner self.

But we must ask ourselves whether the natural Ego, to which the opponent of morality binds all human action, represents the whole of man's life, and whether all endeavour is obliged to serve the interests of natural self-preservation. If a man recognises any kind of spiritual activity in its specific working, he will reject such limitation; and the more he sees in the spiritual life a new and independent phase of reality, the more decisively will he declare that a real self is not contained in the natural Ego, but must first be acquired by means of the spiritual life. In spite of all the subjective force and passion displayed in the self-preservation of the natural Ego, this Ego and its life are without inner significance: it plans and acts, without being absorbed and illuminated by an inner force; it remains alien and dense.

On the spiritual plane, on the other hand, man acquires an individuality, and is able to embrace a whole of reality, into the life of which he submerges himself; and in developing this life, he is able to find full satisfaction and joy. The spiritual life does indeed demand repression, subjection, and even sacrifice of the little Ego; yet the experience of humanity clearly proves that life thereby suffers neither degradation nor disintegration, but rather, that it is thus strengthened and regenerated. Life is certainly not weakened or extinguished in the efforts to gain truth and beauty, in the activity of the scholar and the artist, in social and philanthropic work. By enfranchisement from the little Ego, life has gained in expansion and strength. Man is conscious of finding his real self and of developing his innermost being in such work, not of promoting

ends outside himself. All deeper religions and systems of philosophy have in common this requirement that man should give up his little Ego, and they promise that from this renunciation a new life shall be born, which is of infinitely greater meaning and value than the old life. The movement towards spirituality is not a mere negation, but leads to an assertion founded on the basis of negation. Once man has found the right plane of life, and has acquired a new individuality, the gulf between man and the universe is bridged over. Man can then come into inner relation with reality, and can take possession of the infinite. This is the meaning of Goethe's lines:

> Und so lang du dies nicht hast,
> Dieses "Stirb und Werde!"
> Bist du nur ein trüber Gast
> Auf der dunklen Erde.
> (Till thou hearest the behest
> Saying: "Death is Birth!"
> Thou art but a dreary guest
> On the gloomy earth.)

If this is the case, then all spiritual work contributes to the development of a new, real self; then no blame can be attached to morality for advocating the absolute necessity of this change, and for recognising, in all ramifications of work, the one great task of developing a new human individuality. Morality will not thereby weaken and suppress the impulse of life, but will direct it into the right channel and ennoble it. By treating man's task as a harmonious whole—which at the same time forms part of the one great entity—it will act as a stimulus on all the separate provinces of life. The gravity of this ethical task is heightened by the fact, that we must pass through a negative stage in order to reach one of positive affirmation, and that all action which denies or obscures such negation, remains one-sided and imperfect.

Closely allied to this first objection to morality is the second: the assertion of the

Determinists that human action is but part of an immutable concatenation, and that the decision of the moment arises, with inevitable necessity, from what is and what has been. This is an old assertion, reaching back to the latter days of antiquity. It has frequently aroused men to passion in the domain of religion. It permeates modern philosophy, and has found classical expression in the doctrine of Spinoza. In our day, it is often confirmed by a more careful study of the universe. Favourable to Determinism is also our modern insight into such forces as heredity and social environment, and our greater knowledge of psychology. Everywhere the single atom appears as the result of some cohesion, of which it at the same time forms part. Closer observation only accentuates such dependence; we can no longer consider a separate atom or moment as something absolutely self-centred, nor can we interpret any action as really taking place suddenly. There exists, without doubt, more cohesion and more subordination than was formerly believed, or is often accepted even now.

However legitimate these considerations may be, it does not follow that they exhaust all the possibilities offered by reality. If we declare that man is completely absorbed in such concatenation, we must assume what is by no means unassailable: that man is simply part of a given order of things, of a natural mechanism, of a network of causality. Were he in reality no more than this, there would be no possibility of his own decision, no freedom of action, and consequently no morality. This would destroy, not morality alone, but much that its opponents could not well give up. If our life were merely part of a natural mechanism, it would necessarily cease to be our own life; it would be only a process realised in us without our co-operation, and our attitude to it would resemble our attitude to

our bodily functions. It is difficult to see how we could then be made responsible by society, or how we could ourselves feel any responsibility,—how such conceptions as those of good and evil could come into existence and engross our attention. Neither would there be any real present, for if there is no demand for decision, and no room for original action, all action would, with inevitable necessity, grow out of the past, like a flower out of its bud, without our co-operation.

We might be able to endure such determination of our life for all time, if the various movements could easily meet and mingle in our soul, without any complications. But if our life contains great problems, grave conflicts, various and often opposed planes, then we human beings, did we submit passively and unresistingly, would be chained like Prometheus to a pitiless rock. Determinism, if followed to its logical conclusion, is nothing less than inner annihilation of life.

Such recognition necessarily brings us to the question whether the hypothesis held by the Determinists is unassailable. Do we really appertain absolutely to a given and distinctly limited existence? From the point of view of a new plane of reality manifested by the spiritual life, our reply must be a decided negative. As we have seen, this new phase does not embrace us from the beginning, but must be grasped, appropriated, and developed by us; our own decision and action are here indispensable. Our life must indeed reckon with certain given factors; we must recognise the powerful influence of heredity and environment. Our individuality is determined for us by nature; we cannot in all things remould ourselves as we would wish to do; we are on all sides encompassed by fate. But man is not entirely at the mercy of this fate. The spiritual life which can grow up in him gives him a new, spontaneous source of life; he can originate something new, something entirely his own, and can oppose his own action to fate.

Our life thus becomes a struggle between freedom and fate; and to this struggle it chiefly owes its expansion and greatness. The idea of development is therefore not applicable to the progression of human life. There is no inevitable sequence on a well established basis and in one definite direction; later results are not simply determined by what has gone before; one thing does not follow another naturally and easily, but various elements meet and clash. Time after time, we are in danger of losing what we seemed to have won; over and over again, we must climb to the summit of life. But this struggle constantly calls forth new powers. We see that there is much more in us than appeared at first sight, or than we ourselves were wont to believe. Great shocks and strong emotions often produce new convictions or set free new forces within us. It is, above all, suffering which rouses and regenerates, which teaches us to see and cultivate the deepest that is in us. What hitherto seemed to constitute our whole being, now proves to be but a single stratum, which it is quite possible to transcend.

The real man is only a part, a section of the possible man. The possibilities dormant in us are an integral part of our being; and these possibilities enable us to attain something higher and greater. On this power of inner growth rests the confidence of those who, while recognising the evils of this life, fight bravely and hopefully on the side of progress. The statesman wishing to raise his people from within, builds on such a capacity for inner growth, and believes in the realisation of new possibilities; so does the educator in his efforts to cultivate and ennoble men's souls. Art and religion are ever at work, in order to discover new possibilities and bring them home to man. Were it not for such new possibilities and

the regenerative power of man, his life could retain nothing of its youthful vigour, and would lapse into stagnation and senility. The same would apply to human civilisation: it would drift away from simplicity and truth, and would become more and more artificial.

It is in our own power to maintain our vitality, and to oppose increasing inner strength to all alien and hostile forces. It is by no means certain that we shall always be victorious; it is one of the tragedies of life that a man's soul is filled with longing for something better, yet is held captive by circumstance, and is finally driven back to that from which he would fain escape. And yet it is this struggle which gives to life its vitality and its greatness; and wherever there is religious conviction, there also dwells the hope that what could not gain full victory in our life, will not be lost before God. To quote Browning:

> What I aspired to be,
> And was not, comforts me. . . .
> All instincts immature,
> All purposes unsure, . . .
> All I could never be,
> All, men ignored in me:
> This, I was worth to God.[1]

If all this helps to prove the autonomy of man and his independent power of decision, it does not mean the dissociation of man from all inner cohesion. This freedom only becomes possible by the revelation within him of a new world. There could be no spontaneity of action in single cases, if a world of independent and spontaneous life did not exist and embrace us from within. Thus the individual appertains to the whole, even in the exercise of freedom. That of which he is capable by himself alone, is only his ability to bring his own will into accordance with higher laws. All deep thinkers have seen, in the grasp of the essence of

[1] From "Rabbi Ben Ezra."

life and the development of its possibilities by means of this individual capacity, not an achievement of man alone, but the manifestation of a higher power, a gift of grace. Life did not seem to them to be so divided between grace and freedom, that one of these factors could only be enriched by what was taken from the other; they considered both to be so indissolubly united, that freedom and the power of inner growth appeared to them to be the highest sign of grace. The most energetic natures, if possessed of any spirituality, have generally felt themselves to be instruments of a higher power and compelled by an inner necessity. This feeling gave them the strength and self-confidence indispensable for their work. In the case of achievement for the visible world, this higher power was mostly looked upon as a dark fate, which protects man as long as it needs him, and abandons him as soon as he ceases to be useful. But in the case of inner change and regeneration, this fate was superseded by a power of love and mercy, which sustains man even in the midst of the greatest dangers. In religion especially, the consciousness of complete dependence on a superior power has not led to a suspension or restriction of activity. This is clearly proved by such men as St. Paul, St. Augustine, and Calvin. They were not the soulless vessels of a truth committed to them; they grasped, by their own recognition and decision, what seemed to them to be the truth. Yet in their own consciousness, achievement was of small value compared to what they revered as a gift of grace. "Quid habemus quod non accepimus?" (St. Augustine). "What have we that we have not received?"

Hitherto we have been concerned with refuting widespread objections to the possibility of morality. We must now consider the violent opposition against the appreciation which morality demands—

and must demand. It seems impossible for morality to be unquestionably superior to everything else in life, and to demand absolute obedience to its requirements, since it does not fill the whole of life, but must share men's allegiance with other obligations, and must seek some compromise with them. This objection could only be valid, if our whole life were a homogeneous structure,—if one single aim dominated all activity, and achievement in this direction could alone determine the value of our action. But the case is very different. Even the one fact that two planes unite in our life makes it impossible to apply the same standard to all the variety we encounter. The various values determined by these two planes are too different to be compared with one another. How could we judge sensuous enjoyment and outer success in the same way as we judge values like truth and honour?

Further, morality is not concerned merely with single values appertaining to the higher plane, but with the recognition and appropriation of this higher plane itself: it is a movement from a whole and to a whole. Once the conviction obtains that the spiritual phase of life is something entirely different to nature, the acquisition of it becomes the chief problem of life, and the claim of morality—which upholds the principle of such acquisition—can assert its supremacy over all other claims. Wherever this was contested, the new world revealed by the spiritual life was not fully recognised. The experience of history shows that no artistic or intellectual achievement could prevent a rapid abatement and deterioration of the spiritual life, if the ethical task was not fully recognised. Morality is like religion: neither can take a secondary or even a co-ordinate place; they must be valued *more* than everything else in life, or else they will inevitably come to mean *less*.

We have now seen that the doubts assailing morality generally proceed from a particular conception of the universe and of man's position in it. This more or less naturalistic conception, in spite of all it claims to be, by no means exhausts the resources of human life. As soon as we recognize the limitations of this conception of life and free ourselves from its tyranny, we are able to acknowledge fully the claims of morality. Nay, more: these claims must then appeal to us as being both legitimate and imperative; and what might at first appear to be unintelligible, will become absolutely clear and certain.

IV

## Evolution of the Ethical Principle

Having removed the obstructions which oppose the development of morality, we can now inquire into the special characteristics of the morality based on the spiritual life. Since morality recognises the principle of the spiritual life, which it absorbs into its own volition and being, therefore the nature of the spiritual life will also determine the nature of morality itself. We have already seen that the life of the spirit constitutes a new world as compared to the life which originally encompasses us in nature and society, and which, though it contains certain processes of a spiritual character, is yet mainly and fundamentally bound to the senses. The spiritual element is here disintegrated into separate manifestations, and is never free from the alloy of sense. In the new life, the spiritual gains autonomy, becomes a comprehensive whole, and is able to cultivate its own individuality. It reveals a plane of life essentially superior to that of nature. On man devolves the great task of attaining and developing this plane, on which life first acquires self-concentration and inner significance, and becomes real genuine life.

Let us see how this affects morality. It is not confined to individual provinces of life, but extends over its whole expansion and into every ramification, demanding a change and an uplifting. This refutes a conception of morality which limits it to the relation of man to man, and makes it synonymous with altruism. Morality undoubtedly has much to do in relation to our fellow-men; but does it not also find great tasks in the culture of the soul,—in spiritual work for the world, as expressed in science and art? The quintessence of the Stoical teaching was the development of personality, the proclamation of man's inner autonomy and superiority to the world around him. We can hardly refuse to acknowledge the moral character of this teaching, as also of the Christian teaching, which found expression in men like Augustine, who brought all moral action into immediate connection with God, and derived it from love to Him.

Let us now turn to science and art. We see how, in spite of all inner and outer difficulties, a man like Kant devotes himself in unremitting activity to the lifelong task of finding pure and adequate expression for the perception of truth struggling into consciousness within him. We see how, in the same spirit, an artist scorns all external advantage, and strives only after a pure cultivation and assertion of the creative power within his soul. Must not such fidelity to oneself and to one's own work strike us as being in the highest degree moral? The ethical obligation consequently extends to all ramifications of life. Everywhere we must take possession of the spiritual life for its own sake, transpose ourselves into its inner movement, and exalt it above all concerns of the individual or even of mankind. Therefore we must not seek the highest aim of our actions in the welfare of society, of the community to which we belong.

The welfare of society is a conception

capable of very different interpretations. It may mean the mere subjective well-being of people living together. In that case, a new plane of life is not attained; a social utilitarianism develops, which destroys all inner values, and the sole *aim* of life is to provide the *means* of life. But the condition of society can also be our chief aim because the new plane, with its essentially new values, is best attained through life in the community. Then we do not place ourselves merely in the service of humanity, but we labour for the development of a spiritual world within the life of man. Then humanity as a whole is uplifted, and acknowledges a great task, while social utilitarianism limits life to the human sphere, and takes from it all possibility of inner uplifting. Utilitarianism is the most dangerous opponent of spiritual productive power, for it degrades to a means what should be valued for its own sake and as the highest aim. Utilitarianism does not change its character by becoming *social* utilitarianism. Inner progress of life is only possible if the spiritual values, as the true, the good, and the beautiful, are striven after and appreciated for their own sake, and not as a means for promoting human welfare,—if creative production is not actuated by any consideration of results, but is an inner necessity of a man's own soul.

We have seen that the attainment of autonomy in the spiritual life implies a reversion of the original order of things, and that the whole of life is thus seen in a new light. It follows that no real morality can be engendered merely by developing existing conditions, or heightening natural forces. Wherever this was attempted, closer investigation will always show the presence of both the lower and the higher phase, and the consequent weakening of morality. Here Christianity has achieved something of world-wide historical importance: it clearly demonstrated the gulf between all merely natural development and real moral action; it has also shown us that something essentially new appears in morality, something unattainable by merely ennobling nature.

This was not only the case with religion, for the deepest thinkers of all times have seen in morality not a mere intensification, but a complete transformation. Plato made real virtue dependent on aspiration to the world of ideas. He distinguished this virtue from all that men call virtue, though to him it was little more than physical ability. Kant advocated something similar, by forbidding man to base action on inclination alone. He even went so far as to make action against natural inclination a sign of good principle. The requirement thus formulated does not preclude fruitful moral germs and impulses in the existing order of things; but their full development is only possible when a distinct reversion has taken place, and when an independent spiritual life purifies, unites, and exalts all beginnings. These alone can never, by a slow process of evolution, raise life to the plane of genuine spirituality. As we have seen, the morality of the spiritual life rejects a merely natural origin. But because it represents something essentially new, its main object cannot consist in the denial and suppression of mere nature. This was the aim of asceticism, especially in its development as a reaction against the antique over-estimation of nature. In the latter days of antiquity, life was swamped and enfeebled by a refined form of sensuality. Life could only develop if this sensuality was resisted and full supremacy was advocated for the spiritual. We can understand that those engaged in this struggle went so far as to see the highest morality in the complete suppression of sensual life. This bears witness to admirable personal feeling; and yet it was a dangerous error, for it diverted men from the great task of giving inner significance to life, and of filling it with strong and healthy love. The strictest asceticism can be united to inner hollowness, to spiritual pride, and to want of love. An ascetic element is inseparable from all morality, but only an element subject to higher aims. We feel it to have been one of the great merits of the Reformation, that it set aside the mediæval appreciation of asceticism.

If it is true that autonomy of the spiritual life results in progression towards a new plane, then only such forms of morality can satisfy us as fully acknowledge such progression and the consequent affirmation of life,—as establish the value of man, and stimulate him to strenuous effort. All systems which base morality on pity alone must therefore appear inadequate. Pity does much to free man from narrow egoism, and to inspire him with sympathy for others, even for all mankind; but pity alone shows only one side of life—only limitations and difficulties, suffering and gloom. It restricts man's outlook to this one side of life, so that he can acquire neither glad courage nor any impulse tending to the uplifting of his existence. Pity reveals no new possibilities as love does it; complete resignation here forms the highest pinnacle of the philosophy of life and not the creating of a new world.

Neither can a system of morality satisfy us which only draws up laws and regulations,—which indicates definite channels of action, without vitalising action or giving it any progressive impulse. This might suffice if man only had to take his place in a given order of things. But it is quite inadequate if the whole soul is to be gained for a new plane, and if a new order of things is to be built up within the human sphere. There is, besides, the danger of interpreting morality above all as a narrowing, a police system of life, and of thus forfeiting man's sympathy. We do not deny that the uplifting, inseparable

from spiritual life, demands many struggles and renunciations. We can only rise to an affirmative by means of a decided negation—a negation rendered necessary by the brutality of mere nature and the pettiness of mere man. In the history of mankind, morality at first operated chiefly through prohibition: it was necessary to restrain the wild natural impulses and destructive passions of man, in order to prepare the way for spiritual activity. We have but to think of the frequent recurrence of prohibitive laws in the older legislation of all nations. But there is a great distinction, even in this primitive form of morality. The lower kind may remain permanently on the grade of negation, while higher forms will work their way through the negation to affirmation, and will retain consciousness of this affirmation even in presence of negation. Morality must consequently be productive in character, not merely regulative. Productive morality will press forward, not waiting till man is brought face to face with a new requirement or an opportunity of action, but taking the initiative, seeking new points of attack, bringing everything into movement, and promoting the growth of the spiritual life.

Even then, morality cannot limit its task to the ordering of private life, but must extend its activity to general conditions and human society. Life in the community must be exalted, and fitted to become the representative of spiritual life. It is one of the chief demands of modern times, that not only private life, but the whole of human society, should be subject to moral judgment and moral operation. Hegel condemned as "paltriness of faith" (Kleinkrämerei des Glaubens), men's belief in the guidance of their personal destiny by divine might and wisdom, while at the same time they believed the fate of mankind, as manifested in the history of the world, to be governed by blind unreasonable chance.

We must also combat a paltriness of morality which concerns itself with the private affairs of individuals, but shows no interest and recognises no obligation with regard to what concerns humanity at large. In former times, when man was conscious of his weakness with regard to his environment, the most hopeless situation could be accepted as the will of God or as a decree of fate. But the modern man, with his consciousness of power and of his obligations towards the community, cannot reject the idea of the moral solidarity of all. He must therefore concern himself with the general conditions of mankind, and must display active interest in this direction.

Let us further consider what has been achieved by the autonomy of the spiritual life. We must first of all return to the new depth of life which we have already recognised as one of its most important results. This means that we must cultivate in ourselves a firm basis, a continuous activity which determines, vitalises, and permeates each individual action. We must develop a distinct nucleus, an essential character which is not a mere background to our activity, but an integral part of it. This being the case, morality cannot be satisfied with stimulating man to certain achievements, and setting free the forces within him; it demands of him a new life, in which he must strive to make the deepening of activity we have been considering, an essential part of all his action. This is the ideal we try to realise in the development of personality and moral character. We want not merely to *act* but to *be* something, to make something out of ourselves, to put our own personal self into our action, and to so act that we ourselves thereby grow and advance. Only then life is so concentrated on itself and becomes self-conscious and self-centred—only then can it gain significance; it will otherwise be empty and hollow inwardly, in spite of unremitting activity. This is what justifies the estimation in which the ideas of personality and character are held. Why indeed should we value it so highly, were it but an accumulation of natural forces and impulses, and not the representative and starting-point of a new life?

Not only in individuals must such a depth of being, such a spiritual individuality be developed; but in every community, in every nation, in all mankind. Everywhere must a spiritual character be formed, and this spiritual character must inspire and permeate all action. Only thus can a spiritual atmosphere be created,— can a really civilised nation be differentiated from other nations; only thus, and not by means of outer victories and conquests, can any nation gain lasting significance for all humanity. So, for instance, Greek culture is a possession forever.

In all this, it is evident that in striving for morality, we are not seeking something alien, but rather our own essential being. Yet this being does not already exist in us, but has first to be acquired; it lies not behind us, but in front of us; we cannot take for granted a firm basis and positive continuity, which we see before us as high tasks and ideals. From the imperfect and incomplete life we generally lead, we must resolutely advance towards real and genuine life. While striving after morality, we are at the same time battling for our own spiritual self; we cannot but feel morality as a living inner presence, a source of strength and of joyous impulse to action. Thus understood, morality needs no reward from without; indeed, it sustains grave injury, if action is dominated by the thought of reward. For them the autonomy and independence which are above all aimed at, must be given up; and we force under an alien yoke that life which should be based on itself alone.

Such accentuation of autonomy in life and morality, might seem to exalt man unduly, and to inspire him with self-conscious pride. But we have already guarded ourselves against such misapprehension. We have seen that every undertaking possible to the individual lies within a sustaining and impelling movement of the whole. The recognition of morality is therefore not a matter of personal option or caprice. The life of the whole operates in the individual; but, on the other hand, his decision influences the whole of reality in the direction of progress or retrogression. In this way the conception of duty arises, in which the whole of life, the whole of the cosmic movement formulates a claim on us. Kant rightly pointed out that duty cannot come to us from without, but must proceed from our own being. This can only be the case if our being experiences an inner gradation. A spiritual world speaks within us, not as something alien, but in union with our own innermost being, as the depth of our own soul. The idea of duty is necessary in proportion to the consciousness and recognition of the difference between man as he is, and the inner world which corresponds to his innermost being. Wherever this consciousness grows dim, there morality speedily experiences an inner weakening. Duty is the salt of life. Where it is lacking, life, however brilliant externally, becomes inwardly tame and insipid, while on the other hand, duty can impart inner greatness and dignity to what appears small and insignificant. But as we do not wish the presence of salt to be everywhere perceptible, so also the idea of duty must not always force itself on our consciousness, but must be a latent power in our soul and life, lifting us above all that is arbitrary and capricious. We must take duty up into our inner being, and not place it there as something alien or hostile. Moral life can quite well unite earnestness and joy, reverence and love—earnestness and reverence towards the superior majesty of a higher power operative to us, joy and love arising from the mighty presence of this higher power within us.

Thus constituted, morality can fully acknowledge the various moral impulses at work in the present day; it can, at the same time, oppose their disintegration, and help them as far as possible to promote each other's best interests. We have seen how, in our day, invisible and visible impulses are in operation, which easily come into mutual opposition. The morality of the spiritual life can in such cases acknowledge both aspects, even if it cannot value them equally. For this morality must take up a position in an invisible world, since the progression from a visible to an invisible world goes through the whole of the spiritual life. At the same time work in the visible world is most important for man, if not indispensable. He is driven to it not only by the necessity of natural self-preservation, but also by the real interests of the invisible world. He does not find this invisible world ready for him, or waiting to develop steadily from within, but he must acquire and strengthen it by battling against the visible world and its resistance. The spiritual movement is sure to become subjective and uncertain, as soon as it severs all connection with the visible world, in relation to which our work gains strength and confidence. Love, strength, and continuity are thus acquired, which must then be transformed into activity for our fellow-men. This applies both to individuals and to all mankind. Such valuation of activity for the visible world does not mean that we constitute life out of the visible and the invisible as out of two factors of equal value, for wherever spiritual life develops, the invisible is of paramount importance, and everything else must be brought into relation with it. The visible is valuable only as a means for the development or manifestation of the invisible. But as such, it is of considerable value. Thus the morality of the spiritual life is quite able to recognise—and to benefit by—the great civilising work of the modern age and its untiring social activity, even while insisting on their assimilation by a vaster cohesion which is to vitalise them.

We shall see, later on, that the invisible world cannot hold its own against doubts and obstacles, unless it is aided by religion. But although the morality of the spiritual life must seek to be in close touch with religion, it must do its best to counteract the dangers arising from an exclusively religious system of ethics. Religious morality in former times often directed man's endeavour too much towards a world of faith and hope beyond our world, and was inclined to neglect earthly matters as being of secondary importance. It often transferred to human affairs the humility and pliability born of its relation to God; and it consequently lacked strength and vigour when dealing with the evils of human life. These perils can be counteracted by a morality of the spiritual life, which sees the operation of the Divine Being above all in man, even while acknowledging its superiority to man. Such morality will urge man to seek and appropriate eternal values, not only in a future state, but in this our earthly life. Such morality will teach man not to accept the unreasonable conditions as he finds them, but to struggle against them with all his might, striving to impart reality to the reasonable and reason to reality.

The morality of reason and immanent idealism contains a virile strength and educational power that the morality of the spiritual life is bound to acknowledge. Yet spiritual morality must counteract certain undesirable results frequently brought about by mere rational morality, which is prone to overrate intellect and abstract ideas, to overvalue the strength of the individual, and thus to encourage undue pride and self-consciousness.

Thus great tasks are evident in all directions. From the standpoint of the spiritual life it is possible to take them up hopefully, and to counteract antitheses which would otherwise disintegrate human life. In all these tasks, taken together, we see how life may be quickened and strengthened by the ethics of the spiritual life. Everywhere it is necessary to proceed beyond a given order of things, —to rise above merely human aims and conditions,—to develop the consciousness of a marvellous depth of reality, in which man is privileged to participate. We discover a great cosmic movement, and we see our own greatness in our co-operation in this movement, by which we contribute something to the growth of the spiritual world. To speak with Leibnitz: "Man is not a part, but an image of the divine, a presentation of the universe, a denizen of the City of God."

V

## Morality and Religion

We have hitherto confined ourselves to the inner development of morality, without considering the attitude of the world around us and within us to those claims which morality, from its very nature, is bound to assert. At all times, this question has presented grave complications, which are magnified rather than diminished by the philosophy of the spiritual life.

If morality is the first condition and an essential factor of all independent spiritual life,—if this spiritual life is the central point of reality, and dominates all its manifestations: then we might expect to see, throughout the visible world, the triumph of good, the repression of evil, and the rule of a moral order of things, moulding reality to its requirements. Man's desire for such an order of things does not rise from petty motives, but from an imperative desire for the unquestioned supremacy of the good: what is in itself of such absolute value, must be strong enough to enforce its dominion over reality, otherwise it might come to be considered merely as a subjective illusion.

The world, as we see it, does not come up to this requirement. It evinces—as every impartial observer must acknowledge—absolute indifference, not only to the weal and woe of man, but also to his moral conduct. How often, in the destiny of nations as of individuals, does good succumb and evil triumph! It may be that we often judge too exclusively from external impressions, and that there is more justice in the world than appears at first sight. But this is no more than a possibility, and we cannot assert that it is in any away realised. Much remains dark, and has not been explained away, in spite of the efforts made by religion and philosophy during thousands of years. These efforts have made the darkness less evident, but have not brought light into it. We can deny neither the indifference of nature to our moral action, nor the incapacity of man to enforce, in his own sphere, the triumph and supremacy of the moral idea. And this gulf between what we must demand and what we find in the world, receives further accentuation by the recognition of an independent spiritual life closely allied to morality. For the impotence of morality now appears as the impotence of the whole spiritual life. At the same time, the human sphere seems to lose all its own special significance, since it cannot enforce universal recognition of the power to which it owes its privileged position.

Distressing as is this contradiction between the inner requirement and external experience, it does not necessarily lead to a weakening of the moral obligation. This is plainly shown by religion, more especially by early Christianity. The early Christians were fully conscious of the sorrow and gloom of human life; they realised the unreasonableness of the world we live in, quite as fully as the pessimists of our day. Yet their faith and courage remained unshaken. The contradiction of experience only intensified their inner conviction, and gave it an almost defiant superiority. This was only possible, because the possession of a new life and the certainty of a new world made it easy to bear all the contradictions in the existing order of things. From their certainty of a new world, arose the conviction that the good could only be impotent in a certain phase and for a certain time. The early Christians were so sure of the ultimate triumph of good, that they found strength to persevere in the battle of life.

The present time lacks this joyous certainty of a higher world and a new life. Therefore the contradiction between the course of the world and the requirements of morality, is felt in all its rigour, and doubt is intensified by the unsatisfactory moral condition of human life, by the inner weakness of morality in our day. Single individuals are not without good intentions, but they lack the power of achievement. Spiritual activity is generally treated as of secondary importance; infinitely greater value is attached to the natural self-preservation of individuals and of society. Life in the community ought to give greater prominence to moral claims, and be governed as far as possible by moral law. But on the one hand there is not enough power of volition, and on the other hand there is, here also, a wide gulf between volition and achievement. Social life also displays so much self-interest, selfishness, and passion, so much unreality and hypocrisy, that morality cannot reach any adequate development. The spiritual powers which should raise man to a higher plane are mostly withdrawn into the service of the lower plane, and life is thus diverted into wrong channels. This contradiction between human conditions and the requirements of morality has been expressed in various ways by the great thinkers. Plato lamented, above all, the evanescence and unreality of everyday life; Augustine the overweening conceit of man; Kant the insincerity and injustice everywhere apparent. But to one and all, the moral condition of mankind appeared most unsatisfactory.

All these contradictions, obstructions, and distortions are so deep-rooted, that we can hardly expect any essential progress to result from a gradual amelioration. In other directions—such as science and technical knowledge—humanity may make steady progress; but it is not so easy to prove that humanity will also experience moral improvement. The progress of civilisation brings with it the development of much that is good, but also of much that is evil, for civilisation develops great power, without providing for its moral guidance. History shows us how mankind has always seemed to alternate between periods of moral growth and periods of moral decay; but it is doubtful whether, on the whole, much has been gained. How often have the nations longed to return to simpler and more innocent beginnings!

All these impressions might seem to prove that morality has no power in the life of man. A doubt easily arises as to whether, if morality is so powerless, we ought to acknowledge it as the guide of our life, or whether we should not rather expel it as a mere illusion. But the experience of history shows us unmistakably that the roots of morality lie deeper, and are not so easily removed. Even if moral-

ity is not the ruling power, it is unquestionably efficacious as man's law-giver and judge. Again and again, the nations may resist the claims of morality, and the conceptions of morality itself may be widely divergent; yet wherever human life develops, moral judgment develops with it. Certain actions are highly esteemed, others are decidedly condemned. Something operates in man which is not confined to his own interest, and which forces him to judge his actions. Such judgment must inevitably influence both the action and the spiritual condition of man; in one direction it promotes, in another it represses.

History gives us an indirect proof of the power of morality over man. There are times in the history of mankind when the moral idea, with its decree of duty, recedes into the background, and is even scoffed at as an irksome instrument of control. But such times, however brilliant on the surface, cannot resist inner decay and hollowness, till at last they become unendurable. Then, if there is a return to morality, it is superior to, and triumphant over, all other interests. It was moral earnestness and moral strength that were above all instrumental in causing early Christianity to overcome the pagan world that was, in all outer respects, superior and more powerful. It was moral energy that gave the Reformation its power to advance and conquer, while the soft and beautiful Renaissance perished because it lacked morality. Look where we will, we see that the moral task, if fully and clearly grasped, is stronger than anything else.

It is therefore impossible for mankind to renounce morality. But we have seen that morality, as a rule, has little power over external life or man's soul, and is forced into a subordinate position. This produces inner discord in human life. Man acquires inner insincerity by not recognising and developing the depths of his own being. This inner contradiction can be fully appreciated by a system of philosophy which attaches special importance to the idea of the spiritual life. For in the light of such philosophy, we see one great contradiction pervading the whole of life: the spiritual activity—which ought to lead man to an independent inner life, thus making his existence one of joyous creative work—is used by average life as a mere means and instrument for human ends. Spiritual activity is thus degraded, for the good has mostly to give way to utilitarian considerations. This is the case, when the motive of scientific research is its utility, and not a desire for truth. This is the case, when art does not reveal a new world to man by means of genuine beauty, but appeals only to his senses. This is the case, whenever the subjective welfare of man—either of the individual or of society—is the highest aim,—whenever man is not led to a higher life by spiritual activity, but is only confirmed by it in the lower life.

Such conflicts, such inner discord, such stagnation of life impel morality to seek close contact with religion. We see that man has in himself an ideal, on which depends all the greatness and dignity of his life; but he cannot reach it unaided. Something strives to assert itself within him, without his being able to accomplish it. He remains chained to a lower level, above which his innermost soul longs to rise. Doubt and uncertainty proceed from the fact that what is of the very highest inner value should have so little power in the world and in the sphere of human life. For deep and earnest natures as St. Augustine and as Luther, such uncertainty has often become unbearable; from inner conflicts was born the sure and triumphant conviction of a higher power in the movement towards morality,—a power which not only imposes moral obligations on man, but

which, by the revelation of a new life, gives him strength to fulfil them. Morality here appears as something infinitely superior to the uncertainty of human conditions, and completely independent of man's attitude towards it. If morality does not attain the power due to it in man's life, this is now attributed to the weakness, not of morality, but of man. The majesty of morality is by no means prejudiced by man's line of conduct. Kant could therefore declare that "it is most reprehensible to derive either the origin or any restriction of the laws telling me what I should do, from that which is done by others."

It is the essence of all deep religions, especially of Christianity, that a new life is created in man by a revelation of the Divine by means of a direct union of the soul with God. This new life is held to be superior to the complexity of existing conditions, and is sure to triumph, because it is founded in God. A source of life is thus opened up, which imparts new activity to the life hitherto stagnant. Man regains courage and confidence, because he feels himself sustained by divine strength and love. No contradiction in the world of external realities is now able to weaken man's inner certainty. A powerful impulse towards work and creative activity will be born of the gladness within him. This explains the unquestioning confidence and joyous energy manifested by all the leaders of religious life; the consciousness of their deliverance from dire distress filled them with unbounded gratitude, which sought expression in unremitting work for their fellowmen. Luther says: "From faith flow love and joy in the Lord, and from love a free and joyous spirit of voluntary service of our neighbour, quite irrespective of gratitude or ingratitude, praise or blame, gain or loss."

Further development of life by means of religion is sure to stamp morality with characteristic features. The consciousness of deliverance by a higher power will arouse not only gratitude, but humility and childlike confidence. If everything man has is but a gift, then he will see, in his highest achievement, less his own work than that of God. Gentleness and toleration will gain ground; arrogance and harshness will disappear; all decisive action will have an inner rather than an outer significance. The value of an action depends on loyalty to principle, and not on the greatness of what is achieved. This is shown by Jesus in the parable of the talents.

But this accentuation of softer elements and inner values by no means paralyses activity. For the new life must be energetically developed and bravely asserted against an alien, not to say a hostile, world. Man finds a great task, first of all in his own soul, but then in the whole of his life with other men. We may here apply a principle of the Reformation, which has thus been expressed: "The word of God comes to change and renew the world, whenever it comes." There is one thing on which a philosophy of the spiritual life must emphatically insist: this return to religion must not be confined to the individual, but must embrace all the conditions of human life. Only thus can the whole of man be won. This can only be done by creating a specific religious sphere of life, a specific religious community. Many of us may wish the Church to be, in certain respects, different to what it is; but that should not make us ignore the necessity of a religious community. It is indispensable, if we are to establish the new life in the human sphere, and bring it within the reach of the individual; it is indispensable, if the struggle is to be maintained by great entities, and is not to degenerate into small skirmishes. At the present time, when the state is engrossed by economic and other constantly changing problems of the day,

we need a community which attaches paramount importance to the inner problems of humanity and which directs our life towards eternal aims and values.

In this union with religion, morality will be inclined to see more gloom than light in the life around us. For morality will then judge by higher standards, and will emphasise the insufficiency of human achievement, the unsatisfactory character of the present situation. But morality cannot lead to despondency, once it is emancipated from the world of immediate environment, and has gained a new world. Morality will then see, in the world of strife and antithesis, only a special kind of reality, and not the whole of reality; it will recognise in this world only one act of a great drama, and not the whole drama.

Much that is dark thus remains unexplained. To speak with Goethe, we "walk among mysteries." Even if we cannot enlighten what is dark, the new beginnings established in us will save us from becoming cowed and despondent. We are certain that great things are being accomplished in us and through us,—that a higher power is present within us throughout the struggles of our life. At the same time, we feel sure that our inner renewal is not mechanical, but requires our own decision and action, thus making us co-operate in the movement of the universe, and giving to our activity a significance for the whole. That must and that can be sufficient for us. We can agree with Luther, when he thus characterises human life: "It is not yet done and accomplished, but it is in working order and in full swing; it is not the end, but the way. All does not yet glow and shine, but all is being burnished."

We know that so close a connection between morality and religion is often contested nowadays. But we believe that religious morality can only be attacked by those who have too low an estimate of morality or too high an estimate of the actual condition of humanity. If morality is but a means of tolerable order in the social community of life, and is only looked upon as a controlling force, then it can dispense with religion. But this means a lowering of the moral requirement, the fulfilment of which brings but little gain or profit. It is possible, on the other hand, to value morality more highly, but to over-estimate man, as experience shows him to be. He is looked on as a good and noble being, easily won for the highest aims. Were this a true conception of man, then morality could attain its ends by its own strength alone. But we are clearly shown that this is not the case, both by the conviction of all great religious and philosophical teachers, and by the general impression of human life. At all times, the pessimists—and not the optimists—were held to have the best knowledge of human nature. We need only consider more closely the delineation of human life left us by the so-called optimistic philosophers (like Aristotle and Leibnitz), in order to see that even they found in it much that was dark and gloomy.

If we maintain a high conception of the moral task and an impartial conception of the actual condition of human life, there remains but one dilemma: either complete hopelessness and inner collapse of life, or the acquisition of further cohesions, such as that offered by an alliance with religion. But religion must then mean more than a sum of doctrines and institutions. It must influence the whole soul. It must not only cling to the past, but must, above all, be a power in the living present. It must not only be a source of comfort to individuals, but must raise the whole of mankind to a higher and purer level. In all these aspects, religion is both action and life, not mere thinking about the world, or subjective emotion. A connection of morality

with religion thus understood, can be only a source of profit—not of loss—to morality, which will thus be strengthened in its bearing on external reality, and will experience a great deepening of its inner life.

## VI

## The Present Status of Morality

We must now consider, in conclusion, the position of Morality in our day. Let us see what profit and loss accrues to morality from the present, and what its prospects are for the future. There can be no doubt about the fact that great changes are being effected—changes not only in the world of thought, but in the whole range of life and work. These changes at first result in manifold losses to morality. The pillars which used to support it began to totter, or gave way altogether; new ones arose, but are as yet too weak to offer an adequate substitute for what is lost. We cannot therefore look upon the present status of morality as a satisfactory one.

The weakening of religious conviction and practice is unfavourable to morality. Imperfect as the influence of religion often was on mankind at large, and excessive as was the importance attached to the idea of reward and punishment, men yet recognised a power superior to all human action and all arbitrary human decision. This power was to be an object of reverence; and life was raised above the care for purely material possessions. It was also a gain for moral culture, that religion established the inner solidarity of man, and facilitated mutual understanding. Thus it is a loss for morality, that religion no longer maintains its former ruling position.

The general condition of our intellectual life is unfavourable to morality, inasmuch as this intellectual life lacks a uniform aim which could unite scattered aspirations, strengthen every single undertaking, and counteract, as a whole, the interests of mere individuals. These interests at all times made themselves felt, and life was always in danger of being dominated by petty human considerations. But the difference between period and period depends on whether or not this danger is counteracted and man is raised above himself by some high aim. In our day, such counteraction is lacking. Where have we an aim embracing the whole man, which is common to us all and binds us together to inner communion? Every party and faction preaches some ideal of its own, the attainment of which will, it believes, unite men, making them good and happy. But these individual aims are very different in character; they are a cause of mutual hindrance, and they divide mankind in that which should be a means of union.

Another disadvantage for inner culture is the rapid pace of life, as compared to former times. While we are hastening from moment to moment, we have neither repose nor leisure for the culture of our inner man, for the development of a character, a personality. We are more and more in danger of being absorbed by the whirlpool of life, and robbed of all possibility of self-conscious action. Other perils also beset us. In our thirst for achievement and success, our moral judgment is often repressed; the accentuation of the battle of life can even make us indifferent to the moral quality of the ways and means employed by us. All this necessarily weakens morality, and makes it appear unimportant and shadowy.

To these dangers arising from the general conduct of life, we must add others, which originate in the modern development of work in the community. In former times, the conditions of life were at once narrower and less subject to change. Social environment exercised a stricter and more exclusive control over the individual, holding him within the bounds of law and custom. This influence was often only an external one; correct behaviour was frequently mistaken for moral integrity. This gave rise to much unreality and pharisaical hypocrisy. Still, a certain result was attained in the direction of moral culture; certain restraints were acknowledged, which cannot, without impunity, be dispensed with. Restraints play an important part in the life of the soul, as well as in that of the body. Modern freedom of action makes the individual depend on himself alone, and we must be very optimistic to believe him able to completely withstand, unaided, all the temptations of life.

We cannot omit one characteristic modern development: the change of men's mutual relation from a personal to an impersonal one. We have but to think of the difference between the cordial community of life established by the old arts and crafts, and the cool, almost hostile manner in which, in our great labour complexes, "employers" and "employees" nowadays associate. There is no longer the slightest personal relation or personal sympathy between them.

If we survey all these losses, the balance of the day will hardly appear to be in favour of morality. But we must not forget that the present age has also supplied morality with new and valuable impulses. This is above all the case with labour—the modern form of work to which we have just alluded. There is a strong moral element in the ever increasing formation and organisation of great labour complexes, not only in the factory, but also in science, state organisation, education, and so forth. The individual is thereby obliged to work in close union with others, and in accordance with objective requirements. He must adapt his own activity to the general character of the work; and yet he must do his own part conscientiously, so that the mass of separate achievements may blend harmoniously and ensure the steady progress of the whole. This requires such loyalty, self-control, and sacrifice of personal taste and opinion, that a strong moral effect is undeniable. In this respect, man now learns more implicit obedience than at any former period. Another moral element in modern labour is the concentration of man's whole strength on his work, to the exclusion of all inert repose.

If the impersonal element predominates in work, the social side of modern life offers, on the other hand, more direct union and more reciprocal action between man and man. This was, at first, mainly theoretical. It was pointed out how much one man depends on his fellow-men. People realised that the individual develops with other individuals and as part of the community, with which his aspirations are indissolubly connected, even when he imagines he is striking out a path for himself. But such theories could only have so much influence, because they were in harmony with the realities of life. Modern life, with its technical developments, brought individuals into close touch and created new opportunities of mutual intercourse, uniting men both in success and in failure. Thus grew up the consciousness of human solidarity, the recognition of men's interdependence, the idea of mutual obligation. The result is a wealth of humane activity, which penetrates into all the ramifications of life, attacking and seeking to eradicate all forms of want and misery, instead of merely helping to relieve individual cases. We encounter the earnest endeavour to impart material and spiritual possessions, as far as possible, to all men; to help and strengthen the less favoured section of humanity; to further the interests of as-

piring spirits. These efforts are but various aspects of one great duty, which we feel we cannot ignore; we can no longer look upon them as works of mercy, which it is a virtue to perform. This is at the root of the social idea. And this social idea is, in our day, the greatest bond of union between human beings; not only does it stir individuals, but it also exercises a strong influence on law, education, and so forth. In this respect our time has a right to claim undoubted superiority over all former times.

These moral achievements of the present, valuable as they are, yet have their inner limitations. Nearly all movement here proceeds outward, and is directed towards distinct single achievements, while the culture and welfare of the inner man are mostly treated as of secondary importance. Zeal for surface ends leads to the neglect of the central values of life. Yet all outer achievement only means real gain for us, if it promotes the growth of the whole man, of his soul, of his personality, making him nobler, greater, and happier. If there is no development and strengthening of the centre of life, achievement on the surface is apt to result in grave complications, and all that is great in the present may thereby be driven into the wrong channels. Another danger grows out of the ever increasing tendency to organise work. Owing to the necessity of specialising and differentiating, the amount of work is restricted which the individual can comprehend and master. He is tempted to concentrate his interest on his own little province, to be indifferent to everything outside it, and to lose all consciousness of a leading idea and of a great whole. He thus falls a prey to the narrow conceit of the specialist, and finally pushes aside as worthless accessories all matters of general interest, all the questions and sorrows of humanity at large.

By furthering a spirit of pity for human want and misery, without giving to life an inner value and a higher aim, we are in danger of becoming sentimental and of producing inner languor in spite of all outer activity. We are often more anxious to procure for man a comfortable and pleasant life, than to promote inner growth; and our care for the weak, which is quite justified, leads us to take such weak individuals as a criterion and to lower life to their level.

Modern life often lacks the necessary hardness and vigour; in our care for the rights of individuals, we are inclined to neglect the rights and requirements of the whole and also of the spiritual life. So we are in danger of losing that which according to Goethe, "No one brings with him into the world, yet which is all important if a man is to become a man in every respect: reverence."

If we review the whole and consider the balance of moral profit and loss in our day, the result cannot be a favourable one. No full substitute is offered for what is lost. We have gained in breadth, but we have lost in depth and strength. Above all, morality is in danger of losing its former ruling position, and of having a subordinate one assigned to it. It can therefore no longer call forth reverence, or be treated as an independent aim and ideal. We realise at once the gravity of this loss.

But this unfavourable aspect only holds good, if we consider the present time as something complete and incapable of further development. If, on the contrary, we seek to grasp all that is struggling into life, all the requirements of our time that yet await fulfilment: then the situation is quite different and far more favourable. What mainly told against morality was the prevalent overestimation of everything pertaining to the visible life which surrounds us in nature and in human society. The invisible realms of religion and the ideal have, as

we have seen, often grown dim and shadowy. Many of our contemporaries deny them altogether, and look to the visible world for full satisfaction of all man's wants, even of his spiritual and intellectual requirements. This could only appear possible because, in reality, the invisible world of spiritual values continued to influence even those who denied it, and because it supplemented and completed the achievements of the visible world. It is, however, characteristic of our time, that the old fusion is no longer possible, and the irreconcilable antithesis between these two conceptions of life stands out in bold relief. With increasing zeal, the movement in favour of the visible world—that is to say, Naturalism—tries to eradicate everything appertaining to the invisible world, and to fashion the whole of life in accordance with its own principles. Naturalism tolerates no rival, and declares war to the death to Idealism.

We now see the truth of Bacon's words: *"Veritas potius emergit ex errore quam ex confusione"* (Truth can more easily emerge from error than from confusion). For if we accept naturalism as the only valid conception of life, and develop it consistently in all its bearings, we cannot but see its incapacity to embrace the whole of life. The apparent victory of naturalism thus contains the germ of a defeat, the beginning of a great reaction. What becomes of man and of human life, if the visible world means to him the only form of reality? He is then but part of nature—dark and soulless nature. The vast expansion and range of nature overwhelms him with the consciousness of his own insignificance, while, at the same time, nature is absolutely indifferent to his wishes and aspirations. What he makes of himself and his life has not the very slightest significance for this world of nature. All aspiration which transcends his natural instinct of self-preservation must appear to be mere folly. Such ideals as personality and character are but held to be illusions.

If man turns away from the outer world and takes refuge in his own sphere, in the social life among his fellows, naturalism there shows him a mere juxtaposition, but no inner community which could offer new aims or develop new values. What remains is only a number of individuals inhabiting the same little corner of the universe. Each of these individuals strives to gain recognition of his own merits, and to assert himself, to the detriment of others. Much sordidness and hypocrisy become rampant, and it is impossible to counteract them within so narrow a range, or to hope for the growing up of a nobler and purer race of men. The individual remains bound to the condition of society, which also determines his own nature; he appears to be but a product of the social environment. Having no deeper source of life within himself, how should he be able to escape from the trammels of society, to rise above it or oppose it? Society and environment thus become the destiny of man; and there is no scope for freedom, for initiative, for independent action.

If we survey and appreciate all this with unbiassed minds, this life must appear empty and meaningless and scarcely worth living. At the same time, we shall discern a development of mankind far transcending these narrow limits, as indeed has already been pointed out in this our study of morality. The degradation of life effected by naturalism might be endured in feeble and senile periods conscious of no great tasks, but not in our time, which teems with stupendous tasks it is earnestly striving to carry out. These great tasks and problems can only be grappled with, if we are fully conscious of concentrated energy and increased spiritual power. Modern life has developed in various and opposite directions. Its expansion is greater than its concen-

tration, and this threatens it with disintegration. There is an increasing and imperative need of more unity and cohesion, of some universal and harmonious character of the whole. How should this be attained without a vigorous deepening of life, without the development of invisible values? We observe, in our day, the encounter of an older and a newer age, of a conception of life hallowed by the traditions of history, and a new one that is struggling into existence; there is a sharp conflict between the past and the present. We cannot but admit in the old an imperishable germ of truth, and in the new, an inalienable right to impress and influence us. We must prove and sift, separate and unite. But how were any progress in this direction possible, could we not find a superior point of view, such as can be offered only by a world of thought, not by the visible life? This problem gains vastly in significance by extending to the social life of all humanity. We see here a struggle between an older, more aristocratic form of society, and a newer, more democratic one. This struggle engenders violent passions, especially in the province of economics. We are here placed before a grave question: shall we be able to impart the benefits of civilisation to all men alike, and thus broaden every individual soul, without injury to its inner depths?

These are problems which do not originate in ourselves, but which are forced upon us by the movement of history. Their very necessity bids us hope for progression, in spite of all impediments. The power which has imposed these problems on us will enable us to solve them. But we shall also need to put forth our uttermost strength, and to quicken all our latent spiritual forces; we must grasp our life as a whole, must acknowledge its high aims with all our heart and soul, and must find our real self in these ideals. Only thus can we gain the sense of inner necessity which alone can lead us onward.

In this manner, our aspiration becomes closely linked to morality. Let us see wherein we have already recognised the quintessence of morality. Life and aspiration are detached from the little Ego, and take root in a spiritual world in which we find our own essential being, so that while working for this spiritual world, we are at the same time working for our own depth and spiritual self-preservation. Such a change and reaction, such identification with the movement of the spiritual life, means only that our aspiration has gained a moral character. This moral character brings us, at all points, into touch with our time. By means of our own aspiration, we can now grasp, unite, and deepen all the goodwill, genuine feeling, and untiring activity of our day, which was hitherto inadequate only because it lacked inner unity and quickening spiritual power.

We can thus face the future with courage and confidence. Humanity has by no means exhausted its vital power; it is full of new possibilities which demand realisation; and therefore we may expect an inner progression of life and a rejuvenation of morality.

What is true of mankind in general, is especially true of America. The multitude of grave problems cannot discourage a nation which feels in itself so much youthful vigour, that it will not submit to a dark fate, but is able and ready to mould its own fate, and to aspire to yet greater heights than it has hitherto attained. But to achieve this, moral force is as necessary as unshaken confidence in the power of the spirit. We believe in a bright future for this great country. We believe also in the development in America of such moral strength as will successfully overcome all conflicts and lead to splendid results, for the benefit not only of the American nation, but of all mankind.

# ESSAYS

## By RUDOLF EUCKEN

### *Translated by* Meyrick Booth

---

### *Religion and Civilization*

That the relationship between religion and civilization involves many complications, is indicated, in the first place, by the manifold changes which it has undergone in the course of history. Even in the antique world, especially in its later days, this relationship was no simple matter; but it was upon Christian soil that the problem first developed its fullest intensity. From the very earliest times, men have been divided upon this matter: while some valued civilization and culture, and particularly philosophy, as a preliminary and preparatory stage of divine truth, others were dominated by the idea of the opposition between religion and civilization, and not infrequently uttered pointed expressions of indifference towards, or even of hatred of civilization. The first broad solution was that attempted by St. Augustine, who created an all-embracing system of life, which, while leaving room for the work of civilization, assigned no other task to its entire extent than that of leading man, through all his occupation with the multiplicity of things, and above and beyond this, to the all-dominating unity, the vision of which alone promises certain truth and blessed peace as compared with all the uncertainty and trouble of the rest of life. All the different spheres of spiritual life thus received an immense inspiration and consolidation; but the details of their construction became matters of indifference, and there was a disappearance of all independence and self-value on the part of objective work. The latter found more recognition in the calmer but more superficial mode of thought of scholasticism at the height of the Middle Ages. For although in this case, too, religion continued to form the ruling centre of life, it did not so directly dominate the other spheres; it permitted them a certain degree of independence. In particular, the idea of a series of stages permitted the lower to develop itself undisturbed in its own sphere, while still being subordinate, as a whole, to the higher; the conviction that grace did not supplant nature but completed it (*gratia naturam non tollit, sed perficit*), appeared to remove every difficulty. All impartial authorities upon the Middle Ages are, however, at one in admitting that in reality the outwardly subordinate obtained a powerful influence over that which was set above it, and, in particular, that philosophy gave religion an intellectualistic complexion. Thus it was a desire to liberate religion from disturbing additions, to re-establish its pure condition, which made itself felt at the beginning of the Reformation. Religion and civilization now became more widely separated. Soon, however, and in particular after the beginning of the seventeenth century, civilization began to move along paths which were entirely its own, at the same time more and more emancipating itself from religion. In this respect, the leading civilized nations exhibit different characteristics: the predominating tendency of English life was towards permitting religion and civilization to exist side by side; in the case of the French, the two were apt to fall into irreconcilable conflict; while the German mind sought for an inner harmony, an overcoming of the antithesis. The highest achievement in the latter direction is to be credited to the age of our great poets and thinkers, the period of German Humanism; now religion and civilization seemed each to complete and advance the other, within a comprehensive spiritual life. The nineteenth century again intensified the antithesis, and made the humanistic solution inadequate.

Thus history does not provide us with a solution; nay, it does not even offer us any orientation with regard to the path we should follow; and to-day the antitheses stand out with greater sharpness than ever. Many believe themselves able best to serve the purposes of civilization by means of a radical rejection of religion, as a mere illusion; while on the side of religion we see much vacillation and insecurity. Protestantism has split up into two movements, the first of which remains attached as far as possible to the position of the sixteenth century, granting to modern civilization only such concessions as are quite unavoidable; while the other follows the banner of modern idealism with its panentheism, seeking merely to deepen this with the aid of religion. In Catholicism, too, differences are not lacking. For although the scholastic ideal with its harmonization of religion and civilization is predominantly retained, this takes place in two senses, the one strict and the other looser, and these give

rise to different attitudes towards modern civilization. Thus the Thomism of the present day has not only two different complexions, but also two different centres—Rome and Louvain. At the same time we note the hopeful beginnings of a modern Catholicism with the desire for a separation from scholasticism and a thorough understanding with our more modern civilization. This juxtaposition and competition of different attempts, shows clearly enough what an urgent necessity there is, in this connection, for further work and clarification. And just as the experience of millenniums distinctly shows that every answer carries in itself a conviction with regard to human and divine things as a whole, so in the absence of such a whole conviction there will be no possibility of progress to-day. A passing consideration such as the present cannot do more than pick out a single point and through its discussion endeavour to throw light upon a particular aspect of the problem rather than attempt to solve it. Such will be our aim in the following.

We shall occupy ourselves with a single thought; namely, that while it is necessary that religion and civilization should be independent of one another, yet each is dependent upon the other for its own prosperity. Those who recognize this fact will see the problem of their harmonization from a characteristic standpoint. Union is most easily possible upon the point that religion must be independent of all civilization; those who would reduce it to a means, however essential, not only weaken its force but endanger its truth. For it is essential to religion to reveal, with the relationship to God, a new life incomparably superior to all human aims; this life may well work, nay, it must work towards the reformation of human relationships, but it does this only as a side issue and as a consequence, not of set purpose and as its principal task. Thus wherever religion rises up with original and spontaneous force we invariably perceive a remarkable indifference towards human and worldly things. The great heroes of religion, for example, were never social reformers, not because they lacked feeling for human need and suffering, but because they hoped for the deepest help not from the things of this world, but alone from the revelation of a new world. This independence of content must correspond with an independence of basis. Religion itself has to be responsible for its own truth, to construct its own organ of truth; it may not make itself dependent upon the result of the work of civilization, on philosophy, history or natural science. For such a dependence would bring with it a painful insecurity: it would involve in all the changes of the ages that which, according to its very nature, demands eternity. Where religion must seek this organ of its own, and how it has to develop it, are matters of the severest conflict; immense confusion has resulted, in particular, from the fact that religion, which promised to impart to life a support more solid than knowledge itself, became itself imperceptibly converted into a particular sort of knowledge. But all such conflict, in spite of its dangers, cannot affect the necessity of the fundamental thought.

Moreover, the positions and psychic accomplishments of man appear, in the cases of civilization and religion, to be completely different, nay, opposed. Since civilization calls upon man fully to develop his power and bases his existence as far as possible upon his own activity, it demands self-confidence upon his part: only a firm and joyful faith in his own capacity can enable him to attack difficult tasks with spirit, and sustain him in all the unavoidable doubts. Religion, too, seeks to make man powerful and to elevate his life, but this it does, in contrast to mere nature, as a gift and through grace. The affirmation of life for which it

stands takes place only through a negation of the mere man. A complete upheaval of the natural position is indispensable to the truthfulness of religion.

Such a difference in psychic position proclaims the independence of religion, and not less that of civilization. If from the very beginning man thought little of himself and confined himself to the limits of his capacity, an energetic work of civilization would never come into being. But just as it has its own attitude towards life as compared with that of religion, so civilization needs independence for the content and aims of its work. A work, the result of which is prescribed by an imperative authority (as took place in the mediæval system, and as is still demanded by its disciples) is a miserable hybrid. It lacks freedom, a seeking and struggling of its own, an overcoming of doubt on its own account, and therefore lacks a true soul of its own, a complete taking up of the object in its own being. Moreover, civilization will hardly find the energy and patience to penetrate the object, and hardly achieve the proper conscientiousness in work, if it cannot look upon itself as something with a value of its own, as an end in itself, independent of any outward relationship.

Thus religion and civilization may easily appear as opponents, struggling for the soul of man. At the same time neither would seem able happily to perform its own task if wholly isolated from the other. With the abandonment of all religion, civilization rapidly sinks into littleness, secularism and mere humanism; it threatens to fall away from its own idea. This idea demands a fundamental transformation of reality and an inner elevation of man; and for this purpose it cannot dispense with independence in relation to the immediate state of things, with a freedom from the interests of the mere individual, with a clear separation between a spiritual life founded in itself and governed by its own aims, and the ways and doings of human society. Only in so far is a civilization genuine and full of content as it separates itself, as a spiritual culture, from merely human culture and becomes the revelation of a spiritual world. Is it to be supposed that such a spiritual world can be attained and firmly established in the human sphere, in the face of all the immense inward and outward resistances, without some sort of direction towards religion? In reality a true and transforming civilized life has never been developed without a relationship (though often, perhaps, a concealed relationship) to religion: even if the superworld stands in the background of life it continues to illuminate the latter, and only with its help is the littleness of daily life overcome. Moreover it must not be forgotten that civilization knows not only ages of confident and joyful upward effort, but also ages of error and confusion, of a laborious search for new pathways. And in such days of doubt, of search and of tentative effort, religion provides a support for mankind and maintains faith in the possibility of an inward renewal. Thus civilization, if it takes a high view of itself and of its task, cannot dispense with religion.

If, however, there is an impulse from civilization towards religion, no less is there an impulse from religion towards civilization. Religion must not illuminate human existence as if from an alien world situated without; if it is to become a genuine power in life it must win over the whole man, penetrate the general human relationships and exert its influence in every direction. Otherwise it becomes narrow and petrified, and instead of acting as a world power and elevating the entire level of human existence, kindling at each point a life based upon perfection and eternity, it becomes a mere means of comfort for individuals, nay, only too easily a mere refuge for the weak. There

have been ages which, while the life of civilization remained stagnant, preserved an outward correctness in their religious position. Has religion itself flourished at such times? Has it not rather been shown that it is a blessing for religion to be the central point of a larger sphere, to be surrounded by an atmosphere of a more general spirituality? We should mention, too, that a supernatural construction of reality cannot well attain to full power and truth, unless, in the first place, the capacity of nature has been examined and its limits ascertained through our own experience; the transformation of the world which religion demands and must demand, must base itself and prove itself ever afresh. Not the least of the causes giving rise to a spirit of opposition to religion is to be found in the fact that many of its disciples have looked with contempt upon human capacity, and in particular upon the capacity of knowledge, without ever having put forth their own strength, without ever having seriously taken up the struggle for scientific truth with all its labour and care. An equally serious cause is the idea of the evil world, from which it is said to be our duty to hold ourselves anxiously aloof. A limitation can be overcome truly only by those who have themselves experienced it; and there can be no experience without an entering into the life of the world.

Thus we see that, in actuality, religion and civilization at the same time repel and attract one another, at the same time fly from one another and seek one another. This could not be possible unless life had a characteristic structure, and the life-process a characteristic formation. If spiritual life were in the first place the setting up of a comprehensive formula and a deduction of all manifoldness from this, the antithesis would remain an insoluble contradiction. And such a contradiction can be avoided only if our life is able to form independent points of departure within its own sphere, and to embrace within itself different and even opposed movements, the conflict of which advances life, preserves its freshness, and reveals to it a depth within itself. This subject leads us, however, into larger relationships than those with which we can at present occupy ourselves.

## The Moral Forces in the Life of To-day

In dealing with moral problems, we must distinguish between these two things: the ultimate derivation of morality from our innermost nature, and from our basic relationship to the whole, on the one hand; and its actual unfoldment, its rise and growth within the human sphere, on the other. Those who think themselves able to dispense with the former, condemn their own mode of thought to irrevocable superficiality; those who neglect the latter, renounce the power of morality within human conditions, and the gaining of the whole man. A conclusive treatment must embrace both. But without injury now the one side and now the other may come more to the front. The following study will pursue the second of these two lines of thought.

A consideration of this kind is based upon the conviction that man—empirically regarded—is not already moral, but must first become so; and this he cannot do unless the life process itself so shapes him; experience and work must effect a moral education, a force indwelling in life must lead the individuals beyond their crude natural impulses and their narrow care for personal welfare. The chief means of education consists in that which at first comes to us through the compulsion of outward circumstances, being gradually turned into inner life and appropriated by our feeling; that which at

first operates only here and there, only under particular circumstances and conditions, gradually ceases to be accidental and is extended over the whole of life. To follow out this movement in a given age means to trace the lines of convergence and points of contact which empirical life offers to the work of moral development; it means to seek out the place of morality in the work of the age. And we must adopt this method of procedure in dealing with the moral forces of the present day.

An energetic negation is the primary characteristic of modern life, if we consider it, as we do in this case, in its characteristic manifestation only: it rejects all invisible relationships and supernatural laws. This signifies a thrusting aside of religion and a weakening of its moral impulses. Now the immediate moral effect of religion is certainly often overrated. That which, in the first place, impels men towards religion is, for the most part, nothing other than care for their own happiness, and even within the sphere of religion there is so much envy and hatred, so much selfishness and passion, that under human circumstances, the power of religion does not straightway signify a gain for morality. But only a shortsighted consideration could fail to recognize that, in spite of all this, powerful moral influences go forth from religion. The invisible goods, the acquisition of which was prompted in the first place perhaps by selfish motives only, begin, through their own value, to please and to move the feelings; the mere fact of an occupation with high and distant things, effects an elevation above the petty interests and cares of everyday life; the ideas of eternity and infinity lay hold of men's minds and deeply stir them; supernatural laws, placed by faith in a living present, operate towards the recognition of the limits of everything human, and towards the awakening of reverence and piety. And since, when religion is in a position of secure dominance, this extends over the whole of man's soul, there results a characteristic type of morality, a constant counteraction of the lower and meaner elements in human nature. In so far, an upheaval of religion is at the same time a loss for morality. And who can deny that religion has been severely shaken in the modern era?

Modern life believes itself able entirely and easily to replace the deficiency which thus results by a more energetic grasp of immediate reality and a full employment of the otherwise neglected forces here at hand. Such a movement as this, in the first place opens up an endless manifoldness, but a more accurate examination reveals guiding aims and centres of unity in the midst of all the disintegration. Such a unity is to-day above all the *social idea*, the endeavour to raise the whole of humanity, in all its individual members, to a higher stage of well-being, to destroy necessity and misery at their very deepest roots (not merely to alleviate them here and there), to communicate the goods of a highly developed civilization, not to special classes only, but to everyone bearing the human countenance. It is this goal, in particular, which imparts determination and concentration to the life of the present day. From this standpoint certain truths appear to be matters-of-course and binding upon all. At this point all are drawn together into a great stream. Our age, moreover, acquires a specific moral stamp and characteristic moral forces in that it finds the centre of gravity of its spiritual existence, not like earlier ages, in religion, nor in the building up of the inner man, but in social work.

At this point the consciousness of the solidarity of humanity is aroused, the individual becomes more keenly sensitive to his responsibility for the condition of society as a whole; the need and suffering of the one are more directly felt in sympathy by the others, and from feeling, there is an impulse of previously unknown energy towards vigorous action, towards an untiring working for others and for the whole. An essential feature of this movement is that the social activity is not looked upon as a matter of favour or pity, as an outpouring of mere goodwill, but as a duty on the one hand and a right on the other; this is the point at which the idea of duty (otherwise often but little regarded) approaches the modern man and profoundly stirs him. To recognize a right on the part of another, means to place oneself in his position and to limit one's own desires. Feelings of this kind are to-day finding their way into political life and into the statute-book. The moral influence of art, literature and philosophy also lies in the social direction. The change, as compared with earlier ages, is obvious. Formerly the poets were looked upon as the teachers and creators of humanity, and their function was to elevate the level of human existence through the presentation of lofty ideals; now, they seek, through the clearness and realism of their art, to bring us nearer to reality, to impart to their impressions a greater power of arousing feeling, and to stir us to sympathy by a bold unveiling of the darker side of human existence. Formerly, philosophy advanced the moral development of man, either by insisting, with Plato, upon a high mode of thought, averse to all that is common and degrading, or by calling man, after the fashion of the Stoics, to inner independence and a manly consciousness of duty; to-day it operates, in so far as it operates at all, towards the strengthening of solidarity, and as an impulse to social work.

Thus the social tendency imparts an altogether peculiar character to modern morality. We cannot fail to recognize that it causes morality to become energetic, to direct itself towards tangible achievement, to be moved by the destiny of the whole, and to embrace the whole sphere of life; there is a desire to convert ethics in general into social ethics, without adequately inquiring whether in this way we are not employing a shallow and perverted concept. In general it may be said that the obvious advantages of the new type are apt to lead us to forget its limits and its dangers. Our interest is often wholly absorbed by the outer situation; our entire salvation seems to depend upon its betterment; its thorough transformation is to produce happy and capable men, and create a paradise upon earth. This is accompanied by a neglect of the inner problems, an outward direction of the thoughts, an overvaluation of the human capacity, a breaking out of an insatiable thirst for happiness, and an awakening of tremendous passions.

But within the sphere of modern life itself there is no lack of a tendency to balance and counteract the social movement. This is the movement towards the *liberation and development of the individual,* which has formed a main element in the modern type of life since the passing of the Middle Ages, and still persists throughout every change. In the past, the individual was valued only as a member of a larger whole and all order in his life came from thence; but now this is reversed, in the sense that all spiritual life presents itself, in the first place, to the individual and all common life is erected upon the basis of the individual. This high valuation of the individual involves the abandonment of many of the moral impulses which previously seemed indispensable. The educative power of the great social orders and fixed systems suffers a decline; while authority and tradition are undermined, and manners and customs lose their sacredness. There seems to be nowhere a norm independent of man; while reverence and piety increasingly disappear from human relationships. In addition, the modern devel-

opment of technical science and of facilities for intercourse gives rise to a greater freedom of social movement, and helps to break down the ancient limitations, while at the same time weakening the controlling power of the social environment and of super-individual authority. It is possible for all this to be understood and made use of in such a fashion that the accidental position and mood of the individual becomes the highest court of appeal, and social life signifies nothing more than an encounter (which easily becomes a conflict) of individuals bent upon their own welfare.

But for humanity as a whole, the movement towards the individual is by no means wholly negative; it is also very decidedly positive—even in a moral sense. For the more powerful development of the individual involves the desire for a greater directness and truthfulness of life; man is to regulate his actions not under the influence of outer pressure, but according to his own conviction and feeling; under no circumstances is he to remain a mere unit of the race, or a fragment of an organization. He is to stand upon his own feet, to develop his own nature and express the latter in all his actions.

Following this tendency, freedom is developed, not only in the political and social sphere, but also in all the personal connections of man with man. This is to be seen in the relationship of parents and children, and in the realm of sex relationships. It may be asked: Why should not the freedom of a rational being develop an inner law which shall be more deeply influential than any outward compulsion? And indeed if the word be taken in its deeper sense, individuality, in all its extension, can become a constructive norm. For spiritual individuality is not given ready-made; it is a continuous task; it involves demands and fixes limits; and in its attitude towards matter it works as a transforming and form-giving power. It thus ennobles all personal relationships, and every kind of love, especially (as the strongest dam against the crude natural instinct) sexual love; thus it refines all feeling, permits art and science to see more in the things, makes the particularity of the separate moment more significant, and accordingly effects, throughout, an elevation of life; at the same time, it expels mere self-will, and commits man to the law of his own nature. All this holds, indeed, only in as far as individuality is understood in the higher sense. But why should this not be the case; why should this great idea remain tied to its lowest interpretation?

Just as, rightly understood, individuality contains within its own nature a law and a formative force, so the movement towards the individual evolves from mutual human relationships a wealth of connections and limitations. The freedom which the individual demands for himself he cannot possibly deny to others as their right; thus the separate units are compelled to respect and to limit one another. Here, too, the idea of justice acquires no little power.

Further, the more free movement of modern life brings the individuals into incomparably closer mutual relationship, and this effects an adjustment and a wearing down of individual eccentricities. Thus there results, in social life, a common spiritual atmosphere, accompanied by general opinions and general movements, which in spite of all apparent self-will, firmly surround the individuals and securely hold them together. The attempt to reckon for something in the estimation of one's fellow-men, to find recognition and distinction (or at any rate, to avoid falling) in their eyes, is, in general, a particularly strong motive force in human conduct; and with this growth of mutual relationship and the greater publicity and consciousness of modern life it becomes stronger than ever. Public opinion now becomes a conscience for humanity and for man. And is it not characteristic of its connection with the elevation of the individual that the same thinker who peculiarly emphasized the right of the individual in the state, in society, and in education, namely John Locke, was also the first to desire to see the recognition, side by side with the divine and the political law, of a law of public opinion? It is certainly true that conduct in response to the pressure of public opinion is at first decidedly external and superficial. Yet even the endeavour to obtain a respectable appearance in these matters is not wholly without value; and it is of importance to remember that in this case, too, we may rely upon the movement from without to within, from the action to the inner feeling. That which in the first place was done for the sake of the others can gradually give rise to pleasure for its own sake, and finally, as an end in itself, serve as a guide for our conduct.

While public opinion surrounds man as an invisible power and guides him with invisible reins, there is also no lack, in the modern world, of visible relationships. In the place of the old organizations, work itself produces new links binding men together; out of the different interests which are here in question there are developed groupings which are outwardly free, though inwardly no less united than was formerly the case; and in the place of the old communal sense there arises the fellowship feeling of these free associations. Now, too, the individual finds himself compelled to subordinate himself to a whole and to make sacrifices in its interests; here, too, that which was first taken up from motives of selfish interest can gradually become an end in itself.

An individualization of existence, accompanied by an elevation of man above his petty ego, is brought about in another direction through the idea of nationality.

While the eighteenth century clung to the abstract concept of humanity, the nineteenth discovered and developed a wealth of individual formations; just as the whole life of humanity experienced an immeasurable enrichment in this way, so there resulted from this standpoint, also, a powerful reaction against the egoism of the individual. General tasks become much more immediate to the individual and more imperative for him when people and country hold up the peculiarity of his own specific character on a large scale and in a powerful visible form, and at the same time introduce the passing moment into the current of historical life. The individuality of the nation becomes the bridge from the separate interests of the individual to a devotion to general ends. How much can thus be gained for the strengthening of life and the development of character was magnificently demonstrated by Fichte in his speeches to the German people; though whether the matter was always understood in this noble sense is another question. For the individuality of a nation, just like that of an individual, can be understood in a higher or a lower sense; if a people takes its own character as a great task, as a noble aim, it will unceasingly seek to improve itself, while testing and reviewing the existing state of things; thus it will recognize a general reason beyond all that is special and individual, and will subordinate its own conduct to this. Then the most powerful development of a nation can constitute no disadvantage or danger for any other nation. If, however, the national character, in its immediate condition, is unconditionally retained, glorified, and recklessly and passionately defended, then not only must the inner development of the nation come to a standstill, but there will arise a state of mutual repulsion and hostility amongst the different peoples. All the unfairness and bitterness formerly produced by the inter-religious conflicts may then experience a revival on the basis of nationalism; and in particular we may again see the employment of twofold weights and measures, in the sense that each demands for himself, as a right, that which he denounces as injustice when practiced by the others. Formerly it was said *cujus regio, ejus religio;* now we consider this barbaric. But will later generations think any better of the motto of *cujus regio, ejus natio,* which has to-day attained to such power? But such possibilities need not necessarily develop into actuality. The rational concept of nationality can assert itself, overcome mere nature, and form a main factor of moral education for the people of to-day. It is a retrogression to the eighteenth century to ignore this mighty stream of life and power, and to recognize the idea of humanity only in its abstract form.

Thus modern life is interwoven with a wealth of individual formations; through its whole length and breadth works a process of individualization which, with its form-giving and consolidating power, gives rise to inexhaustible moral impulses. It is another question, however, whether such an individualization of existence is easily reconcilable with that socialization which we have just considered, whether there is not here a sharp conflict of movements, accompanied by a tension between the moral influences. The two movements agree at any rate in one main tendency: in the elevation of man, in the greater care for his well-being, in the more powerful development of his existence. In both cases man forms the central point of reality. But this common feature does not remain free from attack; it encounters serious opposition from a department of life which in the first place should also be concerned only with man's welfare—from the *modern construction of work.*

We need not dwell upon the educative

and moral power of work. The inner development of man's true life, the growth beyond the early natural motives (which is the fundamental idea permeating our whole study), is never more conspicuous than at this point. The object, which man at first lays hold of from without and as a mere means for his purposes, becomes familiar to him and of value in itself, the more his activity becomes bound up with it and represented in it. Thus work becomes an end in itself and a source of pure joy to those who are carrying it forward. Now man can subordinate himself to the tasks of his work and in its success wholly lose sight of his own advantage. Therefore, the more energetic the work becomes, the more it grows to be a matter bound up with the whole man, the more it may serve as a liberation from petty egoism, the more it can contribute to an inner enlargement of man's being. Now it is obvious that the present day is more than any other age devoted to work, more than ever before is man's whole power put forth, more than ever before is our activity bound up with the objects, more than ever before is all success dependent upon their being overcome and appropriated. Thus work, too, should now exhibit its educative influence in the fullest degree. And in reality life does attain an immense earnestness; all idleness is banished, all purposeless activity is thrust aside, all self-will is rejected, when man comes under the disciplinary influence of the object and must obey, without escape, the law of the thing itself. There is here developed a consciousness of duty and an action in obedience to duty, which, in subordination to an objective order, in the recognition of a condition of dependency, at the same time arouses a feeling of dignity and greatness and lends a greater firmness to the whole of life.

At the same time, modern work, with its immense complexes, must force upon the individual the feeling that in himself he is capable of absolutely nothing, but that all success demands the co-operation of many individuals, and that the individual has no value apart from this common achievement. Thus attention is continually directed towards the matter as a whole, while the individual is impressed with a sense of his immeasurable littleness. *Multi pertransibunt et augibetur scientia.*

But this psychic influence on the part of work is subject to a condition: that which is brought by the outward occupation must be converted into inner feeling and be appropriated by the whole man; and everything which hinders this inward direction also endangers the influence. Now it is precisely at this point that the modern type of work exhibits serious dangers. Work has grown more and more beyond the immediate feeling and capacity of the individual; it has become more and more technical in character and has in this way become infinitely refined and differentiated. This increasing division, however, does not permit the individual to perceive more than an increasingly small fragment of the whole; and finally he and his thought, too, become tied down to this fragment. He no longer succeeds in holding the idea of the whole, he becomes a will-less cog in a great machine. Now he can no longer feel the work to be his own; he ceases to take pleasure in it and becomes indifferent or even hostile towards it. The spiritual contact with the object becomes increasingly less real, until ultimately the educative effect of work upon the soul entirely ceases. At the same time the spiritual influence of the work is reduced by reason of its feverish acceleration, which urges man forward from one accomplishment to another, gives rise to unceasing alteration, and does not permit even the strongest impression to strike roots in his soul. Finally the increasing intensity of the struggle for existence, the severe conflict of forces, with all its moral temptations, as produced and unceasingly accentuated by modern life, becomes a direct source of injury to the work of moral education. The excitement and passion of these struggles of individuals, classes and peoples, threatens to stifle all inner joy in the objects themselves and to suppress all feeling of solidarity. Thus work, which should, according to its innermost nature, bind men together, appears sharply to divide them and to drive them to unrelenting hostility.

The core of all these dangers is the separation of work from the soul and the overmastering of man by a soulless external activity. The unrestricted development of this tendency leads to a mechanization of existence, a reduction of man to a mere tool with a soul. The sharp antithesis to the motive forces of which we have just treated is obvious; in their case, man with his feeling and subjective condition experienced an immeasurable enhancement; now, on the other hand, he is deprived of all value in himself. In the former case he was treated as the highest end in itself; in the latter he becomes a mere will-less slave of work, a mere means in a soulless process of civilization. Only a dispirited feeling can endure such a contradiction.

Our study has shown that modern life, especially in its specific characteristics, is rich in moral motive forces. To fling all this away, and to complain of the age in sentimental or pharisaical vein, must therefore be looked upon as a fundamental mistake. But at the same time the movement of the age is shown to be full of problems; both the separate points and their mutual relationship offer great tasks and demand decisions of our own. That which is of spiritual importance has always first to be gained; the age has first to acquire its own ideality. The main points are here set forth as separate theses.

1. In the case of the individual motive forces, the general level of life exhibits a confused mixture of higher and lower conceptions, of action and reaction. An energetic division and a gathering together of the higher elements is in this case needful. And this can never under any circumstances result of itself from this condition of confusion; it demands a movement to the moral principles, a development of morality, not as a mere accompaniment of civilization, but as a complete end in itself.

2. As they exist in their immediate form the moral impulses of the age form an unendurable contradiction. Socialization and individualization draw us in opposite directions. And in sharp opposition to both stands the mechanization of life, an apparently unavoidable result of modern work. Such contradictions as these cannot be removed by means of fainthearted compromises, which may perhaps gladden the heart of academic philosophers, but which leave humanity indifferent. There is need of a courageous deepening of thought and life in order to grasp, in these antitheses, the different sides, tasks and relationships of an all-embracing reality.

3. Characteristic of all the modern motive forces is the movement from without towards within, from action to feeling, the gradual alteration and ennobling of the motives through the process of life. Such a movement is incomprehensible without the assistance of an inner nature, without a depth of the soul, uniting man with a spiritual order. This spiritual basis of our life is to-day obscured. It needs to be worked out and to be brought into prominence. Otherwise life remains empty in all its wealth and spiritless in all its activity.

It is obvious that all three theses point in the same direction. Our spiritual capacity must be more independently developed; our fundamental moral power must be revivified. This can never be given to us by the circumstances of the age. It is, and always must be, a free act on the part of man. Must we not believe that in our case, too, we shall find the courage to develop spiritual power? Can the German people, in particular, permanently forget that it gave rise to such great movements of moral renewal as the Reformation and the critical philosophy?

## Against Pessimism

As in the life of the individual so also in that of humanity we find waves of optimism and pessimism. At one time our whole activity and creative work is accelerated by a spirit of joy and courage; at another, doubt and discontent blight everything to which we lay our hands. These differences of mood do not arise in the first place from outward circumstances; ages filled with difficulty and trouble, and apparently wild, coarse and joyless, have nevertheless often preserved a feeling of joyful life; while, on the other hand, ages of success and pleasure frequently exhibit paralyzing doubt and profound depression. It is clear that the matter is by no means simple, that there are inward complications.

There is to-day a particular reason for studying this question. For it cannot be denied that in the midst of all our restless work and amazing successes there has arisen a pessimistic tendency, which grows ever stronger and stronger; all our brilliant triumphs do not assist us to obtain inward satisfaction and a feeling of joy in life. The very fact that we argue and ponder so much upon the meaning and value of life indicates that the situation is abnormal. We are unmistakably confronted with a problem, and with one that cannot be set aside; for it penetrates too deeply into the situation as a whole and into the state of each individual, too greatly stimulates, and too nearly concerns every one of us. What, then, is the source of this depression, so sharply contradicting the outward appearance of our life? It must surely be connected with experiences and disappointments which we have encountered in the pursuit of our aims. Let us see how the matter stands.

The nineteenth century saw a great movement away from the invisible world of religious faith, philosophical thought and artistic creation, and towards the things of the visible world, a movement bringing with it the victory of realism over idealism; and our common life is still pursuing this path.

This tendency seemed to clear away a heavy mist which had hitherto concealed from man the real nature of things; a much closer linking-up, nay interweaving, of man and his environment was now effected, and our every undertaking and action gained immensely in power and truthfulness. Now, for the first time, life seemed placed upon a secure basis; while at the same time endless tasks were revealed, the treatment and solution of which opened up limitless prospects. In all this there was expressed a mighty thirst for life, which found ever-increasing nourishment; the complete possession of our immediate existence and the task of shaping it to a kingdom of reason seemed to demand man's whole power and to fulfill his entire desire. This movement penetrated the whole of humanity; it rendered nature subordinate to us, both in an intellectual and in a technical sense; it altered the entire character of our work; in social affairs it banished much that was unjust and irrational; it developed justice and humanity incomparably more strongly than had hitherto been the case; it more and more drew every section of humanity into participation in the tasks and goods of life. These results are so obvious as to need no further comment.

We should have expected, when life became so much richer, more plastic, and more pleasurable, and when unceasing progress was made in every direction, that an overflowing happiness would have filled men's hearts. How does it come about that the very opposite has occurred, that we have become depressed rather than elated? This cannot be satisfactorily explained merely by arguing that what is taken up in youthful enthusiasm usually brings with it certain disappointments, that the resistance is apt to prove greater than was expected, that even in the case of success we do not find all that we hoped for, that where proud reason seemed to have established itself much that was irrational lay in concealment; all this would explain a certain lowering of our life-feeling, but not a complete reversal. The latter cannot be understood, unless the experiences of life have made our aims themselves uncertain and destroyed our faith in them. And to a very large extent this has taken place.

It has come to pass in this fashion. The powers which the modern life-impulse called into being have to a great extent separated themselves from our control, have come to dominate us, and threaten to direct themselves against us; now a soulless mechanism and now wild human passion endangers the rationality of life and poisons its joy. We have been proud of our modern work, and of the great relationships it has built up, and through which it accomplishes more than was possible in any previous age; but this work has detached itself from humanity and, heedless of man's welfare, has followed its own necessities alone, with the result that it threatens to reduce him to its helpless instrument. We have rejoiced over the greater mobility of life, with its intolerance of any sort of stagnation, but this mobility has become so vehement and life has grown so breathless that all peace and all true enjoyment of the present threaten to vanish. We have boasted of the thoroughgoing liberation accomplished by modern life in a political, social, and national sense; but this liberation has given rise to so much disintegration, so much embitterment, so much passionate hatred between parties, classes, and peoples, that its fruits are beginning to taste bitter. And here, as indeed throughout the whole, we perceive a development and extension of obscure forces to which we do not feel ourselves to be equal. We are painfully conscious of an inner weakness; and life, thus uncontrolled, becomes vacillating and insecure. Under these circumstances, all elevation may seem impossible and all aspiration futile. And this must be all the more oppressive the higher were our hopes, and the stronger the impulse with which the movement began. If modern life in its whole character thus becomes problematical, it nevertheless holds us much too fast for us to turn back to earlier, simpler, less mobile and less reckless ages; thus the whole outlook becomes clouded over and we can easily understand how it is that in such a situation a dark pessimism should increasingly prevail, and that it should appear impossible to wrest from these obscure forces a meaning and value for our life.

We should not, indeed, strive against a conclusion in this pessimistic vein, if it were really the true expression of the human, and in particular of the modern, condition of life; but we could not fully carry out this conclusion without the whole life-impulse collapsing, all our courage being extinguished, and our desire for happiness being wholly expelled from our souls; and life itself protests against this; it strives to resist such a self-negation, holds us fast, and compels us to seek some way out of the difficulty. In the first place it drives us to make certain whether pessimism itself does not involve complications, whether it does not of necessity lead us beyond itself and call upon us to seek other paths. If, in the pessimism of the present day, we perceive the product of a peculiar condition, this is itself perhaps something gained, for we are thus liberated from the pressure of an immense, obscure power, utterly disheartening us at the very beginning.

In the first place it is easy to perceive that pessimism cannot assert itself as a final conclusion without becoming exposed to an inward contradiction. From this standpoint sorrow and pain are decisive as to the character of the whole of life, and there is no recognition of any independent reality on the part of the good. The most elementary consideration, however, must convince us that we cannot very well begin with a loss, since we cannot lose anything which we do not possess. We cannot be grieved by the loss of anything, unless in the first place we value its possession. Thus ancient Greek and early Christian thinkers stood for the conviction that evil has no real existence of its own, but is merely a deprivation of good, just as the loss of sight is an evil only for those who can see, and would otherwise signify no loss whatever. Such a statement of the case may be open to objection; but at any rate we cannot doubt that all pain, more especially in relation to spiritual things, is ultimately referable to some good, even if the latter be limited or hidden. The experience of history, too, will confirm us in this opinion. Indian thought, for example, was greatly influenced by a belief in the transitory character of all earthly happiness, and the consequent emptiness of all human effort; it was considered folly to attach oneself to anything that must pass by like a shadow; here we are given a moving expression of the unceasing changes of the ages, of the replacement of one moment by another. But we may ask: How could this affect man with deep pain and touch his innermost feeling, if he did not carry within him a desire for eternity, and if his nature did not demonstrate, through the very strength of this desire, the fact that it belongs to a timeless order? How could the changefulness of things disturb us, if, like the flies who are born and die in the same day, we belonged to the mere moment? The very power of this pain itself is the witness of a greater depth in human being. Within Christianity it was the moral condition of man, the inadequacy —nay, the perversity, of his feelings, with which life was in the first place occupied, and which compelled it to a gloomy mode of thought; the idea of moral depravity lay upon men's minds as a terrible burden. But moral error would itself be impossible if man was not in some way fitted for morality; he must possess some capacity for personal decision, some freedom of conduct, in order to be capable of error. Moreover, he could not suffer from his error and feel it as a loss to himself if he did not contain some power of good which was working against evil. Pessimism, in taking a moral turn, makes the mistake of perceiving and valuing the hindrance alone, and not the aspiration which experiences the hindrance. But this aspiration is also a part of life and must be taken into account in our valuation of the whole. Pascal was right when he said: *"Qui se trouve malheureux de n'être pas roi, si non un roi dépossédé?"*

These considerations may well be applied to the situation of to-day; however many hindrances, complications and perversities may weigh upon us and cause us pain, they are able to affect us in this way solely because, in our case, life has acquired a greater energy, has more boldly attacked the most difficult tasks, and has more valiantly striven for freedom in the struggle against fate, than did the life of any earlier age. Thus an impartial vision and a just valuation must perceive that in spite of every hindrance life is growing and must rejoice in the power which springs forth at every point and permeates every relationship. When we compare our own age with the latter days of the antique world (a period with which it is often unjustly associated), we immediately perceive how sharply it should be distinguished from an age which was in reality empty and fatigued, and how characteristic is its effervescing life-energy. When life is predominantly passive it clings, in the first place, to its sensations, and allows itself to be completely dominated by its resistances; if, on the other hand, it is controlled by a powerful impulse towards activity, then the life-process grows beyond the position of mere sensation and ceases to be able wholly to surrender itself to its resistances.

But although such considerations may serve to refute an absolute pessimism, the pessimist in a wider sense need not yet consider himself defeated. For although he is forced to admit that life contains a depth, of what use is this depth if it cannot attain to a proper development? That which is latent within it will not then be able to come together for common action, and life will remain divided and incapable of free development. And this contradiction and the impossibility of overcoming it would justify pessimism, although of a milder type.

Thus all hope of success in the overcoming of pessimism depends upon the possibility of arousing these depths to movement and in some way enabling them to prevail against the resistances. Again, let our consideration of the present be preceded by a glance at the world-historical movement. Within the Indian religions, and within Christianity, it has been found possible to move these depths, but this has not been achieved upon the basis of the broad and immediate experience, but only through an elevation above it, only through a reversal of the immediate condition of life. Thus Indian life ob-tained a liberation from the confusions of time, a rest in an unchanging eternity through its amalgamation with the all-permeating Divine being; thus Christian belief took refuge in an all-powerful love which liberated man from every need, created for him a new and more pure life, and, at the same time, gave his true nature (until then obscured and limited) its fullest realization. Embracing the older types the life-problem presents itself today in a more universal fashion; the possibility of bringing about a movement and a development which shall overcome the resistances now depends wholly upon the capacity, through such an expansion, of reaching a new position; it is a question of whether life as a whole can achieve an inner elevation—nay, a reversal, which shall make it superior to the complications of the human situation. Unless this question can be answered in the affirmative there is no possibility of life taking a positive turn. For it is established beyond doubt that we cannot progress in any essential way beyond the chaos of the present situation as the result of any merely subjective emotion or activity.

We can, however, with confidence return an affirmative answer. Life as a whole contains far more than is apparent from the first impression. For the life of man does not exhaust itself in the life-impulse of the separate points and in the exploitation of the forces to be found here, nor in the activities which result from their competition and conflict. In opposition to this disintegration, life comes together to form a whole, and it is precisely this whole which we call *spiritual life*. In it there becomes visible a cosmic movement, an ascent of reality to a new stage far transcending the desire and capacity of the mere man. Working through all the manifold activities of man, this spiritual life accomplishes an inner construction, and builds up for itself a world of its own. It exhibits a creative capacity in the construction of whole departments of life, with their own contents and norms, such as science and art, law and morality; it raises the movement of life above all the aims of the mere man, and opens up a kingdom of universally valid values lying beyond all utility; it develops a spiritual culture in the face of all superficial and merely human culture; it is able to arouse a self-active and original life in every individual, notwithstanding the claims and ties of the existing situation, a life in which he directly experiences the new world as a whole, thus becoming a world-embracing personality. (This view of the spiritual life, into which we cannot here enter in detail, is more adequately dealt with in *The Meaning and Value of Life,* trans. Lucy Judge Gibson and Professor Boyce Gibson; pub. A. and C. Black.)

In turning to this new life the complications of human existence are by no means eliminated. Our immediate existence holds us fast, and only through setting ourselves apart from it and through appropriating the power it contains, can the work of spiritual construction be successful. Much that is strange and obscure remains mingled with our life, and an optimism which, through a mere change in the angle of observation, believes itself able to convert the whole into life and reason is an untenable thing, and indeed from the earliest times has been found rather in books of philosophy than in the conviction of humanity. But through the recognition of the living presence of this new world we may hold ourselves fully secured against pessimism with its paralyzing power. For henceforth we are surrounded by greater relationships, we are driven by a superior power, and there can be no doubt of a great goal. Such a deepening and consolidation permits of a powerful combination of all that lends a spiritual impulse to our existence, thus making it effective as a whole. Even when our work does not attain to a complete conclusion, a further development of life can take place; in this case even outward loss may prove a gain.

Taking up this standpoint, we find ourselves confronted by a new picture of existence. From the former standpoint the resistance in the things appeared to be excessive, and the movement threatened to go beyond the guidance of reason. That would be a hopeless evil if our power were confined within a given limit and were incapable of any essential expansion. The possibility of such an expansion is provided, however, by the spiritual life in which our being is grounded. This life is not a given and limited quantity: it carries an infinity in its creative power; and the man who participates in the life can continually draw new force from this infinity; he can now make new beginnings, and effect an inner elevation of life. Considered from this point of view the world-historical work no longer appears as a peaceful progress along a predetermined path; doubt and movement are continually attacking the whole; through severe upheavals new tendencies are developed, new forces are brought into being, and new relationships are discovered. That which has thus been exhibited in the past will be valid also for the present and the future. The complications of the age, reviewed from this standpoint, are realized to be indications of a great renewal of life still in a condition of flux, which, in the first place, makes itself felt predominantly as a negation, but which could not possibly penetrate so deeply into the condition of things if constructive forces were not already operative in it. It must be our duty to develop these according to our best capacity and to set them in the foreground of life. A joyful view of human affairs will then return, and in the midst of all the resistances a joyful belief in life will assert itself.

A consideration of our study as a whole permits us to realize what it is which to-day stands in question: the earlier constructions of life have become too narrow for us, doubt and anxiety now extend to life as a whole, and it is our task to deepen the latter and find in it the foundation of a universal spiritual development and culture, which utilizes everything which the past can contribute, while reaching beyond everything thus received to new heights. For the time being, we perceive only the beginnings of this, but even these beginnings make the age, in spite of all its confusion and incompleteness, one of greatness and importance. It is great in the wealth of its tasks, which no longer merely distract us, but become subordinate to a central aim; it is great in the breadth of its life, in the independence of its search and struggle, in the ever-increasing desire for new depths. Never before has life as a whole been in such a condition of flux, never before has the struggle penetrated so deeply into the ultimate things. In the midst of such a conflict we cannot dispense with a firm faith, but what is now needed is not a faith in remote things, but in the spiritual life which breaks through in us and is able to create in us a new being. Such a vital faith we must have and may have, if we remain true to our own being, and at the same time enter into relationship with the infinite creative force. Then the age, which to a timid eye appeared small, can become great, and we can joyfully feel ourselves to be its children. We can find in it a value for our life and be of the firm conviction that to-day, as in former ages, no real work is lost.

From the earliest times, spring (and Easter in particular) have been to seekers after truth a symbol for the capacity of renewal, and the regenerative power of spiritual life; for they represent to us the inexhaustible and perpetually renewed force of nature. Therefore let us hope that now, too,* the contemplation of the budding and blooming life around us may strengthen in us the conviction that spiritual life, as well as nature, possesses an eternal youth, and that we human beings are able to participate in this youth.

## Philosophical Parties

The history of philosophy exhibits not only schools dependent upon particular distinguished personalities, not only sects ramifying out and separating themselves from the general movement of the whole, not merely different tendencies and types of thought, peacefully existing side by side, but also divisions of such a character that they can hardly be described otherwise than as *parties*. For we must speak of parties and of a party conflict when a split is formed which goes beyond any personal relationship, sides coming into being, each of which claims the whole for itself. Each of these sides comprehends its specific character in a thesis, this forming a point of concentration; and at this point it enters upon a severe struggle for existence, a struggle which is able to drag the whole sphere of knowledge into its vortex. An essential characteristic, too, is that each side gains a larger or smaller circle of sympathizers, thus constituting a centre where many persons unite for collective influence and for the purpose of conflict. A division of this kind, within philosophy, embraces departments which may be large or small. We shall be primarily occupied, in the present instance, with those cases in which the division and the conflict extends itself, in an ideal sense, over the whole field. We shall direct our attention not to logical, ethical, or metaphysical

---

* This essay was written in March, 1910.

schisms in particular, but to general philosophical parties.

Does the history of philosophy present the spectacle of a continuous conflict? It would appear not. Only at particular periods does the struggle break out in full force. In between there are periods when different bodies of thought and feeling exist tolerantly side by side, or even when all opposition seems extinguished. Nevertheless, the formation of parties and their conflict, the fact of party divisions, remains a phenomenon of thoroughgoing importance. The more full the life which pulses through philosophy, the more energetic is the division of men's minds; the more rapidly knowledge progresses, the more movement and change of parties it usually brings with it; on the other hand, it demonstrates an undesirable state of things, when there is no concentration of isolated forces in the defence of common convictions, or when divisions which have lost their vitality continue to drag out a meaningless existence. The struggle at the summit, at the critical points, is decisive, in its consequences, for the whole. Even if the conflict ends, the antithesis remains. The difference, once recognized, can never again fully disappear from our consciousness. There is no peace, but only a truce, unless—which is exceptional—the problem itself dies out. It thus remains correct that the effect of the struggle and the party division extends virtually to the whole, that the party division is something which must be taken into account in the general movement of philosophy.

We see, however, that party division and party conflict occur under all kinds of different circumstances. When a new movement works its way upwards, it must attack the old which already holds the field. And the mere fact of war breaking out between them is in itself sufficient to drag down the older body of thought from its position of security, to narrow it to a party thing, to force it into a defensive position; it now sinks to be a mere sect, an antiquated standpoint, just as, in the sphere of religion, the new belief displaces the old, reducing it to the level of a superstition. But the victorious new movement itself cannot long escape division. Soon old antitheses spring up on the new soil, albeit in changed form, and again there is a cleavage of opinion: for example, after the gigantic upheaval brought about by Kant, Spinoza and Leibniz were resuscitated in the persons of Hegel and Herbart. Or possibly the new position undergoes a schism, which so splits up the work and so embitters those who are carrying on the struggle, that the common basis is thereby completely forgotten. This took place at the beginning of the modern philosophical period, after the Cartesian revolution. The movement of knowledge and life is continually producing fresh formations; and it would thus seem as if these must cut across one another and the general situation become more and more complicated. But opposed to this progressive complexity, is the impulse to let fall that which has become useless or unimportant, to subordinate all separate oppositions to one comprehensive antithesis, not to weaken the contrast, but to carry through a single *either–or*. Thus we see at the beginning of the new age, and also in the case of Kant, the disappearance of all previous party division with its ramifications, before the ascending problems. There is thus an opposition in the movement; an impulse towards further ramification and an impulse towards simplification work against one another, and continually create fresh situations and tasks.

The movement enhances an antithesis which springs from the relationship of the person to the party. Those who are engaged in the work cannot very well admit that right is divided among the parties without weakening the firmness of their conviction and the intensity of their energy. There can be only one truth; therefore he who defends a certain conviction must defend it as being exclusive. He can no more permit it to be divided than the true mother who appeared before Solomon could allow her child to be cut asunder. If he were contented, accordingly, to consider his side as a mere party he would be giving up the whole; he must therefore desire it to be more than a party. Furthermore, he cannot allow the other side to reckon as a party, since this would be admitting a certain right on its part and a limit on his own. What is too little for him is too much for another. It follows that the party is not a basis upon which one could ever wish to abide. In reality the conflicting parties are engaged throughout in endeavouring to raise themselves above the party position, while thrusting their opponents below it, and seeking to represent them as sectarians divorced from all universally valid convictions. And just this easily comprehensible, nay unavoidable, endeavour of each party to be more than a party, leads to ever fresh formations, and at the same time to new party divisions. This takes place, more especially, in two different ways. The one investigator strives to rise above the opposition by introducing a new element, presumed to be superior to it, and elevated above party conflict. But hardly is this developed, and to some extent consolidated, before it itself is looked upon by the others as a party, or gives rise to party constructions. What was meant as universal, is not able, as the movement progresses, to escape particularity. Another, on the other hand, will not admit any antithesis at all; the right, he declares, lies wholly on the one side. And now it becomes his duty to stop the conflict at its root, to prove that the opposite side is absolutely devoid of foundation. This, however, will be possible only

if he deepens his own position, and (even if secretly) reconstructs it. Thus the situation continually alters, although those who are participating are not necessarily conscious of this. Hardly anything stimulates the conflict so much as that which was intended to extinguish it. A sort of party mechanism is the result of the combined operation of motive forces due to personal considerations, and those arising from what is inherent in the matter itself. From this particular standpoint it is possible to obtain a characteristic view of the history of philosophy as a whole.

The phenomenon of party division in general necessarily becomes a problem when considered in broad and systematic fashion. There is only one truth, and it belongs to humanity as a whole. Is it not a contradiction of its being when we treat it as a party matter; and must not such a treatment injure the work and imperil its success? The phenomenon is one which undoubtedly demands explanation. It is to be expected, moreover, that the discussion of the matter will throw a peculiar light upon the entire task of knowledge and provoke thoughts or general interest.

The explanation of the phenomenon offered by scepticism is, in appearance, the simplest. Unfortunately, however, this explanation, at bottom, explains absolutely nothing. The continual reconstruction of parties, their restless ascent and descent, the contrast between the claim of the individual to be complete and his actual limitation—all this appears to the sceptic to prove that philosophy is no more than a juxtaposition of individual opinions, all equally right and equally wrong, and that its history is a mere to-and-fro movement of such opinions. But the phenomenon of party division itself contradicts this conception. In the formation of a party there takes place a union of many individuals, a combination of separate forces in a common task; and this is achieved from within and not through outward pressure. How could completely isolated forces effect an inward combination? How is a summation of elements, an even partially permanent concentration upon a given point, possible, if there be no common basis, no capacity for mutual understanding? The conflict could not give rise to so much excitement, so much movement, nay, as a spiritual conflict, it could not come into being at all, if the misunderstanding were complete, if the different circles merely existed side by side, wholly cut off from one another. Why are we not able to permit other convictions to reckon as of equal value with our own, somewhat as in the case of sensuous impressions? Whence comes the impulse common to all parties towards a truth superior to the party position? Everything points to a more deep-lying complication than scepticism is able to explain. There are reasons compelling us to regard the party as more than an accidental aggregation of subjective opinions. But the question of its real nature and significance remains open, and urges us to another explanation.

In the realm of philosophy, as in other departments of life, two factors go to the formation of a party: there must be inherent in the matter itself antitheses, or at any rate different sides, stages or possibilities—without such an inherent basis the party has no hold and sinks to be a mere faction or côterie; and, further, in the special historical position of the period, a particular antithesis must make itself felt above all the others and must enter into the life of the period, dividing men and at the same time drawing them together. Thus whatever formations may be derived from the historical movement will point back to problems inherent in the matter itself.

It is thus easy to perceive in what different ways the task of philosophy can be taken up and directed. In distinction from the ramification of the separate sciences, philosophy strives towards a completeness of knowledge, a view of reality as a whole. But even this first step at once gives rise to complication and division. Has philosophy simply to take up the position communicated to it by the other sciences, or has it to develop this position further, according to the laws and demands which philosophy contains within itself? Is its attitude to be reflective only, or is it also to be productive? Is the desired union a mere selection of the common features, a piecing together of the given material, hardly worthy to be described as a synthesis, or can philosophy in truth bring the things nearer to one another, perhaps precisely in this very way more clearly exhibiting their distinctions? Does its work carry its standard within itself, or must it seek it without? We know what great conflict has raged around this problem, a conflict which has continued down to the present day. On the one hand, the more comprehensive claim is rejected on the score of overboldness and exaggeration, and is regarded as a falling away from scientific work; on the other, the limitation of philosophy is scorned as an abandonment of its independence. The conflict reaches its greatest intensity around the question of the possibility and necessity of metaphysics; for millenniums the metaphysicians and the anti-metaphysicians have stood at daggers drawn. From the earliest times, it has been peculiar to metaphysics to assert that the demands of thought lead to an irreconcilable conflict with the immediate view of reality, and that, in the case of such conflict, thought has the right and the duty to alter this view according to its claims, cleansing it from its contradictions, and causing the inner necessities of thought to prevail against every resistance.

The metaphysical path has not always been pursued with the same energy; and thus the degrees of transformation due to philosophical influence have been different. It is obvious, however, that the work of philosophy has exercised, in various directions, an immense influence upon the world of thought, not, however, without itself undergoing a division to the point of complete opposition. Let us examine these directions and their associated conflicts a little more in detail.

That philosophy overlooks the whole of the human task of knowledge does not signify that it must subordinate multiplicity to a unity, or even cause the former entirely to disappear. For it might well be that this comprehensive review, this consideration of the position of things as a whole, would rather have the effect of bringing out with increased clearness the differences between particular things and between the various departments of life, thus separating them from one another more sharply. We find, accordingly, that there are two different types of thought. The one seeks to view the things together as a whole, treating the differences as secondary and letting them drop as far as possible into the background; it understands and values the separate things according to their places in the whole. In following this path there is a danger of slurring over the specific character of the individual thing, pushing forward too quickly to a smooth conclusion, and producing an artificial simplification, easily accompanied by superficiality. This gives the opposed mode of thought a right to lay the greatest possible stress upon the individuality of particular things, to pay attention to contradictions, and rather to leave the problems unsolved than settle them with too great facility. In this case the concrete content of reality and with it the specific character of human knowledge come far more to recognition; but at the same time there arises the danger of an abandonment of the solidarity of reality and of a premature suspension of the

conflict against the irrational element in the human situation. So the struggle sways now in this direction, now in that, and continually produces new formations. It is obvious that there is here an opposition not merely of opinions, but of types of thought, which no mere logical argument can bring together. According, in each case, to the difference in general tendency there result opposed ideals for the whole of life and conduct. On the one hand, the main demand appears to be for subordination to the whole, for an emphasis upon what is in common, and for the expulsion of all that is specific and distinctive, as if it were no more than an obstacle (*omnis determinatio negatio*); on the other, it is precisely the distinctive which appears important and valuable, and what is uniform presents itself as something lower, as a mere beginning beyond which the movement must progress. When the opposition is so sharp, the parties to which it gives rise can be at one only in the rejection of a mediatory compromise. An overcoming of the opposition would demand a new standpoint, and in the midst of the party strife this appears unattainable.

Philosophy divides the world of thought and sunders life itself, in another direction, in the case of the problem of rest and movement, of time and eternity. The customary view of things provides a mixture of the two which appears unbearably confused when subjected to more energetic methods of thought, and philosophy thus insists upon a separation, thereby itself developing in directly opposite directions. On the one hand, all movement and change appear to be tainted with an inner contradiction, and to be a mere appearance, so that our view of reality should be radically purified of this element; on the other, a resting, stationary being is regarded as an impossibility, and everything of this nature which has found its way into our view of reality seems to be no more than an appearance which it is the task of our thought energetically to remove in order to bring the whole into flux, and to understand all being from the standpoint of becoming. The resultant division of opinion gives rise to fundamentally different ideals of life: in the first instance we have an effort to achieve, as far as possible, a condition of permanence, to find true happiness in a rest superior to the world, in the contemplation and treatment of things *sub specie æterni;* in the second, we have a whole-hearted submergence in the stream of time, a realization of the highest satisfaction in a restless effort to move further and further. In opposition to this division all kinds of attempts are made to overcome the antithesis, and to bring rest and movement, time and eternity into a relationship of mutual completion; but in so far as these attempts go beyond weak compromise, they are apt to produce new schisms and new party formations. Those who take the problem earnestly seem never to come to a resting-point.

Although the previous oppositions penetrate very deeply into the structure of life, we may describe them as being predominantly formal. Still greater becomes the tension when we come to concern ourselves with the problem of content, when we ask the question: Which department of reality has to provide the dominating position for the view of the world as a whole? The main consideration here is that for us civilized people the world seems to be given in twofold fashion: from without and from within, as a physical and as a psychical phenomenon. Once we have become clearly conscious of this antithesis, it seems impossible to allow the juxtaposition quietly to remain; now the one must subordinate itself to the other, and the only question is which is primary and which secondary, which original and which derived. Thus, on the one hand we have an attempt to place

everything psychical—including all spiritual and intellectual work—under the sway of natural concepts, while refusing to recognize anything as true reality which cannot show itself to be natural, in the broad sense of the word. This tendency carries with it a thoroughly characteristic construction of life and civilization; it involves an expulsion of all independent and self-valuable psychic life, a binding down of the whole of life to the environment, and consequently an elevation of sensuous goods to be the main objects of all effort.

On the other hand, we perceive an endeavour to convert the outer world into a mere appearance of the inner life, while building up the latter to be an independent and self-sufficient world, to whose purposes everything is to be subordinated. This is accompanied by the danger of a slurring over of the characteristic features of the outer world, as well as of an emptiness on the part of the inner life, detached as it is from all that is external.

In opposition to an antithesis which reaches down so deeply into the basic structure of life, there arises an aspiration towards reconciliation and an overcoming of the contrast, and we note the development of a "monistic" mode of thought. But along with this there goes a new assertion, which (in as far as when carried out in detail it does not relapse into the antithesis), brings with it a new union, and at the same time a new division of opinion. Further, this "monistic" development gives rise to unlimited differences of opinion as to the more exact comprehension of nature and of the inner life; in the case of nature, for example, it is a question whether the mathematical-physical or the organical-biological side should dominate our concepts; and, in the case of the inner life, it is a matter of dispute what content should be given to the spiritual life. There result possibilities upon possibilities, and these invite to the formation of parties, provided that the historical situation impels to an appropriation of one or other of them, and a conversion of it into living conviction.

The varied life which results from the development and conflict of these possibilities, is able wholly to absorb men's minds as long as the struggle surges to and fro and each party hopes to obtain a final victory. But ultimately there will come a time of relaxation and self-recollection, and then we shall inevitably find ourselves confronted with the question whether the whole yields any sort of secure result, whether all the inexpressible trouble and labour does not lead but deeper into confusion. Then scepticism raises its head; for its principal argument has always been that reason, in its struggle for truth, unavoidably becomes wrapped in contradictions, and that it gives rise to incompatible statements which are equally right and equally wrong, and each of which, although able successfully to attack the opposed doctrine, is impotent to secure its own position.* And those who avoid falling into scepticism cannot simply close their ears to its argument and avoid the difficulties involved in the metaphysics which it attacks. The latter undertook, at any rate in its older form, to draw inferences from thought and apply them to the neighbouring world; being must correspond, it was

believed, to that which was demanded by the necessities of thought. But such a passage from thought to being presupposes an inner relationship between the two, the existence of a common world embracing the two; for in this way alone can that which applies to one side be valid also upon the other.

But how is this supposition to be grounded, and how can we trust this necessity of thought, when it leads in such opposed directions and divides us so seriously amongst ourselves? For every man believes himself to follow the necessity of thought, when he follows his own path.

The consideration and experience of such doubt must shake the old-fashioned metaphysic in the severest possible way; and those who do not give themselves up to negation, must necessarily seek a new concept of truth and must develop the task of philosophy in an essentially new direction. And here there seems to be only one possible path: there must be a movement from the objective to the subjective: even if the world of things is inaccessible to our thought, yet the latter retains its own active influence and governing power, and in place of knowledge of the world there will be the self-knowledge of the thinking and knowing spirit. We know with what power Kant effected this revolution, and how he believed his work to have secured, if not an inert peace, at any rate a safe and right position for all ages, while at the same time putting a definite end to all party division. But it soon appeared that the subject, which was to provide this firm basis, is not so simple and secure; and that as much division and strife could arise as to its proper comprehension as with regard to the attainment of the object. For a world, even if it is only a world of phenomena, cannot be supported by the subject (which thus gains an object of knowledge) unless the latter is something more than an isolated and changeable

---

* Thus, to the older scepticism, the equilibrium of "for" and "against" was a main weapon; a further application of this thought we came across in the case of Bayle; we see it, in its grandest development, in Kant. According to the latter's conviction the inevitable shipwreck of all attempts to obtain an insight into the supersensuous becomes most obvious when we consider that "there are principles in our reason, which, in opposition to every statement explaining these matters, sets up a contradictory statement, apparently just as well founded; and reason herself destroys her own attempts."

point, unless it contains a permanent and common spiritual organization; violent conflict can, nay must, soon arise upon this point. Such an organization, claiming, as it does, law-giving power, goes beyond immediate experience and from the experiential standpoint may be objected to as being metaphysical; those who retain it will, however, easily be driven beyond the Kantian position and be compelled to undertake the development of an independent spiritual world. And here we have fresh complications; in this case human capacity may easily seem overstrained, and the content of the spiritual life appear one-sidedly conceived.

These complications are clearly perceptible in the case of Hegel; whatever may be our opinion of his achievement, no one can assert that his philosophy settled the problem of truth. The strife of parties was not brought to an end by Kant; but has raged since his time more furiously than ever; the movement towards the subject, so far from composing the discord, merely transferred it to another place, a place where uncertainty and division are still less endurable. All the same, a change was effected that cannot be undone; philosophy no longer finds itself confronted with a given and indisputable task, but has itself to shape this task. In this way the struggle takes hold far more deeply of the fundamental concept of life and of our fundamental relationship to reality. In particular it is obvious that a definite relationship between subject and object, between man and world, cannot be presupposed as secure, but is first to be discovered and to be defined clearly. This cannot be accomplished, however, except by beginning with that which it is possible directly to experience; it is thus our task to lay hold of life, and as far as possible to grasp it as a whole, in order from this standpoint to explain the meaning of knowledge and obtain a picture of reality. But the hard-

est conflict of all breaks out with regard to the question of what shall be reckoned the nearest and the most certain.

Now we reach the point at which there is the sharpest and the most irreconcilable cleavage of opinion.

Some look upon the sensations with their relationships as being the immediate and therefore the only real things. This conviction cannot be strictly carried through without the division between an inner and an outer world appearing a superfluity, nay, a disastrous error. Thus all metaphysic vanishes, and with it all possibility in general of any penetration behind the surface and the stream of sensations. There could hardly be any question of a content in life, and of a life of our own, if this type of thought were not imperceptibly complemented by elements borrowed from other relationships. Philosophy in this case would become a mere science of sensations.

Others, however, are driven beyond this position through the consideration that there are no such things as free, isolated sensations but only *my* sensations and *your* sensations, that the ego cannot result from the sensations but is presupposed by them. It is the ego, which, in the life-process, and not merely in the opinion of philosophers, raises itself up from the separate events and is able to offer opposition to them. Life thus acquiring a centre, that which previously seemed to be the whole now becomes peripheral, and the separation of an inward and an outward within life itself becomes unavoidable. At the same time man and the world fall further apart, and there arises a conflict between the two. This results in a characteristic conception of the task of knowledge, and in a characteristic view of reality.

But at the same time complications make themselves felt, and impel us beyond this position. Psychic life confined to particular points could never under any circumstances impart a content to life, or lead to scientific knowledge. The point from which a world has separated itself, would never be able to draw this world back to itself and inwardly to master it. Thus the question crops up, whether life by itself is not able to construct relationships which take on a cosmic character; there arises the question whether a spiritual life does not separate itself from the psychic life, a spiritual life superior to the antithesis of subject and object and able to produce from itself an autonomous reality. The individual man rather gains a part in this life than originates it through his own capacity; his life becomes a striving upward beyond the first position of things; it must transfer its centre of gravity and seek real immediacy and its own firm basis beyond the nearest psychic processes. And this carries with it an assertion pregnant with consequences, compelling a division of opinion; a spiritual life thus growing independent is reckoned by some as the indispensable presupposition of all science and human culture, as well as of all spiritual individuality and personality, while to others this appears as an arbitrary and almost inconceivable hypothesis, a reckless and senseless plunge into the unknown. The antithesis, however, which is here in question reaches far beyond the conscious foundation, and reveals itself in the most varied forms throughout the whole history of philosophy. On the one side, spiritual goods and contents take the first place, seeming to exist independently of man and to communicate themselves to him, to measure him, to raise him to themselves; on the other, they seem to develop from a human basis and not to be able to give up the connection with the human mode of presentment and human interests; in the first case, thought asserts its independence of man's ideas, and the good separates itself from the agreeable and useful; in the second, the former

(*i.e.,* thought and the good) must appear to be produced through the mere further development of the latter (*i.e.,* man's ideas and the agreeable and useful). Thus there arise obviously and fundamentally different types of life and knowledge. Is work carried on upon a merely human basis, or does it depend upon spiritual contents and necessities? The answer to this question divides human conviction more than almost anything else.

Further complications and divisions arise from the different ways in which the relationship of the spiritual life to reality may be understood. The conception of its own core is very closely connected with this problem. The spiritual life will bring a self-dependence on the part of reality (*Beisichselbstsein der Wirklichkeit*); but in our human sphere, however, such a self-dependence must first work its way up in the face of conditions of another kind, and it cannot be thought of without an antithesis. Then the question crops up: What is its attitude towards this other element; is it securely superior to the latter and is it able wholly to subject it, nay, to convert it into itself, or does it encounter a hard resistance, in conflict with this being driven (inwardly, too) beyond the original position? The one side believes itself able to rate the resistance so low that it can be completely overcome, if not at once, bit by bit; it does not regard the disturbance as penetrating to the interior of the spiritual life, and the latter is looked upon as needing only to put forth its entire power, in order to master every resistance. So we obtain an optimistic idealism, under whose influence the task of knowledge must assume a characteristic shape. For if the spiritual life, with its human form, occupies a position of such secure superiority, and if it may regard itself as the core of all reality, it will be able, of itself, to open up knowledge, and possesses the power to penetrate with certainty to the last depths of truth. In this case, speculation, with its inner movement of thought, will maintain a superiority over against all experience.

The situation takes on a totally different aspect if the resistance be conceived as rigid and unconquerable, if the complication affects the very centre of the spiritual life, if an unbridgeable gulf opens up between our human capacity and the tasks which it is impossible for us to avoid. This is the position which gives rise to pessimism, and at the same time to a higher type of scepticism. There is not in this case any denial of a rational task; the laws of thought are recognized as effective, and the concepts of the true and the good are not rejected. But they do not acquire, in the human sphere, a power adequate to secure their prevalence; all the effort they cost us only exhibits the distance which removes them from us and makes us aware of our incapacity; thought will, in this case, dwell more especially upon the contradictions. If, at the same time, the demand cannot be evaded and if it unceasingly confronts man with the entire inadequacy of his accomplishment, nay, with the futility of all his efforts, the contradiction must paralyze the vital nerve of his life and creative work; and the struggle for truth, too, must finally realize its complete hopelessness and collapse. For in the long run this struggle cannot be kept up by continually reminding ourselves of contradictions and thus destroying false imaginings.

Again we find ourselves at a point where opinion divides. The paralyzing influence of pessimism leads some to complete negation; while others find the complications which pessimism points out, to be impulses towards the discovery of new paths, thus making them means and instruments for the deepening of life. For the latter purpose, merely subjective wishing and willing are inadequate; to this end an inner development of spiritual life will be necessary, a penetration to a core inaccessible to the complications. There must be an advance from a universal to a characteristic spirituality. This is the path along which the religions move: but the problem reaches beyond the religions into life as a whole. Throughout it is a question of an inner gradation of life, and of an attempt to carry out, in a sphere of concentrated spirituality and personal conviction, that which could not be accomplished for life as a whole. But such an inner gradation of life would transform its whole appearance; it would work towards the preservation of the task as a whole in the midst of all complications and contradictions. Again, therefore, we have a characteristic type of life and thought, a concrete idealism, which pushes forward through the negation to an affirmation and keeps the yea and the nay in mind at the same time. In this case the task of knowledge must ultimately gain a positive conclusion, after passing through energetic criticism and manifold resignation.

Thus we have a wealth of types of life and thought, all witnessing that the conflict of parties is not a result of freely ranging reflection, impelling some in one direction, and some in another, but rather arises from the fact that the core of life is being sought in different places and the work of thought is accordingly shaping itself in fundamentally different fashions. It is obvious that we are not struggling so much for the interpretation of a common given reality, as for the shaping of reality itself, and in this work the very greatest importance must attach to that which man makes of his own life and to his manner of understanding it. Whether, in its particular manifestations, the development of life goes essentially beyond the customary aim of natural and social self-preservation, and at the same time the inner life wins an independence; whether man finds great tasks in this inner life, and in working at them becomes superior to his entire environment; and whether, finally, difficult complications become noticeable and force us to an inner transformation—all these points are of far greater importance for the formation of the thought-world than anything which may present itself from without. For it is this inner which first communicates to the outer its meaning and value; the same facts can be interpreted in fundamentally different ways, according to whether they are included in this or that relationship, referred to this or that life-centre. As it is with individuals, so it is with peoples and ages; the decisive point in the conflict lies considerably deeper down than the point at which we are accustomed to look for it. The concepts and doctrines are only the appearance of spiritual energies, and if this were not so the passionate conflict they arouse would be inexplicable.

When the problem is thus taken a stage deeper, the formation and development of philosophical parties acquires an enhanced interest. The antitheses themselves, as we find them inherent in our nature and attitude towards the world, are very far from being the source of such division; for this purpose the problem must become prominent and must be appropriated; this will take place, however, under particular historical circumstances, and is therefore to be understood only from the standpoint of history. The nature of the work, the working out of new groups of facts, a fortunate advance of work in a particular direction, the inner condition of humanity, the predominance of a feeling of strength or of weakness, the emergence of dominating personalities who induce humanity to follow their paths—all these factors operate together. If the analysis be sufficiently penetrating, it is possible to obtain, from the standpoint of philosophical party division, a sort of history of the work of thought.

The matter must, it is true, be treated with great caution. For the position of the parties is by no means a pure expression of the spiritual situation. Movements may exist and exert influence in a particular age, and yet not come to a tangible concentration so as to give rise to parties; moreover, party formations made in earlier and inwardly remote ages, may preserve themselves through the dead weight of their existence, and unite and divide men at a point which is no longer the vital centre of the antithesis. To-day, in particular, in philosophy, as well as in politics and religion, we have often to do with party divisions which are inwardly obsolete, and on this account, the real antitheses do not get a chance of adequate unfoldment. As compared with the disintegration into numbers of little circles and factions, there is a lack of great dividing lines of conflict. It is characteristic of the real antitheses of the present day that they penetrate far more deeply down into the basic content of life and are therewith concerned much more with principles than has been the case in most other ages. Formerly men differed as to the paths by which the goal might be reached; but to-day the goals themselves have become uncertain. In former times, for example, men disputed as to the derivation of morality; while, to-day, morality itself has become insecure.* It is only to be wished that the true state of things should attain to full and clear expression in the formation of the parties.

---

* Sorley justly observes: "We have no longer the same common basis of agreement to rely upon that our predecessors had a generation ago. There are many indications in recent literature that the suggestion is now made more readily than it was twenty or thirty years ago that the scale of moral values may have to be revised. . . . Modern controversy would not hesitate to call in question the received code of morality, and to revise our standard of right and wrong."

In reviewing the history of conflicts and parties in philosophy we may feel inclined to ask the question whether, taking the matter as a whole, we have made any progress, whether the movement of thousands of years has carried us beyond certain standpoints and antitheses. A negative answer would seem, in this case, to spring to our lips far more readily than an affirmative, a certain affirmation being rescued, indeed, only with difficulty. For the historical progress of the movement beyond a particular position is not an actual refutation of the latter; the rationality of history is itself a question; the further development may well be looked upon as a mere complication, and the striking out of new ways as an abandonment of the true path. Thus we see, in actual fact, that positions which have seemed obsolete for centuries, nay for thousands of years, are taken up anew again and again; Aristotelianism, which even in Grecian days seemed left far behind, developed new power in the Middle Ages, and through the reawakening of Thomism exercises important influence even down to the present day; nay, the most recent movements in natural science again adopt the hylozoism of the Ionian scientists with such an absence of prejudice that the intervening thousands of years seem to have passed by without a trace. It is true that when the old is thus brought forth into new life, the mode of its defence is different, it is more complicated and is richer in reflection; although this applies more to the representation than to the core of the thing itself. Those alone have the right to speak of an inner advance who are able to separate from all merely human standpoints and opinions, a world-historical evolution of the spiritual life, and to distinguish from the superficies of the age the particular stage of this evolution which is operative in it. This world-historical evolution exhibits itself in the sphere of philosophy far more powerfully in bringing out new problems than in giving conclusive answers, but these problems themselves contain facts, even if they are facts situated deeper down, and the emergence of the problem makes much which until then was considered adequate, obsolete for the world-historical movement. Such obsolete positions are hylozoism and Aristotelianism, no matter how many followers they may command even at the present day. But the recognition of this world-historical movement itself rests upon preliminary assumptions which are by no means matters-of-course. Thus in this direction, too, we do not free ourselves of conflict and in the whole we must convince ourselves that history does not bring to us a ready-made truth but is able only to shape the struggle for truth so that it is greater, more intense, freer from accidents.

# THE LIFE AND WORKS OF
# RUDOLF EUCKEN

## By ARMAND CUVILLIER

RUDOLF CHRISTOPH Eucken was born in Aurich, a town in western Hanover, Germany, on January 5, 1846. He lost his father and his only brother at an early age and was brought up by his mother. Eucken studied first at the University of Göttingen, then in Berlin, where his teacher was the philosopher Adolf Trendelenburg, the originator of a neo-Aristotelian doctrine. Trendelenburg, with whom Eucken formed a close personal relationship, developed an organic conception of the universe, in which both the outer and the inner world combine to form a whole, moving constructively and purposefully toward a definite end. His belief in purpose and finality—what philosophers call the "teleological" view—was probably a decisive influence on the thought of the future Nobel Prizewinner.

After teaching in various secondary schools in Germany, Eucken was appointed "ordinary," or full, professor of philosophy at the University of Basel in the autumn of 1871, and subsequently (in 1874) at Jena University, where he taught until his retirement. In 1912, he went to the United States to lecture as exchange professor at Harvard, and in 1914 he was visiting professor at Tokyo University.

At first he concerned himself mainly with philology and the history of philoso-phy, particularly the philosophy of Aristotle. One of his earliest works combined both fields in a study of Aristotle's vocabulary, *De Aristotelis dicendi ratione* (1866). During this early period all his writings revolved round Aristotle: "Die Methode und die Grundlagen der aristotelischen Ethik" (1870); "Die Methode der aristotelischen Forschung" (1872); "Ueber die Bedeutung der aristotelischen Philosophie für die Gegenwart" (1872); "Aristoteles' Anschauung von Freundschaft and Lebensgütern" (1884). In 1879, he published *Geschichte der philosophischen Terminologie* (History of Philosophical Terminology), which after several reissues was reprinted in 1960 by the Olms publishing house in Hildesheim, and in 1880, a study of the role of images and similes in philosophy, *Bilder und Gleichnisse in der Philosophie* (*Images and Similes in Philosophy*). He never abandoned his active interest in the history of philosophical doctrines. Along with a work on the value of this branch of learning, he wrote essays on the thought of Saint Augustine and Saint Thomas Aquinas, (1886); "La Conception de la vie chez Saint Augustin" (Saint Augustine's Conception of Life) in the *Annales de Philosophie chrétienne* (Paris, 1899). In 1890, he published a major work, on *Die Lebensanschauungen der grossen Denker von Plato bis zur Gegenwart* (*The Views of Life of the Great Thinkers from Plato to the Present*).

Eucken did not carry on this research for the sake of scholarship alone. As the titles of these publications show, his purpose was to find out how the great philosophers saw life, its meaning and its ends, and to determine the features of their philosophies that can be of value to the world today. More and more he came to think along the lines of a philosophy of universal life, a philosophy of neo-idealism that drew its inspiration from the great German idealistic philosopher Johann Fichte. In Eucken's neo-idealism, spiritual life is placed in an order higher than that of the empirical world and the subjective psychology of the individual, although this higher order can only be established by human effort.

In 1878, one of Eucken's central works appeared—*Geschichte und Kritik der Grundbegriffe der Gegenwart* (History and Critique of the Basic Concepts of Modern Thought). It was a review of the main categories of modern thought; subject and object, theory and practice, thought and experience, the mechanistic and the organic, civilization and culture, society and the individual. In 1904, revised and expanded, the book became *Geistige Strömungen der Gegenwart* (*Main Currents of Modern Thought*). The change of title indicates a change in perspective. A historical survey formed the main part of the first edition; in the second, interpretation and discussion were predominant and, as Eucken said in his preface, the book became "first and foremost an expression of a set of personal convictions," an entire philosophy of life. He had gone beyond the purely intellectual conception of philosophy which, as he said, "thinks it can calmly proceed with its scientific work without being disturbed by the questions or doubts" arising from the conflicts in modern life.

All Eucken's subsequent works dealt with "spiritual life and its demands" as opposed to what he called "the spiritual void" of our age, and with the contribution that religion can make to the life of the spirit. In 1896 he published *Der Kampf um einen geistigen Lebensinhalt* (The Struggle for a Spiritual Content of Life), and in 1901 came his most important work on religion, *Der Wahrheitsgehalt der Religion* (*The Truth of Religion*), supplemented six years later by *Hauptprobleme der Religionsphilosophie der Gegenwart* (Main Problems of Contemporary Philosophy of Religion). The year 1907 saw the publication of *Der Sinn und Wert des Lebens* (*The Meaning and Value of Life*), a work that lies at the core of all Eucken's writings. It addresses itself to the essential problems of philosophy: Has life any meaning? Has it any value? What is its meaning and its value? In a form accessible to the cultured public, Eucken summarizes the main themes of his own philosophy. He contrasts what he calls "the answers of time" (those that bear the stamp of a single moment in history) with the creation of a new conception, safeguarding the eternal, timeless characteristics of life.

Tirelessly returning to the same theme, Eucken published *Einführung in eine Philosophie des Geisteslebens* (Introduction to a Philosophy of Spiritual Life) in 1908 and, in 1912, an introduction to the theory of knowledge, *Erkennen und Leben* (Knowing and Living). In the latter book he places life above knowledge, which is no more than one of life's manifestations, and draws a distinction between two kinds of knowledge: intuition, or true knowledge (*Erkennen*), involving integrative activity by the mind, and superficial knowledge (*Kennen*), which does not become part of reality and merely introduces its own subjectivity into the world.

World War I had a profound influence on Eucken's thought. In a book published just before World War II, *The Doctrines of the German Revolution,* Edmond Vermeil discussed "the everlasting German protest against intellectualism" and showed the part played by this philosophical attitude in the birth of the National Socialist mentality. Vermeil explained that on the pretext of denouncing the narrow confines of the intellect, "life and action" are exalted with the end result becoming a defense of what Nietzsche called the "will to power" and of all the passionate, irrational forces of the soul. Eucken was not a Nietzschean and did not engage in this defense of the irrational. Yet as early as 1913, he sounded a call "for the rallying of the spirits," trying to lay the foundations of a new "German idealism" and urging its acceptance by all those who were searching for a secure basis and reliable guidance, amid the confusion, dissension, and strife of the day.

During World War I, he signed the "Manifesto of German Intellectuals" and asserted that the doctrine of the Frenchman Henri Bergson (who had written a most laudatory foreword to *The Meaning and Value of Life*) is "only a worthless patchwork of old Germanic theories." In 1914, Eucken published a pamphlet entitled *"Die weltgeschichtliche Bedeutung des deutschen Geistes"* (The Significance of the German Spirit for World History); in 1915, he wrote another pamphlet on *"Die Träger des deutschen Idealismus"* (The Representatives of German Idealism). Two more pamphlets followed in 1919: *"Deutsche Freiheit: ein Weckruf"* (German Freedom: an Alarm) and *"Was bleibt unser Halt? Ein Wort an ernste Seelen"* (On What Can We Still Rely? A Word to Serious Souls). In *Mensch und Welt: eine Philosophie des Lebens* (Man and the World: a Philosophy of Life), which first appeared in June 1918, he dealt mainly with the modern "spirit-ual crisis" in which many people no longer believe in God and life has lost its meaning. But in the preface to the second edition, published in December 1919, he deplores "the tremendous catastrophe that has befallen the German people," a catastrophe "the like of which no one expected and the history of the world has hardly ever seen," and he declares that the responsibility for it does not lie with one nation, but "involves all mankind."

Rudolf Eucken retired in 1920. He remained in Jena, and published several more works, notably *Lebenserinnerungen* (Memoirs, 1920), *Der Sozialismus und seine Lebensgestaltung* (Socialism and Its Way of Life, 1921), *Prolegomena und Epilog zu einer Philosophie des Geisteslebens* (Prolegomena and Epilogue to a Philosophy of Spiritual Life, 1922) and *Ethik als Grundlage des staatsbürgerlichen Lebens* (Ethics as a Basis for the Life of the Citizen, 1924). He died on September 15, 1926, in the town of Jena, where he had taught for so long. In 1920, an Eucken Society ("Euckenbund") was formed to propagate his ideas; its organ was the journal *Die Tatwelt*.

Eucken's ethnocentrism should not blind modern readers to the value of his work. Despite a certain lack of precision and occasional obscureness, Eucken undeniably made a major contribution to modern philosophy, fully justifying the award of the Nobel Prize in 1908.

Let us try to define the main features of Eucken's philosophy. Its primary characteristic is that it sets out to define and understand the *present*. The problem of the meaning and value of life, Eucken argues, does not arise in the abstract, but in relation to the conditions under which we live and chiefly at times when the individual no longer feels in harmony with the way of life his environment offers him. This is exactly the case with our age, and in almost all his works Eucken constantly returns to the uncertainty and confusion of modern man.

For this reason, philosophy must refuse to be a mere scholastic discipline; it must remain associated with life. Its source, in fact, has always been in life at a particular time, as can be seen from comparisons between the philosophies of different ages and civilizations. At the same time philosophy acts on life in its turn. "What characterizes all truly great philosophical works," we read in *Main Currents of Modern Thought,* "is not only the elucidation of ideas and broadening of the intellectual horizon which take place in them, but the fact that they bring about a development of the actual movement of life, an increase in spiritual reality."

Moreover, philosophy cannot be a mere synthesis of the results of the several sciences. "There must be a distinct science that deals with an object in its totality, above all makes the fundamental fact stand out with absolute clarity and endeavors to determine the content of this fact as well as its position in relation to the world about us; this science is philosophy." Such a science calls for a new principle, different from that of the other sciences. "This principle can neither be given from without nor come from purely intellectual movements; it must be found in the movement of life as a whole." Thus, "The existence of a spiritual life embracing the world is the hub of all philosophical considerations and the axiom of axioms." On this principle, philosophy can be independent, rather than a mere aid to science; it can become "a creative, renovating force."

Eucken rejects the modern tendency to make the intellect "the scapegoat for everything we dislike at the present time." On the other hand, he argues that the intellect, with its propensity toward abstract concepts, cannot give us sufficient knowledge of reality. It should not be taken as the sole guide for our actions, which cannot be conceived of "in the same way as a logical argument" or "forced into rigid patterns," for this would deprive them of all their originality and individuality. Philosophy must be the work of the whole personality, without being reduced to a mere reflection of our individuality. Only those whose personal life possesses strength, breadth, and depth can have access to the fundamental processes of the universe.

Intellectualism is everywhere the ally of naturalism, which was born during the *Aufklärung,* the age of enlightenment, and developed as part of the nineteenth-century cult of science. Naturalism did, it is true, win recognition for the value of facts and clearly pointed up man's relationship with nature. But with its excessive concentration on the outside world, it reduced man's world to the action of physical forces and held that everything that lay outside the exact sciences was illusory. Building in particular upon the theory of evolution, it claimed that man himself is part of nature, and made the life of the mind into a *Nebengeschehen,* a mere secondary process, ignoring the real meaning of spiritual life. But the naturalists forgot one thing: that science itself is the work of the mind and that the scientist's world, in which nature is converted into measurable phenomena, relationships, and laws, is basically different from the world of sensory experience. What is more, when naturalism reduces man to a mere part of nature, it does so only through the agency of the mind. The fact that thought exists and transforms the tangible world is enough to refute the conclusions of naturalism.

The antithesis of naturalism is idealism —but we must be clear about what is meant by idealism. In Eucken's day, the idealism prevailing in German philosophy was the abstract idealism of Georg Hegel, who thought that reality could be deduced from pure concepts and simple "categories." Hegel considered logical contradiction—the contrast between thesis and antithesis—to be productive in itself and capable of giving rise to a creative "synthesis." In Eucken's view, this form of idealism leads back to the errors of intellectualism and, like intellectualism, provides no more than what Bergson was later to call a "closed" philosophy. The fundamental originality of spiritual life, however, lies in the fact that it is in constant progress, trying to reach beyond itself to an ever higher level of spirituality.

Moreover, it is not true that contradiction in itself has any creative power. Is not our own age largely indifferent to the contradictions between various conflicting systems of ideas? For "the cultured," this spiritual disharmony is a game in which they can sharpen their wits; the more contradictions there are in the world, the more "original" and "interesting" they find it. In actual fact, contradiction can be productive only when "problems penetrate to the instinct of spiritual preservation, vital energy develops through them and a sphere of spiritual energy is formed"; then and only then do contradictions become intolerable. It is "the degree of unification, the force of life's synthesis that gives logic the power that it is supposed to have in its own right."

In Eucken's view, the only form of idealism appropriate to our age is one that, far from being opposed to experience, embodies it and goes beyond it. This idealism asserts that there is "a spiritual life superior to man," which reveals itself to him in his consciousness, mingles with his own essential being, and thus becomes real to him. Man is not intended to shut himself up in his own subjectivity. Time and time again, Eucken repeats this idea: "Man is more than mere subjectivity." He must "come out of his petty self"

and become one with spiritual life in its most universal and deepest aspects. This is the only way for him to find spiritual communion with his fellowmen, who will no longer be external "objects" or strangers since they participate in the same life as he.

In another man this form of idealism might have led to pantheism. Eucken does, in fact, give credit to pantheism for directing philosophers' attention to the reason immanent in the world and for rejecting the "splitting" of the universe which would isolate mankind in the realm of being and cuts individual human beings off from one another. But he also denounces the fundamental fallacy of pantheism: its view of reality as something complete and of spiritual unity as something that has already come about. These views would make our life purely contemplative and leave no room for freedom or independent moral action. Eucken was profoundly convinced that life cannot consist simply of contemplation or speculation. From 1896 on he called his own doctrine "activism," by which he meant that truth is a matter of life and action rather than pure intellect. It is in the nature of spiritual life to require continual activity, to be in constant progress. Once it slackens or sinks into inactivity, it descends to the level of habit, and is no longer spiritual life at all. The roots of knowledge lie in the movement of life; knowledge cannot be mere contemplation, nor can it be a reflection or copy of reality. It is, rather, the *creation* of truth: "Truth does not mean exact accordance with external reality, but participation in an all-embracing, original vital process which is constantly self-oriented through all diversity—a vital process the development of which above all gives rise to true reality."

This philosophy, which ascribes so much importance to spiritual activity in the search for truth and even presents truth as a creation of the mind rather than the exact description of an external model, is reminiscent of the pragmatic philosophy of such men as William James. Pragmatism was in fact flourishing in Eucken's time in America and England. Eucken himself, however, explains in *Main Currents of Modern Thought* the radical difference between activism and pragmatism. "For pragmatism," he writes, " 'life' denotes human subjectivity, human existence—whether of the individual or the species, it ultimately amounts to the same thing—while in our search for closer unity of truth and life, we have in mind the life of the spirit, in the sense of a self-contained life which, with its content and values, is something essentially new compared with human subjectivity and even involves the complete overturn of the immediate situation." The phrase "unity of truth and life" does not have the same meaning for both pragmatism and activism. "In the former, truth becomes merely a means of attaining a goal which is considered to be higher and, as far as we are concerned, we regard this as internal destruction. In activism, on the other hand, truth forms an essential, integral part of life itself and may never become a mere instrument." Eucken adds that the two doctrines stand for two radically different attitudes toward the conquest and defense of truth. For pragmatism the criterion is man's interest, man's "convenience." Activism takes its stand on "the enduring quality and substantial content of spiritual life." According to Eucken, "a philosophy may demand great sacrifices of a man *qua* man and make his life difficult rather than easy—this is the case with anything that is truly great—but it can at the same time provide him with a richer, higher spiritual life; on the other hand, something that gives man a life full of convenience may considerably degrade his spiritual life. The fact that periods entirely given up to work and enjoyment may be totally empty in the spiritual sense is amply demonstrated by the age in which we live."

This is the root of the problem. The philosopher's intention is to "put life into activity"; activism is in agreement with pragmatism in this respect. "But," Eucken states, "this does not seem possible to us on the basis of existence as it is, with all its inflexible trammels, but only if we overturn this existence by taking a new starting-point and developing a new life from it." This program, he adds, is "a kind of metaphysics; we do not deny it; we are even plainly calling for a metaphysics, since only the overturn of the given situation can make original, independent life possible and there can be no spiritual preservation without metaphysics, whatever its nature may be." To put it briefly, pragmatism does not go beyond a purely empirical standpoint, while activism calls for a complete metaphysics of life—a metaphysics that does not shrink from asserting "the self-contained life of the spirit, regarded as a new level of reality and the unfolding of reality's innermost being."

Eucken lays great stress on the fact that this metaphysics is as essential to moral action as to knowledge. Moral life is something quite different from natural life. In opposition to the mere workings of self-interest and utilitarian objectives, it builds an essentially different world, a world in which we become independent of the empirical world, free of self-interest. True morality is above all an uplifting of life into the higher realms of spiritual life. It makes our existence a creative effort, a task to be fulfilled, not a pattern of compliance with hard and fast laws. Only through this metaphysics of life can moral values take on their full significance. Duty becomes something other than a mere command from without, "an oppressive yoke or stereotyped organization" acting only through sanctions. The metaphysics of life enables us to understand how that which is "above us" can at the same time be "within us," how moral law can lie in personal will and life even though it rises above them. In the same way, love can break through individual consciousness and become true spiritual communion with others, since all human beings participate in the same spiritual life.

To understand human beings in this way, psychology is inadequate. In the moral sphere it must be supplemented by what Eucken called the "noological" method, which embraces not only the psyche, but also the "noos," the mind itself. According to Eucken, the noological method leads directly to the basic assertion at the root of all religion: the assertion that an absolute spiritual life exists, and though its sphere of action lies in immediate experience, it springs from a much higher source. Even if man does not realize it, every development of spiritual life involves a religious element; or more specifically the conviction that we belong to an infinite life, are subordinate to it, and are duty bound to make it our own. In *The Truth of Religion,* Eucken writes, "Is human life merely a subordinate part of nature or is it the starting-point of a new world? The whole organization of our behavior depends on this question. Religion claimed to raise human existence to a level above the world and thus to save our life from the nothingness in which it would otherwise surely be engulfed. If this undertaking were to suffer the same fate as the flight of Icarus, all hope would collapse with it and even the best and noblest things would appear to be empty fancies, and everything would thus end in unreason."

The religion referred to in this passage is what Eucken calls "universal religion." He considers this indeterminate form of religion inadequate, and argues that we must go beyond it to "characteristic religion"—the historical religions of mankind. These religions have a powerful, vivifying effect on mankind and, since they originate in superior personalities, they are far above popular culture. The danger—and Eucken stresses it—is that they tend to become the servants of temporal powers or interests and to take on a rigid form, reducing themselves to lifeless dogmas and observances. Petrified in this way, religion becomes static and false to spiritual life. "Religion," Eucken maintains, "is not pure contemplation or immobile accord; in its innermost nature it is a break with the former chaos, the concentration within oneself of fundamental life and the pursuit of such life despite all opposition. But it is all this in the certain knowledge that its foundations lie in eternal freedom."

Eucken even criticizes the historical forms of the Christian religion, rejecting the dogma of original sin and of the infallibility of the Church. In his view, the former is liable to make man appear fundamentally bad and to reduce him to impotence, especially when it is associated with a doctrine of predestination. As for infallibility, it pertains to the creative activity of God and to the spirit as an eternal truth, not to the historical forms this truth may take in any particular church or religious organization.

Yet, when Eucken, in *"Können wir noch Christen sein?"* (1911), asks "Can we still be Christians?," his answer is "We not only can, but must." In his view, Christianity is the highest religion, since it regards religion as a spiritual renewal, a striving to rise above life on earth to a world of love and grace. In addition, through the prominence it gives to the personality of Christ, it shows us that the spiritual life is fundamentally a personal activity of participation in the life of the "universal personal being." In this sense, Christianity associates us with the creative activity of the spirit and makes human life into *"Mitschaffen,"* or "co-creation." Eucken adds, however, that "we can be Christians only if Christianity is recognized as a historical movement that is still in flux, breaks free from the rigidity of the Church and is established on a broader basis." To Eucken, the Church is only a means of achieving the kingdom of God. It is even possible, he maintains, to be deeply religious without belonging to any formally organized religion; the main thing is religion as a personal experience.

Eucken did not confine himself to metaphysical and religious speculation. He also applied his ideas to human history and civilization, and his views are still of great contemporary interest.

The naturalistic view of life, he observes, has led to a purely external civilization, a soulless existence in which individuals and nations are governed by material interests rather than ideas. Despite the spectacular progress of technology, modern life is given over to spiritual anarchy, the dissipation of thought, uncertainty over the aims of life, and inner emptiness and isolation. But "the history of mankind does not drift aimlessly on the swiftly-flowing stream of time." The past is not irretrievably lost; it can "become part of a supratemporal present and thus remain a matter of personal life and unremitting effort." Man himself is not a purely temporal being; "all socio-historical spirituality is only the development of a supratemporal spiritual life that rises above all purely human existence," and "civilization has a soul and is true civilization only to the extent that it participates in this spiritual life."

According to Eucken, true civilization is what he calls "essential civilization," that is to say, a civilization based on the "cult of essence." The civilization of antiquity, based on the cult of "form," en-

couraged the benumbing of the mind by the plastic arts, which were supposed to express the eternal for all eternity. Modern civilization, born of the Renaissance and the return to nature, is based on the cult of "force"; it breaks up the essence of things and destroys all stability. Essential civilization, on the other hand, fosters the recognition of the interaction between the eternal and the temporal; through human effort, eternal potentialities become realities, preserved in the form of eternal values. Essential civilization is actually *culture* rather than mere *civilization,* and Eucken makes a distinction between these two terms, pointing out that the word "civilization" mainly designates the social order, while "culture" is education "from within" by which man as a whole is uplifted.

Another distinction exists between individualistic as opposed to social civilization. The former seeks to develop the individual, to strengthen his personality, and to free him of all fetters, even at times his moral obligation. It severs the bonds between men, and exalts egoism, originality (an originality often more apparent than real), and a "pitiful tendency toward super-subtle paradoxes." Social civilization, on the other hand, absorbs the individual in the community; it is characterized by "an inordinate passion for the masses. . . . the lowering of civilization to the level of their interests and intelligence, the adoption of their views and objectives as a yardstick for everything, . . . the subjection of individual freedom to strong pressure." This mass civilization destroys all personal originality; it subordinates spiritual activity to petty interests and makes the spiritual life a mere tool to serve man's creature comforts.

Eucken sees no possibility of reconciling the two tendencies of individualistic and social civilization on the level of purely human civilization. For him the solution lies in "essential civilization," which is suprahuman because it is spiritual and even religious in essence. "If neither purely social civilization," he writes, "nor individualistic civilization is equal to its task, if neither of them provides life with essential content and if, at the same time, it is beyond doubt that only deplorably obtuse people may try to reach a direct compromise between them and make room for both of them in life, we simply must rise above this antithesis. The individual and society are necessary aspects and manifestations of spiritual life; the latter needs individuals to give it originality and society to strengthen it. But the individual and society do not draw their strength and reality from themselves; these come from the spiritual aggregates that surround them." Eucken adds, "Nevertheless it should be observed that the relationship between the individual and society takes a different form in history; when life is mainly in need of strengthening, after periods of disintegration and upheavals, it moves toward society." (This was the case at the end of antiquity, as described in the writings of St. Augustine.) On the other hand, "the movement toward the individual predominates where rising young forces, finding the traditional rules too narrow and inflexible, can only seek new paths by breaking away from them." (This occurred in modern times up to the middle of the nineteenth century.) In other words, the conflict is not so much between two ways of interpreting civilization as between temporary and irreconcilable historical forms of civilization, between "developments of life" at different times and under different circumstances. The only remedy for this "cleavage" lies in the "inner progress of life." Once again, in Rudolf Eucken's view, it is evident that life can only take on meaning and value by transcending the purely human standpoint.

Armand Cuvillier is a professor and literary critic in Paris.
Translated by Annie Jackson.

# THE 1908 PRIZE

## By GUNNAR AHLSTRÖM

It was Rudolf Eucken who received the Nobel Prize for Literature of 1908 because the academic barometer indicated philosophy that year, whereas it had indicated history in 1902, the year in which Mommsen was crowned. Neither one nor the other of these great men represented literature in the sense of "the humanities and poetry." The Swedish Academy enlarged the conception of literature. The legitimacy of such breadth of mind was later to be further confirmed by the award of the Prize to Henri Bergson in 1927 and to Winston Churchill in 1953.

However, the discussions of the Committee of 1908 did not cover principles; they were confined to elementary questions. First of all, who was Rudolf Eucken? Once this question had been answered, people then began to inquire whether this professor from Jena really had the necessary wide-ranging mind to qualify for a Nobel Prize. If it were absolutely essential to pay homage to philosophy, and to German philosophy in particular, why not choose Heinrich Rickert, Hermann Cohen, or Wilhelm Windelband? In his autobiography, published in 1921, Eucken reveals that he was embarrassed and rather irritated by this discussion: but he notes with all the more satisfaction that foreigners were able to appreciate his intellectual prowess.

The pronounced attraction of Eucken to the Academy lay in the words "ideal," "idealism," and "idealist." These are the noble euphonies which secured Eucken his triumph.

In France, in the days of the great Descartes, the concept of the ideal had long ago been ennobled; it had been marked by new stresses under Victor Cousin and had taken on a new lease of life under the influence of Alfred Fouillée. But the expression "idealism" had always been used with economy. Auguste Comte and the vigorous wave of positivism presented a healthy antidote to the ill-considered use of spiritualistic terminology. From this point of view it is, moreover, characteristic that the Académie Française did not include the words "idealism" and "idealist" in its dictionary until 1878. Perhaps one should look on this as a concession to the craze for the thinkers across the Rhine, where the word *Idealismus* was in current use and was lovingly cultivated, like a banal geranium overflowing from professorial and bourgeois balconies. It was a word that was supposed to be full of meaning, and in fact, it meant nothing at all.

Since the advent of romantic philosophy, Swedish culture had several times received an important impetus from German ideas. Fichte, Schelling, and then Hegel had provided the universities and intellectual circles with a spiritualistic orientation. National thinkers, almost all with long-term reputations, had also added their emphatic tributes to an official and conservative idealism. Turning away from the disparate multiplicity of the world of phenomena, they gazed on eternity, searching the heaven of spirituality for a divine spark to guide mankind. The strength of this massive and omnipresent tradition may be measured by the eagerness with which the new generation, with its positivist leanings, rushed to assault its defenses toward the end of the century. To Auguste Strindberg and his writings, idealism was the sworn enemy.

This "professional idealism" that Strindberg stigmatized was held in honor by the Swedish Academy; for the Academy had been charged with the mission, in the terms of Alfred Nobel's will, to judge the literature of the world and decide who were the writers worthy to receive a prize for their "idealist tendencies." In the eyes of the venerable Academicians, this was a natural and legitimate criterion. So the philosopher Eucken seemed to have been made to measure to suit the Nobel Foundation. At last they had got hold of an indisputable idealist. At Jena he had set himself up as the apostle of more or less heavenly truths, and besides being a brilliant lec-turer he was also a writer of great ability.

His candidacy had been proposed by a Swedish colleague and sympathizer at the University of Gothenburg, and it appeared to be supported by a majority. At the end of 1908, the news was made public: Rudolf Eucken was to receive the Nobel Prize. Eucken, like a good philosopher, liked wisdom. When he arrived in Stockholm he declared calmly to a journalist who challenged him, that he had conscientiously studied the rules relating to the Prize and considered that he fulfilled the required conditions. He added that his works were being read more and more throughout the world: "I am in fashion." He did not make a formal acceptance speech and it is not known whether he was able to appreciate the sum awarded to him, since his views were so antimaterialistic, but given that people were still living in a happy age of monetary stability, it is reasonable to suppose that he did not scorn the cash. In the realm of eternal values his place was assured by the diploma which he was awarded for "his earnest search for truth, his penetrating power of thought, his wide range of vision, and the warmth and strength of presentation with which in his numerous works he has vindicated and developed an idealistic philosophy of life."

Translated by Camilla Sykes.

# Anatole France

## 1921

---

"In recognition of his brilliant literary achievements, which are characterized by nobility of style, magnanimous human sympathy, charm, and a true French temper"

---

*Illustrated by* JEAN OBERLÉ

# PRESENTATION ADDRESS

## By E. A. KARLFELDT

PERMANENT SECRETARY
OF THE SWEDISH ACADEMY

ANATOLE FRANCE was no longer a young man when, in 1881, he captured the attention of the literary public in France and subsequently in the civilized world with his curious novel, *Le Crime de Sylvestre Bonnard*. He had behind him a long stretch of years during which his development had been carried on without attracting wide attention. But if, during this period of slow growth, his literary efforts had been infrequent and not very energetic, the work to which he had subjected his intellect, his thought, and his taste had been proportionately wider and more vigorous. No immoderate desire for fame moved him. Ambition seems to have played a small role in his life. Indeed, he tells the story that at the age of seven he wanted to be famous. Excited by the legends of saints told to him by his good, pious mother, he wanted to settle in the desert and as a hermit match the glory of St. Anthony and St. Jerome. His desert was the *Jardin des Plantes* where the huge beasts lived in houses and cages, and where God the Father seemed to him to raise His arms to heaven blessing the antelope, the gazelle, and the dove.

His mother was frightened by such vanity but her husband soothed her: "My dear, you will see that at twenty he will be disgusted with fame." "My father was not mistaken," France says. "Like the King of Yvetot, I lived quite well without fame and no longer had the least desire to engrave my name on the memory of men. As for the dream of becoming a hermit, I refashioned it every time I believed I felt life was thoroughly bad; in other words, I refashioned it every day. But every day nature took me by the ear and led me to the amusements in which our humble lives pass away." At the age of fifteen the young Anatole France dedicated his first essay, *"La Légende de Sainte Radegonde, Reine de*

France," to his father and his beloved mother. This work is now lost, but even much later, when his faith in saints had vanished, he was still able to write legends with a pen dipped in the gold of haloes.

In the old book store of his worthy father, he soon felt a thirst for knowledge, amidst the noble dust of old books. Into this shop came collectors and bibliophiles to examine the recently acquired treasures and to discuss authors and editions. Thus the young Anatole, always a good listener, was initiated into the mysteries of erudition, a pursuit he considered the highest pleasure of a peaceful life. We need only look at the Abbé Coignard, all beaming as he leaves the grill room of the *"Reine Pédauque"* where he pays for the material pleasures of this world by giving some lessons to a young spit-turner and by dispensing the treasures of an eloquence full of wisdom, irony, and Christian faith; we see him turn toward the library to feast his spirit free of charge on the latest books arrived from Holland, the country of classical editions. And, bored with domestic tedium, here is Mr. Bergeret, who comes to pass the finest hours of his day in conversation with friends gathered around the library's display shelves. Anatole France is the poet of libraries and bookworms. His imagination revels in the visions of bibliophiles, as when he praises that marvellous *Astaracienne,* a giant collection of books and manuscripts in which a noble cabalist sought proofs to bolster his superstition. "More fervently than ever," says Coignard toward the end of his adventurous career, "I want to sit down behind a table, in some venerable gallery, where many choice books would be assembled in silence. I prefer their conversation to that of men. I have found diverse ways of life and I judge that the best way is to devote oneself to study, to support calmly one's part in the vicissitudes of life, and to prolong, by the spectacle of centuries and of empires, the brevity of our days." Love of intellectual work is a fundamental characteristic of Anatole France's personal religion and just like his Abbé, he prefers, from the height of the ivory tower of knowledge and thought, to turn his gaze toward far-off times and countries. His irony lives in the present, his devotion in the past.

Yet though our existence is fragile, beauty lives everywhere, and for the writer it materializes in form and style. Anatole France's vast studies and great meditation have bestowed a rare solidity on his work, but no less serious is the labor he has devoted to the perfecting of his style. The language which he had to shape is one of the noblest; French is the most richly endowed daughter of the mother tongue Latin. It has served the greatest masters. Now grave, now merry, it possesses serenity and charm, strength and melody. In many places France calls it the most beautiful language on earth and lavishes the most tender epithets on it as to a beloved woman. But as a true son of the ancients, he wishes it *simplex munditiis*. He is an artist, certainly one of the greatest, but his art aspires to keep his language, through severe purification, as simple and, at the same time, as expressive as possible. In contemporary Europe, where a flourishing superficial dilettantism is a danger to the purity of languages, his work is a richly instructive example of what art can do with true resources. His language is the classical French, the French of Fénelon and Voltaire, and rather than contribute new ornaments to it, he gives it a slightly archaic stamp which admirably suits his subjects, often taken from antiquity. His French is so transparent that one would like to apply to it what he said of Leila, daughter of Lilith, one of the luminous and fragile beings sprung from his imagination: "If crystal could speak, it would speak in this fashion."

Let us recall now, for our own pleasure, some of the works which have secured for the name of Anatole France the worldwide renown which he has so little desired but which nevertheless he cannot avoid. By so doing we will often encounter France himself, for he is less inclined than most writers to hide behind his characters and words.

He is recognized as a master of the tale, which he has made a wholly personal genre, in which erudition, imagination, serene charm of style, and depth of irony and passion combine to produce marvellous effects. Who can ever forget his Balthazar? The Negro King of Ethiopia comes to pay a visit to Balkis, the beautiful Queen of Sheba, and soon wins her love. But shortly the fickle queen forgets him to give herself to another. Wounded to death physically and emotionally, Balthazar returns to his country to devote himself to the highest wisdom of the seers, astrology. Suddenly an astonishing and sublime light spreads over the intense gloom of his passion. Balthazar discovers a new star and, high in the heavenly concourse, the star speaks to him, and in the light it sheds he joins with two neighboring kings. No longer can Balkis hold him. His soul is detached from voluptuousness and he undertakes the pursuit of the star. The star which spoke was no other than the star which led the Three Wise Men to the manger at Jerusalem.

Another time France opens before our eyes a mother-of-pearl casket filled with priceless jewels, chased by the hand of a master of antiquity.

We find in it the legend, slightly ironic but most seductive, of Célestin and d'Amyers, of the old hermit and the young faun singing together the Easter Alleluia, the one exalting in the return of Christ and the other in the return of the sun, worshipers communing in a single innocent piety, reunited at last—under the alarmed eye of the historian—in a single sacred tomb. This story shows us France in a realm in which he delights, the realm between paganism and Christianity, where twilight and dawn are mingled, where satyrs meet with apostles, where sacred and profane animals wander, where ample materials are found to exercise his fantasy, his contemplation, and his spiritual irony in all its nuances. One often does not know whether to call it fiction or reality.

Romantic chastity is celebrated in the legends of the saints Oliverie and Liberette, Euphrosine and Scolastica. These are pages taken from the chronicles of saints, literary pastiches perhaps, executed with talent and a sense for the miraculous.

Still another time France takes us to the pits outside of Sienna where, in the spring twilight, a sweet barefooted Carmelite narrates the story of St. Francis of Assisi and St. Claire, the daughter of his soul, and that of the holy satyr who served masters as different as Jupiter, Saturn, and the Galilean, a profound if hardly edifying legend, but recounted by France in the most exquisite style.

In his famous novel *Thaïs* (1890) he enthusiastically penetrates the Alexandrine world at the time when the scourging thorns of Christianity were ravaging among the last effeminate survivors of Hellenic civilization. Asceticism and voluptuousness are at their heights here, mysteries and esthetic orgies flower side by side, angels and demons incarnate press around the Fathers of the Church and the neo-Hellenic philosophers, disputing over human souls. The story is steeped in the moral nihilism of that era, but it includes beautiful passages such as the magnificent descriptions of the desert solitude in which the anchorites preach from atop their columns or are subject to nightmares in the mummies' tombs.

However, one must put *La Rôtisserie de la Reine Pédauque* (*At the Sign of the Reine Pédauque,* 1893) in the first rank of Anatole France's novels. There he has sketched a group of true-to-life characters, legitimate or natural offspring of his mind in their own colorful world. The Abbé Coignard is so alive that one can study him as a real character who reveals all his complexity only when one has penetrated his privacy. Perhaps others have had the same experience I had. At first I had but little sympathy for this clumsy, loquacious priest and doctor of theology, who has so little concern for his dignity that sometimes he even steals or commits other equally heinous crimes, which he nevertheless defends with shameless casuistry. But he improves on better acquaintance, and I have learned to love him. He is not only a brilliant sophist, but an infinitely amusing character who exercises his irony not only on others but also on himself. There is profound humor in the contrast between his lofty views and his shabby life, and one must regard him with the smiling tolerance of his creator. Coignard is one of the most remarkable figures in contemporary literature. He is a new and vigorous plant in the Rabelaisian vineyard.

A type at once grotesque and lovable is the cabalist of Astarac. The crude mystic obviously belongs in a novel dealing with eighteenth-century manners. But the beings this magician evokes are of a singularly ethereal species; freed of earthly bonds, he enjoys the sweet and useful society of salamanders and sylphs. As proof of the talents of these beings, d'Astarac tells how once a sylph obliged a French scholar by arranging delivery of a message to Descartes, who was then living in Stockholm where he was teaching philosophy to Queen Christine. Sworn enemy of superstition that he may be, Anatole France should be grateful to that superstition for all the happy suggestions it has given him for his work.

Admirably rendered is the accent of pious simplicity with which the Abbé's student, the young spit-turner, recounts all these turbulent events. When his master, revered despite everything, after having suffered to his last moments the assault of the powers of darkness, finally dies a holy death in a Church he had never ceased to recognize openly, the student traces in Latin an ingenuous epithet praising the Abbé's wisdom and virtues. The author himself, in a later work, delivers an obituary eulogy for his principal hero. Presenting him as a blend of an Epicurean with a St. Francis, one who scorned men tenderly, France speaks of his benevolent irony and his merciful scepticism. Aside from the religious aspect, this characterization applies equally well to Anatole France himself.

Let us accompany him then without fear in his philosophical strolls in the garden of Epicurus. He will teach us humility. He will say to us: the world is infinitely large and man is infinitely small. What do you imagine? Our ideals are luminous phantoms but it is in following them that we find our only true happiness. He will say that human mediocrity is widespread, but he will not exclude himself from it. We may reproach him for the sensuality that occupies too large a place in some of his works and for the hedonistic sentiments, for example, which he describes under the sign of the red lily of Florence, and which are not made for serious minds. He will reply, according to the maxims of his spiritual father, that the pleasures of the mind surpass by far those of the flesh, and the serene calm of the soul is the port into which the wise man steers his boat in order to escape the tempests of sensual life. We shall hear him express the wish that time, which deprives us of so many things, may allow us compassion for our fellow man, so that in our old age we do not find ourselves shut up as in a tomb.

Following this inclination Anatole France left his esthetic seclusion, his "ivory tower," to throw himself into the social fray of his time, to clamor like Voltaire for the restoration of the rights of persons unjustly condemned as well as of his own wounded patriotism; and he has gone into the workers' quarters to look for means of reconciling classes and nations. His old age has not become a walled tomb. The end has been good for him. After having been accorded many sunny years at the court of the Graces, he still throws the glint of gay learning into the idealistic struggle that, at an advanced age, he wages against the decadence of societies and against materialism and the power of money. His activity in this regard does not interest us directly, but we obtain from it the inestimable advantage of being able to fix his literary image against the background of a lofty nobility of sentiments. There is nothing of the careerist about him. His much discussed work on Joan of Arc, which has cost him enormous toil and which was intended to tear the veil of mysticism from the inspired heroine of France and to restore her to nature, to real life, was a thankless enterprise in an era prepared to canonize her.

"The Gods Are Athirst!" The great drama of the Revolution unfolds and, as with the battle of ideas, the trivial destinies of men are reflected in blood. Do not believe, however, that France would wish to present this squaring of accounts as being definitive. A century is far too short a period of time to permit delineating distinctly the march of men toward more tolerance and humanity. How events have fulfilled his predictions! Several years after the appearance of this book the great catastrophe occurred. What beautiful arenas have been prepared now for the games of salamanders! The smoke of battles still hangs over the earth. And out of the fog surge gnomes, sinister spirits of the earth. Are these the dead who return? Somber prophets announce a new revelation. A wave of superstition threatens to flood the ruins of civilization. Anatole France wields the subtle and corrosive weapon which puts to flight the ghosts and the false saints. For our times, faith is infinitely necessary—but a faith purified by healthy doubts, by the spirit of clarity, a new humanism, a new Renaissance, a new Reformation.

Sweden cannot forget the debt which, like the rest of the civilized world, she owes to French civilization. Formerly we received in abundance the gifts of French Classicism like the ripe and delicate fruits of antiquity. Without them, where would we be? This is what we must ask ourselves today. In our time Anatole France has been the most authoritative representative of that civilization; he is the last of the great classicists. He has even been called the last European. And indeed, in an era in which chauvinism, the most criminal and stupid of ideologies, wants to use the ruins of the great destruction for the building of new walls to prevent free intellectual exchange between peoples, his clear and beautiful voice is raised higher than that of others, exhorting people to understand that they need one another. Witty, brilliant, generous, this knight without fear is the best champion in the sublime and incessant war which civilization has declared against barbarism. He is a marshal of the France of the glorious era in which Corneille and Racine created their heroes.

Today, as we in our old Germanic country award the world Prize of the poets to this Gallic master, the faithful servant of truth and beauty, the heir of humanism, of the lineage of Rabelais, Montaigne, Voltaire, Renan, we think of the words he once spoke at the foot of Renan's statue —his profession of faith is complete in them: "Slowly but surely humanity realizes wise men's dreams."

Mr. Anatole France—You have inherited that admirable tool, the French language, the language of a noble and classical nation, which is reverently guarded by the famous academy you adorn and is maintained by it in an enviable condition of purity. You have that brilliant tool of piercing sharpness, and in your hand it acquires a scintillating beauty. You have used it masterfully to fashion chefs-d'oeuvre very French in their style and refinement. But it is not your art alone that charms us: we revere your creative genius as well, and we have been enticed by the generous, compassionate heart which so many exalted pages of your works reveal.

# ACCEPTANCE SPEECH

## By *ANATOLE FRANCE*

---

I HAVE CHERISHED the prospect of visiting in the evening of my life your beautiful country which has brought forth brave men and beautiful women. With gratitude I receive the prize that crowns my literary career. I consider it an incomparable honor to have received this Prize established by a man of noble sentiment and awarded to me by judges so just and competent. Invited by you as a member of the French Academy to give advice on the Nobel Prize for Literature, I have several times had the pleasure of directing your choice. It happened in the case of Maeterlinck, who combines a brilliant style with thought of great independence; it also happened in the case of Romain Rolland, in whom you have acknowledged a lover of justice and peace and who has been able to defy unpopularity in order to remain a good man.

Perhaps I am overstepping the limits of my competence, if I now talk about the Peace Prize of the Norwegian Storting. If I do it, nonetheless, it is to praise the choice that the Storting has made. I may perhaps be permitted to say that in my view you have honored in Branting a statesman impassioned for justice. Would that the destinies of peoples could be guided by such men! The most horrible of wars has been followed by a peace treaty that is not a treaty of peace but a continuation of war. Unless common sense finally finds its place in the council chambers of ministers, Europe will perish. If one cannot with good reason hope for the triumph of union and harmony among the countries of Europe, I wish at least to believe, gentlemen, that under the influence of brave, just, and loyal men like you the good will sometimes prevail.

# THE GODS ARE ATHIRST

## By ANATOLE FRANCE

*Translated by* Alec Brown

---

### I

Évariste Gamelin, an artist and pupil of David, member for the Pont-Neuf ward (formerly the Henry IV) has gone round to the former Barnabite church early—for three years now, since May 21st, 1790, the building had been the headquarters of the Ward General Assembly. The church gave on a gloomy, narrow square, a step from the Law Courts railings. On the frontage, consisting of two classical orders, with reversed corbels and flaming urns for ornament, and fouled by all and sundry, the religious symbols had been chipped out and the Republican device "Liberty, Equality, Fraternity—or Death" inscribed in black letters over the door. Évariste Gamelin went straight through into the nave; the arches, which used to hear the surpliced clergy of the new community of St. Paul sing divine service, now saw red-capped patriots assemble to elect municipal magistrates or discuss Ward affairs. The saints had been dragged from their niches and replaced by busts of Brutus, Rousseau and Le Peltier. The Table of the Rights of Man was established on the stripped altar.

It was here, twice weekly, from five to eleven P.M., that the public assemblies were held. The pulpit, draped with the tricolour, served as tribune for the speeches. Opposite, on the lectern side,

rose a platform of rough-hewn planks, intended for the women and children, who came to the meetings in great numbers. This particular morning, seated at a desk under the pulpit, in red bonnet and red jacket, was Citizen Dupont *senior,* a cabinet-maker from the Place de Thionville, and one of the twelve members of the Watch Committee. On the desk stood a bottle and some glasses, a writing-desk and a folder containing a copy of the Petition calling on the Convention to expel from its bosom the twenty-two unworthy members.

Évariste Gamelin took the pen and signed.

"I had no doubts," declared the artisan magistrate, "about you coming to add your name, Citizen Gamelin. You're a true one. But there's no warmth in the Ward; it lacks spunk. I've put it up to the Watch Committee not to issue civic papers to anybody who doesn't sign the Petition."

"I am ready to sign with my own blood," said Gamelin, "to have those federalist traitors proscribed. They willed the death of Marat; let them perish!"

"It's this spirit of indifference that's ruining us," Dupont *senior* replied. "A Ward with nine hundred citizens with the right to vote, and not fifty who turn up at assemblies. We were twenty-eight yesterday."

"Very well," said Gamelin, "we shall have to compel them, under penalty of a fine."

"Steady there!" said the cabinet-maker, with a frown, "if they all came, the patriots would be in the minority. . . . Citizen Gamelin, will you drink a glass of wine to the health of all good sansculottes?"

On the wall of the church, along the Gospel side, was a black hand, the index-finger pointing to the passage leading to the cloisters, with the words: *Administration Committee, Watch Committee, Welfare Committee*. A few steps farther, one came to the door of what had been the vestry, over which stood: *Military Committee*. Gamelin pushed it open, to find the Committee Secretary writing, at a huge table cluttered with books, papers, steel ingots, cartridges and specimens of nitrate-bearing soils.

"Greetings, Citizen Trubert, how are you?"

"Me . . . I'm fine."

This was the Military Committee's secretary Fortuné Trubert's invariable answer to those who enquired about his health, less to inform them how he was than to cut short any talk on that subject. At twenty-eight he had a dry skin, sparse hair, hectic cheeks and bent shoulders. An optician of the Quai des Orfèvres, he owned a very old house, which in '91 he made over to an old assistant, to give himself up to his municipal duties. A charming mother, who died when only twenty, leaving tender memories in a few men of the district who were now old, had given him her lovely, soft, passionate eyes, her pallor and her shyness. From his father, optician and instrument-maker to the Crown, carried off by the same complaint before he was thirty, he had inherited a spirit of exactitude and assiduity. Without stopping his writing, he asked: "And you, Citizen, how are you?"

"Very well. What's the news?"

"Nothing, nothing. You can see: everything's calm here."

"And the general situation?"

"The general situation is unchanged."

The general situation was frightful. The finest army of the Republic was surrounded in Mayence; Valenciennes was besieged; Fontenay had fallen to the Vendéens; Lyons had rebelled, the Cévennes were risen in arms, and the frontier open to the Spaniards; two-thirds of France were invaded or risen against them; Paris, without money and without food, lay under the Austrian cannon.

Fortuné Trubert wrote on calmly. The Wards had been charged by a Decision of the Commune to raise twelve thousand men for the Vendée, he was drawing up instructions for the recruitment and arming of the unit which the Pont-Neuf (formerly the Henry IV) Ward was to supply. All the muskets of their armoury were to be handed to the recruits. The War National Guard would be armed with shot-guns and pikes.

"I've brought the inventory of the bells to be sent to the Luxembourg Palace for making into cannons," said Gamelin.

Although he was penniless, Évariste Gamelin had been enrolled as one of the executive members of the ward, a prerogative legally reserved to citizens well enough off to provide three working-days —to be eligible, an elector had to find the cost of ten working days. But the Pont-Neuf Ward, smitten with equality and jealous of its autonomy, considered any citizen who could pay his own National Guard uniform to be an eligible elector. Such was the case of Gamelin, who was a *citoyen actif,* or executive citizen of his Ward and a member of the Military Committee.

Citizen Trubert put down his pen. "Citizen Évariste, will you now go to the Convention and ask for instructions to be sent us to excavate all cellar floors, and wash the soil and rubble, to collect nitrate. Cannons are not everything, we also need gunpowder."

A little hunchback with a pen behind his ear and a handful of papers entered the one-time vestry. This was Citizen Beauvisage, of the Watch Committee.

"Citizens," he said, "bad news is coming in: Custine has evacuated Landau."

"Custine is a traitor," cried Gamelin.

"He shall be guillotined," said Beauvisage.

In his rather breathless voice Trubert, with his usual calm, declared: "The Convention did not set up a Public Security Committee for nothing. Custine's doings shall be investigated by it. Whether merely incompetent, or traitorous, he shall be replaced by a general determined to win, and *ça ira!*"

He looked through the papers, his wearied eyes flashing over them: "To enable our soldiers to do their duty without worries or weakness, they need to know that those they have left by the fireside are looked after properly. If you agree, Citizen Gamelin, you will join me, at the next Assembly, in requesting the Welfare Committee to work in with the Military Committee and lend support to every poor household which has a relation at the front." He smiled, and began to hum the *Ça ira.*

Working twelve or even fourteen hours a day, at his deal table, in the defence of the imperilled Fatherland, this obscure secretary of a Ward Committee saw no disproportion between the vastness of the task and the frailty of his means, so long as he felt united to all patriots in the common task, so long as he was part of the body of the people, so long as his life merged in the life of a great nation. He was one of those persistent yet inspired people, who, after any defeat, set about preparing for impossible, certain victory. For they simply had to win. These nobodies, who had destroyed the monarchy and overturned the old world, these Tru-

berts, these little instrument-making opticians, these Évariste Gamelins, these obscure artists, could expect no mercy from their enemies. They had no choice between victory and death. Hence their fervour and their calm.

## II

When he left the Barnabite building, Évariste Gamelin set out in the direction of the Place Dauphine, now renamed the Place de Thionville, in honour of an inconquerable city.

Situated in the busiest part of Paris, this square had lost its elegant lines nearly a century ago; the mansions built on three sides of it in the days of Henry IV, of uniform red brick interlined with white stone, for grand magistrates now, having exchanged their noble slate roofs for two or three miserable lath-and-plaster attics—or even been razed to the ground and shamelessly replaced by badly limewashed houses, presented only a miserable, grimy, irregular frontage, with countless narrow windows of all shapes and sizes, bright with pots of flowers, bird cages and drying linen. Here a concourse of artisans, jewellers, metal-craftsmen, lock-smiths, opticians, printers, sempstresses, dressmakers, laundresses and a few old lawyers who had not been swept away together with monarchical justice, in the flood, now lived.

It was morning and it was Spring. Young rays of sunlight, heady as young wind, smiled on the walls and flooded cheerfully into the attics. The window-sashes were all up and under them showed the unkempt heads of the housewives. The Clerk to the Revolutionary Tribunal, leaving the building to go to work, patted the cheeks of children playing under the trees. You could hear the treason of infamous Dumouriez being cried on the Pont-Neuf.

Évariste Gamelin lodged in a house on the corner of the Quai de l'Horloge dating from Henry IV, which would have still been reasonably handsome, had it not been for the little tiled attic which had been added to it under the tyrant before the last. To adapt the domicile of some old member of the Parliament to the needs of the middle-class and artisan families now quartered there, there was a multiplicity of partitions and false floors. Thus Citizen Remacle, house porter and jobbing tailor, was crammed into a half-floor as limited in height as it was in breadth, where you could see him through the glass door, legs crossed on his work-table and his neck up against the floor boards above, stitching away at the uniform of a national guard, while Citizeness Remacle, whose stove had for chimney only the well of the staircase, poisoned all the lodgers with the fumes of her stews and her fries and, on the threshold, little Joséphine, their daughter, her face all treacle but lovely as daylight, played with the cabinet-maker's dog Mouton. Citizeness Remacle, generous of heart, bosom and hips, was alleged to grant her favours to Citizen Dupont *senior*, one of the twelve of the Watch Committee. At least, her husband was full of violent suspicions, and the Remacle ménage filled the hours with their rows, alternating with their peacemakings. The upper floors of the house were occupied by Citizen Chaperon, a goldsmith, who had his little shop on the Quai de l'Horloge, by a health official, a lawyer, a goldbeater and a number of lawcourts clerks.

Évariste Gamelin mounted the ancient staircase, to the fourth and upper floor, where he had a studio, including one room for his mother. Here the wooden stairs, ornamented with tiles, to which the grand stone stairway of the

lower floors had given way, came to an end. A ladder against one wall led to a loft, from which a heavily-built man, getting on in years, with handsome, florid, pink cheeks, was just descending, with a huge bundle perilously clutched in his arms, yet without ceasing to hum:

*J'ai perdu mon serviteur.*

Breaking off his refrain, he gave Gamelin a polite *good-day,* which Gamelin returned, helping him down with his bundle, for which the old man thanked him.

"There," he said, taking up the bundle again, "there you see some dolls which I am straight away going to deliver to a toy-seller in the Rue de la Loi. There is a whole community of them: my creatures; I have given them a perishable body, exempt of joy or suffering. I have not given them the power of thought, for I am a kind God."

It was Citizen Brotteaux, one time tax-collector, an ex-noble; his father, having made a pile in tax-collecting, had bought himself a title. In the good old days Maurice Brotteaux had called himself Monsieur des Ilettes and at his town house in the Rue de la Chaise had given exquisite dinner-parties which a Madame de Rochemaure, the wife of a court purveyor, a woman of parts, had illuminated with her eyes—her fidelity to her husband never being in question—so long as the Revolution had not touched Maurice Brotteaux des Ilettes' offices, income, house, lands and name. But the Revolution did take them away. He earned his living painting portraits at the door, making pancakes and doughnuts on the Quai de la Mégisserie, writing speeches for representatives of the people and giving your citizenesses dancing lessons. And now, in his attic, to which you scrambled up a ladder, and without head-room, Maurice Brotteaux, with a pot of glue, a ball of string, some water-colours and scraps of paper as capital, manufactured dolls, which he sold to wholesale toy-merchants, who re-sold to hawkers who hawked them in the Champs-Élysées, at the end of a fishing rod, dazzling bait for little children. Throughout troublous times, and despite the terrible ill-fortune which had assailed him, he maintained a placid state of mind, reading for solace the Lucretius which he carried every-where in the bulging pocket of his puce frock-coat.

Évariste Gamelin pushed open the door of his rooms without difficulty. His poverty spared him any concern about locks, and if by habit his mother did shoot the bolt, he would say: "What's the point? People don't steal cobwebs . . . least of all, mine." In his studio, under a thick layer of dust, or turned face to the wall, were piled his *toiles d'araignée*—the canvasses on which, in the days when, following the fashion, he painted scenes of gallantry, with feeble, hesitant brush he had begun fiddling with empty quivers and birds in flight, risky pastimes and dreams of happiness, tucking up the pet-ticoats of goose-girls and sticking rose-hued buttons on the breasts of shepherd-esses.

But it was not a genre that suited his temperament. These scenes with their cold treatment were evidence of the incurable chastity of the painter. Con-noisseurs were never deceived, and Gamelin had never been accepted as an erotic artist. Today, though still under thirty, these subjects seemed to him to date from ages ago. In them he saw mon-archical depravity and the shameful re-sults of court corruption. He blamed himself for ever having taken up such a despicable kind of painting and shown his spirit to be debased by slavery. Now, citi-zen of a free nation, with bold strokes of his charcoal he would sketch Liberty, the Rights of Man, French Constitutions, Republican Spirits, Hercules of the

People trampling underfoot the Hydra of Tyranny, and fill every one of his pictures with all the fervour of his patriotism. Alas, this did not earn his bread-and-butter. It was a bad time for artists. No doubt, the Convention was not to blame, for flinging armies in all directions against the Thrones, the Convention which, proud, impassive and determined against a united Europe, was perfidious and cruel to itself, rending itself with its own hands, making terror the order of the day, instituting, for the punishment of conspirators, an implacable tribunal to which it was shortly to give its own limbs to be devoured, but which, at the same time, calm, reflective and enamoured of science and beauty, was reforming the calendar, instituting special schools, start-ing national contests of painting and sculpture, with foundation of prizes to spur artists on, organising annual exhibi-tions, opening a Museum and, on the model of Athens and Rome, lending pub-lic holidays and funerals a sublime char-acter. Yet, French painting, formerly so well known in England, Germany, Rus-sia, and Poland, now had no outlet to abroad. The connoisseurs of painting, art collectors, nobles and financiers, were ruined, had emigrated or were in hid-ing. The men whom the Revolution had enriched, peasants who had collared national properties, commission-agents, army contractors, law courts gamblers, still did not dare show their opulence—and for that matter were indifferent to painting. One needed either the reputa-tion of Regnault or the push of young Gérard, to sell a picture. Greuze, Frago-nard, and Houin were reduced to pov-erty. Prud'hon could barely support wife and family by drawing things for Copia to make stippled engravings of. Henne-quin, Wicar, and Topino-Lebrun, patri-otic painters, suffered starvation. Game-lin, unable to earn the expenses of a picture—neither pay the model nor buy the paints—had abandoned the first rough sketch of his vast *Tyrant in Hell Pursued by the Furies*. It covered half his studio with incomplete outlines of terrible aspect, more than life size, with a huddle of green snakes each of which was thrusting out two in-curved pointed tongues. In the foreground, to the left, could be distinguished a fierce, emaciated Charon in his skiff, a powerful fragment, well drawn, though redolent of the art school. There was much more gift and naturalness in a smaller canvas, also unfinished, hanging in the best lit corner of the studio. This was an Orestes, being raised from his bed of suffering by his sister Electra. One could also see the young girl drawing back the tangled locks concealing her brother's eyes, with a moving gesture. Oreste's head was tragic and handsome and one could detect in it a certain resemblance to the painter himself.

Gamelin often gazed sadly at this composition; on occasion his arms, quivering with a longing to paint, would reach out to Electra, whose features were mainly sketched in, and then fall back again helpless. The artist was all enthusiasm and his soul was attuned to great things. But he was compelled to exhaust himself on orders which he painted indifferently, because he was obliged to satisfy the taste of the man in the street and also because he was not big enough to stamp the slightest thing with the imprint of genius. He drew little allegorical compositions, which skilfully enough his comrade Desmahis engraved for black and white or colour reproduction, to be taken at a cheap rate by a print seller named Blaise in the Rue Honoré. But the print trade was going from bad to worse, according to Blaise, who latterly had refused to buy any more.

But on this occasion Gamelin, made ingenious by necessity, had evolved an idea which was happy and new, or at least, so he thought, and ought to make

the print seller's fortune as well as their own, and that was, a pack of patriotic playing-cards, in which he was going to substitute Liberties, Equalities and other Ideas, for the Kings, Queens and Knaves of the old world. He had already sketched all his characters, and even completed some, and was anxious to get those he thought ready for engraving into Desmahis' hands. The one he thought had come out best was of a volunteer in his cocked hat, with blue coat edged with red, yellow breeches and black gaiters; he was seated on a big drum, with his feet on a pile of bullets and his gun between his legs. This was Citizen Hearts—replacing the Knave of Hearts. For more than six months Gamelin had been drawing volunteers, with unflagging passion. He had sold a number; fervour was at its height. There were several hanging on his studio wall. Five or six, in water-colour, gouache, two chalks, lay about on table and chairs. In the July of '92, when there were recruiting platforms erected all over Paris, and every bar, gay with greenery, rang with cries of "Long live the People! Liberty or Death!" Gamelin could never cross the "new bridge" or the town hall without his heart leaping towards the beflagged marquee in which magistrates with their sash on were inscribing volunteers to the sounds of the *Marseillaise*. But if he had joined the forces, he would have left his mother to starve.

Preceded by the sound of her hard breathing, widowed Citizeness Gamelin entered the studio, all a-sweat, flushed, breathless, the national cockade dangling carelessly from her cap and ready to fall off. She planted her basket on a chair, and then, still standing, the better to get her breath, grumbled about the cost of foodstuffs.

Citizeness Gamelin had till her husband's death been the spouse of a cutler of the Rue de Grenelle-Saint-Germain (at the sign of the *Town of Châtellerault*)—

now she was only the poor housekeeper of her painter son, who was the elder of her two children. As for her daughter, Julie, formerly in the gown business in the Rue Honoré, the best thing was to forget what had come of her, for there was no good in telling everybody that she had emigrated with an aristocrat.

"Almighty God!" sighed Citizeness Gamelin, showing her son a heavy, dun-coloured cottage loaf, "bread is too dear for anything; they might at least make it of pure wheat! There's not an egg or a vegetable or a cheese in the market. If we go on living on chestnuts we shall turn into chestnut trees ourselves."

After a long silence, she resumed: "I came on some women who haven't a thing to feed their little ones with. Poor people are suffering terribly. And there'll be no change till things are restored."

"Mother dear," said Gamelin, with a frown, "the shortages we are suffering from are caused by men who corner the market and speculators who starve the nation and try to reach understanding with external enemies to make the Republic hateful to its citizens and destroy Liberty. That is where the conspiracies of your Brissot crowd and the treacheries of your Pétions and Rolands lead! We shall be lucky if the armed federalists do not get to Paris to massacre the patriots whom famine kills too slowly. There is no time to be lost: flour will have to be taxed and any person speculating on the nation's food, stirring up revolt or treating with abroad, guillotined. The Convention has just set up a special Court to try conspirators. It is made up of patriots; but will its members have sufficient drive to defend the country against all its enemies? Let us have faith in Robespierre; he has guts. Let us above all trust in Marat. That's a man who loves the people, perceives its true interests and serves them. He had always been the first to unmask traitors and scent out conspiracies. He is

incorruptible and fearless. He alone is capable of saving the Republic in its hour of danger."

Citizeness Gamelin, with a toss of her head, made the neglected cockade drop from her cap.

"That's enough, Évariste; your Marat is a man like any other, not one whit better than the rest. You are young, you are all illusions. What you say now of Marat, you used to say of Mirabeau, of La Fayette, of Pétion, of Brissot."

"Never!" cried Gamelin, genuinely forgetful.

Freeing an end of the deal table, with its litter of papers, books, brushes and chalks, the citizeness laid out an earthenware tureen, two pewter bowls, two iron forks, the grey round loaf and a jug of cheap wine.

Mother and son ate their soup in silence, finishing their dinner with a fragment of fat bacon. The mother put her fried scrap on her bread, then with a pocket knife conveyed it morsel by morsel to her toothless mouth, chewing with respect the food which had cost so dear.

She had left the best piece for her son, who remained lost in thought.

"Eat up, Évariste, eat up," she kept enjoining him, at regular intervals.

On her lips, the words acquired the solemnity of a religious commandment.

She had resumed her lamentation on the dearness of foodstuff. Gamelin again proclaimed taxation as the sole remedy to these ills.

But her view was: "There's no more money. The refugees have taken it all. There's no more confidence. It makes you despair about everything."

"Silence, mother, silence!" cried Gamelin. "Do our privations or our sufferings matter an instant? The Revolution is going to mean centuries of happiness for the human species."

The good lady dipped her bread in her wine; her outlook cleared, and she smiled, dreaming of her youth, when on the King's birthday she danced on the greensward. She also recalled the day when Joseph Gamelin, cutler by calling, asked her hand. And she told over every detail, one after the other. Her mother said: "Go and dress. We're going to the Place de Grève, to M. Bienassis the goldsmith's shop, to see Damiens quartered." They had great difficulty, getting through the crowd of sightseers. At M. Bienassis's shop the young girl found Joseph Gamelin, in his best pink coat, and guessed at once what was afoot. All the time she stood by the window to see the regicide drawn, drenched with molten lead, quartered by four horses and tossed into the fire, M. Joseph Gamelin, standing behind her, kept up his compliments on her complexion, her coiffure and her figure.

She drained her glass and went on recalling her life story.

"I brought you into the world, Évariste, sooner than I expected, through a fright I had while I was pregnant, on the bridge, where I was nearly knocked down by sightseers at the execution of M. de Lally. You were so small when you were born, that the surgeon doubted whether you would survive. But I was sure that God would be kind to me and preserve you. I brought you up as well as I could, never sparing care or expense. It is fair to say, Évariste dear, that you have shown me your gratitude and that ever since you were only a boy you have done all you could to repay me. You were gentle and affectionate by nature. Your sister was not bad at heart, but she was selfish and hot-tempered. You were always more sorry for the unfortunate than she was. When the little rascals of the district pulled birds' nests down from the trees, you tried to get the little birds away from them, to give them back to their mother, and often enough you only gave up when they had got you down and beaten you about terribly. When you were seven, in-stead of quarrelling with bad boys, you would walk so nicely down the street, saying your catechism; and you used to bring all the poor people you found home for help, though I had to whip you to break you of that little way. You could not see anybody suffer without crying. When you had grown up, you became very handsome. To my great astonishment, you seemed ignorant of it, which was very different from most handsome boys, who are conceited and proud of their fine faces."

The old mother spoke the truth. Évariste at twenty had a serious countenance of some charm, handsome both in an austere and a feminine sense, the features of a Minerva. Now his dull eyes and colourless cheeks were expressive of a sorrowful, temperamental soul. But for a moment his glance, when he turned towards his mother, reassumed the gentleness of early youth.

She continued: "You could have made the most of what Nature gave to you, to go after bad girls, but you preferred to stay at my side, in the shop, and there were even times when I had to tell you to detach yourself from my petticoats and go and have some fun with your friends. To my dying day, Évariste, I shall be your witness that you were a good son. After your father's death, you pluckily took responsibility for me; though your position hardly brings in anything now, you have never let me want a thing, and though today we are both of us destitute and in poverty, I cannot blame you; it is all the fault of the Revolution."

He made a gesture of reproach, but she shrugged her shoulders, and continued.

"I am no aristocrat. I knew the great in all their power and I can tell you that they abused their privileges. I once saw your father beaten by the Duke of Cana-leilles' men for not getting out of the road of their master briskly enough. I never could abide the Austrian—she was too haughty and too much a spendthrift. As for the King, I thought he was kind, and it was only his trial and condemnation made me change my mind. In fact, I do not crave after the old régime, for all that I spent some happy moments under it. But don't tell me the Revolution will bring in equality, because men will never be equal; it's not feasible, and there's no point turning the country upside down, there will always be great and small, fat and lean."

And while she spoke, she put away the crockery. The painter paid no attention to her. He was trying to get at the outline of a sansculotte in red cap and jacket, who in his pack of cards was to replace the rejected knave of spades.

There was a scratch at the door, and a girl appeared, a country lass, broader than she was high, red-polled and bandy, a wen concealing the left eye, the right eye so pale blue that it seemed white, and with enormous lips and protruding teeth.

She asked Gamelin if he was the painter, and if he could do her a portrait of her fiancé, Ferrand (Jules), volunteer of the Ardennes army.

Gamelin replied that he would gladly do the portrait, when the good warrior returned.

The girl, with persuasive gentleness, insisted that she wanted it at once.

The painter, smiling in spite of himself, objected that he could do nothing without the model.

The poor thing made no answer; she had not envisaged this difficulty. Her head drooping to her left shoulder, her hands clasped on her belly, she stood there, dumb, apparently overcome with grief. Touched, and interested by such simplicity, the painter, to distract the unhappy loving girl, thrust into her hand one of the volunteers he had just done in water-colour, and asked her if this fiancé in the Ardennes was at all like this.

She applied her doleful eye to the sheet of paper, it gradually came to life, then flashed fire, and was glorious; her broad features expanded into a radiant smile.

"That's the very image of him," she said, at last; "that's Ferrand (Jules) in the flesh, that's the very spit of Ferrand (Jules)."

Before the painter could think of taking the sheet from her, she had folded it carefully in her coarse red fingers and made of it a minute square, which she dropped over her heart, between stays and shift, then handed the artist a five livre treasury note, wished him and his mother good night, and hobbled nimble and smiling out of the room.

## III

On the afternoon of the same day, Évariste went to see Citizen Jean Blaise, print seller, who also dealt in boxes of wood and cardboard and a variety of toys, in the Rue Honoré, opposite the Oratory, near the Messageries, at the sign of the *Amour Peintre*. The shop was on the ground floor of a house about sixty years old, and gave on to an alcove the keystone of which was a grotesque horned head. The alcove was covered with an oil painting representing "The Sicilian or Love the Painter," after a composition of Boucher's, that Jean Blaise's father had had put up in 1770, but which had steadily deteriorated since then through sun and rain. On either side of the door a similar alcove, with a nymph's head as keystone, and furnished with the largest plate-glass window it had been possible to find, offered to the eye fashionable prints and the latest colour engraving novelties. Today one could see scenes of gallantry, treated with a somewhat dry charm by Boilly—*Lessons of Conjugal Love* and *The Gentle Art of Resistance*, which scandalised the Jacobins and had been denounced to the Society of the Arts by the single-minded; also the *Promenade* by Debucourt, with a dandy in green breeches sprawling over three chairs, some horses by Carle Vernet the Younger, some balloons, *Virginia Bathing,* and some classical figures.

Of all the citizens swept by the flood past this shop, it was the most ragged who dawdled longest at these two lovely displays, being avid for distraction and pictures and greedy, if only by ocular vision, to participate in the good things of this world; they marvelled open-mouthed, whereas the aristocrats just glanced, frowned and hurried on.

From as far off as he could discern anything, Évariste raised his eyes to one of the windows above the shop, that on the left-hand side, where there was a pot of red pinks behind the ironwork railing of the balcony. That window lighted the room of Jean Blaise's daughter, Élodie. The print seller and his daughter occupied the first floor of the house.

Évariste, pausing a moment as if to take breath at the shop, turned the door-handle. He came on Citizeness Élodie just when, having sold some engravings, two compositions, by Fragonard son, and Naigeon, most carefully selected from among many others, before putting away the notes she had taken in the till, was holding them up between her lovely eyes and the daylight, to examine the hachuring, the borders and the watermark, being worried, for there was as much bad paper money about as good, which was most harmful to trade. As formerly those who imitated the Royal signature, forgers of the national currency were punished by death; all the same, treasury note blocks could be found in any cellar; the Swiss were bringing false treasury notes in by the million; whole bundles were left about in inns; every day the English deposited whole bales of them on the coast,

to discredit the Republic and reduce the patriots to poverty. Élodie was afraid of taking bad money, and still more afraid of tendering it and being treated as an accomplice of Pitt, though she always had faith in her good luck and was confident of getting out of any tight corner.

Évariste examined her with that gloomy look which is more eloquent of love than any smile. She looked at him with a rather mocking pout which puckered her black eyes, and that expression came of the knowledge of being loved and of not being annoyed to be, and also because that sort of expression provoked a suitor, prompted him to bewail his lot, and led him on to a declaration, if he had not already made one, which was the case with Évariste.

Putting the notes away in the cash-box, she drew from her work-basket a white scarf which she had begun to embroider, and set to work. She was industrious and a coquette too, and as she instinctively handled her needle to please as well as to make herself a pretty piece of ornament, she embroidered differently, according to who was watching her; she embroidered in a slapdash way for those to whom she wished to communicate a gentle languor; she embroidered with temperament for those she liked to make rather desperate. She began embroidering carefully for Évariste, in whom she wished to inspire genuine feeling.

Élodie was neither very young nor very pretty. She could even look ugly at first sight. She was dark, with olive skin, and beneath the voluminous black kerchief carelessly knotted under her chin, from under which the blue-black locks of her hair escaped, her fiery eyes charred their orbits. In her round face, with its prominent cheek-bones, a smiling face with slightly snub nose, a face both rustic and voluptuous, the painter could see the head of the Borghese faun, the divine roguishness of which, seen in a cast, he had admired. Slight moustaches emphasised her sensuous lips. A bosom which seemed ripe for loving puffed out the crossed shawl of that year's fashion. Her supple waist, her agile legs, the whole of her sturdy body was animated with lovely, untamed charm. Her glance, her breath, every quiver of her flesh spoke to the heart and promised love. Behind the tradesman's counter she rather suggested a dancing nymph, a bacchante from the Opera, stripped of her lynx skin, her thyrsis and her ivy garlands, and by some enchantment constrained into the modest envelope of a Chardin housewife.

"My father is out," she told the painter, "wait a little, he will be back soon."

The small swart hands made the needle flash to and fro through the lawn.

"Does my design please you, M. Gamelin?"

Gamelin was incapable of pretence. And love, firing his courage, increased his frankness.

"You embroider with skill, Citizeness, but, if you wish for my opinion, the design you have drawn is not simple enough, not bold enough, it is too reminiscent of the affected taste which in France has for too long dominated the art of decorating materials, furniture, canopies; all these knots and garlands recall the petty, mesquin style which was in favour under the tyrant. Taste is being reborn. Alas, we have a long way to go. There was something Chinese about decoration under the infamous Louis XV. Chests of drawers were made pot-bellied, with handles ludicrously contorted, only fit to be put on the fire to warm patriotic folk; simplicity alone is beautiful. We must go back to classic shapes. David has designed some beds and armchairs after Etruscan vases and the paintings of Herculanum."

"I have seen those beds and chairs," said Élodie, "they're lovely. Soon people

will refuse anything else. Like you, I adore classical things."

"Then, Citizen," Évariste replied, "had you ornamented this shawl with a Greek border, ivy leaves, snakes or interlaced arrows, it would have been worthy of a woman of Sparta—and of yourself. But you could keep this pattern, by simplifying it, reducing it to straight lines."

She asked him what she should take out.

He bent over the shawl; his cheeks brushed against Élodie's curls. Their hands met on the lawn, their breath mingled. In those instants Évariste tasted unlimited delight; yet, when he felt Élodie's lips near his own, he was afraid he might have offended her, and brusquely withdrew.

Citizen Blaise loved Évariste Gamelin. She thought him marvellous with his large, burning eyes, his fine oval countenance, his pallor, his thick black hair, parted down the centre and falling richly over his shoulders, his solemn bearing, his cold manner, his restrained approach, his determined speech, without a trace of flattery. And, since she loved him, she lent him a proud artistic genius, which some day would burst into masterpieces and make him famous, and she loved him the more for that. Élodie Blaise made no cult of male purity, her moral sense was not troubled by a man yielding to his lusts, his tastes, his desires; she loved Évariste, who was austere; she did not love him because he was austere; yet in the fact that he was austere she found some advantage of not giving a thought to jealousy or suspicion, or fearing any rival.

All the same, at the moment she did find him a little too reserved. Though Racine's Aricia, loving Hippolytus, did admire the young hero's savage rigour, it was in the hope of getting the better of it, and she would soon have complained of a rigour of morals which he would not slacken on her account. And, the moment she found the opportunity, she more than half declared herself, to compel him to declare himself. On gentle Aricia's model, Citizen Élodie Blaise was not very far from holding that in love the woman ought to make the advances. "Those who love the most," she told herself, "are the shyest; they need help and encouragement. Such, for that matter, is their simplicity of heart that the woman can go half way or even more to meet them, without their noticing it, thus leaving them all the outward appearance of making a bold attack, and the glory of the conquest." What put her mind at rest regarding the final result was that she was quite certain (nor was there any doubt about it) that Évariste, before the Revolution had made a hero of him, had had a very human affair with a woman, a humble creature who was porter at the Academy.

Élodie, who was no novice, was aware of different kinds of love. The feelings that Évariste inspired in her were profound enough for her to consider linking her life with his. She was quite prepared to marry him, but expected her father would not approve of the union of his only daughter to an obscure and penniless artist. Gamelin had nothing; the print dealer turned over large sums. The *Amour Peintre* brought in a lot, commission more still, and he was associated with a contractor who supplied the Republican cavalry with trusses of rushes and musty oats. In short, the son of the Rue Saint Dominque cutler was very small beer beside the print publisher with a European name, related to the Blaizots, the Basans, the Didots, and *persona grata* in the Saint-Pierre and Florian households. It was not as obedient daughter that she held her father's consent to be necessary to her marriage. The father, widowed early, greedy and shallow, a great wencher, with a keen nose for a deal, had never bothered himself with her, letting her grow up untrammelled, without either counsel or friendship, more anxious to turn the blind eye than to supervise a daughter whose hot temperament, and means of seduction powerful in quite a different way from a pretty face, he appreciated with the eye of a connoisseur. Too warm-hearted to preserve her virginity, too clever to squander it, sensible in her follies, she had never let her taste for love make her forget the social forms. Her father was infinitely grateful for that prudence, and, as she had inherited from him a business instinct and taste for commercial ventures, he never gave a heed to the mysterious reasons which kept so marriageable a girl from the altar and preserved her at home, where she was worth a house-keeper and four assistants to him. At twenty-seven, she felt she had years and knowledge of the world enough to make her own life, and felt no need whatsoever to ask advice from, or follow the whims of a father who was young, easygoing and careless. But for her to be able to marry Gamelin, it would have been necessary for M. Blaise to settle something on so poor a son-in-law, engage him in the business, guarantee him work, as he did to a number of artists, in short, in one way or another find´ means for him; and that, she considered it out of the question for either the one to propose or the other to accept, so long as they had so little in common.

This stumbling-block worried gentle, but practical Élodie. Without the least trepidation she was contemplating a secret liaison, with the author of the universe as sole witness of their mutual love. Her outlook on life found nothing reprehensible in such a union, which was made feasible by the independence she enjoyed, and to which Évariste's straight and sturdy character lent a sort of moral support; yet Gamelin had great difficulty in keeping his head above water and supporting his ageing mother—it did not look as if so cramped an existence had room even for a love reduced to the simplicity of nature. For that matter, Évariste had not even declared himself, or communicated his own intensions. Citizen Élodie Blaise was however counting on being able to force him to it before very long.

Suddenly she interrupted her thoughts and her needle. "Citizen Évariste," she said, "I shan't like this shawl unless you like it too. Please design me a pattern for it. While you do, I like Penelope will undo what was done in your absence."

With gloomy fervour he replied "I accept the task, Citizen. I will make you a design of Harmodius' sword: a sword in a garland."

And, taking out his pencil, he made a sketch of swords and flowers, all in the bald, sober style he liked. And while he did so, he outlined his beliefs.

"A regenerated French nation," he said, "should reject the whole legacy of servitude—bad taste, bad form, bad drawing. Watteau, Boucher and Fragonard worked for tyrants and slaves. Their works are devoid of any sense of good style or clean line; no nature, or truth. Masks, dolls, fashions, apeing. Posterity will scorn their shallow works. In a hundred years all Watteau's work will have perished, despised, in attics; in 1893 art students will cover Boucher's canvasses with their early attempts. David has shown the way; he is drawing near the classical, though he is still not simple or grand or stark enough. Our painters have still many secrets to learn from the Herculanum friezes, the Roman reliefs, and Etruscan vases."

He spoke at great length of the classical beauties, then came back to Fragonard, whom he harried with unquenchable hatred: "Do you know him, Citizen?"

Élodie nodded; she did.

"Then you also know old Greuze, laughable enough, in all faith, with his scarlet coat and his sword. But he looks like a Greek sage beside Fragonard. I met him, some time back, poor old man, mincing along under the Palais-Égalité arcades, powdered, gallant, frisky, bawdy, frightful. At the sight I felt, failing Apollo, that I'd like to see some tough friend of the arts string him up to a tree and flay him like Marsyas, an eternal warning to bad painters."

Élodie pinned him with her dancing, sensuous eyes. "You know how to hate, Monsieur Gamelin, am I to take it you also know how to l . . . ."

"Is that you, Gamelin?" came a tenor voice, that of Citizen Blaise, returning to his shop, boots squeaking, trinkets jangling, skirts flying, in an enormous black hat, the extremities of which came down to his shoulders.

Taking her basket, Élodie retired to her room.

"Well, Gamelin," Citizen Blaise demanded, "brought me anything new?"

"Perhaps," said the painter.

And he outlined his idea. "Our playing cards are in shocking contrast to our ethics. Such titles as *knave* and *king* are offensive to the ears of a patriot. I have invented and designed a new revolutionary pack of cards in which *Liberties, Equalities and Fraternities* have been substituted for *kings, queens* and *knaves;* the *aces,* surrounded by *fasces,* are named the *Laws* . . . You call a Liberty of Clubs, Equality of Spades, Fraternity of Diamonds, or Law of Hearts . . . I think I've made a good job of the designs; I thought of having Desmahis engrave them on copper, and taking out a patent."

And, drawing from his folder a number of figures finished in wash, the artist handed them to the print dealer.

Citizen Blaise would not take them. He turned away. "Young man," he said, "take it all round to the Convention, you may be the star turn of the sitting. But do not hope to get a penny piece out of your novelty, for it isn't novel. You've overslept. This is the third revolutionary pack I've had brought me. Your pal Dugourc last week offered me a picquet set with four Geniuses, four Liberties, and four Equalities. He suggested another pack with wise men and heroes, Cato, Rousseau, Hannibal and who knows not who else . . . And, my dear boy, the cards were better than yours by being crudely designed and engraved in wood with a penknife. How little you know men, to believe that gamesters would use cards designed à la David and engraved à la Bartolozzi! Besides, what self-deception, to think that you need to go to such lengths to make the old playing cards fit the ideas of the moment. Good sansculottes correct anything unpatriotic themselves, by calling 'The tyrant!' or simply: 'The old swine!' They go on using their filthy old cards and never do buy new ones. The greatest consumption of card packs is in the gambling dens of the Palais-Égalité: my advice to you is to go and offer the croupiers there your Liberties, your Equalities and your—what did you call them?—your Laws of the heart . . . then come back and tell me what they made of it."

Citizen Blaise seated himself on the counter, flicked some grains of snuff off his nankeen breeches and, regarding Gamelin with gentle commiseration, said: "May I give you a word of advice, Citizen Painter? If you want to earn your living, drop your patriotic card packs, drop your revolutionary symbols, your Hercules, your hydras, your Furies pursuing wrongdoing, your geniuses of Liberty, and paint some pretty girls, my boy! The regenerating fervour of citizens grows lukewarm in course of time, but men will always love women. Do me some pretty women, with dainty feet and dainty hands. And get it into your skull

that interest in the Revolution's dead and nobody wants to hear any more of it."

Évariste Gamelin reared at once: "What? nobody wants to hear any more of the Revolution? But the establishment of liberty, the triumphs of our armies and the punishment of tyrants are events which will astonish the most distant posterity. How can we fail to be struck by them! What! the age of sansculotte Jesus lasted nearly eighteen centuries, and the worship of Liberty is going to be abolished after scarcely four years' existence?"

But, with an air of superiority, Jean Blaise said: "You live in dreamland; I live in the real world. Believe me, my friend, the Revolution bores people; it has gone on too long. Five years of fervour, five years of love and kisses, massacres, speech-making, the *Marseillaise,* alarms, aristocrat hunting, heads on pikes, women straddling cannons, trees of liberty with red caps, young girls and old men dragged through the streets in flowered waggons and white robes, of imprisonments, guillotining, ration-cards, public proclamations, cockades, plumes, sabres, red jackets—it's too much. Besides, people come to losing their bearings in it all. We've seen too many great citizens elevated to the Capitol only to be cast down the Tarpeian Cliff—Necker, Mirabeau, La Fayette, Bailly, Pétion, Manuel—and a crowd of others. Who can say you are not preparing the same fate for your latest heroes? . . . One gets lost."

"Name them, Citizen Blaise, name the heroes we are now preparing to sacrifice!" cried Gamelin, in a tone which reminded the print dealer not to be foolhardy.

"I am a Republican and a patriot," he replied, his hand on his heart. "I am as republican as you are, and as patriotic as you are, Citizen Évariste Gamelin. I cast no suspicion on your sense of public duty, and lay no accusation of your being a turncoat. You let me remind you that my sense of public duty and my devotion to the national cause are proved by numerous deeds. Here are my principles: I give my confidence to any man capable of serving France. I take my hat off to those to whom the voice of the nation grants the dangerous honour of legislative power—such as Marat, such as Robespierre; I am prepared to lend them my assistance to the extent of my feeble means and to offer them the unpretentious support of a good citizen. The Committee can testify to my zeal and devotion. In association with true patriots, I have supplied oats and forage to our glorious cavalry and boots to the men. Why, only today, I had sixty bullocks despatched from Vernon to the Southern Army, right through a countryside infested with brigands and bands of Pitt and de Condé's men. I don't talk; I act."

Gamelin calmly put his water-colours back into the folder, tied the strings and put it under his arm.

"Strange contradiction," he said, through clenched teeth, "to help our soldiers carry throughout the world a liberty which one betrays at home, by sowing alarm and unrest in the hearts of its defenders . . . Salut, Citizen Blaise."

Before turning down the alley beside the Oratory, Gamelin, whose heart was big with love and indignation, turned back to cast a glance at the red pinks blooming on a certain window-sill.

He had not lost faith in the salvation of the Fatherland. To Jean Blaise's unpatriotic language he opposed his revolutionary faith. However, he was obliged to recognise that the dealer was not without some semblance of reason when he asserted that the people of Paris had already lost interest in what was happening. Alas! it was only too clear that a general indifference had taken the place of the fire of the early days, and one would never again see the tremendous unanim-

ity of the crowds of Eighty-nine, one would never again see millions of hearts being together as they did in 1790 round the altar of the Federates. All right, then good citizens would have to double their zeal and their dash and awaken a slumbering nation again, giving it a choice between liberty and death.

Thus Gamelin reflected, and thoughts of Élodie reinforced his confidence.

As he reached the Quais, he saw the sun sink to the horizon under heavy clouds, which were like mountains of incandescent lava; the roofs of the city were bathed in golden light; the window panes flashed lightning. And Gamelin then saw Titans forging Dike, a city of brass, from the glowing fragments of the old world.

Being without even a scrap of bread for his mother or himself, he dreamt of sitting down to an endless table, at which the whole universe would be welcome and a regenerated humanity would dine. Meanwhile, he persuaded himself that the country, like a good mother, would suckle its faithful child. He stiffened himself against the print-dealer's scorn, and worked himself up into believing that his notion of a revolutionary pack of cards was novel and good, and that in the successful water-colours under his arm he held a fortune. "Desmahis will engrave them," he thought. "We shall publish the new patriotic game ourselves and we can be sure of selling ten thousand, at twenty sols, in a month.

And, in his impatience to realise the idea, he made off with great strides to the Quai de la Ferraille, where Desmahis lodged, over a glass-cutter's shop.

The entrance was through the shop. The glasscutter told Gamelin that Citizen Desmahis was out, which was no great surprise for the artist, who knew his friend to be a sot and a vagabond, and was indeed always astonished that one could engrave so much and so well with so little application. Gamelin decided he would wait a while. The glass-cutter's wife offered him a chair. She was gloomy and complained of business being bad, though one might have thought that by smashing all the windows the Revolution would have made a glass-cutter's fortune.

Night was falling; Gamelin gave up the idea of waiting for his friend, and bid the glass-cutter's wife good-night. As he made his way across the Pont-Neuf, he saw mounted national guards emerging from the Quai des Morfondus, pushing back pedestrians and carrying torches, as they escorted a tumbril slowly drawing a man whose name nobody knew, a former noble, to the guillotine—the first man to be condemned by the new revolutionary tribunal. He was indistinctly discernible between the hats of the guards, seated, his hands bound behind his back, his head bare, tossing limply towards the tumbril tailboard. The executioner was standing beside him, leaning on the side of the tumbril. Passers-by, halted, observed one to another that it must be somebody who had been starving the country, and paid little attention. Drawing near, Gamelin observed Desmahis among the spectators, trying to force a way through the crowd and across the procession. He called to him and lay a hand on his shoulder: Desmahis turned. He was young, handsome and powerful.

In the old days, at the Academy, it used to be said that he carried Bacchus's head on Hercules' body. His friends called him Barbaroux, because of his resemblance to that representative of the people.

"Let's go," Gamelin said, "I've something important to discuss with you."

"Let me be!" cried Desmahis. And he added something that Gamelin could not make out, while he looked for the possibility to make a dash forward. "I was on the trail of a marvellous wench, in a straw hat, a dressmaker's assistant, with golden hair down her back," he said, "when this blasted tumbril came between us . . . She went on ahead, she's already at the end of the bridge."

Gamelin tried to hang on to his coat, assuring him the business was important. But Desmahis had already slipped through horses, guards, sabres and torches and was following the dressmaker's girl.

## IV

It was ten A.M. The April sun drenched the tender foliage of the trees with its light. The air, lighter after the night storm, was marvellously soft. At long intervals, riders in the Allée des Veuves, broke the silence and the solitude. Beside that shady ride, up against the cottage "of the fair maid of Lille," Évariste sat on a wooden bench, awaiting Élodie. Since that day when their fingers met on the piece of lawn and their two breaths mingled, he had not once been back to the *Amour Peintre.* For a whole week his haughty stoicism and his shyness, which was rapidly becoming desperate, had kept him apart from Élodie. He had written her a serious, gloomy, burning letter, in which, outlining what he now had against Citizen Blaise, but silent on the subject of his love, and concealing his agony, he had announced his determination never again to visit the print shop, showing more determination in the execution of his resolve than could be pleasing to a loving mistress.

Élodie, being of a stubborn disposition, and inclined to stick out for what was hers on every occasion, immediately put her mind to recapturing her loved one. Her first thought was to go to his place, the studio in the Place de Thionville. But, knowing him to be touchy, and judging from his letter that he was outraged, fearsome lest he included the daughter in the annoyance he felt against the father, and made a point of never seeing her again, she thought it best to offer him a sentimental, romantic meeting-place which he would not be able to avoid, and where she would have ample time to convince him and please him, and solitude would be with her in the plot to enchant and vanquish him.

At this time in every one of the English gardens, and on all the fashionable walks, there were cottages built by learned architects to flatter the rustic taste of townsfolk. The "Fair Maid of Lille" cottage, with a lemonade-seller as tenant, rested a pretended poverty on the artistic imitation of a ruined tower, so as to combine village enchantment and the melancholy of ruins. And as if a thatched cottage and a ruined tower were not enough to touch sensitive hearts, the lemonade-seller had erected a tomb under a willow—a pillar with a funeral urn and the inscription "Cléonice to his Faithful Azor." Thatched cottages, ruins, tombs: on the eve of their own decease the aristocracy had built these symbols of poverty, destruction and death in their family parks. And now patriotic townsfolk found pleasure in drinking, dancing and making love in these fake cottage homes, in the shade of fake cloisters in fake ruins and amidst fake tombs, for one and the other were lovers of Nature and disciples of Jean Jacques Rousseau and had hearts identically sensitive and full of philosophy.

Having reached the rendezvous before the appointed hour, Évariste was waiting, and, as if by the pendulum of a clock, measured the time by his own heart-beats. A patrol passed by, convoying prisoners. Ten minutes later, a woman dressed from tip to toe in pink, a bouquet in her hand, as was the custom, slipped into the cottage with a cavalier in cocked hat, red coat and striped vest and breeches, both of them so like the gallants of the old régime that one really ought to agree with Citizen Blaise that there was something in human nature that revolutions did not change in the slightest.

A moment or two later came an old woman, from Rueil, or Saint-Cloud, with a cylindrical box, painted in bright colours, held at arm's length, and sat down on the bench where Gamelin was waiting. She put the box down in her lap; there was a pointer on the lid, for drawing lots. For the poor woman offered little children in their parks a "try." She also sold "pleasures" which was a new name for the little biscuits that used to be called "oublies"—chosen either because the immemorial name had in it an unfortunate suggestion of an offering or debt, or else because people got tired of it, and it was their whim to have a new one.

With a corner of her apron the old woman wiped the sweat from her forehead and then breathed her woes to Heaven, accusing God of injustice in making life so hard for his creatures. Her husband kept a pub down by the river at Saint-Cloud, and every day she trudged up to the Champs-Élysées, swinging her rattle and crying "Pleasures, good ladies, pleasures!" Yet with all their efforts they could not get enough to support their old age.

Seeing the young man on the bench disposed to be sorry for her, she spread herself on the cause of her misfortunes. It was the Republic which, by stripping the rich, had taken the bread out of the mouth of poor people. And there was no hope of any improvement, either. On the contrary, she could tell, from many a sign, that things were going to get worse. There was a woman at Nanterre had given birth to a child with a viper's head; the Rueil church had been struck with lightning and the cross on the tower melted; a werewolf had been seen in Chaville Woods. Masked men were poisoning the springs and scattering powders which caused illnesses . . .

Évariste saw Élodie jump down from her cab. He ran towards her. The young woman's eyes sparkled in the transparent shadow cast by her straw hat; her lips, red as the pinks she held in her hand, smiled. A black silk shawl, crossed over her bosom, was tied at her back. Her yellow gown revealed the quick movements of her knees and feet, trim in low-heeled shoes. Her hips were almost completely unencumbered, for the Revolution had liberated women's figures; nevertheless, the skirts, billowing again beneath the loins, concealed Élodie's true shape, exaggerating it and veiling the truth by magnified curves.

He wanted to say something, but could not find a word, and was angry with himself for this shyness, which Élodie preferred to the sweetest of receptions. She also noticed—and took for a good sign—the fact that he invested more skill than usual in the tie of his cravat.

"I wanted to see you," she said, "and have a talk with you. I did not answer your letter; it annoyed me; I did not find you in it. It would have been more pleasing if it had been more natural. It would be doing your character a wrong to believe that you won't come to the *Amour Peintre* any more because you had a trifling dispute about politics with a man much older than yourself. You can be sure you've no reason to fear my father not welcoming you, when you do come. You do not know him; he neither remembers what he said to you or what you replied. I won't pretend there is much sympathy between you; but there is no bitterness in him. I tell you frankly, he's not much concerned with you . . . or with me. His only thought is for his business and his pleasures."

She made her way towards the shrubbery round the cottage, where he followed her, with some repugnance, knowing that it served as rendezvous for bought love and momentary caresses. She selected the most concealed table.

"What a lot of things I have to tell you, Évariste! Friendship has its rights—may I use mine? I want to tell you a lot about yourself . . . and a little about me, if I may."

The lemonade-man had brought a carafe and some glasses, and, good housewife, Élodie poured herself out a glass; then she told him about her childhood, told him of her mother's beauty, which she liked to dilate upon out of filial piety and also as the source of her own beauty; she praised the vigour of her grandparents, for she was proud of her bourgeois blood. She told him how, losing that adorable mother when she was sixteen, she had lived with neither tenderness or anything she could rely on. She depicted herself as she was—lively, sensitive, plucky and then added:

"Évariste, I have had too sad and too lonely a childhood not to know the value of a heart like yours, and I tell you frankly, I shall never give up, willingly or without a fight, a sympathy on which I used to think I could count, and valued."

Évariste gazed at her tenderly. "Élodie, can it be that you are not indifferent to me? Can I believe . . . ?"

He stopped short, afraid of saying too much and so abusing so trusting a friendship.

She held out her hand, small and unpretentious, half-emerging from tight long sleeves flounced with lace. Her bosom rose and fell in long sighs.

"Évariste, lend me all the feelings you choose for yourself, and you will not be mistaken about how my heart feels."

"Élodie, Élodie, I wonder whether you will repeat what you have just said, when you learn . . ."

He hesitated.

She lowered her eyes.

He concluded, in a lower voice: ". . . that I love you?"

Hearing the final words, she blushed; from delight. Yet, while her eyes expressed a tender passion, in spite of herself a mocking smile curled up a corner of her lips. She was thinking "And he thinks he is the first to have told me this . . . and may even be afraid of making me angry."

But, with kindness, she said: "My dear, did you not see that I love you?"

They thought they were alone in the world. Évariste was so beside himself that he raised his eyes to the heavens, all a-sparkle with light and the azure infinity: "Look," he said, "the sky is watching us! It is adorable and full of kindness, as you are, my beloved; brilliant like you, gentle like you, smiling like you."

He felt himself united to the whole of nature, and associated the universe with his happiness and his triumph. In his eyes the chestnut blossoms lit up like candelabras and the giant torches of the poplars blazed to celebrate their betrothal.

He exulted in his strength and magnificence. She, softer and also more subtle, more supple, more malleable, took advantage of her own frailty, and as soon as she had conquered him, submitted to him; now that she had got him under her domination, she recognised the master in him, her hero, her god, burning to obey him, to marvel at him, to give herself to him. In the shade of the thicket he gave her a long kiss, under which she threw back her head and, in Évariste's arms, felt her whole body melt, like wax.

Forgetting the world, they told each other much more about themselves. Évariste mainly expressed hazy, lofty thoughts, which were ravishing to Élodie. She told him things which were tender, useful and individual. Then, when she thought she could stay no longer, she rose determinedly, gave her love the three red pinks from her window and jumped quickly into the cabriolet which he had brought her. It was a yellow-painted cab from the square with very high wheels, without the least thing strange about it or the driver. But Gamelin never took cabs, nor did the people he had to do with. Seeing her mounted on those swift large wheels gave him a heart pang and he felt overcome with gloomy presentiments; by a sort of hallucination which was entirely mental, he had the impression that that hired horse was bearing Élodie away beyond reality, from the present into some wealthy, hilarious metropolis, towards haunts of luxury and delight he would never enter.

The cab vanished. Évariste's disturbance faded, though leaving him with a dull pain and a feeling that the moments of tenderness and oblivion he had just lived through he would never know again.

He passed down the Champs-Élysées, where women in light gowns were chatting or embroidering on wooden chairs while their children played under the trees. A *plaisirs* seller, with his drum-shaped box, reminded him of the old woman in the avenue, and he had the impression that between one encounter and the other a whole age had passed. He crossed the Place de la Révolution. In the Tuileries he caught the distant sound of that tremendous murmur of the grand days, that unanimity of the crowd which the enemies of the Revolution maintained self-destroyed for all time. He quickened his pace in the growing din, reached the Rue Honoré, to find it packed with men and women, shouting: "Long live the Republic! Long live Liberty!" The walls of the gardens, windows, balconies, roofs, all were full of onlookers, waving hats and handkerchiefs. Preceded by a sapper clearing a way for the procession, surrounded by municipal functionaries, national guards, gunners, gendarmes, hussars, a bilious-looking man above the heads of the populace was slowly approaching, his forehead bound with a fillet of oak-leaves, his body wrapped in an old green surtout with ermine collar. The women were pelting him with flowers. He kept looking on all sides with his piercing yellow eyes, as if coming through this fervent multitude to pick out still more enemies of the people to denounce, traitors to punish. As he passed by, Gamelin, bareheaded, joined his voice to the hundred thousand others, and cried: "Long live Marat!"

The triumphal figure entered the Hall of the Convention like Destiny. While the crowd dispersed slowly, Gamelin, seated on a curb-post of the Rue Honoré, clutched his pounding heart. What he had just witnessed filled him with the loftiest emotion and burning ardour.

He venerated, he cherished Marat, who, a sick man, his arteries inflamed, and devoured by ulcers, was drawing on the remnants of his strength to serve the Republic and, in his poor home, open to everybody, received him with open arms, spoke to him fervently of the public good, or perhaps, on occasion, put him questions about what the villains were plotting. He marvelled to see how the enemies of *the Just,* plotting his ruin, had prepared his triumph; he blessed the revolutionary court which, acquitting the Friend of the People, had given back to the Convention the most zealous and most single-minded of its legislators. Again his eyes could see that fever-scorched head, bound with the civic crown, that countenance printed with unwavering pride and implacable love, that face so ravaged, decomposed and powerful, that contorted mouth, that broad bosom, that dying colossus who, from the heights of the living chariot of his triumph, seemed to be telling his fellow citizens to be, as he was, patriots to their last breath.

The street was deserted, night wrapping it in shadows; the lantern-man passed with his cresset, and Gamelin murmured: "To the last breath!"

## V

At nine A.M., in the Luxembourg gardens, Évariste found Élodie awaiting him on a bench.

During the month since they exchanged their vows of love, they had met every day, at the *Amour Peintre* or the studio in the Place de Thionville, always very tenderly, though still subject to a reserve in their intimacy dictated by the character of a lover who was solemn and full of virtue, a deist and good citizen who, though ready to be united with his beloved mistress before the law or before God, as circumstances willed, wished only to do so in broad daylight, publicly. Élodie was well aware of how honourable that resolve was, yet, despairing of a marriage which everything ruled out, and loth to fly in the face of social convention, in her own heart she contemplated a liaison which secrecy would keep decent till time had made it respectable. She expected some day to be able to overcome the scruples of a lover whose respect for her was excessive; and, anxious not to delay certain essential confessions, had asked for an hour together in the deserted gardens next the Carthusian Convent.

Giving him a glance full of tenderness and frankness, she took his hand, had him sit down beside her and with great concentration began: "I prize you too much to hide anything from you, Évariste. I believe myself worthy of you, but I should not be, if I did not tell you everything. Hear me and be my judge. There is nothing vile I have done, to reproach myself with, nothing low or even selfish. I was weak and credulous . . . My dear one, do not forget the difficult circumstances in which I was placed. You know—I no longer had a mother; my father, still young, thought of nothing but his own distractions and never paid any attention to me. I was sensitive; nature gave me a tender heart and a generous spirit; and, for all that it also did not refuse me solid commonsense, at that time my feelings did get the better of my reason. Alas, it would be the same today, did not the two agree, Évariste, and give me to you, body and soul, for ever!"

She told her story in stages, without faltering. She had prepared her words; she had been determined to make her confession for some time, because she was a frank character, because she liked to imitate Rousseau and because, sensibly enough, she told herself that some day Évariste would learn the secrets which were not hers alone, and it was far better for him to learn by an open avowal, dependent entirely on her own discretion, than for him to be informed of it later, to her shame. Tender-hearted and sweet-natured as she was, she did not feel very guilty, and that made the confession less painful; besides, she did not intend to say more than she need.

"Ah!" she sighed, "Évariste darling, why did you not come to me when I was alone, abandoned . . ."

Gamelin had taken her request for him to be her judge *au pied de la lettre*. Prepared by his character and his literary education to administer domestic justice, he was ready to hear Élodie's avowal. As she seemed to hesitate, he told her to speak. Quite simply, she said: "A young man, apart from his bad qualities, had some good ones too, and only revealed those, found some attraction in me and took me up with a persistence which was surprising in him; he was in the flower of his youth, full of charm and had liaisons with a number of delightful women who never concealed their worship of him. It was neither his good looks nor his intelli-

gence that engaged my attention . . . He knew how to get at me by showing me affection, and I do believe he genuinely loved me. He was kind and pressing. I asked no pledge but his heart, but that was fickle . . . I only blame myself; I am making my own confession, not his. I am not complaining of him, as he is now a complete stranger. Oh, Évariste, I swear to you, he might never have existed."

She was silent. Gamelin made no answer. He folded his arms; his glance was rigid, gloomy. At one and the same time he thought of his mistress and his sister Julie. Julie too had listened to a lover; but she was very different, he told himself, from the unfortunate Élodie; she had let herself be seduced, not by the mistake of a sensitive heart, but, far from her own folk, to find luxury and pleasure. In his severity he had condemned his sister and he had been on the point of condemning his mistress.

In a very sweet voice, Élodie resumed: "I was soaked in philosophy; I thought all men were honest by nature. It was my misfortune to come upon a lover who had not been formed in the school of Nature and ethics, one whom social prejudices, ambition, self-esteem and a false notion of honour had made egotistical and false."

These well worked-out words produced the desired effect. Gamelin's eyes softened. He asked: "Who was your betrayer? Do I know him?"

"No, you do not."

"Tell me his name."

She had foreseen this request and was determined not to satisfy it. She gave her reasons. "Spare me that, please. I have already said too much, for either of us."

But, as he insisted, she said: "In the sacred interests of our love, I shall tell you nothing which could give that unknown person precise form in your mind. I do not want to feed your jealousy with a ghost; I do not want to place a superfluous shade between you and me. I am not going to introduce you to the man whom I myself have forgotten."

Gamelin pressed her to tell him the name of her betrayer; this was the term he insisted on using, for he was quite sure Élodie had been betrayed, tricked, led astray. He could not even conceive otherwise, or that she had given way to her desires, irresistible desires, given ear to the inward voice of flesh and blood; he could not conceive of this voluptuous, tender-hearted creature, this lovely piece of prey, offering herself; to satisfy his very nature he had to see her as taken by force or by some trickery, raped, caught in a snare laid in her tracks. He put her question after question, all moderately worded, but precise, searching, embarrassing. He wanted to know how the liaison began, whether it had lasted a long or a short time, whether it had been calm or tempestuous, and how it was broken off. And he kept coming back to the means this man had used to seduce her, as if he had been obliged to adopt some unheard-of, extraordinary means. But all these questions he put in vain. With obstinacy both gentle and pleading, she kept her silence, her lips tight and her eyes swollen with tears.

However, when Évariste demanded where the man now was, she replied: "He has left the Kingdom," then swiftly corrected herself and amended to: "France."

"An émigré!" cried Gamelin.

She shot him a silent glance, both relieved and saddened to see him creating his own truth on the lines of his political passions, giving his jealousy a gratuitous Jacobin twist.

In fact, Élodie's lover was a little lawyer's clerk, a very handsome young fellow, a cherubic guttersnipe whom she had adored, and the memory of whom, after three years, still warmed her heart. He was a specialist in wealthy old women;

he left Élodie for a most experienced woman who recompensed him for his qualities. Entering the Mayor's offices, after the suppression of the system of lawyers, he was now a sansculotte dragoon and a former noblewoman's paramour.

"A noble! An émigré!" Gamelin repeated, while she took care not to undeceive him, never having wanted him to know the truth. "And he deserted you like a rotter?"

She nodded.

He pressed her to him. "Darling sacrifice of monarchical corruption, my love shall avenge you. May Heaven bring him across my path! I shall know him!"

She turned her face away, at once saddened and smiling, disappointed. She would have liked him to be more knowledgeable in love matters, more primitive, more brutal. She felt that he only forgave her so quickly through a frigidity of imagination, and because the confidences she had made in him had failed to awaken any of those pictures that are the agony of lecherous persons, and in short that her seduction was for him merely a moral or social fact.

They had risen and were strolling down the green alleys of the gardens. He was telling her that he honoured her the more for having suffered. Élodie had not asked for so much; yet, such as he was, she loved him, and marvelled at the artistic genius she saw glow in him.

As they left the Luxembourg gardens they came upon crowds of people in the Rue de l'Égalité and all round the National Theatre, which was nothing to surprise them; for some days there had been much ferment in the more patriotic wards; people were denouncing the d'Orléans group and Brissot's accomplices, who, people said, were plotting the ruin of Paris and a massacre of the republicans. Gamelin himself had for that matter quite recently signed the Petition of the Commune calling for the expulsion of the Twenty-one.

Just before passing under the arcade which joined the theatre and the adjoining building, they had to make their way through a group of red-jacketed citizens whom a young soldier as handsome as a Cupid of Praxiteles under his panther-skin helmet was addressing. This fascinating soldier charged the Friend of the People with slackness. He cried: "Marat, you sleep, and the Federalists are forging our fetters."

Élodie had scarcely set eyes on the man when she cried: "Let's go, Évariste!" She said the crowd frightened her, she was afraid of fainting in the crush.

They parted in the Place de la Nation, swearing eternal love.

The same morning, early, Citizen Brotteaux had made Gamelin's mother the magnificent present of a capon. It would have been imprudent of him to say where he had got it, for it came from a lady of the Market at the Pointe Eustache for whom he sometimes acted as clerk, and it was known that these ladies cherished royalist sympathies and were in correspondence with émigrés. Citizeness Gamelin had accepted the capon with a grateful heart. At this time one rarely saw such lovely things; foodstuffs were rising. The general public were afraid of a famine; it was said that the aristocrats wanted one, and the market-riggers were preparing it.

Citizen Brotteaux, begged to share the capon at midday dinner, accepted the invitation and congratulated his hostess on the sweet culinary odours which were to be imbibed in her dwelling. The artist's studio was indeed redolent of a rich chicken soup.

"You are very kind, Monsieur," the good lady replied. "To prepare the stomach to receive your capon, I have made a soup with herbs and a bacon rind and a shin bone. There is nothing to soften a soup like a marrow-bone."

"A praiseworthy maxim, Citizen," old Brotteaux replied. "And you would do well to put the precious bone back in the pot tomorrow, the day after tomorrow, and all the week, for it will not fail to add its scent. The sybil of Panzoust did thus: she made a potage of green cabbage with a smoked bacon rind and an old *savorados*. This in her country, which is also my own, they call the medullary bone, so tasty and so succulent."

"This lady you mention, Monsieur," said Gamelin's mother, "was she not a trifle too keen, to serve up the same bone so long?"

"She was in a small way," Brotteaux replied. "Though she was a prophetess, she was poor."

At this point, Évariste Gamelin arrived home, all upset by the confession he had just heard, and full of resolve to find out Élodie's betrayer, at one stroke to avenge the Republic and his love.

After commonplace courtesies, Citizen Brotteaux resumed the interrupted thread of his disquisition: "It is rare," he said, "for those whose profession it is to foretell the future, to get rich. Their frauds are too soon found out. Their imposture earns them detestation. Yet, if they really did tell one the future, they would be hated even more. For man's life would be unbearable, if he knew what was to come to him. He would learn of coming ills, from which he would suffer in advance, and would fail to enjoy the good things of the moment, because he would be able to see the end. Ignorance is an essential condition of human happiness, and one must admit that men generally are pretty successful at it. We are ignorant of nearly everything in ourselves, and everything in others. Ignorance gives us peace of mind; lies give us contentment."

Citizeness Gamelin put the soup on the table, said grace, bid her son and her guest take their places, and herself began her meal standing, refusing the seat which Citizen Brotteaux offered her beside him, for, as she would say, she knew the obligations of good manners.

## VI

Ten A.M. Not a breath of wind. It was the hottest July in living memory. In the narrow Rue de Jérusalem, there were about a hundred citizens of the ward queuing at the baker's door, watched over by four national guards, standing at ease, smoking their pipes.

The National Convention had fixed maximum prices, and immediately grain and flour vanished. Like the Israelites in the desert, the people of Paris had to be up before daybreak if they wanted to eat. All and sundry, crushed together, men, women, children, under a sky of molten lead which heated the garbage in the gutters and intensified the odours of sweat and dirt, elbowed, bickered and exchanged looks of all the feelings of which human beings are capable regarding one another—antipathy, disgust, self-interest, attraction, indifference. By painful experience they had learned that there was not enough bread to go round, so the last come tried to slip into the queue, those who lost ground complained bitterly, lost their tempers and vainly claimed their scorned rights. Women used elbows and hips savagely, to keep their place or get a better one. If the crush became too stifling, there would be cries of "Stop shoving there!" Then everyone protested that it was he who had been shoved.

To avoid these daily disorders, the officers appointed by the ward had had the notion of tying a rope to the baker's door, for each person to hold in order; but hands too close to each other would clash and start fighting. Anybody who let go never managed to get hold again. Malcontents or practical jokers would cut the rope, and the idea had to be abandoned.

In this queue people were stifled, thought they were going to pass out, joked, bandied smut, abused the aristocrats or federalists as the cause of all their woes. When a dog passed, jokers called it Pitt. Now and then a resounding box of the ears could be heard, applied by some good woman's palm to a rude cheek, while on the other hand a servant-girl, being squeezed by the man next her, half-closed her eyes, lips parted, and heaved soft sighs. At every word, gesture, or attitude capable of prompting that charming French smutty wit, a group of young wasters set up singing the Ça ira, notwithstanding the protests of an old Jacobin, who was outraged to hear a tune expressive of Republican faith in a future of justice and well-being debased by dirty double meanings.

His ladder under his arm, a bill-poster came to put up a Commune order on the wall opposite the baker's, rationing butcher's meat. Passers-by stopped to read the notice, still wet with glue. A cabbage-vendor, trudging by under her back-basket, yelled in her loud, cracked voice: "All gone, all the decent bullocks, now we're going to rake out the offal!"

Suddenly such a gust of putrefaction came up from a drain-pipe that several felt sick; a woman felt ill and two of the national guards carried her a few paces away, to a pump. People held their noses; the crowd began to mutter; expressions of agony and horror were exchanged. Was it some animal buried there, or even poison purposely planted, or a noble or priest of the September massacre forgotten in one of the cellars?

"So this is where they stuffed 'em, is it?"

"They're everywhere."

"Must be one from the Châtelet prison.

On the second, I saw a pile of three hundred on the Exchange Bridge."

The Parisians were full of fear of the vengeance of those former nobles who, dead, were now poisoning them.

Évariste Gamelin came to take his place in the queue; he wanted to save his old mother the long time of waiting. His neighbour, Citizen Brotteaux, was with him, tranquil, smiling, his Lucretius in the gaping pocket of his puce surtout.

The old fellow praised the scene, and said it was a "jollity" worthy of the brush of a modern Teniers.

"These porters and housewives," he said, "have more charm than the Greeks and Romans so dear to our painters to-day. I must say I have always liked the Flemish school."

Out of commonsense and good taste he failed to mention that he had once possessed a gallery of Dutch works which only M. de Choiseul's collection had equalled in number and standard.

"The only beauty is classical beauty," the painter replied, "and what is inspired by it, though I grant you that Tenier's, Steen's and d'Ostage's sprees are worth more than Watteau's, Boucher's or Van Loo's frills and flounces; though they do make humanity more ugly, they do not debase it, as your Baudouin or Fragonard do."

A newsboy came along, crying the "Revolutionary Court Bulletin . . . list of condemned!"

"One Revolutionary Court is not enough," said Gamelin. "We need one in every town . . . What am I saying, in every commune, every canton. Every father, every citizen should be made a magistrate. With the country under enemy cannon and the knives of traitors, indulgence is parricidal. Why! we have Lyons, Marseilles and Bordeaux in revolt, Corsica in revolt, la Vendée ablaze, Mayence and Valenciennes fallen into the hands of the coalition, treason on the benches of the National Convention, treason throughout the countryside, in the town, in camps, treason present, map in hand, at our generals' councils of war . . . The guillotine must save the Fatherland!"

"I have no fundamental objection to the guillotine," old Brotteaux replied. "Nature, my sole mistress and teacher, in no way indicates that human life has any value; on the contrary, Nature teaches us in many ways that it has no value. The sole end of all beings appears to be to serve as pasture to other creatures destined to the same end. Murder is a natural right; hence the death penalty is legitimate, on condition it is not applied either by virtue or justice, but out of necessity or for some advantage. But I must have perverted instincts, for I have a horror of bloodshed, and there you have a defect of character that all my philosophy has still failed to correct."

"The Republicans," Évariste replied, "are human and men with feelings. It is only despots who hold that the death penalty is an essential attribute of authority. One day the sovereign people will abolish it. Robespierre was against it, and every patriot with him; the law curtailing it must be promulgated at the earliest possible moment. Yet it must not be brought into force till the last enemy of the Republic has perished under the Sword of Justice."

Gamelin and Brotteaux now had some later-comers behind them, among them a number of women of their ward; among others a stalwart knitter of great beauty, in kerchief and wooden clogs, with a sabre slung from one shoulder, a lovely blond wench, her hair a mop, the kerchief badly crumpled, and a young mother, pale and thin, suckling a sickly baby.

The little one, finding the breast dry of milk, was whimpering, but feebly, the sobs choking it. It was pitiably small, with pallid, muddy skin, inflamed eyes, and the mother kept looking down at it, painfully worried.

"How young," said Gamelin, turning to the luckless baby, crying at his back, crushed in by the latest to join the queue.

"Six months, the poor love! . . . It's father is in the army. He is one of those who repelled the Austrians at Condé. His name is Dumonteil (Michel), he's a draper's assistant by calling. He joined up when they put up a booth in front of the town hall. My poor darling wanted to defend his country and see something of the country . . . he writes to me to be patient. But how am I to feed Paul . . . (he's called Paul) . . . when I can't feed myself?"

"Oh!" cried the handsome blond girl, "we've another hour ahead of us, and this evening we shall have to begin again at the grocer's. You risk your life to get three eggs and a quarter of a pound of butter."

"Butter?" Citizeness Dumonteil sighed, "it's a good three months since I saw any!"

And the chorus of women lamented the scarcity and high price of foodstuffs, addressing curses to all émigrés and consigning to the guillotine Ward Commissioners who for shameless favours gave dragtail creatures fat hens and quartern loaves. Disturbing stories were spread of oxen drowned in the Seine, sacks of flour emptied down drains, loaves thrown into privies . . . It was all the work of royalists, Rolandists, Brissot's men, out to cause starvation and wipe out the people of Paris.

All at once the handsome blond girl with the crumpled kerchief set up a yell as if her petticoats were afire, and was shaking them wildly and turning out her pockets and declaring that somebody had stolen her purse.

At news of this theft a great wave of indignation took possession of these little folk, who had laid waste the Faubourg Saint-Germain mansions and invaded the Tuileries Palace without taking a thing, all of them artisans' wives, who would have enjoyed burning down the Versailles castle, but believed themselves dishonoured to take as much as a pin. The young wasters tried some dirty jokes about the pretty young person's misfortune, but these were soon drowned by the general mutter. There was immediate talk of stringing the thief up on the spot. A noisy, partisan enquiry was started. The burly knitting woman pointed to an old man whom she suspected of being a defrocked monk and swore that that was the "Capuchin" who had done it. The crowd, swayed in an instant, demanded death.

The old man so swiftly denounced to public vindictiveness had been stationed very quietly just in front of Citizen Brotteaux. He certainly did look most like a former monk. He had quite a venerable appearance, though marred by the anxiety which the violent mood of the crowd and his still lively memory of the September days were causing him. The fear depicted on his countenance made him suspect to the masses, who are always ready to assume that only the guilty fear condemnation, as if the ill-considered precipitation with which they condemn were not sufficient to scare even the most innocent.

Brotteaux made it a rule never to go against popular sentiments, particularly if these seemed ridiculous or savage, "because in such moments," he said, *"vox populi vox dei."* But Brotteaux was inconsistent, and he now declared that this man, whether capuchin monk or not, could not have robbed the citizen, for he had not been near her for a single instant.

The crowd concluded that the man who took the thief's part must be his accomplice, and now talked of treating both evildoers the same, and when Gamelin stood security for Brotteaux, the wisest heads spoke of taking him round to the Ward with the other two.

But suddenly the pretty wench was delighted to announce that she had found her purse. Immediately she was the butt of booing and threats of a public whipping, as a nun.

"Sir," said the monk to Brotteaux, "thank you for defending me. My name is of little account, but I owe it you to tell you: I am Louis de Longuemarre. I am indeed a regular, though not a Capuchin, as these ladies say. Very much the contrary; I am a regular clerk of the Order of the Barnabites, which has given the Church many a learned head and many a saint. It is not sufficient to trace our origins back to St. Charles Borromeo; we should consider the apostle St. Paul himself to be our true founder—his monogram is incorporated in our coat of arms. I have been obliged to leave my monastery, which has become the Headquarters of the Pont-Neuf Ward, and put on secular clothes."

"Father," said Brotteaux, casting his eye up and down M. de Longuemarre's long-tailed coat, "your get-up is ample proof that you have not abandoned your status; to see it, one would imagine you had reformed your order rather than left it. And by such austere appearance you do rather gratuitously expose yourself to the insults of the disbelieving crowd."

"All the same," replied the monk, "I cannot wear a blue coat, like a dancer."

"Father, I say what I do of your clothes to express my respect for your character and to warn you against the danger you run."

"Monsieur, it would on the other hand be more suitable to encourage me to declare my faith. For I am only too prone to fear danger. I have abandoned my vestments, Monsieur, in itself a kind of apostasy; I wish at least I had not been obliged to leave the four walls where

throughout so many years God vouchsafed me the mercy of a sheltered, tranquil existence. I did get permission to stay on, and kept my cell, while they transformed church and cloisters into a sort of miniature town hall which they call the Ward. Sir, I saw, I tell you, I saw the symbols of holy revelation effaced; I saw the name of the Apostle Paul replaced by a felon's cap. On occasion I was even present at ward councils, and I heard astounding errors expressed there. At last I left such profaned quarters, and on the pension of one hundred *pistoles* which the Assembly has granted me I have taken up my abode in some stables, the horses of which have been requisitioned for army service. I serve mass there to a handful of faithful souls, who come to witness the eternity of the Church of Jesus Christ."

"As for me, Father," the other replied, "if it pleases you to know, I am Brotteaux, former stockbroker."

"Sir," replied Father Longuemarre, "the example of St. Matthew tells us that from a man of your profession a kind word may be expected."

"Father, you are too kind."

"Citizen Brotteaux," said Gamelin, "you should marvel at these good folk for being hungrier for justice than bread; not one here but was prepared to lose his place, to punish a thief. These men, these women, in their poverty, the victims of such privations, are so strictly honest that they cannot bear a dishonest act."

"You must admit," replied Brotteaux, "that in their great desire to hang the thief these folk would have given this worthy monk, his defender and the defender of his defender, short shrift. Their greed and their egotistical love of their own goods drives them to it; by attacking one of them, the thief threatened them all; they find protection in dealing out punishment . . . Otherwise, no doubt the majority of these handworkers and housewives are honest and do respect other people's goods. Those are sentiments which have been inculcated in them from childhood by fathers and mothers who have whipped them sufficiently, getting the virtues into them through the backside."

Gamelin did not conceal from old Brotteaux that such language seemed to him unworthy of a philosopher.

"The virtues," he said, "are inborn in man; God planted the seed in men's hearts."

Old Brotteaux was an atheist, and found his atheism a rich source of satisfaction.

"I perceive, Citizen Gamelin," he said, "that, for all you are a revolutionary on earth, as far as heaven goes you are conservative, even reactionary. Robespierre and Marat are too. And I find it peculiar that the French, who will no longer put up with a mortal king, insist on keeping an immortal one, who is much more tyrannical and fierce. For what was the Bastille, what was the *Chambre ardente,* compared with hell? Humanity models its gods on its tyrants, and you, who abolish the original, keep the copy!"

"Come, Citizen," cried Gamelin, "are you not ashamed to say such things? Can you confound the menacing divinities which ignorance and fear conceived, with the Author of all Nature? Belief in a good God is essential to ethics. The Supreme Being is the source of all the virtues, and you are no Republican if you do not believe in God. Robespierre was well aware of that, when he had the bust of the philosopher Helvetius removed from the Jacobin Hall, for Helvetius was guilty of predisposing the French to servitude by teaching them atheism . . . I do at least hope, Citizen Brotteaux, that when the Republic does institute the worship of Reason, you are not going to refuse to support so sensible a religion."

"I love reason," Brotteaux replied, "but

I am not fanatical about it. Reason guides us and lights our path; if you make a divinity of it, it will dazzle you and get you to commit crimes."

And feet planted in the gutter, Brotteaux continued to reason, just as he had once reasoned in one of Baron d'Holbach's gilded armchairs which, as he put it, had served as foundation to natural philosophy: "Jean-Jacques Rousseau," he said, "who did exhibit some gifts, particularly in music, was a nit-wit who made out he drew his ethical system from Nature, when he really got it out of Calvin's principles. Nature teaches us to devour one another and provides us with the example of every crime and every vice that organised society corrects or glosses over. One ought to love the virtues; but it is good not to forget that they are a simple expedient invented by men, so as to live together comfortably. What we call ethics are merely a desperate attempt of our kind to counter the nature of things, which is—struggle, bloodshed, and the blind play of opposing forces. Nature is self-destructive, and the more I think on it, the more convinced I am that the universe is mad. Theologians and philosophers, who make God the prime cause of Nature and Architect of the Universe, make him ridiculous and malicious in our eyes. They say he is kind, because they are afraid, yet they cannot but agree that he behaves in a terrible way. They lend him a malignity rare in man. And that is how they make him loveable on earth. For our kind would never devote a religion to gods which were just or kindly, whom it would not have to fear. It would not feel a trace of gratitude for their beneficence, for it would have no point. Without purgatory and hell your good God would be a very poor fellow indeed."

"Sir," said Father Longuemarre, "you should not speak of Nature; you do not know what it is."

"Heavens alive, I know as much about it as you do, Father!"

"You cannot, since you have no religion, and it is only religion that can tell us what Nature is, or where Nature is benign or malevolent. For that matter, do not expect I am going to answer you; to refute your errors God has granted me neither warmth of language or strength of mind. I should fear lest by my insufficiency I merely gave you opportunity for blaspheming or reason to harden your heart, and though I feel a keen desire to be of service to you, the sole fruit of my rash charity would be . . ."

This speech was interrupted by a tremendous clamour which, starting from the head of the queue, told all these famished creatures that the baker had opened his shop. They began to move forward, with infinite slowness. A national guard let them in, one by one. The baker, his wife and his boy were aided in the sale by two municipal officers with tricolour arm bands on the left arm who had to verify that each purchaser belonged to the ward and that nobody got more than the share proportionate to the mouths he had to fill.

Citizen Brotteaux made the quest of pleasure the sole aim of his life; in his view neither reason nor the senses, which in the absence of a deity were the sole arbiters, could conceive any other. So now, as he found the artist's views too fanatical, and the monk's views too simple to afford much satisfaction, this sensible fellow, out to match his conduct to his ideas under the conditions of the moment and to while away a wait which was still going to be lengthy, drew from the bulging pocket of his puce surtout his Lucretius, which had remained his greatest satisfaction and real solace. The red morocco binding was chafed by use, and Citizen Brotteaux had been prudent enough to scratch out the coat of arms, those three little isles of gold, which his finan-

cier father had bought for hard cash. He opened the book at the place where the poet philosopher, anxious to cure men of the pointless perturbations of love, discovers a woman in the arms of her domestics in a state which would hurt a lover's feelings. Citizen Brotteaux read these lines, though not without his eyes wandering to the golden down-covered nape of the pretty wench in front of him, not without a voluptuous snuffle at the little slut's perspiring skin. The poet Lucrèce knew only one form of wisdom—his disciple, Brotteaux, had more than one.

He read on, taking two steps every quarter of an hour. His ear, soothed by the stately flow of cadence of the Latin muse, was deaf to the harsh wordy bombardment of the good ladies concerning the rise in the price of bread, sugar, coffee, candles and soap. Thus he at last reached the threshold of the baker's shop, in a state of serenity. Beyond him, Évariste Gamelin could see the gilded sheaf of corn of the grating which filled the arch over the door.

His turn come, he entered the shop: the baskets and trays were empty; the baker handed him the only loaf left, which did not weigh two pounds. Évariste paid, the gate was shut on his heels, lest the rebellious crowd invaded the shop. But there was no need to fear that: these poor folk, taught to be obedient by their former oppressors and their present liberators, went their way, hanging their heads, dragging their feet.

When he reached the corner of the street, Gamelin saw Citizeness Dumonteil, her baby in her arms, seated on a corner stone. She was immobile, colourless, tearless, sightless. The child was sucking greedily at her finger. Gamelin stood in front of her for a moment, shy and undecided. She did not seem to see him.

He stammered something, then took

out his knife, a horn-handled clasp-knife, cut his loaf in half and put one in the lap of the young mother, who stared in astonishment at it, but he had already turned the corner of the street.

When he got home, Évariste found his mother sitting at the window, darning stockings. Cheerfully he put the remainder of the bread in her hand.

"Do forgive me, mother dear. I was so tired, standing so long, in the street, exhausted by the heat that I have eaten half our ration, bit by bit, on the way home. There's only your part left."

And he pretended to brush the crumbs from his vest.

## VII

Using a very old figure of speech Citizeness Widow Gamelin had declared that "by dint of living on chestnuts, we shall turn into chestnuts." On this particular day, July 13th, she and her son had just made their midday meal of a chestnut pudding. They were just finishing this austere repast when a lady opened the door and immediately filled the room with her brilliance and her scents. Évariste recognised Citizen Rochemaure. Thinking she had mistaken the door and was looking for Citizen Brotteaux, her former friend, he was on the point of showing her the ex-noble's attic or, to spare an elegant woman clambering up a miller's ladder, calling Brotteaux down; but it was immediately clear that her business was with Citizen Évariste Gamelin, for she announced how glad she was to find him, and to be his servant.

They were not entirely strangers—they had met many times at David's studio, at a box in the Assembly, at the Jacobin club, and Vénua's restaurant; she had been struck by his good looks, his youth, and his interesting air.

Wearing a hat as be-ribboned as a roundabout and as plumed as the headdress of some ambassadorial personality, Citizeness Rochemaure was bewigged, painted, be-patched and be-musked, though her flesh was still fresh despite such condimentation; these strident tricks of the fashion were revelative of women's haste to grab at life, revelative of the feverish quality of those awful days, none of which was sure of the morrow. Her bodice, which had enormous revers and tremendous tails to it, and was all aglitter with steel buttons, was blood red, and she was at the same time both so aristocratic and so revolutionary that it was impossible to tell whether she was wearing the colours of the victims or their executioner. She was accompanied by a young soldier —a dragoon.

A long mother-of-pearl walking-stick in her hand, tall beautiful, plump, generous of bosom, she made the tour of the studio and, holding a two-armed gold lorgnon to her grey eyes, examined the canvases with smiles and little cries, prompted by the good looks of the artist to admire, and flattering, to be flattered.

"What," she demanded, "whatever is this picture of a gentle pretty girl beside a sick young man, it's so noble, so moving?"

Gamelin replied that it was meant to be *Orestes Watched Over By His Sister Electra,* and that, had he been able to complete it, this would perhaps have been his least unworthy picture.

"The subject," he added "is taken from Euripides' *Orestes.* I read a scene of the tragedy in a very old translation, and it struck my imagination—the scene in which the young Electra, raising her brother from his bed of sickness, wipes away the froth which sullies his lips, draws the locks back from the eyes they blind and begs her dear brother to hear what she is going to read him in the silence of the Furies . . . Reading the translation again and again, I felt a sort

THE GODS ARE ATHIRST

of mist concealing the forms of Greece from me and could not disperse it. I imagined the original must be more highly strung and different in tone. I felt such a keen desire to get an exact impression that I went to ask M. Gail, who was then professor of Greek in the Collège de France (this was in '91), to explain the scene to me, word by word. He did as I wished and I realised that the classic authors are far more simple and intimate than one had thought. Thus, Electra says to Orestes: 'Dearest brother, how happy I am you have had a good sleep! Shall I help you get up?' And Orestes answers: 'Yes, help me, take me and wipe away the traces of froth sticking to my lips and eyes. Lay your breast against mine and draw my tangled hair back from my face, for it hides my eyes . . .' Full of that poetry, so young and so alive, full of those direct, strong expressions, I sketched the picture you see, Citizen."

The artist, who usually was so reserved about his work, did not even then dry up. Encouraged by the sign Citizeness Rochemaure made him, raising her lorgnon, he continued:

"Hennequin had done the madness of Orestes in masterly manner. But Orestes moves one even more in his sorrow than his madness. What a fate his was! It was from filial piety, in obedience to sacred orders, that he committed the crime of which the gods have to absolve him, but which men will never forgive him. To avenge outraged justice, he denied Nature, made himself inhuman, tore out his own entrails. He remains a proud figure, under the burden of that horrible, unflinching penalty . . . That is what I wished to show in this brother and sister group."

He went up to his canvas and looked at it with self-satisfaction.

"Some parts," he said, "are very nearly finished; Orestes' head and arm, for example."

"It is a wonderful thing . . . And Orestes is like you, Citizen Gamelin."

"You think so?" the painter asked, with a solemn smile.

She took the chair Gamelin offered her. The young dragoon remained standing, by her side, his hand on the back of her chair. By which one could see there had indeed been a Revolution, for, under the old régime, in company, a man would never have laid so much as a finger on the chair which contained a lady, being moulded by upbringing to the limitations of good manners, which were sometimes pretty exacting, though for that matter he could consider that restraint observed in public lent a special value to secret abandon, and that you cannot fling aside respect without first having it.

Louise Masché de Rochemaure, daughter of a Lieutenant of the Royal Hunt, widow of a Court Purveyor, and for twenty years faithful mistress of the financier Brotteaux des Ilettes, had accepted the new principles. In July, 1790, she had been seen digging in the Champ de Mars. Her marked leaning for the powers had borne her lightly from the Feuillants to the Girondists and then the Mountain, while an accommodating spirit, a fervour for conversion and something of a gift for intrigue still linked her with the aristocrats and counter-revolutionaries. She moved widely in society, being regularly seen in suburban café gardens, theatres, fashionable restaurants, gambling dens, drawing-rooms, newspaper offices and the lobbies of this or that Committee. The Revolution brought her novelty, distraction, smiles, delights, business deals and profitable schemes. Combining sexual and political liaisons, playing the harp, sketching landscapes, singing songs, dancing Greek dances, giving dinners, receiving pretty women, such as the Countess of Beaufort and Descoings the actress, running night-long parties of vingt-et-un, biribi, or roulette, she still found the time to be charitable to her friends. Inquisitive, meddling, a muddle-maker and fickle, connoisseur of men, but a fool regarding crowds, as ignorant of the views she shared as of those that were to be rejected, without the slightest notion what was happening in France, she appeared enterprising, courageous and a marvel of audacity, though never grasping the danger and unlimited confidence in the power of her own fascination.

The soldier with her was in the flower of his youth. A copper helmet topped with a panther-skin, the crest tricked out with scarlet silk, shielded a cherubic head and precipitated a long, frightful mane down his back. His red vest, more like a bodice, avoided reaching down to his hips, so as to reveal their flow. At his waist he carried an enormous sabre, the hilt of which represented a glittering eagle's beak. Pale blue breeches with flaps shaped themselves to the elegant muscles on his legs, while dark blue braid flourished in rich arabesques up his thighs. He looked like a ballet-dancer costumed for some gallant martial part, in *Achilles at Scyros* or *Alexander's Feast,* by some pupil of David who was taking care to exaggerate the style.

Gamelin had a hazy notion he had already seen him before. It was indeed the soldier he had come upon, a fortnight before, speechifying to the crowd from the Théâtre de la Nation gallery.

Citizeness Rochemaure introduced him: "Citizen Henry, member of the Revolutionary Committee of the Rights of Man Ward."

He was always at her skirts, a reflection of love and a living certificate of patriotism.

Citizen Rochemaure congratulated Gamelin on his gifts and asked him if he would not consent to design a card for a fashionable milliner in whom she was taking an interest. He would treat some suitable subject—a woman trying a scarf before a psyche, for example, or a young workwoman with a hatbox under her arm.

As artists are capable of doing a little thing like this, she had been told of Fragonard *junior,* young Ducis and also of somebody named Prudhomme; but she preferred to approach Citizen Gamelin. All the same, she made no concrete proposal about it, and one felt she had produced the order solely as a pretext for conversation. She had indeed come for quite another purpose. She wanted Citizen Gamelin to do her a good turn: knowing that he knew Citizen Marat, she wanted him to introduce her to the Friend of the People, with whom she wished to have a talk about something.

Gamelin replied that he was too small a person to introduce her to Marat, and that as far as that went, she had no need for any introduction; though he was snowed under with business of one sort and another, he was not the invisible personality people said. And Gamelin added: "If you are in distress, Citizen, he will see you, for his great heart makes him accessible to misfortune and full of pity for all sufferings. He will see you, if you have anything to reveal to him concerning the public good; he has consecrated his life to unmasking traitors."

Citizen Rochemaure replied that she would be delighted to pay her respects to Marat, as an illustrious citizen, who had rendered his country great services, and was capable of rendering still more, and that she hoped to be able to put the legislator in contact with men of good will, philanthropists favoured by fortune and in a position to provide him with new means for satisfying his burning passion for humanity.

"It is desirable to get the wealthy to play their part in public prosperity."

In fact, she had promised Morhardt

the banker to arrange a dinner for him with Marat.

Morhardt, a Swiss, like the Friend of the People, had joined hands with a number of deputies of the Convention, Julien (Toulouse), Delauney (d'Angers), and the former Capuchin Chabot, for speculation in the India Company's shares. Their very simple game consisted in bringing shares down to six hundred and fifty livres by proposals for expropriation, so as to be able to buy as many as possible at that price, and then to put them up to four or five thousand livres by re-assuring proposals. But Chabot, Julien and Delauney were too transparent. Lacroix, Fabre d'Eglantine, and even Danton were under suspicion. The commission agent, Baron de Batz, was on the look out for new accomplices in the Convention and had advised Morhardt to see Marat.

This idea of the counter-revolutionary commissionmen was not so peculiar as at first sight it seemed. Those gentry were always making efforts to get into touch with the powers of the moment, and, in popularity, writings and character, Marat was a formidable power. The Girondists were foundering; the Dantonists, beaten by the tempests, had lost the helm. Robespierre, the idol of the crowd, was of jealous probity, suspicious and unapproachable. It was important to get round Marat and make sure of his benevolence, against the day when he became dictator, and everything pointed that way—his popularity, his ambition, and his readiness to recommend sweeping measures. And perhaps, after all, Marat was going to bring back order, finance and prosperity. He had frequently risen against fanatics who wanted to out-bid him in patriotism; for some time he had been denouncing demagogues almost as much as moderates. After inciting the crowd to hang speculators in their ruined offices, he now exhorted citizens to remain calm and to be prudent; he was becoming an administrator.

In spite of certain rumours spread against him, as against all the other figures of the Revolution, these money pirates did not believe him to be bribable, yet they did know he was vain and credulous; it was their hope to get him by flattery, and above all by condescending familiarity, which they for their part considered the most seductive form of flattery. Thanks to him, they counted on blowing hot or cold on all the values they wished to buy or re-sell, and push him into serving their interests, while he thought he was only serving the public interest.

Go-between in the grand style, for all that she was still of an age to have love affairs, Citizeness Rochemaure had undertaken bringing together the journalist legislator and the banker, and in her crazy imagination she could see the man of the cellars, his hands still red with September's blood, caught in this financier's game for which she was the agent, cast by his very sensitivity and frankness into mid-speculation, in this world of market-cornerers, purveyors, foreign emissaries, gamblers and gallant women which she adored.

She now insisted on Citizen Gamelin taking her to the Friend of the People, who lived quite near, in the Rue des Cordeliers, near the church. After putting up a little resistance, the artist agreed to her request.

Henry the dragoon, invited to join them, declined, his pretext being that he meant to maintain his freedom, even regarding Citizen Marat, who doubtless had rendered the Republic some service, but was now growing feeble; had not Marat in his newspaper just advised the people of Paris to be resigned?

And the youthful Henry, in melodious tones, with lengthy sighs, deplored the Republic betrayed by those in whom it had placed its hopes: Danton rejecting the notion of a tax on wealth, Robespierre opposing the permanence of the wards, and Marat, whose pusillanimous advice was undermining the public drive.

"Ah!" he cried, "how weak these men do look, against a Leclerc or a Jacques Roux! . . . Roux, Leclerc! You are the true friends of the people!"

Gamelin did not hear all this, which would have outraged him; he had gone into the next room to put on his blue coat.

"You can be proud of your son," said Citizeness Rochemaure to Citizeness Gamelin. "He is great in both gifts and character."

Citizeness Widow Gamelin, in answer, testified warmly in her son's favour, though without any boasting about him to so superior a lady, for in her childhood she had learnt that the first duty of little people was humility towards the great. She was inclined to complain, and not without reason, too, and find in her complaints some solace for her troubles. She would pour out her misfortunes to anybody she believed capable of assuaging them, and Madame de Rochemaure seemed to her to be one of those. And so, making hay while the sun shone, in the same breath she told all about mother and son's poverty, how they were both dying of starvation. It was impossible to sell pictures any more; the Revolution had killed that trade, cut it off with a knife. Provisions were scarce and at fantastic prices . . .

Thus the good lady addressed her lamentation as volubly as her flabby lips and thick tongue would allow, in order to get them all off before her son reappeared, for his pride disapproved of that sort of talk. She lent all her forces to touching the heart of a lady whom she believed wealthy and influential in the shortest possible time, and interesting her in the fortunes of her child. She also had a feeling that Évariste's good looks were her secret ally in this attempt to move a lady of noble birth.

Citizeness Rochemaure did indeed show feeling; the thought of Évariste's sufferings and those of his mother disturbed her and she wondered how she could lessen them. She would get the well-to-do among her acquaintances to buy his pictures.

"For," she said, with a smile, "there is still money in France, only it keeps hidden."

Better still: since art was lost, she would get Morhardt, or the Perregaux brothers, or some army contractor, to give Évariste a job in their offices. Then it occurred to her that perhaps that was not quite what a man of character would want, and, after an instant's thought, by a gesture she indicated that she had found the solution.

"A number of jurors on the Revolutionary Tribunal have to be appointed. A juror, a magistrate, now there's something that would suit your son. I am in touch with the members of the Committee of Public Safety; I know the elder Robespierre; his brother often dines at my place. I shall have a word with them. I'll talk to Montané, Dumas, Fouquier."

Gamelin's mother, touched and grateful, lay a finger to her lips; Évariste was returning to the studio.

He accompanied Citizeness Rochemaure down the dark stairs, the boards and tiles of which were thick with ancient dirt.

On the Pont-Neuf, where the sun, already low, was drawing out the shadow of the pedestal on which the Bronze Horse had formerly stood, but now capped by the tricolour, a crowd of men and women, divided into small groups, was listening to some people speaking in low tones. The crowd was consternated, and except for periodical groans, or a cry of anger, maintained silence.

Many were already hurrying away towards the Rue de Thionville, formerly the Rue Dauphine; slipping into one of the groups he learned that Marat had been assassinated.

Gradually the news gained confirmation and detail: he had been in his bath, it was a woman who had come from Caen purposely to kill him.

Some maintained that she had escaped, but the majority said she had been arrested.

There they all were, like a flock of sheep without a shepherd.

They were thinking: "Marat, sensitive, humane, benevolent, Marat is no longer here to guide us, Marat who never made a mistake, who guessed everything, who shrank from revealing nothing. What is to be done, what will happen now? We have lost our counsellor, our defender, our friend." They knew the origin of this stroke, who had guided the woman's hand. They groaned: "Marat was struck down by the criminal hands that wish to destroy us. His death is a signal for the slaughter of all patriots."

There were a variety of versions of the circumstances of this tragic demise and the last words of the victim; questions were asked about the assassin, concerning whom they only knew that it was a young woman sent by the federalist traitors. Women bared finger-nails and teeth, and wished the criminal tortured; they thought the guillotine too gentle, and demanded flogging, the wheel, quartering, even invented new tortures.

Some armed national guards came along, taking a young man with determined bearing to the Ward. His clothes were in shreds; there were rivulets of blood on his pale cheeks. He had been caught declaring that Marat had merited his fate, by incessant incitement to loot and murder. And it had been only with difficulty that the police got him away from the popular fury. He was pointed to

as an accomplice of the murderer, and threats of death pursued him.

Gamelin was stupified with grief. Arid tears dried as they formed in his burning eyes. His filial sorrow was mingled with patriotic concern and a national piety which distressed him. He said to himself: "Le Peltier, then Bourdon, and now Marat! I see to what patriots are fated: to be massacred on the Champ de Mars, at Nancy, in Paris—they will perish one and all." And his thought of the traitor Wimpfen who so recently had been marching on Paris at the head of sixty thousand royalists, and had valiant patriots not halted him at Vernon, would have razed to the ground this heroic, but condemned city.

And what countless other dangers, what criminal schemings, what treason, solely the wisdom and vigilance of Marat could decipher and outplay. Now he was gone, who could denounce Custine idle in the camp of César, refusing to relieve Valenciennes, Biron passive in the Vendée, letting Saumur be taken and Nantes beseiged, or Dillon, betraying the Fatherland in the Argonne?

Meanwhile, all round him, the menacing clamour increased: "Marat is dead, the aristocrats have killed him."

As, his heart bursting with pain, hatred and love, he went his way to pay his last respects to the martyr of liberty, an old peasant woman in a kerchief of the Limoges district came up to him and asked him if this Monsieur Marat, who had been assassinated, was not perhaps the Reverend Mara of Saint-Pierre-de-Queyroix.


## VIII

The day before the festival, in the evening, which was breathless and bright, Élodie strolled up and down the *Champ de la Fédération* on Évariste's arm. Workmen were hastily finishing the erection of columns, statues, temples, a mountain and an altar. Monster symbolic figures, Hercules of the people brandishing his club, Nature watering the Universe from inexhaustable breasts, were suddenly erected in this capital that was harried by famine and terror and trying to catch—if it could not hear it already—the sound of the Austrian cannon on the Meaux road. The Vendée was making amends by dashing victories for the check before Nantes. A circle of iron, flame and hatred encircled the great revolutionary city. Notwithstanding, Paris continued to receive with the magnificence of the sovereign of a vast empire deputies of those basic assemblies which had accepted the constitution. Federalism was vanquished: a Republic one and indivisible would master its every foe.

With a sweeping gesture over the densely crowded fields, "There," said Évariste, "there it is that on July 17th, 1791, that villain Bailly ordered fire on the people at the foot of the altar of the Fatherland. Grenadier Passavant, witness of the massacre, went home, ripped his tunic in two, cried: 'I swore to die with liberty; it is no more; I die'—and blew out his brains."

All this time peaceful artists and townsfolk were quizzing the preparations for the festival, and on their features was stamped a love of life as dismal as their life itself; the greatest of events, entering their being, were adapted to their dimensions and became as insipid as they were. Every couple in the promenade either carried in their arms or dragged by the hand or had run on in front children not one whit more handsome than their parents, and with no promise whatsoever of being more happy, and destined to give life to still other children, just as middling as themselves in happiness or looks. Yet from time to time one did see a finely built girl with a pretty face who as she passed inspired young men with noble longings, and old men with regret for the sweets of life.

Near the Military Academy, Évariste showed Élodie some Egyptian statues which David had designed after Roman models of the Augustan period. At the same moment they heard a powdered Parisian getting on in years cry: "One could imagine oneself on the banks of the Nile!"

During the three days since Élodie had last seen her love, there had been serious happenings at the *Amour Peintre*. Citizen Blaise had been denounced to the Committee of Public Safety for frauds in government supply. Luckily the print dealer was known to his Ward; the Watch Committee of the Piques Ward had stood surety for his patriotism with the Committee of Public Safety and got him off completely.

Having related all this with much feeling, Élodie added "Our minds are at rest now, but it was a tight moment. My father was very nearly clapped in prison. If the danger had lasted many more hours, I should have gone to you, darling, to say something in his favour to your influential friends."

Évariste did not reply. Élodie was far from plumbing the depths of that silence.

Hand in hand, they wandered along beside the Seine, telling each other their love in the language of Julie and Saint-Preux; good old Rousseau had furnished them with the means for depicting and prinking out their love.

The municipality had achieved the miracle of making plenty rule in the starving town for a day. Booths were set up in the Invalides square, down by the river; there were men on this fair ground selling sausages, saveloys, chitterlings, hams in bay, Nanterre cakes, gingerbreads, pancakes, quartern loaves, lemonade and wine. There were also stalls selling patriotic songs, cockades, tricolour ribbons, purses, white-metal chains and all sorts of little trinkets. Pausing at the display of a humble jeweler, Évariste chose a silver ring with a relief of Marat's head depicted in a silk kerchief. He put the ring on Élodie's finger.

The same evening, Gamelin went to the Rue de l'Arbre-Sec, to see Citizeness Rochemaure, who had sent for him on urgent business. He found her in her bedroom, reclining on a *chaise-longue,* in charming intimacy.

While the posture of the Citizeness was expressive of voluptuous idleness, everything round her was eloquent of her accomplishments, her diversions and her gifts: a harp beside an open clavecin, a guitar in an armchair, an embroidering frame with a piece of satin on it, on a table, the first stage of a miniature, papers, books, and a bookcase upside-down just as a fair hand, as greedy for knowledge as sensation, had left it. She held out her hand to be kissed, and said:

"Salut, citizen, juror . . . Today as ever is, Robespierre the elder gave me a letter on your behalf to President Herman, a very well put letter, which said approximately: 'I suggest Citizen Gamelin, to be recommended for his gifts and his patriotism. I felt it my duty to inform you of a patriot of principle and stalwart in following the revolutionary line. You will not fail to be of service to a republican . . .' I didn't waste a minute about taking the letter to President Herman, who received me with perfect courtesy and immediately signed your appointment. It's done."

After an instant of silence, Gamelin said:

"Citizeness, though I have not a scrap of bread to give my mother, I swear on my honour that I only accept the duties of juror to serve the Republic and avenge all its enemies."

She considered this form of thanks frigid, and the compliment stark. She had a suspicion that Gamelin lacked charm. But she was too fond of youth not to pardon a degree of crudity. Gamelin was handsome; she found him worth it. "We'll shape him," she told herself. And she invited him to her little dinners; any day, after the theatre, he would be welcome.

"In my house you will meet brilliant minds and great talents: Elleviou, Talma, Citizen Vigée, who turns improvised verse with wonderful skill. Citizen François read us his *Paméla,* now on at the National Theatre. It is in an elegant, pure style, like everything that comes from Citizen François' pen. A moving play, too; it made us cry. Little Lange is going to play Paméla."

"I accept your judgement, Citizeness," Gamelin replied. "Yet the National Theatre is not very national. And it is aggravating for Citizen François to have his work played on boards debased by Laya's wretched doggerel; one has not forgotten what a reception *L'Ami des Lois* . . ."

"Citizen Gamelin, do what you like with Laya; he is not a friend of mine."

It was not from unadulterated kindness that the citizeness had used her credit to get Gamelin an envied position; after what she had done, and what more she might do for him, she calculated on attaching him closely to her, and so guaranteeing herself some support against a justice with which some day or other she might have to reckon, for after all she did send a great many letters to all parts of France and to abroad, and such correspondence was just now under suspicion.

"Do you often go to the theatre, Citizen?"

At this point, Dragoon Henry, more gracious than the young Bathyllus, entered the room. He had two enormous pistols in his belt.

He kissed the fair citizeness's hand,

and she said: "Here is Citizen Gamelin on whose account I have spent all day at the Committee of Public Safety but who is not at all grateful to me. Scold him."

"Oh, Citizeness," the soldier cried, "you have just seen our legislators at the Tuileries. What a distressing sight! Should the representatives of a free people meet under the roof of a despot? The same lustres once shone on the plots of Capet and the orgies of d'Antoinette now illumine the night watches of our legislators. Nature must shudder."

"My friend, congratulate Citizen Gamelin," she replied, "he has been appointed to the Revolutionary Tribunal."

"My compliments, citizen!" said Henry. "I am glad to see a man of your character invested with these functions. Yet, I must confess, I have little faith in your methodical justice, the work of the moderates of the Convention, this lighthearted Nemesis which is considerate to conspirators, spares traitors, scarce dares touch the federalists and is afraid to put that Austrian woman in the dock. No, this is not the Revolutionary court which will save the Republic. They are very guilty, all who, in the desperate situation in which we are, halt the drive of popular justice."

"Henry," said Citizeness Rochemaure, "pass me that scent bottle . . ."

Returning home, Gamelin found his mother and old Brotteaux playing picquet in the light of a smoky candle. Without the least shame, Widow Gamelin called "three kings."

When she learned that her son had become a juror, she was so delighted she kissed him, telling herself that it was a great honour for them both, and that henceforth they would both dine every day.

"I am happy and proud to be the mother of a juror," she said. "Justice is a lovely thing, the most necessary of all;

without justice, the weak would constantly be injured. And I consider that you will judge well, my dear Évariste, for ever since you were a boy I have found you just and benevolent in all things. You cannot bear wrong doing and you oppose violence with all your powers. You have pity on the unfortunate, and that is the finest jewel in the crown of a judge . . . But, tell me, Évariste, how do you dress in this great court?"

Gamelin told her that judges wore a hat with black plumes, but that the jurors had no uniform, and wore ordinary coats.

"It would be far better," said Citizeness Gamelin, "if they wore a gown and a wig; they would inspire more respect. Though you generally dress carelessly, you are a handsome man and make the most of your clothes, but most men need some sort of decoration if they want to seem substantial; it would be far better if the jurors had wig and gown."

Gamelin's mother had heard that being a juror of the Revolutionary Tribunal brought in something, and she had no compunction about asking if one earned enough to live decently, for, as she said, a juror ought to cut a good figure in public.

She learned with satisfaction that the jurors received monetary compensation of eighteen livres a court sitting and that the great number of crimes against State security would oblige them to sit very often.

Old Brotteaux collected his cards, rose and said to Gamelin:

"Citizen, you have been invested in a lofty and awe-inspiring office. I congratulate you for lending the light of your conscience to a tribunal which is more certain and less fallible than perhaps any other, for it perceives good and evil not as such, as absolutes, but solely in relation to tangible interests and obvious loyalties. You will have to determine between hatred and love, which is done spontaneously, not between truth and error, to discriminate between which the feeble mind of men is impotent. Judging by the impulse of your hearts, you will run no risk of error, for the verdict will be good, provided it satisfies the great love which is your sacred law. But all the same, were I your president, I should imitate Bridoie, and resort to the dice. In questions of justice that is still the most reliable way."

## IX

Évariste Gamelin was to commence duty on September 14th, on the reorganised Tribunal, now in four sections, with fifteen jurors to each. The prisons were overflowing; the public prosecutor was working eighteen hours a day. To defeats in the field, revolt in the provinces, plotting and treachery, the Convention was opposing terror. The Gods were thirsty.

The first step of the new juror was to pay a courtesy visit to President Herman, who enchanted him by the suavity of all he said and the urbanity of his manners. A friend of Robespierre, whose views he shared, and from the same part of France, he revealed a heart which was sensitive and upright. He was thoroughly imbued with those humane sentiments which had for too long been alien to judges' hearts and constitute the eternal glory of a Dupaty or a Beccaria. He was proud of the recent diminution of harshness, in court procedure, in the abolition of torture and ignominious or cruel forms of execution. He was overjoyed that the death penalty, formerly lavishly applied, and as a means of suppressing the most petty crimes, had become more rare, and was reserved for major crimes. Had it depended on him like Robespierre, he would gladly have abolished it for all offences except those touching public se-

curity. But it would in his view have been to betray the State, were crimes against the sovereignty of the nation not punished by death.

That was the view of all his colleagues: the Revolutionary Tribunal was animated by the old monarchical conception of State expediency. Eight centuries of absolute power had shaped the judicial mind, and Herman judged the enemies of liberty by the principles of divine right.

The same day, Évariste Gamelin called on the public prosecutor, Citizen Fouquier, who received him in the office where he worked with his clerk. He was a sturdy fellow, with a rough voice, cat eyes, whose vast pock-marked cheeks and leaden complexion showed what damage a sedentary, cloistered life can cause powerful men, made for open air and fierce exercise. At his back files of papers rose mountainous as the walls of a tomb, yet it was clear that he loved that frightful mass of dead paper, which looked as if it was trying to suffocate him. He talked like a hard-working judge who was devoted to his duty and whose mind never emerged from the narrow circle of his functions. His heated breath smelled of brandy which he took to keep him going and which did not seem to go to his head, so lucid were all the invariably commonplace things he said.

He lived in a small flat in the Law Court buildings with a young wife, who had presented him with twin boys. This young person, his Aunt Henrietta and a maid named Pelagia constituted his whole household. He was clearly gentle and kind to these women. In short, an excellent person, both as family man and professionally, poor in ideas and devoid of imagination.

Gamelin could not help noticing with some distaste how much these judges of the new order resembled in spirit and manner the judges of the old régime. After all, they were old régime men:

Herman had been Advocate-General to the Council of Artois; Fouquier was a former Châtelet prosecutor. They had kept their character. But Évariste Gamelin was a believer in revolutionary rebirth.

Leaving the public prosecutor's office, he crossed the Lawcourts arcade and paused at the shops where a variety of goods were artistically displayed. At Citizeness Ténot's stall he glanced through works on history, politics and philosophy: *The Chains of Slavery; Essay on Despotism; The Crimes of Queens.* "We're getting on!" he said to himself, "now these *are* republican writings!" And he asked the bookseller if she sold many of these books. She shook her head: "Only songs and novels," she said. And, drawing a little book from a drawer, "Here," she said, "is a good thing."

Évariste read the title: *The Nun in Her Shift.*

Outside the neighbouring shop he came on Phillipe Desmahis, who, magnificent and gallant amid the scented waters, the powders and the sachets of Citizeness Saint-Jorre, was trying to convince that pretty person that he loved her, promising he would draw her picture and begging for a meeting in the Tuileries gardens that evening. He was handsome. Persuasion brimmed from his lips and sparkled in his eyes. Citizeness Saint-Jorre was listening to him without a word; her eyes were on the ground; she was ready to believe him.

To familiarise himself with the awesome duties with which he was invested, the new juror had the idea of mingling with the public and attending a trial before the Tribunal. He climbed the stairs, where an immense crowd was seated as if in an amphitheatre, and made his way into the former hall of the Parliament of Paris.

People were crowding to see a general tried. For, as old Brotteaux had said, the Convention was following the example of His Britannic Majesty and trying defeated generals, in default of generals who were traitors, for these avoided trial. Brotteaux also said that this was not because a defeated general was necessarily criminal, because clearly you have to have one such in every battle. But there was nothing like condemning one general to encourage the rest.

Quite a number of them had already taken their place in the dock, flighty, pigheaded military men, with birds' brains in oxen's skulls. The present defendant did not know a thing more about the sieges and battles for which he had been responsible than did the judges who interrogated him; accusation and defence got lost in effectives, objectives, munitions, marches and counter-marches. And the crowd of citizens who followed these obscure, endless debates saw behind the half-witted soldier a Fatherland open to the enemy and rent asunder, suffering a thousand deaths; and they used their eyes and their voices too to influence the jurors, calm on their bench, to bring their verdict down like a club on the enemies of the Republic.

Évariste was fervently convinced that what deserved to be struck at in this poor wretch was twofold—the frightful monsters which were rending France: rebellion and defeat. What did it matter, hang it all, if this soldier was innocent or guilty!? At a juncture when the Vendée was raising its head again, Toulon capitulating to the enemy, the Rhine army in retreat before the victors of Mayence, the Northern army, withdrawn to César's camp, in danger at any minute of being mastered by a blow of the Imperial forces, the English, the Dutch, the masters of Valenciennes, what was essential was to teach the generals to win or die. At the sight of this decrepit, besotted old regular fumbling with maps as if he were lost out there in the northern plains,

Gamelin hurried from the court, or he would have had to shout "Death!" with the crowd.

At the Ward Assembly, the new juror was congratulated by President Olivier, who had him swear to the old high altar of the Barnabites, now the altar of the Fatherland, that in the sacred name of humanity he would stifle any human weakness in his heart.

His hand raised, Gamelin called on the august spirit of Marat, martyr of liberty, whose bust had just been placed against a column of the former church, opposite the bust of Le Peltier, to witness his oath.

There was some applause, mixed with a mutter of voices. The assembly was unruly. At the head of the nave a group of members of the ward, armed with pikes, were squabbling. "It is anti-republican," said the President, "to carry arms at an assembly of free men."

He then ordered them immediately to deposit their guns and their pikes in the former vestry.

Citizen Beauvisage, of the Watch Committee, a hunchback with darting eye and upturned lips, mounted the pulpit under the red cap.

"The generals are betraying us," he declared, "and delivering our armies into the hands of the enemy. The Imperial forces are thrusting cavalry detachments out round Péronne and Saint-Quentin. Toulon has been handed to the English, who are disembarking fourteen thousand men there. The enemies of the Republic are plotting in the very bosom of the Convention. In the capital there are innumerable plots being hatched to free the Austrian woman. While I speak the rumour is going round that the Capet brat has escaped from the Temple and is being borne in triumph to Saint-Cloud; they want to restore the tyrant's throne for him. The rise in food prices and depreciation of our paper money are due to ma-

nœuvres carried through in our midst, under our eyes, by enemy agents. In the name of public safety, I charge the Citizen Juror to be merciless with plotters and traitors."

While this man went back from the tribune, voices in the Assembly could be heard: "Down with the Revolutionary Tribunal! Down with the Moderates!"

Obese and florid, Citizen Dupont *senior,* cabinet-maker of the Place de Thionville, mounted the tribune, desiring, he said, to put a question to the Citizen Juror. He then asked Gamelin what attitude he would take in the trial of Brissot's adherents and of the Capet widow.

Évariste was timid, and had not the least idea how to speak in public. But indignation inspired him. He rose, pale, and in a colourless voice said, "I am a magistrate. I am responsible solely to my conscience. Any promise which I made to you would be contrary to my duty. I am to speak in Court and be silent everywhere else. I no longer know you. I am a judge: I know neither enemy, nor friend."

The assembly, of many minds, undecided and fluctuating like all assemblies, approved this. But Citizen Dupont *senior* came back to the attack; he could not forgive Gamelin for occupying a place he had coveted himself.

"I understand," he said, "and even approve the scruples of the Citizen Juror. He is said to be a patriot; it is for him to see whether his conscience allows him to take his place on a tribunal aimed at the destruction of the enemies of the Republic but resolved to spare them. There are forms of complicity from which a good citizen should refrain. Is it not said that a number of jurors on the tribunal have let themselves be corrupted by the gold of the accused, and that President Montané misdirected, to save the head of the Corday girl?"

At these words, the building echoed

with energetic applause. The final bursts of this were still echoing against the vaulted ceiling when Fortuné Trubert mounted the tribune. He had grown much thinner during the last few months. His red cheekbones pierced the skin of his pale cheeks; his eyelids were inflamed and his pupils glassy.

"Citizens," he said, in a feeble, slightly breathless voice, which was peculiarly penetrating, "one cannot suspect the Revolutionary Tribunal without at the same time suspecting the Convention and the Committee of Public Safety, in which it has its origin. Citizen Beauvisage has alarmed us by pointing out President Montané altering the procedure in favour of a guilty person. Why did he not add, to put our minds at rest, that, on being denounced by the public prosecutor, Montané was dismissed and imprisoned? Can we not keep our eye on public security without broadcasting suspicion everywhere? Is there no more talent, no more uprightness, in the Convention? Are not Robespierre, Couthon, Saint-Just straight? It is noteworthy that the most violent suggestions are made by men whom one has never seen fighting for the Republic. Their words are precisely those to make the Republic detestable. Citizens, less noise, and more work! France will not be saved by chatter, but cannon. Half the cellars of this ward are still to be dug in. Quite a number of citizens still hold considerable quantities of bronze. We can remind the wealthy that their best guarantee is in patriotic gifts. I recommend to your generosity the daughters and the wives of our soldiers who are winning their laurels at the frontier or on the Loire. One of them, Hussar Pommier (Augustin) formerly a cellarman's apprentice of the Rue de Jérusalem, on the tenth of last month, before Condé, taking some horses down to water, was attacked by six Austrian cavalrymen; he killed two and took the others prisoner. I ask this

Ward to declare that Pommier (Augustin) has done his duty."

This speech was applauded and the members of the ward went their ways with shouts of "Long Live the Republic!"

Remaining alone in the nave with Trubert, Gamelin shook his hand: "Thank you. How are you?"

"Me, fine, fine!" replied Trubert, and with a gurk he coughed blood into his handkerchief. "The Republic has many enemies, without and within; as for our Ward, it has rather a large number of them. It's not with chatter but iron and laws that empires are made . . . Goodnight, Gamelin; I have a number of letters to write."

And handkerchief to lips, he entered what had been the vestry.

Citizeness Widow Gamelin, with her cockade now fixed on her head-dress a little more seemingly, had overnight assumed a stout middle-class solemnity, republican pride and the dignified bearing that became the mother of a "Citizen Juror." The respect for justice in which she had been reared, the admiration which she had felt for magisterial robes ever since she was a child, and the august terror she had always felt at sight of those to whom the Almighty himself had delegated his earthly rights of life and death —all these feelings had turned the son whom hitherto she had looked upon as almost a child into an august object, something venerable, holy. In her simplicity she imagined a continuity of justice right through the revolution, quite as strongly as the Convention legislators saw a continuity of the State through all mutations of régimes, and to her the Revolutionary Tribunal seemed to be of equal majesty to all the former courts, which she had learned to respect.

Citizen Brotteaux showed the young law-dispenser interest with an admixture of surprise, and forced deference. Like

Citizen Widow Gamelin, he too saw a continuity of justice through successive régimes; but in contradistinction to that lady, he despised the revolutionary courts just as much as he did those of the old régime. Not daring to express his views openly, nor able to reduce himself to absolute silence, he plunged into paradoxes which Gamelin saw through just sufficiently to suspect something antipatriotic.

"The august court in which you will soon take your place," Brotteaux told him on one occasion, "has been set up by the Senate of France for the salvation of the Republic; now it was without question a most proper intention on the part of our law-makers to provide their enemies with judges. I can see the magnanimity of it, but I don't think it was good policy. In my view, it would have been more clever of them to have struck down their most irreconcilable enemies in the dark and won over the others by gratuities or promises. A court strikes slowly and hurts less than it terrifies; its principal effect is exemplary. The shortcoming of yours is that it reconciles all whom it frightens and so makes a chaos of mutually contradictory interests and passions into a great party capable of common and powerful action. You disseminate fear; it is fear more than courage that engenders heroes; is there not a danger, Citizen Gamelin, of some day seeing prodigies of terror burst against you?"

Desmahis the engraver, enamoured this particular week of a Palais-Égalité prostitute, brunette Flora, a giant, nevertheless did find five minutes to congratulate his old friend and tell him that this was an appointment that did great honour to the fine arts.

As for Élodie, though she unconsciously detested everything revolutionary, and feared public duties as the most dangerous rivals likely to dispute with her a lover's heart, that gentle creature nevertheless was influenced by the rise of a magistrate summoned to pronounce life and death. Besides, Évariste's appointment had surrounded her with happy results, which she was sensitive enough to appreciate: in an outburst of masculine affection Citizen Jean Blaise visited the Place de Thionville studio to congratulate the juror.

Like all counter-revolutionaries, he had proper respect for the powers of the Republic, and ever since he had been denounced for fraud in army supplies, the Revolutionary Tribunal inspired him with respectful apprehension. He could see he was too prominent a personality and too mixed up in business to enjoy complete security: Citizen Gamelin looked like the sort of man to be on the right side of. Besides, was one not a good citizen, friend of the law?

He held out his hand to the artist magistrate, showed himself to be warm-hearted and patriotic, well inclined towards the arts and liberty. Gamelin, being big-hearted, shook the hand so generously offered him.

"Citizen Évariste Gamelin," declared Jean Blaise, "I appeal to your friendship and your talent. Tomorrow I am going to take you to the country for a couple of days: you will sketch and we can chat."

Several times a year the print dealer made a two or three day excursion with some artists who sketched the landscapes and ruins he indicated. Skilfully picking out what was likely to please the public, he would bring back from these trips pieces which, finished off in the studio and brightly engraved, provided red-chalk or multi-coloured prints, from which he earned a good profit. The sketches were also used to have door friezes and panels made for between windows, which sold quite as well, if not better, than Hubert Robert's decorations.

This time the juror had so much improved the painter that he wanted to take Citizen Gamelin with him, to design some fabrics. Two other artists were to be in the party—Desmahis, who was an excellent draughtsman, and unknown Philippe Dubois, who did fine work in the style of Robert. According to custom, Citizeness Élodie, with her friend Citizeness Hasard, was to accompany the artists. Jean Blaise, who was good at combining concern for his interests with care for his pleasures, had also invited a Citizeness Thévenin to join the party—a Vaudeville Theatre actress, said to be his great mistress.

## X

On Saturday, at seven in the morning, Citizen Blaise, wearing a black cocked-hat, a scarlet waistcoat, leather breeches, yellow turn-back top boots, rapped with the handle of his crop on the studio door. He found Citizeness Widow Gamelin having a polite exchange with Citizen Brotteaux, while Évariste stood before a scrap of mirror, tying his high white cravat.

"Bon voyage, Monsieur Blaise!" said the Citizeness. "But, as you are going to paint landscapes, why not take Monsieur Brotteaux, he paints."

"Very well, then," said Jean Blaise, "Citizen Brotteaux, will you join us?"

Once assured that he would not be in the way, Brotteaux, who was of a sociable nature and loved amusements, accepted.

Citizeness Élodie came all the way up the four flights just to embrace Citizeness Widow Gamelin, whom she called her dear mother. She was dressed all in white, and scented with lavender.

An ancient cross-country two-horse berlin, the hood down, was waiting for them in the square. Rose Thévenin did not budge from the rear seat, with Juli-

enne Hasard. Élodie made the actress sit on the right, took the left-hand side herself, and put Julienne, who was slight, between them. Brotteaux took his seat back to the horses, opposite Citizeness Hasard; Évariste, opposite Élodie. As for Philippe Desmahis, he reared his athletic torso on the driving seat, on the left of the coachman, whom he astonished with an account of how in one part of America chitterlings and saveloys grew on trees.

Citizen Blaise, an excellent horseman, did the journey on horseback, keeping a good lead, not to get the carriage dust.

As the wheels devoured the cobbles of the city outskirts, the travellers forgot all their cares; and when they saw the fields, trees, open sky, their thoughts were all laughter and sweetness. Élodie began to imagine herself born to rear chicken with Évariste at her side—a country magistrate—beside a river—with a wood nearby. As they entered the villages the mastiffs dashed diagonally at the carriage and barked under the horses' feet, and there would be a fat spaniel asleep in the middle of the road who would get up unwillingly, the hens would rush all ways, invariably to the opposite side of the road, while the geese would close their ranks and retreat with dignity. Grubby-faced children would watch the vehicle pass. It was a warm day, the sky without a cloud. The parched soil awaited rain. They got down at Villejuif. As they made their way through the little town, Desmahis went into a fruit shop to buy cherries to refresh the ladies. The saleswoman was pretty; Desmahis did not appear. Then Philippe Dubois called him out by the name they all knew him with: "Hallo there, Barbaroux! Barbaroux!"

Hearing that hated name, passers-by pricked up their ears and faces showed at every window. But when they saw a handsome young man emerge from the shop, waistcoat unbuttoned, neckerchief

dangling loose on an athlete's chest, a basket of cherries on his shoulder and his coat dangling at the end of a stick, some sansculottes mistook him for the outlawed Girondist, seized him roughly and despite his indignant protests were on the point of leading him off to the town offices, had not old Brotteaux, Gamelin and the three young women vouched that the citizen's name was really Philippe Desmahis, that he was a copper-engraver and a good Jacobin. All the same, the suspect was obliged to show his identity card, which by good fortune he had on him, for he was very careless about things of that sort. Thus he escaped from the hands of the local patriots with no more damage than having one of his lace cuffs torn off; but that was a trifling loss. He even obtained an apology from the national guards who had handled him most roughly and now wanted to bear him off in triumph to the Town Hall.

Free, surrounded by Citizenesses Élodie, Rose and Julienne, Desmahis shot Philippe Dubois, whom he did not like and suspected of treachery, a bitter smirk and, looking him up and down from head to feet, said: "Dubois, if you call me Barbaroux again, I shall call you Brissot; Brissot's a stout, farcical little creature with greasy hair, oily skin and sticky hands. Nobody will doubt you're the infamous Brissot, enemy of the people; and there'll be republicans so horrified and so disgusted to see you, they'll string you up to the nearest lamppost . . . Understand?"

Citizen Blaise, coming back from watering the horses, made out that he had saved the situation, though everybody else thought it had been arranged without him.

They got back into the carriage. As they continued, Desmahis informed the coachman that in this flat Longjumeau country a number of people had fallen from the moon some years back in shape

and colour rather like frogs, only much taller. Philippe Dubois and Gamelin discussed their painting. Dubois, a pupil of Raphaël, had been to Rome. He had seen Raphaël's tapestries, which he considered superior to all masterpieces. He admired Correggio's colour, Hannibal Caracci's imagination, and Domenichino's drawing, but thought there was nothing to compare in style with the pictures of Pompeio Battoni. At Rome he had often been to see M. Ménageot and Madame Lebrun, who had both come out against the Revolution, so he did not say a word about them. But he praised Angelica Kaufmann, who had taste and knew the classical world.

Gamelin found it deplorable that the height of French painting—so late, since it only dated from Lesueur, Claude and Poussin, and answered to the decadence of the Italian and Flemish schools, should have been followed by so rapid and profound a decline. He put that down to the social complex and to the Academy, which reflected it. But, fortunately, the Academy had now been liquidated, and under the influence of new principles, David and his school were evolving an art worthy of a free people. Among the younger painters, Gamelin unenviously gave top place to Hennequin and Topino-Lebrun. Philippe Dubois preferred his teacher, Regnault, to David, and saw the hope of painting in young Gérard.

Élodie had nice things to say to Citizeness Thévenin about her red velvet toque and her white gown, while the actress praised the get-up of the two other women and gave them hints how to improve upon them—her idea was that they needed to limit the trimmings.

"You cannot dress too simply," she said. "We learn that in the theatre, where costume has to reveal every pose we take. Therein lies its beauty, it needs no other."

"Very true, my dear," replied Élodie, "but simplicity is the most expensive kind of dress. And it is not always through bad taste we put on frills; we sometimes do it to cut down expense."

With great eagerness they discussed the autumn fashions, with their gowns in but one piece, and high waists.

"So many women make frights of themselves by following the fashion," la Thévenin said. "One ought to dress according to one's figure."

"Only cloth simply laid on the body and draped is beautiful," said Gamelin. "Everything tailored and stitched is frightful."

Such ideas, which would have been better in a book by Winkelmann than on the lips of a man talking to some ladies of Paris, were rejected with scorn and indifference.

"For next winter," said Élodie, "they are making Laplandish quilted gowns, in taffeta and muslin, and coats à la Zulime, with round yoke and a Turkish zouave."

"Hiding the poverty underneath," said la Thévenin, "ready-made stuff. I've a little dressmaker who works like an angel; cheap, too; I'll send her round to you, my dear."

Thus the talk fluttered, nimble and light, unfurling and flying fine textiles, striped Florence silk, self-colored Shantung, muslin, voile, nankeen.

And old Brotteaux, listening, sadly savoured all these transparencies of a season to be cast over enchanting forms which lasted for years and were eternally springing up like the flowers of the fields. And his eyes, wandering from the three young women to the cornflowers and poppies in the furrows, moistened with smiling tears.

They reached Orangis a little before nine and put up at the Auberge de la Cloche, where a couple named Poitrine provided for man and beast. Citizen Blaise, straightening his clothes, handed the ladies down. After ordering dinner for midday, they set out on foot, with a little village lad preceding them with their paintboxes, their boards, their easels and their sunshades, and went through the fields to where the Orge and the Yvette mingled their waters, a delightful site whence one looks over the verdant level lands of Longjumeau, with the Seine and the Sainte-Geneviève woods on the far side.

Jean Blaise, who led the way, exchanged funny stories with the former financier, and without rhyme or reason they passed from Verboquet the openhanded to Catherine Cuissot the pedlar, the Chaudron girls, Galichet the wizard and those more modern characters, Cadet-Rousselle and Madame Angot.

Évariste, when he saw harvesters tying their sheaves, was suddenly taken with love of Nature, and felt his eyes well with tears; his heart flowed over with dreams of harmony and love. Desmahis busied himself puffing the light dandelion seeds into the ladies' coiffures. As all three had city girls' taste for bouquets, they went gathering mullein blossoms, which cluster round the stem like ears of wheat, bell-flowers, with their tiny tiers of lilac-coloured bells, delicate sprays of verbena, dwarf elder, mint, weld, milfoil, all the wild flowers of the end of summer. And, since Rousseau had made botany fashionable for town girls, all three knew both the names and the love meanings of these flowers. As the delicate pearls, languid from the drought, came away in her arms and rained at her feet, Citizeness Élodie sighed: "The flowers are going off already."

Each of them then set to work trying to express his or her view of Nature, but each saw it as some master had already seen it. In no time Philippe Dubois had patched up an abandoned farmhouse in the style of Hubert Robert, with trees blown down and a dried up stream. Beside the Yvette, Évariste Gamelin found Poussin landscapes. Philippe Desmahis tackled a dove-cote—in the picaresque style of Callot or Duplessis. Old Brotteaux, who prided himself on imitating the Flemish painters, drew away painstakingly at a cow. Élodie sketched a thatched cottage, and her friend Julie, whose father was an artist's colourman, prepared her palette. Some children clustered round, watching her paint. She kept getting them out of the light, calling them midges and giving them lollipops. And Citizeness Thévenin, when she found pretty ones, cleaned them up and stuck flowers in their hair. She fondled them with melancholic gentleness, because she had not the fortune to be a mother, also to make herself more beautiful by expressing tender feelings and at the same time to practice her art of pose and grouping.

She was the only one who neither drew nor painted. She busied herself with learning a part, but more still with pleasing. Notebook in hand, she flitted from one to the other, frail and enchanting. Women said she lacked complexion, figure, body and voice, yet she made emptiness full of movement, colour and grace. Faded, pretty, fatigued yet tireless, she was the delight of the party. Moody, yet always jolly, touchy and irritable, yet easily won over and ready to fit in, a tongue for smut most elegantly told, vain, modest, faithful, treacherous and delightful, Rose Thévenin managed her affairs badly, yet if she was no goddess, it was the age which was at fault and the fact that there was no more incense, nor altar in Paris for the Graces. Citizeness Blaise, who always made a face when she spoke of her and called her "my godmother" could never see her without giving way to her charms.

At Feydeau's theatre they were rehearsing *Les Visitandines* and Rose was proud of playing her part most realistically. It was realistic acting she wanted, pursued, and achieved.

"So we shan't see *Paméla?*" handsome Desmahis enquired.

The National Theatre had been closed and the actors sent to the Madelonettes and Pélagie prisons.

"Is that liberty?" cried Rose Thévenin, raising her lovely eyes heavenwards.

"The actors of the National Theatre," said Gamelin, "are aristocrats, and Citizen François' play suggests one should regret the end of noble privileges."

"Gentlemen," said la Thévenin, "can you only listen to those who flatter you?"

Towards midday the little band returned to the inn with a grand appetite.

Évariste, walking with Élodie, reminded her with a smile of how they first met: "Two little birds had fallen from the roof where their nest was, on to your windowsill. You fed them with a spoon; one of them lived and flew away. The other died in the cotton-wool nest you made for it. 'That was the one I liked best,' you said. That day you had a red ribbon in your hair."

Philippe Dubois and Brotteaux, a little behind the others, spoke of Rome, where they had both been, the one in 1772, the other during his last days at the Academy. And old Brotteaux could still recall the Princess Mondragone, to whom he would certainly have breathed his love, had Count Altieri not stuck to her like a leech. Philippe Dubois made a point of saying that he was invited to dinner by the Cardinal de Bernis and the cardinal was the kindest of hosts.

"I knew him," said Brotteaux, "and I am not flattering myself if I say that during several months I was his closest friend: he had a taste for the dregs of society. He was a delightful fellow, and though he made telling fairy-stories a regular practice, there was more commonsense philosophy in his little finger than there is in the skulls of all your Jacobins with their wish to make us all god-fearing prigs. Upon my word I prefer our crude god-eaters, who neither know what they say or do, to these rabid law-makers, who are now going to guillotine us to fill us with the virtues and sober behaviour and make us worship a Supreme Being who made them in his own image. In the old days I used to have mass said in the family chapel by a poor old wretch of a parson who when he'd had a drop would say: 'Let us not disparage sinners; we priests, unworthy as we are, live by them.' I'm sure you agree that prayer-monger held sound views on government. That's what we ought to get back to, and govern men as they really are and not as we'd like them to be."

Rose Thévenin now came up to old Brotteaux. She knew he had once lived on a grand scale, and by that dazzling memory her imagination transformed the present poverty of the former financier, which she thought less humiliating since it was general, the result of national ruination. With great interest and considerable respect, she saw in him the debris of those generous Croesuses of whom older actresses she knew told such glowing stories. Besides, the manners of this nice old gentleman in plum-coloured surtout so shiny but so clean pleased her.

"Monsieur Brotteaux," she said, "it's no secret that formerly, in lovely gardens, on luminous nights, you would slip into the myrtles with actresses and ballet girls, to the distant sound of flutes and violins . . . Alas, they were more beautiful, were they not, those goddesses of yours of the Opera and the Comédie Française, than we poor little national actresses?"

"Don't you believe it, Mademoiselle," Brotteaux replied, "and let me tell you that if in those days one had met anybody at all like yourself, she would have been paraded all by herself, unrivalled sovereign, however little she wanted it, in that park which you please to imagine in such charming shape . . ."

The Hôtel de la Cloche was rustic. A branch of holly hung over the courtyard doors, through which one entered a courtyard which was permanently damp, with poultry picking. The building was at the bottom of the yard, one floor up, one down, with a steep roof of mossy tiles, and walls lost under old rambler roses in full bloom. On the right, close-trimmed fruit trees raised their peaks above the low garden wall. On the left were the stables with an outside hay-rack and a half-timber barn. There was a ladder against the wall. On this side there was also a lean-to full of farm implements and tree-stumps and an old dog-cart from which a white cock was surveying his hens. The yard was thus enclosed by farm buildings, in front of which, a magnificent mountain, there rose a muck heap which a girl broader than she was high with straw-coloured hair was just forking over. The liquor trickling into her wooden clogs was splashing her bare feet, the saffron-yellow heels of which every now and then rose out of the *sabots*. Her tucked-up petticoats revealed the dirt of her enormous, low-set legs. While Philippe Desmahis was watching her, with astonishment and interest in the trick of nature which produced so immense a beam, the landlord shouted: "Hallo there! Tronche! Fetch some water!"

She turned, showing a scarlet face and an immense mouth with a gap in it. It had needed a bull's horn to breach that powerful set of teeth. Fork on shoulder, she laughed. Her arms, bare to the elbows, and like two thighs, sparkled in the sunlight.

The table had been laid in a downstairs room, where the chickens were just finishing roasting under the hood of the fireplace, with its old fowling pieces. More than twenty paces long, this dining-room, with lime-washed walls, was lit only by the greenish glass of the door and a single window, framed with roses, near which the grandmother of the house sat at her spinning-wheel. She was wearing a coif with lace frilling in the Regency style. Her earth-stained, knotted fingers clutched a distaff. Flies settled on the edge of her eyelids, but she made no effort to drive them away. While in her mother's arms, she had seen Louis XIV drive through the place.

It was sixty years since she had been to Paris. In a weak sing-song voice she told the three young women, standing round her, that she had seen the Town Hall, the Tuileries and the Samaritaine, and that when she was crossing the Pont-Royal bridge, a barge taking apples to the Mail market broke up and the apples floated down the river, which was purple with them.

People had told her about the recent changes in the kingdom, especially of the strife between juror and non-juror priests. She also knew there had been wars, famines and signs in the heavens. She refused to believe that the king was dead. They had got him away, she said, by an underground passage and had delivered an ordinary man to the executioner in his place.

At the grandmother's feet was the latest Poitrine, in his cradle—Jeannot, just teething. Rose Thévenin raised the wicker cradle and smiled at the baby, which whimpered feebly, worn out by fever and convulsions. It must have been very ill, for they had called in the doctor, a citizen Pelleport, who, one must admit, being a deputy to a Convention deputy, made no charge for his visits.

Rose Thévenin, born and nurtured on tour, was at home anywhere; dissatisfied with the way Tronche had washed the dishes, she gave another wipe to plates, glasses and forks. While Citizeness Poitrine brought the soup to the boil, which as good innkeeper's wife she tried, Élodie sliced up a quartern loaf still warm from the oven. Gamelin, seeing her at it, said:

"The other day I was reading a book by a young German, whose name I can't remember, which had been put into French very well. In it was a pretty girl named Charlotte who cut the bread just like you, and just like you did it with charm, so prettily that when he saw her, young Werther fell head over heels in love with her."

"And did it end in marriage?" asked Élodie.

"No," replied Évariste, "it ended with Werther coming to a violent end."

They dined well, for they had enormous appetites; but the food was rather poor. Jean Blaise complained about it; he was very particular about his food, and made good eating a rule of life; and no doubt the general scarcity made him make his greedy eating a regular system. In every house the Revolution had overturned the stewpot. The average citizen had nothing to get his teeth into. Clever folk, who like Jean Blaise made a fortune amid general poverty, regularly went to the restaurant, where they showed their intelligence by stuffing. As for Brotteaux, who, in the year II of Liberty, was living on chestnuts and dry crusts, he could remember supping at Grimod de La Reynière's at the beginning of the Champs-Élysées. Anxious to prove his claim to a fine palate while he dealt with Madame Poitrine's fat pork and cabbage, he produced a steady flow of recondite kitchen recipes and good trencherman's tips. And when Gamelin laid it down that a republican scorned the pleasures of the table, the old entrepreneur, expert in antiquities, gave the young Spartan the true formula for the Spartan black broth.

After dinner, Jean Blaise, who never neglected serious business, had his itinerant school make sketches and notes of the inn, which he found dilapidated enough to be romantic. While Philippe Desmahis and Philippe Dubois were drawing the farm buildings, Tronche came out to feed the pigs. Citizen Pelleport, health officer, happened at the same instant to emerge from the dining room, where he had been to tend the Poitrine baby, and he went up to the artists, and after complimenting them on their gifts, most edifying for the whole country, he pointed to Tronche among her porkers.

"See that creature," he said, "that's not a girl, as you might think, but two girls. Understand me, I am speaking literally. I was so astonished by the dimensions of her foundation of bone, that I examined her and found that most of her bones are double: each thigh has two femurs, welded into one, each shoulder, two humeruses. She also has double muscles. In my opinion it's a case of very closely associated twins, twins melted into one, so to speak. An interesting case. I drew Monsieur Saint-Hilaire's attention to it, and he was most grateful. What you see there, citizens, is a monster. The locals call her 'Tree-trunk'—Tronche—what they ought to say is *Tree-trunks,* as there are two of them. Nature has its waggeries. Good-afternoon, Citizen painters! There's going to be a storm tonight . . ."

After a supper by candle light, the Blaise school, with the assistance of a Poitrine son and daughter, played blindman's buff in the inn yard, in which the young women and the young men too displayed a liveliness for which their age is explanation sufficient for us not to try to find a reason for their ardour in the violence and insecurity of the age in which they lived. When it grew completely dark, Jean Blaise suggested some harmless games in the dining-room. Élodie wanted "hunt my heart" which they all agreed to. Under her instructions, on walls, doors and furniture Philippe Desmahis chalked seven hearts, that is to say, one less than there were players, for old Brotteaux had obligingly joined in. They danced "Look out, La Tour," in a ring, and on a sign from Élodie, each ran to put his hand on a heart. Gamelin, absent-minded and clumsy, found them all occupied; he had to give a forfeit—the little six sous knife he had bought at the Saint-Germain fair and cut the starving mother half the loaf with. They began again, and in turn Blaise, Élodie, Brotteaux, and Rose Thévenin failed to touch a heart and paid their forfeits—a ring, a vanity bag, a little morocco-bound book, a bracelet. Then the forfeits were drawn for in Élodie's lap and each then had to buy back his property by showing his drawing-room talents, singing a song or reciting some poetry. Brotteaux recited the speech of the patron saint of France in the first canto of *La Pucelle:*

*I am Saint Denis and a saint by trade,*
*And love my Gaul . . . .*

Citizen Blaise, for all that he was less well-read, responded at once with Richmond's reply:

*My worthy Saint, 'twas not worth while*
*Celestial domains to quit.*

At that time the whole world was reading and rereading the French Ariosto's masterpiece with the greatest delight; the most serious of men smiled over the love of Jeanne and Dubois, the adventures of Agnes and Montrose, and the exploits of the winged ass. Every educated man knew the fine passages of that amusing and philosophical poem by heart. Even Évariste Gamelin, for all has austerity of temperament, when he came to recovering his two penny knife from Élodie's lap, made a good show of reciting Grisbourdon's entry into hell. Citizeness Thévenin sang Nina's song—*Quand le bien-aimé reviendra*—without accompaniment. To the tune of *La Faridondaine,* Desmahis sang:

*Unknown persons took the pig*
*Of our good Saint Anthony,*
*Putting on the pig a cowl*
*Piggie turned into a monk,*
*'Tis the cowl that makes the monk . . .*

Nevertheless, Desmahis was worried. At the moment he was ardently in love with the three women whom he was playing forfeits with, and was dispensing hot, languishing glances on each of them. In Rose Thévenin he loved her charm, her subtlety, her mastery of her art, her flashing glances and her voice, which pierced him through and through; he loved Élodie, who, he felt, was a generous soul, with much to give and readiness to give it; and he loved Julienne Hasard, in spite of her bleached hair and colourless lashes, her freckles and her lack of bust, for, like the Dunois of whom Voltaire related in *La Pucelle,* he in his greatness of heart was always prepared to offer the least prepossessing woman some mark of love, the more so since at the moment it looked to him as if she was the most disengaged, hence the most accessible. Free of any vanity, he never counted on being accepted, though he also always counted on the possibility that he might be. So he was always making the offer, on the off chance. Taking advantage of the favourable moments forfeits had provided, he had made some gallant suggestions to Rose, who was not in the least annoyed, though she could hardly be expected to respond, under the jealous eye of Jean Blaise. He had spoken still more amorously to Élodie, whom he knew to be Gamelin's girl, but he was not so exacting as to insist on exclusivity. Élodie might not be able to love him, but she found him handsome and had not quite succeeded in concealing that from him. Finally, he had plied the most vigorous suit to Citizeness Hasard, who had responded by an air of bewilderment which might equally well have meant abject submission or bored indifference. But Desmahis was quite sure she could not be indifferent.

There were only two bedrooms in the inn, both upstairs, opening off the same landing. That on the left, the better room, was papered with a flowered paper and as decoration had a mirror as large as your hand, the gilt frame of which had suffered the outrages of flies ever since Louis XV was a little boy. There, under a single muslin canopy, stood two beds equipped with feather pillows, eiderdowns and counterpanes. This room was allotted to the three ladies.

When the hour for retirement came, Desmahis and Citizeness Hasard, each with a candle, wished each other goodnight on the landing. The amorous engraver slipped the colourman's daughter a note asking her to come to him, as soon as everybody was asleep, on the loft over the girl's room.

A practical man, with foresight, during the day he had studied the lay-out and explored this loft, which was full of strings of onions, fruit drying under swarms of wasps, chests and old trunks. He had even found a rickety old folding bedstead there, though he thought that was unusable, but there was also a gutted straw mattress jumping with fleas.

Opposite the girls' room was a three-bedded room, pretty small, where the gentlemen were to do as best they could. But Brotteaux, who was a sybarite, made off for the barn, to sleep in the hay. As for Jean Blaise, he had vanished, while Dubois and Gamelin were soon sound asleep. Desmahis had got into bed, but, when the silence of the night, like still waters, had enveloped the house, he got up and climbed the wooden ladder, which creaked under his bare feet. The loft door was half open. From it came a stifling heat and the acrid odour of rotting fruit. On the rickety folding bed was Tronche asleep, mouth open, shift drawn up, legs widespread. She was huge. A ray of moonlight coming through the skylight poured azure and silver over her skin which, in between scales of dirt and splashes of muck-heap liquor, gleamed with youth and freshness. Desmahis flung himself at her; thus wakened by surprise, she was frightened and called out; but, the moment she grasped what was afoot, her fears vanished, she showed no astonishment or opposition, but pretended to be still sunk in half-sleep, which made her unaware what was really happening and authorised some enjoyment . . .

Desmahis at last made his way back to the bedroom, where he slept through to daybreak without budging.

The following day, after another session of work, the wandering school took the road back to Paris. When Jean Blaise settled with Poitrine, paying in notes, Poitrine expressed his regret at seeing this "square money" and said he would be damned thankful to any man who brought back the "yellow boys."

He offered the ladies flowers. Under his instructions Tronche mounted the ladder, in clogs and kilted skirts, and cut and cut at the climbing roses. The blooms rained down from her massive hands, torrents, an avalanche, into the laps which Élodie, Julienne and Rose held for them. The carriage was full. When they got home that night each of them had armfuls and their sleep and wakening was perfumed with roses.

# XI

On the morning of September 7th, Citizeness Rochemaure, calling on Juror Gamelin, whom she wished to interest in one of her acquaintance who had fallen under suspicion, on the landing met former nobleman Brotteaux des Ilettes, whom in happy times she had loved. Brotteaux was on his way to take a gross of the dolls he made to a toy-dealer of the Rue de la Loi. And to carry them the more easily he had decided to stick them at the end of a pole, just as the street hawkers do. He was always the grand gentleman to any woman, even where long familiarity had skimmed the cream of their attraction, which must have been the case with Madame de Rochemaure, unless, now she was seasoned by betrayal, absence, faithlessness and superfluous flesh, he could find her appetising. Anyway, he now greeted her, on this sordid landing with its loose tiles, exactly as he used to do on the grand staircase of des Ilettes, and begged her to do him the honour of visiting his attic. She mounted the ladder pretty nimbly, to find herself under a sloping roof of rafters and tiles, with a skylight. It was not high enough to stand upright in. She took the only chair to be seen and then, with a sweeping glance over the gaping tiles, demanded, with some astonishment and sorrow:

"So this is where you live, is it, Maurice? Scarcely any need to fear spongers. One'd have to be a demon or a cat to find you."

"I have not much room," the ex-noble replied. "And I will not conceal that it sometimes rains on my miserable bed. A trifling inconvenience, for on clear nights I can see the moon above me, symbol and witness of human love-making. For, Madame, the moon has always been lovers' reference, and when full, and pale and rotund, calls a man's mind to the object of his desire."

"Agreed," said the citizeness.

"When in season," Brotteaux continued, "the cats kick up a fine din in that guttering. But when love fills human life with torture and crime, one must forgive love that merely miaows and swears on the roofs."

They both were wise enough to take each other just as if they had parted but last night, going to bed; and though they had become mutual strangers, they conversed with good grace and intimacy.

Nevertheless, Madame de Rochemaure seemed worried. The Revolution, which for a long time had smiled upon her and been fruitful, was now bringing her worries and alarms; her suppers were becoming less brilliant, less gay. The sounds of the harp no longer brightened gloomy countenances. The richer gamblers had abandoned her gaming parties. Quite a number of her intimates, become suspect, were in hiding; banker Morhardt, her lover, had been arrested, and it was on his account that she had come to solicit Juror Gamelin's support. She was even under suspicion herself. The National Guard had searched her house and ransacked her chests of drawers, lifted flooring, stuck bayonets through mattresses. They had found nothing, apologised, and drunk her wine. But they had just managed to miss her correspondence with an émigré named d'Expilly. Friends she had among the Jacobins had warned her that handsome Henry, her plaything, was beginning to give her a bad name politically; he was too extreme to convince one of his sincerity.

Elbows on knees, her cheeks on her clenched fists, pensive, she asked her old friend, who was seated on his straw mattress, what he thought of it all. "Tell me, Maurice."

"I find," he said, "these good folk provide a philosopher and one who loves public scenes quite sufficient to keep him both preoccupied and entertained, but, my dear, that it would be better for you to get out of France."

"Maurice," she demanded, "where will that take us?"

"That's just what you asked me, Louise, one day in a carriage beside the Cher, on the Ilettes road, when our horse took the bit between its teeth and bolted. What inquisitive creatures women are! You still want to know where we are going. Ask fortune-tellers that. I'm no good at it, my sweet. And philosophy, even the wisest, is poor help for knowing the future. It will come to an end, because everything comes to an end. One can

foresee a number of conclusions. A Coalition victory and the allies entering Paris. They are very near it; yet I doubt if they will succeed. These soldiers of the Republic get beaten with a fervour that nothing can extinguish. Robespierre may even marry Madame Royale and have himself appointed Protector of the Kingdom till Louis XVIIth comes of age."

"You really think so?" cried the citizeness, who would have given anything to have a finger in so lovely a plot.

"Or it is even possible," continued Brotteaux, "that the Vendée will win and a government of parsons rear its head over mountains of ruins and piles of corpses. Dear friend, you just cannot conceive what power the clergy have over most donkeys . . ." Here des Brotteaux's tongue slipped, for, saying *donkeys* or *ânes,* he had—or at least so he averred—meant to say *souls,* or *âmes.* "But the most likely thing," he went on, "is in my opinion that the Revolutionary Tribunal will bring about the destruction of the régime that has instituted it; it threatens too many heads. Those it frightens are innumerable; they will get together and, to destroy the tribunal, they will destroy the régime. I believe you had young Gamelin appointed to that court. He is single-minded; he will be terrible. The more I think of it, my dear friend, the more convinced I am that this tribunal, established to save the Republic, will destroy it. Like the Monarchy, the Convention would insist on having its supreme personal court, and ensure its own security by magistrates of its own appointing, dependent on it. But how much inferior the Assembly in this respect, compared with the Monarchy! This Revolutionary Tribunal is dominated by a spirit of crude justice and levelling equality which will soon make it hateful and farcical, and disgust the whole world. Louise, did you know that this Tribunal, which intends to try the Queen of France and twenty-one leg-

islators, yesterday troubled to try a servant-girl accused of shouting 'Long live
the King!' with evil intent, and with the
idea of destroying the Republic? Our
judges, all black plumes, work like that
William Shakespeare so dear to the English, who introduces coarse clowning into
the most tragic scenes."

"Well, well, Maurice," the citizeness
rejoined, "are you still fortunate in love?"

"Alas," Brotteaux replied, "the doves
all fly to the white cock pigeon and never
settle on ruins."

"You are still the same . . . Au re-
voir, my friend."

That evening, Dragoon Henry, calling
uninvited on Madame de Rochemaure,
found her sealing a letter on which he
read the address of a *Cit. Rauline,* at
Vernon. That, he knew, was a letter for
England. Rauline received Madame de
Rochemaure's mail by *messageries* cou-
rier, and had a fishwoman get it into
Dieppe. When night fell, a fishing-smack
skipper passed it on to a British warship
patrolling the coast, and an émigré
named d'Expilly received it in London,
and, if he found it useful, passed it on to
St. James's Palace.

Henry was young and handsome;
Achilles buckling on the weapons with
which Ulysses presented him did not
combine more charm or strength. But
Citizeness Rochemaure, having had her
bout of susceptibility to the charms of the
young hero of the Commune, now
averted her eyes from him, her thoughts
too, ever since she had received information that this young soldier, being denounced to the Jacobins as an extremist,
might compromise her and ruin her.
Henry's opinion was that quite possibly
his heart would not be broken by ceasing
to enjoy Rochemaure's favours; but he
did dislike being snubbed. He had
counted on her to cover certain outlay to
which the service of the Republic had

obliged him. Finally, considering to what
lengths women could go, and the way
they have of switching in an instant from
the most fiery passion to the coldest indifference, and how easily they cast to the
wolves what they once held most dear
and destroy what they worshipped, he
had a suspicion that this ravishing Louise
might one day get him thrown into
prison, just to be rid of him. That is why
he had come armed with all his charm.
He drew near, withdrew, drew near
again, to touch and to flee from her, according to the rules of seduction. Then,
throwing himself into an armchair, in
that inconquerable voice, that voice
which went straight to a woman's bowels,
he sang praises of Nature and solitude
and with sighs suggested a trip out to
Ermenonville.

But all she did was pluck stray harmo-
nies on her harp and cast about her eyes
full of impatience and boredom. All at
once, Henry straightened his back and,
full of gloom and determination, announced that he was off to join the army
and would be at Maubeuge in a few days.

She nodded approval, without a trace
of doubt, or astonishment.

"Then you congratulate me on my decision?"

"I do."

She was expecting a new lover who
was infinitely more to her taste and from
whom she expected great advantage;
something quite different from this type;
a successful Mirabeau, a spruced up Danton turned State Purveyor, a lion who
spoke of throwing all patriots into the
river. Every instant she thought it was the
door-bell and started.

To get rid of Henry she did not say a
word, but yawned, fingered some music,
yawned again. Seeing that he was not going to leave, she told him she had to go
out, and went to her dressing-room.

In a broken voice he called: "Adieu,
Louise . . . Shall I ever see you again?"

—while his fingers rummaged in the open writing-desk.

Out in the street he at once opened the letter addressed to Citizen Rauline, reading it with interest. For it contained a strange picture of the state of public feeling in France. There was talk of the Queen, of Rose Thévenin, of the Revolutionary Tribunal, and a statement of various confidential observations made by good old des Brotteaux.

Finishing his reading, he put the letter back into his pocket, undecided for some moments; then, like a man whose mind is made up and tells himself that the sooner the better, he made for the Tuileries and entered the lobby of the Committee of Public Safety.

The same day, at 3 P.M., Évariste Gamelin took his seat on the jury bench with fourteen other jurors, most of whom he knew, frank, simple-minded patriotic persons, scholars, artists and artisans—a painter like himself, a designer, both very gifted, a surgeon, a cobbler, a former marquis, who had given great proofs of patriotism, a printer, some little business men, in short, a cross-section of the people of Paris. There they sat, in working clothes or townsman's rig, hair cropped Titus-fashion or bunched on the nape, cocked hat jammed down on the eyes, or round hat tipped back off the forehead, or with a red cap hiding their ears. Some wore waistcoat, coat and breeches, as in the old days, others the red smock and striped trousers of the sansculottes. In high boots, buckled shoes or wooden clogs, they presented all the varieties of masculine costume of the moment. Having done jury duty several times already, they seemed quite at their ease and Gamelin envied their calm. His heart was thumping, his ears drumming, his eyes misty, and everything around him was livid.

When the usher announced the Tribu-nal, three judges took their places on a rather small podium, in front of a green table. They wore cockaded hats with large black plumes and a cloak of office with a tricolour sash from which dangled a heavy silver medallion. Before them, under the platform, sat the deputy public prosecutor, in similar garb. The Court clerk sat between the Judges and the empty defendant's chair. These persons all looked to Gamelin different from what they had looked hitherto, more handsome, more solemn, more disturbing for all that they assumed easy-going postures, turning over papers, calling an usher or leaning back to hear what some juror or court official had to say.

Above the Judges were hung the Tables of the Rights of Man; to the right and left of these, against the ancient walls of this feudal structure were busts of Le Peltier, Saint-Fargaux and Marat. Opposite the jury bench, at the back of the hall, rose the public benches. The front row was ornate with women, all, blond, brunette or grey-haired, in high headdresses, with pleated tuckers which hid their cheeks; on their bosoms, to which fashion lent the uniform amplitude of wet nurses, were crossed the ends of a white shawl or the bulging bib of a blue apron. They kept their arms folded on the ramp of the tribune. Behind them could be seen scattered over the rising tiers of seats citizens attired with that diversity of style which at this particular time gave any crowd a peculiar though picturesque appearance. On the right, towards the entrance, behind a solid partition, was a space where the public could crowd standing. On this occasion there were few there. The case which this section of the Court was to deal with only interested a few spectators, and no doubt the other sections, in session at the same time, had more stirring cases before them.

This it was rather reassured Gamelin, whose heart, threatening to fail, could not have borne that overheated atmosphere of great hearings. His eyes picked out the tiniest details; he noticed the cotton-wool in the Court Clerk's ear and an ink-blot on the Deputy Prosecutor's folder. As if under a lens he could see the chapter sculped at a time when all knowledge of the ancient orders had been lost, and they put garlands of nettle and holly on Gothic columns. But his eyes came back each time to that chair, of antiquated shape, upholstered in red Utrecht velvet, the seat threadbare and the arms blackened. There were armed National Guards at all the doors.

At last the defendant appeared, under grenadier escort, unfettered, as the law prescribed. It was a man in his fifties, thin, wiry, dark, very bald, cheeks hollow, lips thin and purple, dressed in old style with an oxblood colour coat. No doubt owing to fever, his eyes glistened like precious stones and his cheeks might have been varnished. He sat down. His legs, which he crossed, were of excessive thinness and his immense gnarled hands easily encompassed them. He was called Marie-Adolphe Guillergues and was charged with misappropriation of State forage. The charge enumerated a considerable number of serious facts—none of which was absolutely definite. On interrogation, Guillergues denied almost everything, explaining the remainder in his own favour. He spoke precisely and coldly, and with exceptional skill and gave the impression of a man it was better not to do business with. He had an answer for everything. When the presiding Judge put an embarrassing question, his features remained calm and his voice confident, but his two hands, clasped in front of him, twisted with anxiety. Gamelin noticed this and whispered into his neighbour's ear (a painter like himself):

"Look at his thumbs!"

The first witness to be heard adduced crushing facts. On him the whole charge rested. Those called subsequently, on the contrary, proved favourable to the accused. The Deputy Prosecutor was vehement, but stuck to generalities. The defence lawyer spoke with the tone of truth, which gained the accused sympathy he had been incapable of himself exciting. The hearing was suspended and the jurors assembled in the jury room. There, after a discussion which was obscure and muddled, they split into two groups, almost equal in number. On one side were the indifferent, the lukewarm, the reasoners, whom no strong feelings stirred, and on the other those who let themselves be guided by sentiment, and proved little open to logic, but judged with the heart. The former were always for condemning. They were good patriots, single-minded; their only thought was to save the Republic and nothing else concerned them. Their attitude impressed Gamelin very much, and he felt at one with them.

"This man Guillergues," he argued, "is a clever rascal, a rogue who has been speculating in forage for our cavalry. To find him not guilty would be to let a traitor slip through our fingers, in other words, betray the Fatherland, commit the army to defeat." And Gamelin already saw the Republican hussars, their mounts giving way, sabred down by the enemy cavalry . . . "But what if Guillergues was innocent . . . ?"

Suddenly Jean Blaise came into his mind—also suspected of fraud in supplies. There must be so many more acting like Guillergues and Blaise, making way for defeat, ruining the Republic. They ought to make an example? Yet, what if Guillergues was innocent?

"There is no proof," said Gamelin, out loud.

"There never is any proof," replied the foreman, shrugging his shoulders—he was a good one, single-minded.

In the end, there were seven for condemnation and eight for acquittal.

The jury returned to the court and the hearing was resumed. The jurors were required to give reasons for their finding; each in turn spoke, facing the empty dock. Some were lengthy, others satisfied with a word; there were one or two who were quite incomprehensible.

When his turn came, Gamelin rose and said: "Faced with a crime so serious as robbing the defenders of the Fatherland of the means of victory, one requires formal proof which we lack."

By a majority, the accused was declared *not guilty*.

Guillergues was brought back into court, to the accompaniment of a favourable murmur from the public which told him of his acquittal. It was another man. The dryness of his features had melted, his lips gone flaccid. He looked old; his countenance was expressive of innocence. The President read, with some emotion, the verdict of acquittal; the court burst into applause. The Gendarme who had brought Guillergues in rushed to his arms. The President called Guillergues forward and gave him a brotherly kiss. The jurors all embraced each other. Gamelin wept burning tears.

In the courtyard of the Law Courts, under the last rays of daylight, a howling crowd was milling to and fro. The day before, the four sections of the Tribunal had pronounced thirty death sentences, and there were knitters squatting on the steps of the main approach, waiting for the tumbrils to leave. But as he made his way down the steps in the flood of jurors and public, Gamelin neither saw nor heard anything but his act of justice and humanity and his self-congratulation for having perceived the man's innocence. In the courtyard, Élodie, deathly pale, in tears and smiling, threw herself into his arms and hung there, in abandonment. And when she had recovered her voice, she said:

"Évariste, you are handsome, you are kind, you are generous-hearted. In that court the sound of your voice, so masculine and gentle, went right through me, with magnetic waves. I was electrified. I watched you as you sat there. I saw but you. But you, my love, did you not feel I was there? Did nothing tell you of my presence? I was in the second row, to the right. Dear God, how good it is to do good! You saved that poor fellow. Without you, it would have been all up with him: he was lost. You gave him back life, gave him back to the love of his family. You must have his blessing now. Évariste, how happy and proud I am to love you!"

Arm in arm, pressed close, they walked through the streets, feeling so light they might have been flying.

They were going to the *Amour Peintre*. When they reached the Oratory, Élodie said: "Don't let's go through the shop."

She took him in by the carriage door, then up to the flat. On the landing, she took a large iron key out of her bag.

"You'd think it was a prison key," she remarked. "Évariste, you are my prisoner."

They went through the dining-room, and there they were in the girl's room.

Évariste felt the passionate freshness of Élodie's lips on his. He crushed her in his arms. Head fallen back, eyes dying, hair fallen loose, body yielding, half fainted, she slipped from him and ran to push the bolt . . .

Night was well advanced when Citizeness Blaise opened the door of her flat for her lover and in the darkness whispered:

"My love, adieu. This is the time my father comes home. If you hear anything on the stairs, hurry up to the floor above and don't come down till there is no more danger of his seeing you. To have the street door opened, give three taps on the concierge's window. Adieu, my life, adieu, my soul!"

When he had reached the street, he saw Élodie's window open slightly, and a small hand gathered a red carnation, which fell at his feet, like a drop of blood.

## XII

One evening, when old Brotteaux had taken a gross of dolls to Citizen Caillou, in the Rue de la Loi, the toy-merchant, who was usually suave and smooth among all his dolls and Punches, gave him a very bad reception.

"You look out, Citizen Brotteaux," he said, "you look out! It isn't always laughing time; jokes are not always nice; a member of the Ward Public Safety Committee, who inspected my shop yesterday, saw your dolls and found them counter-revolutionary."

"Jesting," said Brotteaux.

"Oh no, Citizen, oh no no. He's a man who never jokes. He said that these little dolls are a malicious caricature of National Deputies, and especially of Couthon, Saint-Just and Robespierre, and he impounded them. It's a dead loss for me, not to speak of the danger it exposes me to."

"What? These Harlequins, Gilles, Scaramouches, Colins and Colinettes, which I've done just like Boucher fifty years ago, are mockery of Couthon and Saint-Just? No man in his right senses could suggest such a thing!"

"Quite possibly," replied Citizen Caillou, "you have acted without malice, though one should always be on one's guard against a man of your intelligence. But it's a dangerous game. Shall I give you an example! Natoile, who runs a little theatre in the Champs-Élysées, was arrested the day before yesterday for counter-revolutionary sentiments, because he put the Assembly in his Punch and Judy show."

"Now look here," said Brotteaux, raising the cloth which covered his little dangling figures, "just take a look at these masks and physiognomies, are they anything else but characters of farce and pastoral? However did you let yourself be persuaded, Citizen Caillou, I ask you, that I was making fun of the National Assembly."

Brotteaux was astounded. For all his readiness to admit human idiocy, he would never have believed that it could ever go so far as to suspect his Scaramouches and Colinettes. He protested both their innocence and his own. But Citizen Caillou would not hear a word.

"Citizen Brotteaux, please take away your dolls. With all due respect to you, I'm not going to be either accused or worried on your account. I'm a law-abiding citizen. I mean to remain one, and to be treated as one. Good-night, Citizen Brotteaux; take your dolls away."

Old Brotteaux made his way back to his dwelling, with his suspected counter-revolutionaries at the end of a pole over his shoulder, mocked by children who thought he was a man who sold rat poison. His thoughts were gloomy. No doubt his dolls were not his sole source of a living; he did twenty *sol* portraits under archways and in one of the market cellars, side by side with the women who did mending, and there were numerous young fellows going off to the war who wanted a portrait for their mistress. But these little works cost him extreme trouble, and he was not nearly so good at portraits as he was at dolls. He sometimes did secretarial jobs for the market ladies, but that meant getting mixed up in royalist plots and the risk was enormous. He then remembered that in the Rue Neuvedes-Petits-Champs, near the former Vendôme Square, there was another toy-shop kept by a man named Joly, so he decided to go there first thing tomorrow to offer him what the cowardly Caillou refused.

It had begun to drizzle. Brotteaux, afraid of this damaging his dolls, quickened his pace. Just as he was crossing the Pont-Neuf and turning the corner of the Place de Thionville, in the light of a street-lamp he saw a thin old man, on a corner post, looking exhausted by fatigue and hunger, yet still with a venerable air about him. He was wearing a torn surtout, but no hat, and looked well over sixty. Going up to the old unfortunate, Brotteaux recognised Father Longuemarre, whom he had saved from lynching, six months earlier, while they were both in the queue at the Rue de Jérusalem butcher's. Being interested in the monk by his first service, Brotteaux went up to him, introduced himself as the sometime tax-farmer who had been at his side in the midst of the scum, one day of great shortage, and asked him if he could perhaps be of help.

"You look tired, Father. Take a drop of cordial."

And from the pocket of his plum-coloured tail-coat Brotteaux drew a small flask of brandy which had been nestling next his Lucretius.

"Drink. Then I'll help you home."

Father Longuemarre pushed hand and flask aside and tried to get up, but fell back on to the stone.

"Sir," he said, in a feeble but self-confident voice, "the last three months, I have been living at Picpus. Warned that they had come to arrest me at five this afternoon, I have not been back. I have nowhere to go. I am wandering the streets and am a little tired."

"Then, Father," said Brotteaux, "do me the honour of sharing my attic with me."

"Sir," said the Barnabite, "please grasp that I am a suspect."

"So am I," said Brotteaux, "and so are my dolls, which is the worst. You can see them, under that thin cloth, exposed to this drizzle which chills us through. For you should know, Father, that after ceas-ing to be a tax-farmer I live by making dolls."

Father Longuemarre took the hand offered him by the former financier, and accepted the proffered hospitality. In the attic, Brotteaux offered him bread and cheese, with wine, which, being a sybarite, he had put out in the gutter to chill.

Having appeased his hunger, "Monsieur," said Father Longuemarre, "I must tell you what brought me to fly and cast me up half dead on that corner-stone where you found me. Expelled from my monastery, I lived on the slender pension the Assembly made me; I gave lessons of Latin and Mathematics and wrote pamphlets on the persecution of the Church in France. I even wrote a work of some length, to prove that the constitutional oath of the priesthood is contrary to ecclesiastical discipline. The progress of the Revolution robbed me of all my pupils, and I could not draw my pension through not having the certificate of political reliability the law requires. I did go to the Town Hall to get one, feeling sure I deserved it. As member of an order instituted by the Apostle Saint Paul himself, who had the advantage of being a Roman citizen, I prided myself, in imitation of him, in being a good French citizen, respectful of all human laws not in opposition to divine law. I put in my request to Monsieur Colin the pork-butcher and municipal official, in charge of issuing these certificates. He asked me all about what I was. I told him I was a priest; he asked if I was married, and, when I said I was not, told me it was all the worse for me. In the end, after a variety of questions, he asked if I had proved my reliability on August 10th, on September 2nd and May 31st. 'Certificates,' he added, 'can only be given to those who have proved their political reliability by their conduct on those three dates.' I was unable to give him a satisfactory answer. All the same he took my name and address, and promised to have immediate enquiry made into my case. He has kept his word, and it is as conclusion of his enquiries that two Commissaries of the Picpus Committee of Public Safety, supported by armed guards, came to my dwelling when I was out, to take me to prison. I do not know of what crime I am accused. But you must agree that one must be sorry for M. Colin, having such a troubled mind that he has to reproach a priest for not having shown his political reliability on August 10th, September 2nd, and May 31st. A man capable of thoughts like that is very deserving of pity."

"Nor have I a certificate," said Brotteaux. "We are both suspects. But you are tired. Go to bed, Father. We shall see about your safety tomorrow."

He gave his guest the mattress and kept the palliasse for himself, but the monk demanded the palliasse so humbly and so persistently that he had to let him have it, or the man would have lain down on the boards.

Having arranged all this, Brotteaux blew out the candle both from economy and prudence.

"Monsieur," said the monk to him, "I am well aware what you are doing for me, but, alas, you are not very concerned whether I am grateful. May the Almighty reward you. That would be of infinite value to you. But God takes no notice of what is not done in his glory and is but the result of inborn decency. That is why, Monsieur, I do beg you to do what you felt bound to do for me, for His sake."

"Father," replied Longuemarre, "do not worry yourself and do not be grateful. What I am now doing, and you exaggerate the merits of, I am not doing for love of you; for after all, charming as you may be, Father, I know you too little to be fond of you. Nor do I any more do it out of love for humanity, for I am not such a simpleton as Don Juan as to think

with him that humanity has rights of its own; and that prejudice, in a mind as free as his was, I find upsetting. I act as I do from that egoism which inspires all man's acts of generosity and devotion, making him see himself in every unfortunate, disposing him to regret his own misfortune in the misfortune of others, and prompting him to aid a mortal similar to himself in make-up and fate, to such extent that by assisting the other he imagines he is assisting himself. I also do it out of idleness, for life is so insipid that one has to find distraction at all costs, and good works are a pretty dull amusement one gives oneself, solely in the lack of something more piquant; I do it out of pride, and to get the better of you; I do it, in short, because that's my system and also to show you what an atheist is capable of."

"Do not calumniate yourself, Monsieur," replied Father Longuemarre, "I have received more grace from God so far than he has accorded you; yet I am less worthy than you, and much your inferior in natural merit. All the same, allow me to be your superior in one thing. Without knowing me, you cannot be fond of me. But, sir, without knowing you I love you better than myself; God orders me to do so."

Having thus spoken, Father Longuemarre knelt down on the floor, and, after saying his prayers, stretched himself out on his straw mattress and fell peacefully asleep.

## XIII

It was Évariste Gamelin's second jury service. Before the hearing he chatted with his fellow jurors about the news which had come in that morning. There was much that was hazy and inaccurate; but what one could make of it was terrifying. The coalition armies, masters of all the roads, on the march together, the Vendée was victorious, Toulon delivered to the English, who were disembarking forty thousand men.

For these magistrates these were as much matters of domestic concern as events of world interest. Confident they would perish if the Fatherland perished, they made public security their business. The interests of the country then mingled with their own and dictated opinions, passions, conduct.

While on the bench Gamelin received a letter from Trubert, secretary of the Defence Committee; notification of his appointment as Commissar of Gunpowder and Saltpetre.

*"You will excavate every cellar in this Ward, for the extraction therefrom of material necessary for the manufacture of gunpowder. The enemy may be at the gates of Paris tomorrow; the soil of the Fatherland must provide the thunderbolts we shall cast at its aggressors. I am sending you herewith directions from the Assembly concerning the treatment of saltpetre."*

At this point the accused was brought in. It was one of the last of the vanquished generals whom the Assembly was delivering to the Tribunal—and the most obscure. At sight of him, Gamelin shuddered: he might have been seeing the officer whom, in the crowd, three weeks back, he had seen condemned, on his way to the guillotine. It was the same man, with a stubborn, stupid look; it was the same trial. His answers were surly and rude in manner, ruining his best replies. His quibbles were hair-splitting, and the way he blamed his subordinates made one forget that this was all part of the perfectly reasonable job of defending his honour and his life. Everything in the matter was uncertain, disputable, position of forces, number of effectives, mu-

nitions, orders issued, orders received, troop movements: all unknowns. Nobody understood a thing about these chaotic, ridiculous, pointless operations—but which had ended in a disaster; nobody, the defending counsel and accused no more than the prosecutor, the judges and the jury; yet, strangely, nobody either admitted to himself or anybody else that he did not understand. The judges were pleased to draw maps and make disquisitions on tactics and strategy; the accused revealed his inborn tendency to quibble.

The argument was endless, and during all this debating, Gamelin could see ammunition waggons stuck in the mud on those bleak northern roads, and cannon upturned in the ditches, while beaten columns of men trooped in confusion down all the roads, with the enemy cavalry pouring on all sides from the abandoned approaches. And from that betrayed army he could hear a tremendous clamour rise, accusing this general. When the hearing ended shadows were filling the hall, and the hazy figure of Marat looked like a phantom over the President's head. The jury, called upon to pronounce a verdict, was divided. In toneless voice, choked in his throat, yet determined, Gamelin pronounced the general guilty of treason to the Republic, and a mutter of approval, rising from the crowd, flattered his youthful single-mindedness. The verdict was read by torchlight, the livid glow quivering on the hollowed temples of the condemned man, where beads of sweat now showed like pearls. When he went out down the steps where the tumult of cockaded womenfolk was seething, and he could hear his name being called, Gamelin was accosted by the knitting-women who shook their fists and demanded the head of that Austrian bitch.

The following day, Évariste had to pronounce on the fate of a poor widow named Meyrion, who took bread round. She pushed a barrow, with a tally stick dangling at her waist with notches to count the bread she delivered. The deputy prosecutor showed an extreme of violence towards this unfortunate creature, who, so it appeared, had on a number of occasions cried: "God Save the King!" and made counter-revolutionary observations at the houses where she delivered bread every day, and got deep into a plot to get the Capet woman out of prison. When the judge questioned her, she admitted all alleged facts; whether by simple-mindedness or fanaticism, she pronounced most fervent royalist sentiments and destroyed herself.

The Revolutionary Tribunal assured the triumph of the egalitarian principle by being as severe with porters and skivies as aristocrats and financiers. Gamelin did not see how it could be otherwise under a régime of the people. He would have considered it scorn and insult of the people to withhold the death sentence from them. It would so to speak have been considering them unworthy of punishment. Reserved for aristocrats, the guillotine would have looked like a unique privilege. Gamelin was beginning to turn punishment into a religious, mystic concept, lending it inherent goodness and merits of its own. He considered penalties something one owed to criminals, and that to cheat men of them was to do them a wrong. He declared this woman Meyrion guilty and worthy of the supreme penalty, with mere expression of regret that fanatics who had ruined her and were more guilty than she was were not there to share her fate.

Évariste went nearly every evening to the Jacobin club, which met in a former church of the Dominicans, vulgarly known as the Jacobins, in the Rue Honoré. The church, built in a poor and boorish style, with headdress of clumsy tiles and bare gable-end with one fanlight and an arched doorway, opened on to a courtyard with a Tree of Liberty—an aspen with ceaselessly murmuring foliage —and was topped by the tricolour flag and a Liberty bonnet. The Jacobins, like the Cordeliers and the Feuillants, had taken up the quarters and adopted the name of the monks they had dispossessed. Gamelin, formerly a frequenter of the Cordelier meetings, missed the wooden clogs, red coats and Dantonist shouting at the Jacobins'. Administrative wisdom and bourgeois solemnity ruled in Robespierre's club. Since the Friend of the People was no more, Évariste had been following the instruction of Maximilien, whose thought dominated in the Jacobin gatherings, and thence spread through a thousand affiliated societies throughout France. While the minutes were read he passed his eyes over the gloomy bare walls which, having once sheltered the spiritual progeny of the Grand Inquisitor of heresy, now looked down on the gatherings of fervent inquisitors of crimes against the Fatherland.

Here, without pomp, acting through the word alone, was the greatest power of the State. It governed the city of Paris, the Empire, and dictated the decrees of the Assembly. These architects of the new order, so law-abiding that in 1791 they had remained royalist, and through stubborn attachment to the Constitution, would have liked to be royalist again when the King came back from Varennes, were friends of established order, even after the Champ-de-Mars massacres; they were never revolutionaries against the Revolution, strangers to popular stirrings, but in their solemn powerful heart cherished a love of France which had given birth to fourteen armies and erected the guillotine. Évariste admired their vigilance, their suspicion, their dogmatism, their passion for rules, their art of domination, their imperial commonsense.

The men assembled in that hall produced no other sound but a unanimous, regular tremor, like the foliage of that Tree of Liberty which rose at their threshold.

Today, Vendémiaire 11th, a young man with receding brow, piercing eye, pointed nose, sharp chin, pock-marked face and chilly manner slowly mounted the tribune. His hair was snowy with powder and he was garbed in a blue coat which showed his figure. He had a precise carriage and studied gait which made some say mockingly that he was like a dancing master and from others earned him the title of "the French Orpheus." In a clear voice Robespierre made an eloquent speech against the enemies of the Republic. With devastating metaphysical argument he struck at Brissot and his accomplices. He spoke at great length, exhaustively, and with sense of form. Soaring into the heavenly world of philosophy, he cast down lightnings at the plotters who writhed on the ground below.

Évariste heard and understood. Hitherto, he had accused the Girondists of preparing the restoration of the monarchy or the triumph of the Orléans group, and of plotting the destruction of the heroic city which had saved France and one day would save the whole world. Now he discovered more lofty and more pure truths in the voice of this wise man; he perceived a revolutionary philosophy, raising its concept above all coarse reality of circumstance, beyond the reach of errors of the senses, into the realm of absolute certainty. In themselves all things were chaotic and full of confusion; facts were so complex that one could get lost among them. Robespierre simplified them for him, revealing to him good and evil in simple, lucid formula. Federalism, indivisibility; salvation in unity and indivisibility, damnation in federalism. Gamelin was tasting the profound delight of the believer who knows the word which saves and the word which ruins. Henceforth the Revolutionary Tribunal, like the ec-

clesiastical courts of former days, would recognise absolute crime, the crime of the word. And because of this religious cast of mind, Évariste accepted these revelations with dour fervour; his heart was filled to overflowing and he was overjoyed that henceforth he was in possession of a symbol by which to distinguish between crime and innocence. Oh treasures of faith, you take the place of everything else!

Wise Maximilien also enlightened him on the scurrilous aims of those who would like to equalise all property and divide up the land, suppress wealth and poverty and establish a happy medium for all. Seduced by their tenets, he had first supported their aims, which he held to be in harmony with the principles of a true republican. But by his speeches to the Jacobins, Robespierre had laid bare their knavish tricks and revealed that these men whose purposes seemed so far above reproach were aiming at undermining the Republic, and merely menaced the wealthy in order to nurture powerful and implacable enemies of legitimate authority. Indeed, the moment property was threatened, the whole nation, with an attachment to its goods in direct proportion to its poverty, had suddenly begun to be hostile to the Republic. Menacing vested interests was paramount to plotting. Under the show of preparing universal happiness and the reign of justice, those who proposed equality and community of goods as an aim worthy of good citizens were traitors and rogues more dangerous than the federalists.

But the greatest revelation which the wisdom of Robespierre afforded him was what crime, what infamy, atheism was. Gamelin had never denied the existence of God; he was a deist, believing in a Providence that watched over men; but, with the inward admission that he had no more than a very hazy notion of a Supreme Being, and being very attached to freedom of conscience, he had been ready to concede that men who were not rogues could—like Lamettrie, Boulanger, Baron d'Holbach, Lalande, Helvétius and Citizen Dupuis—deny the existence of a Deity, provided they set up a natural system of ethics and themselves made that the source of justice and the rules of a virtuous life. He had even felt a degree of sympathy with the atheists, when he saw them insulted or persecuted. Maximilien Robespierre had opened his mind and unsealed his eyes. By his single-minded eloquence, the great man had shown him the true nature of atheism, its character, its sins, its effects; shown him that this doctrine, elaborated in the drawing-rooms of the aristocracy, was the most perfidious invention the enemies of the people could have imagined, to demoralise and enslave them; that it was criminal to tear from the hearts of unhappy men and women the soothing notion of a rewarding Providence and deliver them up, without either guide or brake, to the lusts which abuse man and make a vile slave of him, and finally that the monarchist epicureanism of a Helvétius led to immorality, to cruelty, to every crime. And, now that the lessons of a great citizen had informed him, he detested the atheists, especially when they were open-hearted and cheerful atheists, like Brotteaux.

The following days, Évariste had to pronounce on one after the other, an ex-noble convicted of destroying corn to starve the nation, three émigrés come back to foment civil war in France, two Palais-Égalité prostitutes, and fourteen Breton plotters, women, old men, youths, masters and servants. The crime was proved, the law explicit. Among the guilty was a woman of twenty, glorious with the splendour of youth in the shadow of the end at hand, an enchanting creature. A blue ribbon contained her golden hair, her lawn fichu revealed supple white shoulders.

Évariste stuck to the verdict of death, and all the accused, except an old gardener, were sent to the scaffold.

The following week, Évariste and his section mowed down forty-five men and eighteen women.

The judges of the Revolutionary Tribunal made no distinction between men and women, in this being inspired by a principle as old as justice itself. And if a President Montané, moved by the courage and beauty of Charlotte Corday, did try to save her by amending procedure, thus losing his position, women were generally interrogated with no favour, by rules common to all the tribunals. Juries were afraid of them, mistrusting their wiles, their way of pretending, their tricks of seduction. By equalling the men in courage, they invited the court to treat them like men. Most of those who judged them, being only moderately sexual, or sexual only at certain times, were not in the least troubled by them. They condemned or acquitted these women according to their conscience, their prejudices, their zeal, and whether their love for the Republic was feeble or fierce. The women almost all appeared with their hair painstakingly dressed and ordered with as much art as their unfortunate condition permitted. But there were not many young ones, and fewer still who were beautiful. Prison and worry had faded them, the harsh light of the courtroom revealed their fatigue, their anxieties, emphasised their lined eyes, their blotchy skin, their tight-drawn bloodless lips. Nevertheless the fateful armchair did receive more than one woman who was young and beautiful in her pallor, even when funereal shadows clouded their glance like the veils of desire. At such a sight, how many jurors could not but be moved or exasperated, or in the depths of his depraved feelings what magistrate but try to scan the most intimate secrets of a woman he could at the same time imagine both living and dead, and, exciting in imagination things both voluptuous and sanguinary, find some frightful satisfaction in consigning to the executioner a body so desired, on all of which, perhaps, one should preserve silence, though one cannot deny it, if one knows what men are. Évariste Gamelin, cold, intellectual artist, knew no beauty but the classical, and beauty did not so much excite him as awaken his respect. His classical taste was so strict that he rarely saw a woman who satisfied him. He was as unmoved by the charms of a pretty face as by Fragonard's colour or Boucher's shapes. He had never known desire, except in the depths of love.

Like the majority of his fellow-jurors of the Tribunal, he considered women more dangerous than men. He detested former princesses, imagining them, in horrific dreams, helping Elizabeth the Austrian make shot to slaughter patriots; he even hated all those lovely mistresses of financiers, philosophers and men of letters, guilty of having known the delights of the flesh and the mind alike and lived in an age when it was sweet to live. He hated them without ever admitting his hatred to himself, and when one of them was brought up before him for trial, he condemned her with bitterness, thinking this to be just, and in the public interest. Thus his decency, his masculine modesty, his unemotional wisdom, his devotion to the State—in short, his virtues—thrust one lovely head after another under the axe.

But what is all this; what does this miracle mean? Till quite recently they had to ferret the guilty out, labour to discover them in their lairs and compel them to confess their crime. Now that hunt with countless hounds, that pursuit of timorous prey, is no more; now victims present themselves on all sides. Nobles, virgins, soldiers, whores mob the Tribunal, rend too tardy condemnation from judges, demand death as a right they cannot wait to enjoy. That multitude with whom the zeal of informers has filled the prisons and whom public prosecutor and acolytes wear themselves out arraigning is not sufficient; punishment must be provided for these others who cannot wait. And so many more still more ready, and prouder, envious of judge and executioner alike wielding death, strike with their own hands. To the fury of slaughter an antiphonal fury of dying. For example, in the Conciergerie Prison, a handsome, athletic, much loved young soldier, who leaves behind him a lovable mistress who said "Live for my sake!" He does not want to live either for her, or for love or for fame. He lights his pipe with his indictment, and though a republican, for he breathes liberty through every pore, he makes himself royalist in order to die. The Tribunal strives to find him not guilty, but the defendant is the stronger; judge and jury are obliged to give way.

Évariste's mind, by nature restless and scrupulous, was supercharged by the Jacobin lessons and the sight of life with suspicions and alarms. By night, making his way through the badly lit streets to Élodie, he imagined that through each cellar-grating he could see the plank which concealed counterfeited banknotes; at the rear of empty baker's or grocer's shops he suspected swollen stores of hoarded provisions; through the sparkling restaurant windows he thought he heard the plotting of commission agents who were preparing the ruin of France by emptying bottles of Beaune or Chablis; in poisonous back alleys he could see prostitutes ready to trample the national cockade underfoot, to the applause of elegant youth; he saw plotters and traitors on all sides. And he reflected: "Republic, against so many enemies, secret or declared, you have but one salvation, Oh Holy Guillotine, save my country!"

Élodie would be waiting for him in the little blue room, over the *Amour Peintre*. To signal that he could come in, she would put her little green watering-can on the window-sill, near the pot of carnations. He now terrified her, and seemed to her a monster; she was afraid of him and worshipped him. The whole night long, pressed desperately together, bloodthirsty lover and sensual girl exchanged silent, savage embraces.


## XIV

Rising at daybreak, Father Longuemarre first swept his room, then went to say mass in a little church in the Rue d'Enfer, served by a non-juror priest. There were thousands of like retreats in Paris, where refractory parsons secretly assembled little flocks of the faithful. The ward police, though vigilant and full of suspicions, turned the blind eye to these hidden folds, both from fear of a maddened flock and from a remnant of respect for holy things. The Barnabite bid farewell to his host, who had great difficulty in persuading him to come back for dinner, but at last exacted a promise by assuring him the food would be neither plentiful nor fine.

Brotteaux, alone, lit a little tiled stove, then, while he prepared a midday meal for the monk and the epicurian, re-read in Lucretius and meditated on the state of mankind.

This sensible fellow was not astonished that miserable creatures, who were trifling toys of the powers of Nature, should most often be in ridiculous and painful positions; but he was weak enough to be of the opinion that the revolutionaries were more evil and more stupid than other men, in which he re-lapsed into ideology. For that matter, he was no pessimist, and did not hold that life was entirely bad. He marvelled at many facets of Nature, particularly the mechanics of the heavens and physical love and made his peace with the labours of life in expectation of that not distant day when he would know no more either of fear or desire.

He painstakingly made some dolls, and made a Zerline like Rose Thévenin. He liked that wench, and his epicurianism praised the particular order of atoms by which she was constituted.

These cares engaged him till the Barnabite returned.

"Father," he said, opening the door to him, "I certainly told you our repast would be a scanty one. We have nothing but chestnuts. The more reason then for seasoning them well."

"Chestnuts!" cried Father Longuemarre, with a smile, "there could be no more delicious dish. My father, sir, was a poor gentleman of Limoges, whose only property was a completely dilapidated pigeon-house, a wild orchard and a few chestnuts. He, his wife and his twelve children lived on huge green chestnuts, and we were all strong and tough. I was the youngest and the most unruly: my father used to joke and say he would have to send me to America to be a pirate . . . Oh, Monsieur, how lovely that chestnut soup does smell. It reminds me of that table with its garland of children over which my mother smiled."

The meal over, Brotteaux went to see Joly the toy shop man in the Rue Neuve-des-Petits-Champs, who took the dolls which Caillou had refused and gave an order, not for a gross as Caillou used, but for two gross as a start.

When he came to the former Rue Royale, Brotteaux caught a glimpse of a triangle of steel gleaming between two wooden uprights on Revolution square: the guillotine. There was a huge cheerful crowd of inquisitive people pressing round the scaffold, waiting for the tumbril-loads. Women with trays on their bellies were hawking Nanterre buns. Lime-tea sellers were ringing their bells; at the base of the Statue of Liberty an old man was running a peep-show in a little tent with a monkey a-swing on top. Dogs under the scaffold were still licking at yesterday's blood. Brotteaux struck back towards the Rue Honoré.

Back in his attic, where the Barnabite was reading his breviary, he wiped the table down carefully and spread out his box of colours and tools and materials of his trade.

"Father," he said, "unless you consider such an occupation unworthy of the sacred condition with which you are invested, will you perhaps help me make dolls? This very morning a certain M. Joly has made me a rather large order. While I paint those figures which are ready, you would be a great help if you would cut out some heads, arms, limbs and trunks from these patterns. You couldn't have better ones; they're taken from Watteau and Boucher."

"Well, sir," said Longuemarre, "what I really think is that Watteau and Boucher would be just the men to make gimcrack things like these; it would have been more to their good name if they'd stuck to harmless little dollies like these. I shall be glad to help you, only fear I may not be skilful enough."

Father Longuemarre was right to doubt his skill; after a number of unhappy attempts, it had to be admitted that he was not gifted at cutting out pleasing shapes with the point of a penknife in thin card. But when, at his request, Brotteaux gave him some string and a bodkin, he proved very good at endowing these little things he had not been able to cut out with movement and making them dance. Then with evident pleasure he tried them and made each one do

a few gavotte steps, and when they responded to his attention, a smile crept over his stern lips.

On one occasion, as he plucked rhythmically at the string of a Scaramouche, he said: "Monsieur, this little mask reminds me of a strange story. It was in 1746: I was just completing my novitiate, under the direction of a Father Magitot, a man getting on in years, of profound knowledge and austere morals. At that time, perhaps you remember, marionette dolls, primarily intended to amuse children, had an extraordinary attraction for women and even men young and old; they were all the rage at Paris. The fashionable shops were full of them; you found them in the houses of people of standing, and it was not rare in the park or in the street to see quite a serious person dandling his dollie. Neither the age nor the character, nor even the profession of Father Magitot preserved him from catching the fever. When he saw everybody busy making a little cardboard mannikin dance, his fingers felt an impatience which in the end became quite insistent. One day when he was calling on M. Chauvel, a Parliament lawyer, on some important business which interested the whole Order, he spotted a dollie hanging over the fireplace, and felt a terrible temptation to tug at its string. It was only by tremendous effort that he mastered his impulse. But the frivolous desire to do it pursued him and gave him no more rest. In his studies, his meditations, his prayers, at church, in chapter, at confession, in the pulpit, he was obsessed by it. After some days consumed by frightful agitation, he told the General of the Order, who luckily at the moment happened to be in Paris, all about the extraordinary business. This was an eminent doctor and prince of the Church in Milan. He advised Father Magitot to satisfy a longing so innocent in principle, though with overpowering results, the excess of which threatened to cause a spirit which was prey to it the most serious disorder. On the advice, or rather, on the orders of the General, Father Magitot went back to M. Chauvel, who received him, as he did the first time, in his study. There, finding the mannikin hanging over the fireplace, he went quickly up to it and asked his host to allow him to have a pull at the string. The lawyer gladly permitted him to do so, and confessed that he sometimes made Scaramouche dance (that was the name of this doll) while he was preparing a pleading, and that only the previous day he had used the movements of Scaramouche to draw up his peroration in defence of a woman wrongly accused of poisoning her husband. Father Magitot, all atremble, took the string, and under his hand saw Scaramouche dance like a mad creature being exorcised. Thus satisfying his whim, he was freed from the obsession."

"Your story does not astonish me, Father," said Brotteaux, "such obsessions do happen. But it is not always cardboard figures that cause them."

Father Longuemarre, being in a religious order, never discussed religion; Brotteaux never stopped. And, feeling sympathy of the Barnabite, he found pleasure in embarrassing him and worrying him by raising objections to various articles of Christian doctrine.

On one occasion, while they were making Zerlines and Scaramouches together, he said: "When I contemplate the events that brought us where we are, and wonder which lot in the universal madness has been the most mad, I am prone to think it was the court crowd."

"Sir," the monk replied, "all men become mad, like Nebuchadnezzar, when God abandons them; yet no man in our time has plunged so deep into ignorance and error as the Abbé Fauchet, and no man was so fatal to the Kingdom as he was. The Lord must have been extremely exasperated by France to send it the Abbé Fauchet."

"I should have thought we had seen other wrong doers, beside poor Fauchet."

"Monsieur, the Abbé Grégoire also showed much malice."

"What of Brissot, Danton, and Marat, and a hundred others, Father?"

"Monsieur, they are laymen; laymen cannot be so responsible as men of the church. They do not do wrong from the same heights, and their crimes are not universal."

"And your God, Father, what have you to say of his conduct in the present revolution?"

"Monsieur, I do not understand you."

"Epicurus said: Either God wished to prevent evil and cannot, or can and will not, or neither can nor wishes to, or else both wishes to and can. If he wishes and cannot, he is impotent; if he can and will not, he is perverted; if he neither can nor would, he is both impotent and perverse; while if he would and could, why does he not do so, Father?"

And Brotteaux shot his interlocutor a complaisant glance.

"Monsieur," the man of religion replied, "there is nothing more contemptible than the difficulties you raise. When I examine the reasons for incredulity, I feel like an ant sticking up a blade of grass to dam the torrent coming down from the mountains. Permit me not to argue the point; I should have too many reasons and too little ingenuity. For that matter, you will find yourself dealt with in the Abbé Guénée and twenty others. I will merely inform you that what you say Epicurus said is nonsense, for it judges of God as if he were human and subject to moral law. But let be, Monsieur, incredulous men from Celsus to Bayle and Voltaire have made a fool of fools with similar paradoxes."

"Just see, Father," said Brotteaux, "to what your faith leads you. Not satisfied with finding the whole of truth in your theology, you would also like to find none in the works of so many fine minds who thought differently from you."

"You are quite mistaken, Monsieur," replied Longuemarre, "quite to the contrary, it is my belief that nothing in man's thought can be entirely false. Atheists are on the bottom rung of knowledge, but even at that level there are still glimmers of sense and flashes of truth, and, even when darkness drowns him, man does raise up a forehead into which God puts intelligence; that is Lucifer's fate."

"Well, sir," said Brotteaux, "I am not going to be so large-hearted, and I assure you that in the works of the theologists I do not find an atom of good sense."

Nevertheless, he protested that he had no desire to attack religion, which he considered people needed; he would merely have preferred it to be administered by philosophers and not controversialists. He deplored the Jacobins' desire to replace it by a religion younger and more evil, the religion of liberty, equality, the republic and the fatherland. He had observed that it was in the vigour of their youth that religions were the most insensate and cruel, and that as they got older they grew more docile. He would also prefer to see Catholicism retained, for it had devoured many victims in the days of its strength, but now, borne down by the weight of years, was of only middling appetite, and satisfied with four or five heretic roasts per century.

"For that matter," he added, "I have always got on well enough with your God-eaters and Christ-worshippers. I had my own chaplain at les Ilettes: he used to say mass every Sunday; all my guests attended. The philosophers were the most intense, and chorus-girls from the Opera the most ardent. I was happy in those days and had numerous friends."

"Friends," cried Father Longuemarre, "friends! . . . My dear sir, do you really think they were your friends, all these philosophers and courtesans, who so debased your spirit that God himself would have had difficulty in recognising in it one of the churches he erected to his own glory."

Father Longuemarre stayed a week with the former tax-farmer without being perturbed. As far as he could, he followed the rules of his community and rose from his straw pallet to kneel on the floor and recite the night offices. Though both men had nothing but wretched scraps to eat, he observed fasts and abstinences. Smiling yet troubled witness of these austerities, one day the philosopher asked him if he really believed that God found any satisfaction in seeing him suffer cold and hunger like that.

"God himself," replied the monk, "gave us an example of suffering."

On the ninth day of the Barnabite's stay in the philosopher's attic, the latter set out as night fell to take some toys to Joly the toy merchant in the Rue-Neuve-des-Petits-Champs. He was on his way back pleased with having sold them all, when, in the former Place du Carousel, a prostitute in a cloak of blue satin edged with ermine, running with a limp, flung herself into his arms and clutched him in the way supplicants have always clutched.

She was trembling, and the swift beat of her heart was audible. Wondering at the pathos she showed in all her commonness, Brotteaux, old theatre goer, reflected that Mademoiselle Raucourt would not have seen her without profit.

She spoke breathlessly, lowering her voice in fear of being overheard by passers-by: "Take me somewhere, citizen, hide me, have pity . . . They are in my room, Rue Fromenteau. As they came up, I slipped into my neighbour Flora's room, then I jumped out of the window into the street, so that I sprained my ankle . . . They are coming; they want to put me in prison and kill me . . . Last week, they killed Virginie."

Brotteaux of course guessed she was speaking of men of the Ward Revolutionary Committee or commissars of the Committee of General Security. At this time the Commune had a straitlaced public prosecutor, Citizen Chaumette, who pursued prostitutes as the most dangerous enemies of the Republic. He was out to regenerate morals. True enough, the young ladies of the Palais-Égalité were not very great patriots. Several of them had already been guillotined as plotters, and their tragic fate had excited a great spirit of emulation in the rest.

Citizen Brotteaux asked the girl by what crime she had caused a warrant for her arrest to be out.

She swore she knew nothing, that she had done nothing they could bring against her.

"All right then, my lass," Brotteaux told her, "you're not under suspicion; you've nothing to fear. Go home to bed, and don't bother me."

Then she confessed everything. "I tore off my cockade and shouted: 'Long live the King!' "

He set off along the deserted embankment with her. Clinging to his arm, she said: "It's not because I love the king; why, did I ever know him, and no doubt he was not much different from other men. But these are so spiteful. They are cruel to us poor girls. They plague me, they exasperate me and they insult me all ways; they'd like to stop me plying my profession. I haven't got any other. You can be sure that if I had, I wouldn't work at this one . . . What are they after? They're savage against little folk, weak folk, the milkman, the charcoal man, the water carrier, the washerwoman. They'll never be content till they've set the whole world against them."

He examined her; she had the expres-

sion of a child. She was no longer afraid. She was almost smiling, lighthearted with a tiny limp. He asked her name. She said she was called Athénais, and was sixteen.

Brotteaux offered to take her wherever she liked. She did not know anyone in Paris, but she had got an aunt, who was in service at Palaiseau, and would keep her.

Brotteaux's mind was made up. "Come along, my child," he said.

Back in his attic, he found Father Longuemarre, reading his breviary. He showed him Athénais, whom he held by the hand. "Father, here is a girl from the Rue Fromenteau who has been shouting: 'Vive le roi!' The revolutionary police are on her tracks."

Father Longuemarre closed his breviary. "If I grasp you," he said, "you are asking me if this young girl, who like me is under the threat of an arrest warrant, can pass the night in the same room as myself, for her temporal salvation."

"Yes, Father."

"By what right could I oppose it? And can I be sure to be worth more than she is, before I feel insulted by her presence?"

For the night he established himself in a broken-down old armchair, insisting that he could sleep there quite well. Athénais lay down on the mattress. Brotteaux stretched himself out on the pallet and blew out the candle.

The hours and the half-hours sounded from the churches round; he could not sleep, and listened to the mingled breathing of the monk and the prostitute. The moon, symbol and witness of his former loving, rose and projected a silver ray into the attic, illuminating the fair hair, the golden lashes, the rounded and red lips of Athénais, who slept with clenched fists.

"Look," he said to himself, "what a terrible enemy of the Republic!"

When Athénais woke up, it was daylight. The monk had gone out. Brotteaux, under the skylight, was reading Lucretius, training himself by the lessons of the Latin muse to live without fears and without desires; yet still was devoured by regrets and unrest.

Opening her eyes, Athénais was stupefied to see the rafters of an attic over her head. Then she remembered, smiled at her rescuer and, to caress him, reached out her grubby but pretty little hands.

Raising herself on her bed, she pointed to the armchair where the monk had passed the night.

"He has gone? . . . He hasn't gone to denounce me, has he?"

"No, my child. You could not find a more decent man than that old madman."

Athénais asked in what the madness of the gentleman consisted, and, when Brotteaux told her it was religion, she reproached him gravely for talking like that, and said that men without religion were worse than animals and that, for her part, she frequently prayed to God, hoping he would forgive her sins and receive her in his holy mercy.

Then, noticing that Brotteaux had a book in his hand, she concluded it was a book of the mass, and said: "Look, you see you say your prayers too. God will reward you for what you have done for me."

When Brotteaux told her that the book was not a prayer book and that it had been written before the notion of the mass was introduced to the world, she concluded it was a "Key to Dreams" and asked if it perhaps contained the interpretation of a remarkable dream she had had. She could not read and had only heard of these two sorts of books.

Brotteaux replied that all this book explained was the dream of life. The pretty child, finding this answer difficult, gave up trying to understand and dipped the tip of her nose in the earthenware bowl which replaced the silver basins Brotteaux had once used. Then with great pains and serious attention she did her hair in front of her host's shaving mirror. With white arms bent behind her head, at long intervals she made observations.

"You—you were rich?"

"What makes you think that?"

"I do not know. But you have been rich, and you are an aristocrat, I am sure of it."

From her pocket she took a tiny Virgin of silver set in ivory, a piece of sugar, some thread, some scissors, a flint and steel, two or three little cases, and when she had selected what she needed, began to mend her skirt, which was torn in several places.

"For your safety, my child, put this on your head!" Brotteaux told her, giving her a tricolour cockade.

"Willingly, sir," she replied, "but out of love for you, and not for the nation."

When she was dressed and her toilet done to the best advantage, she took her skirt in both hands and curtseyed to Brotteaux, as she had learned in her village, and said: "Sir, I am your humble servant."

She was prepared to oblige her benefactor in any way, though she found it very proper that he asked for nothing, so offered nothing herself; she found it nice to get off like that, and good-mannered too.

Brotteaux put some treasury notes in her hand, to take the coach to Palaiseau. It was half his fortune, and though he was known for his prodigality to women, he had never before given one half his worldly goods.

She asked him his name.

"Maurice," he said.

With some regret, he opened the attic door: "Fare thee well, Athénais."

She kissed him.

"Monsieur Maurice, whenever you think of me, call me Marthe; that's what I was christened, and what they called me home in the village . . . Farewell, and thank you . . . Your humble servant, Monsieur Maurice."

## XV

The prisons had to be emptied, because they were over-full; they needed to try cases and try cases without rest or respite. Backs to the old walls with their tapestry of fasces and red bonnets, like their fellows of the fleurs-de-lys, the judges maintained the solemnity and ominous calm of their royal predecessors. The public prosecutor and his deputies, exhausted with fatigue, burned by insomnia and brandy, could only shake off their exhaustion by violent efforts, and their ill health made them tragic. The jurors, diverse in origin and character, some educated, others ignorant, dastardly or warm-hearted, gentle or savage, hypocritical or sincere, but all of whom, in the peril of Fatherland and Republic, experienced— or pretended to experience—the same anxiety, were consumed by the same flames, all of them frightful from single-mindedness or craven heart, formed but a single creature, a single head, deadened yet exacerbated, a single mind, a mystic animal which, by the normal working produced an abundance of death. Kindly or sentimentally cruel, subject to sudden spasms of pity, they would tearfully acquit a defendant whom an hour earlier they would have condemned with biting tongue. The further they progressed in their task, the more impetuous were they to follow the moods of their heart.

They heard cases through that fever and somnolence which came from excess of work, subject to promptings from without and commands from the sovereign people, subject to sansculotte threats and the threats of the knitting-women who crowded on to the public benches, following frenetic evidence, guided by fantastic denunciations, in a pestiferous atmosphere which weighed on every brain, made the ears hum and the temples throb and cast a curtain of blood over their eyes. Vague rumours were circulating abroad about jurors bought by defendants' gold. But at any such story the whole body of jurors replied by outraged protest and merciless condemnations. In short, they were just human, neither better nor worse than the rest. Innocence is generally a piece of luck, not a virtue; any other who consented to take their place would have acted as they did and tackled appalling tasks with mediocre mind.

Antoinette, long awaited, came at last to take her place on the fatal chair, in a black gown, amid such a symphony of hatred that it was only the certainty about the issue of the trial that ensured respect for form. To deadly questions the accused woman replied now with the instinct of self-preservation, now with her usual haughty manner, and once, because of the dastardly accusation one person laid against her, with the majesty of a mother. Witnesses were only allowed to insult and slander; the defence was frozen with terror. The Tribunal forced itself to stick to the rules, scarce able to wait to get through it all, to fling that Austrian woman's head in the face of Europe.

Three days after the execution of Marie-Antoinette, Gamelin was summoned by Citizen Fortuné Trubert, in his death throes, thirty paces from the military bureau where he had drained his life away, on a sacking bed in the cell of an expropriated Barnabite. His livid head was sunk in the pillow. His eyes, which could no longer distinguish things, turned their glassy pupils towards Évariste; his desiccated hand gripped that of his friend and clenched it with surprising strength. He had had three hæmophthises in forty-eight hours. He made an attempt to speak; his voice, veiled and weak to start with, a mere rustle, grew in strength, grew in volume: "Wattignies!" he cried, "Wattignies! . . . Jourdain has breached the enemy camp . . . relieved Maubeuge . . . We have re-taken Marchiennes . . . *Ça ira . . . ça ira . . .*" And he smiled.

These were not the hallucinations of a sick man, but a clear grasp of reality, throwing its light on this brain down upon which eternal darkness was sinking. From now onwards the invasion might be stemmed; the generals, terrorised, had perceived that the best thing they could do was to win. What voluntary recruitment had not produced—a large, disciplined army—conscription was providing. One more effort and the Republic would be saved.

After half an hour of exhaustion, Fortuné Trubert's face, furrowed by death, lit up, and he raised his hands.

He pointed out to his friend the sole piece of furniture in the room, a little walnut writing-desk.

Then, in a weak, gasping voice, though guided by a limpid mind, he said, "My friend, like Eudamidas, I leave my debts to you: three hundred and twenty livres, of which you will find account . . . in that red notebook . . . Farewell, Gamelin. Do not sleep. Watch over the defence of the Republic. *Ça ira.*"

The shades of night poured into the cell. One could hear the dying man's troubled breath, his hands clutching at the sheet.

At midnight, a string of disconnected words came from his lips: "More saltpetre . . . Have the muskets delivered . . . My health? Fine . . . Take the bells down . . ."

He passed away at five in the morning.

By order of the Ward, his body was laid out in the nave of the former Barnabite Church, at the foot of the altar of the Fatherland, on a camp bed, under a tricolour cloth, the brows crowned with oak leaves.

Twelve veterans wrapped in Roman togas, with palm branches in their hands, twelve young girls, with long veils trailing and carrying flowers, surrounded the funeral couch. At the feet of the dead man two children stood, each holding an upside-down torch. In one Évariste recognised the daughter of his concierge, Joséphine, and by her child's solemnity and enchanting beauty the little one reminded him of those spirits of love and death that the Romans carved on their sarcophagi.

The funeral procession went to the Saint-André-des-Arts Cemetery, to the singing of *La Marseillaise* and *Ça ira.*

When he pressed a farewell kiss on Fortuné Trubert's brow, tears started to Évariste's eyes. He was sorry for himself, envious of the man at rest, his task accomplished.

When he reached home, he received notification that he had been appointed a member of the General Council of the Commune. A candidate for four months now, he had been elected by about thirty votes; they had a number of re-counts but nobody came near him. People no longer cast their votes; the wards were deserted; rich and poor alike were solely concerned with how to avoid public duties. The greatest events no longer stirred the slightest enthusiasm or curiosity; people had stopped reading the newspapers. Évariste doubted whether more than three or four thousand out of the seven hundred thousand inhabitants of Paris still had a republican spirit.

The same day, the Twenty-one came up for trial.

Innocent or guilty of the misfortunes or crimes of the Republic, vain, incautious, ambitious and frivolous, both moderate and extreme, weak as much from fear as from feelings of mercy, impetuous to declare war but slow to wage it, dragged before the Tribunal on their own example, they were still the dazzling youth of the Revolution; they had been its charm and pride. This Judge, about to interrogate them with cunning partiality; that pallid accuser, at that little table over there, preparing their death and dishonour; these jurors, about to try to crush their defence; this crowd on the public benches, now hurling invective and cat-calls at them—judges, jurors, people, not so long ago applauded their eloquence, praised their talents and virtues to the skies. But they had forgotten.

Évariste formerly deified Vergniaud and in Brissot saw an oracle. He no longer recalled it, and, if there was any trace of his old marvel in his memory, it was now employed to persuade himself that these were monsters who had se-duced the flower of the country.

Returning home after the hearing, Gamelin heard heart-rending shrieks. It was little Joséphine, whose mother was whipping her for having been playing with some little rascals in the square, and dirtying the nice white frock she had put on for Citizen Trubert's funeral.

## XVI

Having for three months daily sacrificed to the Fatherland victims both illustrious and obscure, Évariste now had a trial of his very own; he made a defendant his own.

Ever since he had been on the Tribunal he had been eagerly trying to spy out Élodie's seducer in the crowd of culprits who passed before him, having in his indefatigable imagination composed a no-tion of the man, some features of which were quite precise. He imagined him young, handsome, haughty, and had con-vinced himself that the man had fled to England. He now thought he had picked him out in a young émigré named Mau-bel, who, back in France and denounced by the proprietor of a Passy hotel, had been arrested there, so that the case had come with a thousand others before Fou-quier-Tinville. Letters had been found on him which the accusation regarded as proof of a plot hatched between Maubel and Pitt's agents, though in fact they were merely letters to the émigré from some London bankers with whom he had deposits. Maubel, who was young and handsome, seemed above all to have been busy with love affairs. His notebook showed a link with Spain, then at war with France; these letters were in reality personal and if the court of enquiry did not find *no true bill* against the man, that was in virtue of the principle that justice should never let a prisoner go.

Gamelin had a report of the first pri-vate interrogation of Maubel and was struck by the young ex-noble's character, which seemed to him just like that he at-tributed to the man who abused Élodie's confidence. From then on, closeted long hours in the Court Clerk's office, he studied the papers fervently. His suspi-cions grew strikingly when in a quite old note-book of the émigré's he found the address of the *Amour Peintre,* though, it is true, it was coupled with the *Singe Vert,* the *Portrait de la Dauphine (for-mer)* and a number of other print and picture shops. But the moment he learned that in this very same notebook had been found a number of red carnation petals, carefully wrapped in tissue paper, with the thought that the red carnation was Élodie's favourite flower, which she cul-tivated on her windowsill, wore in her hair, and (as he knew) gave away as love token, Évariste had no more doubts.

Then, making it a certainty, he decided to interrogate Élodie, though without telling her the way he discovered the cul-prit.

As he climbed the stairs to his studio,

right from the bottom landing he caught a heady odour of fruit, and there in the studio was Élodie herself, helping Citizeness Gamelin make quince preserve. While the old housewife was lighting the stove, all preoccupied with how to save coal and moist sugar without spoiling the preserve, Citizeness Blaise, seated on a straw-bottomed chair, with a brown holland apron tied about her, and her lap full of the golden fruit, was peeling the quince and throwing the quarters into a copper bowl. The points of her kerchief were thrust back and ebony locks of hair were tumbled over her perspiring forehead; she emanated a domestic charm and intimate beauty which inspired gentle notions and unruffled thoughts of love.

Without stirring, she shot her lovely glance of molten gold at her lover and said: "See, Évariste, what we are making for you. You will be able to have lovely quince jelly all the winter, it will steady your stomach and keep you cheerful."

But Gamelin went up to her and whispered in her ear, "Jacques Maubel . . ."

At that point Combalot the cobbler came and stuck his red nose through the half-open door. With some shoes which he had re-heeled he had brought a bill for his repairs.

Afraid of being taken for a bad citizen, he used the new calendar. Citizeness Gamelin, who liked to get her accounts straight, got lost in these Fructidors and Vendémiaires.

She sighed. "Jesus! They want to change everything, days, months, seasons, the sun and the moon. Almighty God, Monsieur Combalot, what on earth does this pair of goloshes on the 8th Vendémiaire mean?"

"Citizeness, take a look at your calendar and you'll see."

She took it down, glanced at it, then, looking up at once: "It doesn't look Christian," she said, overcome.

"Not only that, Citizeness," said the cobbler, "but we've only three Sundays now, instead of four. And that's not all: we shall have to count different, there aren't going to be any more ha'pennies and farthings, it's all going to be done by distilled water now."

At this observation Citizeness Gamelin's lips quivered, she raised her eyes to the ceiling and sighed: "They go too far!"

Then, while she lamented, just like a figure in a country crucifix, a smoky piece of coal, which in her absence had flared up in the embers, began to fill the studio with its stench, which, together with the heavy scent of quinces, made the air unbreathable.

Élodie complained of her throat scratching, and wanted the window opened. But as soon as the cobbler had gone, and Citizeness Gamelin was back at her stove, Évariste repeated the name in Élodie's ear: "Jacques Maubel."

She looked at him in some astonishment and then, very calmly, without ceasing to quarter a quince—"Well, and what about Jacques Maubel?" she asked.

"That's who it is."

"Who? Maubel?"

"You gave him a red carnation."

She insisted that she did not understand, and asked him to explain.

"That aristocrat! That émigré! That scoundrel!"

She shrugged her shoulders, and very convincingly denied ever having heard of a Jacques Maubel.

She had indeed never heard of him.

She denied giving anybody a red carnation but Évariste; though perhaps on this point her memory was not very good.

He knew little about women, and had never penetrated very deep into Élodie's nature; all the same, he thought her very capable of pretending and of deceiving a man more skilled than himself.

"Why deny it?" he cried. "I know."

Once again she asserted that she had never even heard of a Jacques Maubel.

And as she had finished peeling her quince, she told him to fetch some water because her fingers were sticky.

Gamelin brought her a basin. And while she washed her hands, she repeated her denial. He repeated that he knew, and then she said nothing.

She failed to see where her lover's question led, and was a thousand leagues from suspecting that this Maubel, of whom she had never heard, was to be tried by the Revolutionary Tribunal; she could make neither head nor tail of the suspicions which obsessed him, but she did know there was no foundation in them. That is why, though she now had little hope of dissipating them, she also was not particularly interested in doing so. So she stopped declaring she had never known anybody named Maubel, preferring to let her jealous one follow a false trail, when, at any instant, the smallest trifle might put him on the right road. Her former little clerk, now a patriotic handsome dragoon, had at last quarrelled with his aristocratic mistress. Whenever he came on Élodie in the street he gave her a look which seemed to say: "Come, my pet, I have quite a feeling I may forgive you for having let you down, and am quite prepared to show you my respect." So she made no more effort to cure what she called her lover's bee in the bonnet; thus Gamelin retained his conviction that it was Jacques Maubel who seduced Élodie.

During the days which followed, the Tribunal strove unrelentingly to destroy federalism, which, like a hydra, had threatened to devour liberty. Those were very full days, and the jurors, exhausted by their labours, dealt as summarily as possible with the case of the Roland woman, who had inspired and plotted in the crimes of the Brissot group.

All this time, Gamelin went to the court offices to hurry on the Maubel case.

Certain important pieces of evidence were at Bordeaux; he got them to send a special messenger to fetch them. At last they arrived.

The Deputy Prosecutor read them, pulled a face and said to Évariste:

"Not much, all this—there's nothing in it—all fiddle-faddle . . . If only one were certain this ex-count de Maubel did emigrate . . ."

At last Gamelin succeeded. Young Maubel was served with his indictment and brought before the Revolutionary Tribunal on Brumaire 19th.

From the very outset of the hearing, the President showed that gloomy, menacing expression he always took care to assume when he had to steer a badly built-up case through. The Deputy Prosecutor tickled his chin with his pen and assumed the serenity of one whose mind is perfectly clear. The Clerk read the indictment; never had anything so devoid of substance been heard.

The President asked the accused if he had been unaware of the anti-émigré laws.

"I knew them and observed them," Maubel replied, "and I left France with a passport in order."

On the reasons for his journey to England and his return to France, he produced a satisfactory explanation. His countenance was rather pleasant, with an air of frankness and pride which pleased. The women in the public gallery eyed him with favour. The accusation tried to make out that he had stayed in Spain just when that country was at war with France; he asserted that at this time he had not once left Bayonne. One point only remained obscure. Among the papers which he had thrown into the fireplace, at the time he was arrested, and of which only scraps had been recovered, there were some words of Spanish and the name "Nieves."

Jacques Maubel refused to give the ex-

planation of this detail which was demanded of him. And when the President observed that it was the in the accused's own interest to make this clear, he replied that one should not always act in one's own interest.

Gamelin only wished to convict Maubel of one crime; three times he pressed the President to ask the accused if he could inform the court about that carnation the dried petals of which he treasured so carefully in his notebook.

Maubel replied that he did not feel called upon to answer a question which had nothing to do with the law, since the flower in question had not been found to contain any message.

The jury retired to the jury room, with a favourable impression of this young man whose case, though puzzling, seemed rather to have a love mystery behind it. This time even the good patriots, the single-minded, would willingly have acquitted. One of them, a former noble, who had given pledges to the Revolution, said: "Are we to reproach him his birth? I too had the misfortune to be born in the aristocracy."

"Yes, but you have got out of it," replied Gamelin, "and he has not."

He then spoke with such astonishing vehemence against this plotter, this emissary of Pitt, this accomplice of Cobourg, who had crossed seas and mountains to aid the enemies of liberty, and demanded the condemnation of the traitor so fervently that he stirred up the eternally restless unchanging severity of the patriotic jurors.

One of them said cynically: "There are services one cannot refuse a colleague."

The verdict of death was obtained by a majority of one.

The condemned man heard his sentence with smiling calm. He swept his glance, unruffled, over the court, but when his eyes lit on the features of Gamelin, they expressed unspeakable scorn.

Not a person applauded the sentence.

Jacques Maubel, conducted back to the Conciergerie Prison, in expectation of the execution, which was to take place that very evening, by torchlight, wrote a letter:

*"My dear Sister, the Tribunal is sending me to the scaffold, giving me the only happiness I have been able to feel since the death of my darling Nieves. They have taken from me the only thing of hers I still had, a pomegranate blossom, which, I can't tell why, they would call a carnation.*

*I have loved the arts: in happier times in Paris I used to collect paintings and engravings, which are now in a safe place, and will be delivered to you as soon as feasible. Dear Sister, I beg you, keep them in memory of me."*

He cut off a lock of his hair, put it in the letter, which he folded, and then addressed:

*Citizeness Clémence Dezeimeries, née Maubel, La Réole.*

He gave all the money he had on him to the turnkey, begging him to see the letter delivered, asked for a bottle of wine and drank it, bit by bit, while waiting for the tumbril . . .

After supper, Gamelin ran round to the *Amour Peintre* and burst into the blue room where Élodie awaited him every night.

"You are avenged," he told her. "Jacques Maubel is no more. The tumbril taking him to death has just passed under your window, surrounded with torches."

She understood him "Wretch! It's you killed him, and he never was my lover. I never even knew him . . . I never even saw him . . . What was he? He was young, and nice . . . and innocent. And you have killed him, you beast, you beast!"

She fell in a faint. Yet, in the shadows

of this fragile dying she felt at once submerged both by horror and sexual desire. She half revived; her heavy eyelids lifted from the whites of her eyes, her bosom swelled, her arms, blindly, in the air, sought her lover. She crushed him, suffocating him to herself, dug her nails into his flesh, and with lips torn apart gave him the mutest, blindest, longest, most painful and most delicious of kisses.

She loved this man with all her flesh, and the more frightful, cruel, savage he seemed to her, the more she saw on him the blood of his victims, the more she hungered and thirsted for him.

## XVII

The 24th Frimaire, at 10 A.M., under a crystal-clear, rose-blush sky, which was thawing the ice-film of the preceding night, Citizens Guénot and Delournel, Delegates of the Committee of General Security, went to Barnabite house and had somebody take them to the Ward Control Committee, in the Capitulary Hall, where they found Citizen Beauvisage piling logs on the hearth. But for a moment they did not see him, on account of his short, squat build.

In a hunchback's cracked voice, Citizen Beauvisage had the delegates take a seat and placed himself entirely at their disposal.

Guénot asked him if he knew a former aristocrat named des Ilettes, domiciled near the Pont-Neuf. "It's a person," he said, "whom I'm charged to arrest." He showed the Committee of General Security warrant.

Beauvisage, after ransacking his memory for some time, replied that he knew nobody named des Ilettes, that the suspect thus designated might not live in that Ward at all, as there were parts of other Wards—the Museum, the Unité, the Maret-et-Marseille—adjoining the Pont-Neuf; that, if he did live in that Ward, it must be under another name than that the Committee gave, but that all the same they'd soon find out.

"Don't let's lose any time!" said Guénot. "He's been pointed out to us by a letter of one of his co-plotters who is already under arrest and was passed on the Committee a good fortnight ago, of which Citizen Lacroix learned only yesterday. We are snowed under; denunciations are coming in from all sides, so many you don't know whom to listen to."

"Denunciations," replied Beauvisage, with pride, "also pour in to the Vigilance Committee of this Ward. Some do so by sense of public duty, others, by the appeal of a hundred sol note. A large number of children denounce their parents, because they want to get at their inheritance."

"This letter," Guénot resumed, "originates from a former noblewoman named Rochemaure, an old tart in whose place they used to play biribi, and it was addressed to a Citizen Rauline; but it's really addressed to an émigré in the service of Pitt. I brought it with me to pass on to you what it says about this type, des Ilettes.

"It begins with lengthy details about those members of the Convention whom, at least so this woman says, they might win over by the offer of sufficient money or the promise of a high post in a new government, more permanent than this one. Then comes this passage:

*"I have just come from M. des Ilettes, who lives near the Pont-Neuf, in an attic where you'd have to be a cat or a devil to find him; he has been reduced to making puppets to earn a living. He has sense; that is why I am going to give you the gist of what he said. He does not think the present state of affairs will last long. He does not think*

*it will end in a coalition victory; and
events seem to be proving him right;
for you know that for some time the
news from the fronts has been bad. He
is more inclined to believe in a revolt
of the little people and the womenfolk
of the common people, still deeply attached to their faith. He holds that the
general terror caused by the Revolutionary Tribunal will soon unite the
whole of France against the Jacobins.
'This Tribunal,' he said, joking, 'which
tries both the Queen of France and a
bread roundswoman, is like that William Shakespeare, so admired by the
English . . .' and so on. "He does not
think it out of the question that Robespierre will marry Madame Royale and
have himself declared Protector.*

"*I should be grateful if you would
forward me the sums now due me, i.e.,
one thousand pounds sterling, by the
route you usually use, but take care not
to write to M. Morhardt: he has been
arrested and clapped in prison . . .*"
and so forth."

"Milord des Ilettes makes puppets,"
said Beauvisage, "that's a valuable clue
. . . though there are a fair number of
little businesses of that sort in our Ward."

"That reminds me," said Delourmel, "I
promised to take my little daughter Nathalie a doll, the youngest one, she's down
with scarlet fever, the rash came out yesterday. There's not much to fear in scarlet fever, but you have to take care. And
Nathalie's very forward for her age, very
precocious intelligence too, and delicate
in health."

"I've only one," said Guénot, "a boy.
He plays hoops, gets them off barrels, and
is always blowing up paper bags to make
little Montgolfier balloons."

"Often enough," Beauvisage observed,
"children play best with things which
aren't toys at all. My nephew Émile, a
kid of seven, very clever, entertains him-

self the whole day with little blocks of
wood, building things with them . . .
Are you an addict?" And Beauvisage
held out his open snuff-box to the two
delegates.

"Now we must grab our rapscallion,"
said Delournel, who wore long moustaches and rolled his eyes. "I've a bit of
an appetite this morning for aristocrat's
lights, washed down with white wine."

Beauvisage suggested to the delegates
they should go and find his colleague Dupont senior at his shop in the Place Dauphine, as he was sure to know this fellow
des Ilettes.

They made their way into the fresh air,
followed by four grenadiers of the Ward.

"Have you seen *The Last Judgment of
the Kings?*" Delournel asked his companions; "it's well worth it. The author shows
you all the kings of Europe as refugees
on a desert island, at the foot of a volcano which swallows them up. A patriotic play."

At the corner of the Rue du Harlay
Delournel caught sight of a little cart,
gleaming like a shrine, and pushed by an
old woman with a waxed canvas hat on
top of her kerchief.

"What's the old woman sell?" he demanded.

She answered herself: "Take a look,
gentlemen, and make your choice. I keep
beads and rosaries, crosses, St. Anthonys,
holy cerecloths, Saint Veronica handkerchiefs, *Ecce homo, Agnus Dei,* St. Hubert horns and rings, and all other religious objects."

"An arsenal of fanaticism!" Delournel
cried.

He at once began a summary interrogation of the old woman, who to every
question replied: "My son, I've been selling religious requisites for forty years."

One of the delegates of the Committee
of General Security, spotting a bluecoat
going by, had him take the astonished old
woman round to the Town Hall.

Citizen Beauvisage pointed out to Delournel that it should have been for the Watch Committee to arrest this old hawker and take her to the Ward; in any case one could never be clear what attitude to take to the former cult, if one wanted to do what the Government thought right, and he asked, ought one let them have full liberty, or prohibit it all?

As they drew near the cabinet-maker's shop, the delegates and the commissar caught the sound of angry shouting, mingled with the scroop of a saw and murmur of a plane. A quarrel had just blown up between the cabinet-maker Dupont senior and his neighbour, porter Remacle, concerning Citizeness Remacle, whom an invincible attraction constantly brought right inside the carpenter's shop, whence she returned to the lodge covered with chips and shavings. The outraged porter kicked Mouton, the cabinet-maker's dog, just when his own daughter, little Joséphine, was tenderly hugging the animal. Joséphine was most indignant, and broke into imprecations against her father. The carpenter was at the end of his nerves and yelled: "You wretch, I forbid you to strike my dog."

"And I," replied the porter, raising his broom, "I forbid you . . ."

He did not finish; the carpenter's jointing-plane brushed by his head.

The instant he caught sight of Citizen Beauvisage and the Delegates, he ran to him and said: "Citizen Commissar, you are a witness that this rascal just tried to kill me."

Citizen Beauvisage, red cap on head, as sign of office, held out his long arms in a pacifying attitude and then, speaking both to porter and carpenter: "One hundred sols," he said, "to whichever of you can show us where to find a suspect, whom the Committee of General Security wants—a former noble named des Ilettes, who makes Punches."

Both men, porter and carpenter, to-gether pointed to Brotteaux's lodging, their only quarrel now, which was to receive the hundred sols promised to the informer.

Delournel, Guénot and Beauvisage, followed by the four grenadiers, Remacle the porter, Dupont the cabinet-maker, and a dozen little rascals of the district, marched up the stairs, which shook under their feet, then up the mill ladder.

Brotteaux, in his attic, was cutting out dolls while Father Longuemarre, opposite him, was joining the scattered limbs with thread, smiling as he saw rhythm and harmony thus born under his fingers.

At the sound of muskets on the landing, the monk shook all over, not because he had less courage than Brotteaux, who remained unmoved, but because social observance had not trained him to keep a composed countenance. Citizen Delournel's questions revealed to Brotteaux the origin of this stroke, and, rather too late, he saw that one does wrong to confide in a woman. Called upon to follow the Citizen Commissar, he took his Lucretius and his three shirts.

"This citizen," he said, pointing to Father Longuemarre, "is an assistant I have taken to make my dolls. He is domiciled here."

But as the monk could not furnish a certificate of reliability, he was arrested together with Brotteaux.

When the procession passed the concierge's lodge, Citizeness Remacle, leaning on her broom, gazed at her tenant with that air of virtue seeing crime in the hands of the law. Little Joséphine, scornful and pretty, held Mouton back by his collar, as he would have liked to lick the friend who gave him sugar. A crowd of inquisitive persons filled the Place de Thionville.

Brotteaux, at the foot of the stairs, came up against a young peasant girl just about to go up. On her arm she had a basket full of eggs and in her hand a cake wrapped in a linen cloth. It was Athénais, coming from Palaiseau to bring her rescuer some token of her gratitude. When she saw that magistrates and four grenadiers were taking "Monsieur Maurice" away, she was astounded, asked if it could be true, then went up to the commissar and said gently: "You're not really taking him away? It's not possible . . . But you don't know him. He is as good as the good God himself."

Citizen Delournel pushed her aside and signalled to the grenadiers to come forward. Then Athénais poured out a string of the foulest insults and most obscene oaths against magistrates and grenadiers, who felt as if all the jerries of the Palais-Royal and Rue Fromenteau brothels were being emptied over their heads. Then, in a voice which filled the Place de Thionville from one end to the other and made the crowd of sightseers shiver, she yelled: "Long live the King! Long live the King!"

## XVIII

Citizeness Gamelin had been fond of old Brotteaux, and held that he was both the most lovable and most worthy man she had ever had dealings with. She did not bid him farewell when he was arrested, because she would have been afraid to thwart the authorities, and because in her humble position she considered cowardice a duty. But it was a blow she could not recover from.

She could not eat, and sadly lamented losing her appetite just when she at last had something to satisfy it with. She still admired her son, but she no longer dared think of the terrible work he was doing and was very pleased indeed to be only an ignorant woman, so that she did not have to judge anybody.

The poor mother had managed to re-discover an old rosary at the bottom of a chest; she was not very instructed in how to use it, but her trembling fingers now busied themselves with it. Having lived into old age without practising her religion, she now turned pious, praying all day long, by the fire, for the salvation of her child and that kind monsieur Brotteaux. Élodie was a frequent visitor, they avoided each other's eyes, but sat huddled, talking at random about trifling things.

One day, in Pluviôse, when the snow, falling in large flakes, had blotted out the sky and silenced all the noises of the city, mother Gamelin, alone in the flat, heard a knock at the door. She started violently; for some months now the slightest sound had made her shudder. She opened the door. A young man of eighteen to twenty years, a hat on his head, entered. He was wearing a bottle green box-coat, the three capes of which concealed chest and shape. He had on English style turnback high-boots. His chestnut hair tumbled in locks about his shoulders. He came forward to the centre of the studio, as if to obtain all the light the window-panes and snow let pass, and remained for some moments, motionless, without speaking.

At last, while Citizeness Gamelin stared at him in amazement—"Do you not recognise your daughter?"

The old lady clasped her hands: "Julie! . . . You . . . God, can it be?"

"Why, of course it's me! Kiss me, mummy!"

Citizeness Gamelin, widow, clasped her daughter in her arms, and dropped a tear on the cape of the box-coat. Then, in alarmed tones: "You! In Paris!"

"Oh, mummy, why ever did I not come alone! . . . Nobody would ever recognise me in this get-up."

The box-coat did indeed conceal her shape and she did not differ from many a very young man who, like her, wore his hair long and parted into two loose masses. Her features, fine-cut and pleasing, but sun-burned, lined with fatigue and hardened by cares, had an expression that was bold and masculine. She was of slight build, with long, straight legs, her movements were unconstrained; only her high-pitched voice could have betrayed her.

Her mother asked her if she was hungry. She replied that she would gladly take something, and when bread, wine and ham were put before her, set to work on them, one elbow on the table, lovely and greedy as Ceres in old witch Baubo's hut. Then, with her glass still at her lips—"Mummy, do you know when my brother will be back? I have come to see him."

The fond mother gazed in trouble at her daughter, but made no answer.

"I must see him. My husband was arrested this morning and taken to the Luxembourg prison."

The man she called "husband" was Fortuné de Chassagne, a former noble and officer of Bouillé's regiment. He had loved her when she worked in a gown shop in the Rue des Lombards, then took her away with him to England, where he emigrated after August 10th. He was her lover; but to her mother she found it more seemly to call him husband. She also told herself that misfortune had certainly married them and ill luck was a sacrament.

Her mother made no answer, only gazed at her with sorrowful expression.

"Don't you understand me, mummy? Time presses, I must see Évariste at once; only he can save Fortuné."

"Julie," the mother replied, "you would do best not to say a word to your brother."

"What? What is that you say, mother dear?"

"I say you would do best not to say a word about Monsieur de Chassagne to your brother."

"Mummy, but I must, whatever happens."

"My child, Évariste has never forgiven Monsieur de Chassagne for having taken you away. You know how angrily he spoke of him, what names he called him."

"Yes, he called him a corrupter," said Julie, with a wheezy little laugh, and a shrug of the shoulders.

"My child, he was mortally outraged. Évariste has vowed never again to mention Monsieur de Chassagne. Two years now he has not breathed his name. But his feelings have not changed; you know him; he has never forgiven you or him."

"But, mummy, now that Fortuné has married me . . . in London . . ."

The poor mother raised eyes and hands: "It is enough that Fortuné should be an aristocrat, an émigré, for Évariste to treat him as an enemy."

"Now, mother dear, tell me. Do you think that if I beg him to do whatever's necessary with the public prosecutor and the Committee of General Security to save Fortuné, that he will not consent? . . . But, mummy, it would be monstrous, if he refused."

"My child, your brother is a fine man and a good son. But do not ask him, oh, do not ask him to take Monsieur de Chassagne's part . . . Listen to what I say, Julie. He never tells me what he thinks, and I even doubt whether I should be able to understand it anyway . . . but he is a judge; he has his principles; he acts as his conscience tells him. Ask nothing of him, Julie."

"I can see you understand him now. You know that he is cold, devoid of feeling, that he is a bad man, that all he knows is ambition and vanity. And you always did prefer him to me. When we all three lived together, you suggested I should be his model. His measured way of going about and solemn talk impressed you; you could see all the virtues in him.

As for me, you always disapproved of what I did, you ascribed all the vices to me, because I was open, and because I climbed trees. You never could bear me. You only loved him. Very well then, I hate him, your Évariste; he's a hypocrite."

"Silence, Julie; I was a good mother to you as well as to him. I had you taught a trade. It wasn't my fault you did not remain a decent girl and have not married in your own class. I have always been very fond of you, and am still. I forgave you and I love you. But do not say bad things of Évariste. He's a good son. He has always looked after me. My child, when you left me and abandoned your trade and your shop, to go and live with Monsieur de Chassagne, what would have become of me without him? I should have died of poverty and starvation."

"Do not talk so, mummy; you know very well we should have looked after you in every way, Fortuné and I, if you hadn't turned away from us, on Évariste's prompting. Don't make me angry! He's incapable of a kind deed; he only took it on himself to look after you, to make me hateful to you! He—love you? Is he capable of loving anyone? He has neither heart nor intelligence. He's devoid of gifts, absolutely. You need a more sensitive soul than his, to paint."

She flashed a glance at the canvases in the studio—they were exactly as she had left them.

"There you've got it—his character— he has put it into his canvases, cold and gloomy as it is. His Orestes, his Orestes, those stupid eyes, that evil mouth and looking as if he's impaled, that's him through and through . . . So you don't understand anything, mother dear? I cannot let Fortuné remain in prison. You know them, these Jacobins, these patriots, all Évariste's gang. They'll have him killed. Mother, dearest mother, dear little mother, I cannot let him be killed. I love him, I love him! He has been so kind to me, and we have been so unhappy together. Look, this box-coat, that's one of his. I haven't a shift to my back. One of Fortuné's friends lent me this waistcoat, and I worked for a lemonade-seller at Dover, while he worked for a hairdresser. We knew well enough we were risking our lives by coming back to France, but we were asked if we would go to Paris on an important mission . . . We consented; we should have taken on a mission for the devil himself. They paid our fare and gave us a letter of exchange on a Paris banker. We found his office closed; the banker is in prison and is going to be guillotined. We were without a penny piece. Everybody we were in contact with, to whom we might have gone, is in flight or in prison. Not a door to knock at. We had been sleeping in a stable in the Rue de la Femme-sans-tête. A kind shoeblack, who slept next us in the straw, lent my lover one of his boxes, with a brush and a pot of polish quarter full. For a fortnight Fortuné earned our living cleaning shoes in the Place de Grève. But on Monday a member of the Commune put his foot on the box and wanted his shoes done. It was a man who had been a butcher, whose backside Fortuné kicked in the old days for giving under weight. When Fortuné raised his head to ask his two sous, the villain recognised him, called him an aristocrat and threatened to have him arrested. A crowd gathered; there were some decent people and some rogues who shouted: 'Death to the émigré!' and called for gendarmes. I was just taking him some soup. I saw him taken to the Ward and shut up in the Saint-Jean church. I wanted to kiss him, they pushed me away. I spent the night like a dog on the church steps . . . This morning, they took him away . . ."

Julie could not finish her story; she was choked by her sobs.

She threw her hat on the floor and knelt at her mother's feet.

"This morning they took him to the Luxembourg prison: Mother dear, mother dear, do help me save him; have pity on your daughter!"

Sobbing bitterly, she opened her box-coat and, the better to convince her mother she was her daughter, and she was in love, uncovered her bosom; taking her mother's hands, she pressed them on her palpitating breasts.

"My dear, dear daughter, my Julie, my Julie!" widow Gamelin breathed, and pressed her tear-wet cheek against the young woman's.

For some moments they were silent. The poor mother racked her brains, how to help her daughter, and Julie closely followed those swimming eyes.

"Perhaps," Évariste's mother wondered, "perhaps, if I speak to him, he may be persuaded. He is kind, he is gentle. If politics had not hardened him, if he had not come under the influence of the Jacobins, he would never have started acting so harshly, which frightens me, because I can't understand it."

She took Julie's head in her two hands. "Listen, my child. I shall speak to Évariste. I shall prepare him to see you, to hear you. Sight of you might enrage him and I feel afraid about his first reaction . . . Then, I know him; this coat would outrage him; he is so strict on anything to do with what is proper . . . I was a little surprised myself to see my Julie dressed like a boy."

"Oh, mummy, but emigrating and all this frightful disorder in the Kingdom have made disguises like this very common. People assume them to follow a trade, not to be recognised, or to fit in with a borrowed passport or certificate. In London I saw little Girey dressed like a girl, and a very pretty girl he made too; and you'll agree, mummy, that disguise was more shocking than mine."

"My poor child, you have no need to try to put yourself in the right to me, neither for that or anything else. I am your mother; you will always be innocent to me. I shall speak to Évariste, and tell him . . ."

She broke off. She sensed what her son had become; she sensed it, but she refused to believe it, she did not want to admit it.

"He is kind. For me he will . . . for you he will do what I ask of him."

And the two women, worn out, were silent. Julie fell asleep with her head on the knees on which she had rested as a child. Meanwhile, rosary in hand, the sorrowful mother wept silently over the evils she felt ahead, amid the calm of this snowy day, in which all was silence, footsteps, wheels, sky.

Suddenly, with keenness of hearing that anxiety had sharpened, she caught the sound of her son coming up the stairs.

"Évariste!" she cried. "Hide!"

She pushed the girl into her own room.

"Well, mother, how goes it today?"

Évariste hung his hat on the stand, put on a working waistcoat in place of his surtout and sat down at his easel. For some days he had been making a charcoal sketch of Victory placing a crown on the forehead of a soldier fallen for the Fatherland. He would have treated this subject with great ardour, but the Tribunal absorbed most of his days and took all his soul, and his hand, out of the way of drawing, had become sluggish and clumsy.

He began humming the *Ça ira*.

"You sing, my child," said Citizeness Gamelin, "your heart is glad."

"Mother, we should all be glad; good news has come in. The Vendée is crushed. The Austrians are defeated; the Rhine army has broken through Lautern and Wissembourg's lines. The day is near when a triumphant Republic will show its mercy. Why must the boldness of the plotters increase in proportion to the growth of strength of the Republic, and traitors scheme to strike the country in the dark just when it is striking down the enemies who attack it openly?"

Citizeness Gamelin, knitting a stocking, peered at her son over her spectacles.

"Berzélius, your old model, has been to ask for two livres you owed him; I paid him. Little Joséphine has had her tummy out of order through eating too many sugar plums, that the cabinet-maker gave her. I made her some lime-tea . . . Desmahis came round to see you; he was sorry not to find you in. He wants to engrave one of your drawings. He thinks you very gifted. The dear fellow looked through your sketches and marvelled at them."

"When peace is restored and the plot crushed," the painter said, "I shall resume my Orestes. I am not in the habit of self-praise, but that's a head worthy of David."

In one majestic line he drew Victory's arm.

"She's holding out palms," he said. "But it would be more beautiful if her arms themselves formed the palms."

"Évariste."

"Mother?"

"I've had news . . . guess of whom . . ."

"I can't tell . . ."

"Julie . . . your sister . . . She is not happy."

"It would be scandalous if she were."

"Don't say things like that, my dear boy; she is your sister. Julie is not bad; she has good impulses, which have been fed on misfortune. She's so fond of you. I can assure you, Évariste, what she longs for is a life of labour, an exemplary life, and only dreams of being reconciled with her own people. Nothing prevents you seeing her again. She has married Fortuné Chassagne."

"She has written to you?"

"No."

"Then, Mother, how have you this news?"

"Not by letter, my dear, but . . ."

He rose and interrupted her in terrible tones:

"Silence, mother! Do not tell me that those two have come back to France! If they must perish, let it not be through me. For them and for you, for me, keep the fact they are in Paris from me . . . Do not compel me to know it; or . . ."

"What do you mean, my child? You would . . . you would dare . . ."

"Mother, listen to me: if I knew that my sister Julie was in that room . . ." (and he pointed to the closed door) "I should go straight round to the Ward to denounce her to the Ward Watch Committee."

The poor mother, white as her kerchief, let the knitting fall from her trembling hands and, in a voice weaker than the merest murmur she sighed: "I did not want to believe it, but I see it clearly . . . he is a monster. . . ."

As pale as his mother, spittle on his lips, Évariste rushed from the studio and hurried round to Élodie to find oblivion, sleep, a delightful fore-taste of annihilation.

## XIX

While Father Longuemarre and Athénais the prostitute were being interrogated at the Ward, Brotteaux was escorted by two gendarmes to the Luxembourg prison, where the porter refused to let him in, saying there was no more room. The old financier was then taken to the Conciergerie and put in the gaoler's office, a fairly small room, divided in two by a glazed partition. While the gaoler entered his name in the gaol-entry, through the planking Brotteaux saw two men, each on a poor mattress, lying immobile as dead men, their motionless eyes seeming sightless. Plates, bottles and remnants of bread and meat covered the floor all round them. These were two men condemned to death, waiting for the tumbril.

Former des Ilettes was then taken to a cell where, in the light of a lantern, he glimpsed two persons stretched out, one wild in appearance, mutilated, frightful, the other charming and gentle. These two prisoners offered him a little of their own mouldy straw, which was full of vermin, so that he should not have to lie down on the earth, which was foul with excrement. Brotteaux sank on to a bench in the stinking darkness, and held his head against the wall, silent, still. His misery was so great that he would have smashed his head against the wall, if he had had the strength. He could not breathe. His eyes filmed; a din as still as silence filled his ears, he felt his whole being sink deep into a delightful nothingness. For one incomparable second all was harmony to him, limpid clarity, gentleness. Then he ceased to be.

When he came to himself, the first thought that captured his intelligence was to regret that faint, and, philosopher even to the stupefaction of despair, he reflected on how he had had to come into the depths of a sewer while awaiting the guillotine, to experience the most acute sense of bodily enjoyment he had ever tasted. He made an effort to lose his sense of actuality again, but without succeeding, but on the contrary, he gradually became aware of the foul air of this prison cell bringing to his lungs, together with the warmth of life, awareness of his unbearable wretchedness.

All this time his companions saw in his silence a cruel insult. Brotteaux, who was sociable, tried now to satisfy their curiosity, but when they learned that he was what was called "apolitical," one of

those whose trifling crime was one of word or thought, they neither respected him nor sympathised. The facts against these two prisoners were more tangible: the senior of the two was a murderer, the other had counterfeited treasury notes. They were both quite reconciled to their position, and even found some compensations in it. Brotteaux now began reflecting all at once that over his head everything was movement, noise, light and life, and the pretty shop-girls of the Palais, from behind their display of perfumery or haberdashery, were smiling on happy, free passers-by, and that thought increased his desperation.

Night came, imperceptible in the gloom and silence of the dungeon, yet heavy and depressing. One leg extending on his bench and his back against the wall, Brotteaux sank into a sort of sleep. Then he saw himself seated under a tufty beech-tree, where birds were singing; the setting sun had flung liquid flame over the river and the edge of the clouds was tinged purple. A burning fever was tormenting him and straight from his pitcher he drank water which made him still worse.

The next morning, the gaoler, bringing soup, promised Brotteaux to put him in a paid room, if he had the means, as soon as a place was free, which would not be long. And indeed, the following day he invited the old financier to leave his dungeon. With each step higher, Brotteaux felt energy and life return to him, and when he saw a truckle-bed with a miserable woollen counterpane stand before him on the boards, he shed tears of delight. The gilded bed with billing doves which he had once had made for the prettiest dancer of the Opera-house, had never looked so nice or promised such delights.

This truckle-bed stood in a huge hall, which was fairly clean and contained seventeen others, separated by high planking. The company living there, consisting of ex-nobles, merchants, bankers, artisans, was not displeasing to the former financier, who knew how to rub along with all sorts of men. He noticed that these men, deprived just as he was of any solace, and threatened by the executioner, showed great cheerfulness and a lively taste for joking. Being little disposed to admire the human species, he attributed his companions' good spirits to the frivolity of their minds, which prevented their giving any great attention to their situation. Moreover, he was confirmed in this notion by noticing as well that the more intelligent of them were profoundly miserable. He soon observed that in the main they drew their good spirits, which immediately assumed a violent and sometimes rather a crazy form, from wine and brandy. They were not all of them brave; yet they all showed bravery. Brotteaux was not astonished at this; he knew that a man will readily admit to cruelty, anger, even avarice, but never cowardice, for such an admission, whether among savages or in any polite society, would put him in mortal danger. That was why, he reflected, all peoples are peoples of heroes and all armies consist only of brave men.

Still more than wine and brandy, the sound of weapons and keys, the grinding of bolts, the challenging of sentries and the impatient trampling of citizens at the door of the Tribunal, intoxicated the prisoners, inspiring in them melancholy, delirium or madness. There were some brought to cutting their throats with a razor or jumping out of a window.

Brotteaux had been on board three days, when he learned from the turnkeys that Father Longuemarre was lying bedless in the stinking straw and vermin together with thieves and murderers. He had him accepted too as a boarder, in the same room as himself, the moment a bed was vacated. Having undertaken to pay for the old monk, the old financier, who had not so very much money on him, started making portraits at a crown apiece. Through the gaoler he obtained tiny black frames in which to put the minute pictures done in human hair, which he made pretty skilfully. Such works moreover were in great demand in a community of men preoccupied with leaving some memory behind them.

Father Longuemarre maintained good heart and a lively mind. While awaiting the hearing of his case by the Revolutionary Tribunal, he prepared his defence. Making no distinction between his own cause and that of the Church, he told himself he was going to offer his judges an exposition of the irregularities and shocking results to the Spouse of Christ resulting from putting the clergy on an ordinary civic footing; he was going to tackle the task of depicting the eldest daughter of the Church waging a sacrilegious war against the Pope, with the clergy of France robbed, outraged and under hateful subjection to the laity, while the regular orders, the true militia of Jesus, were despoiled and dispersed. He was going to quote Saint Gregory the Great and Saint Ireneus, and bring forward a large number of articles of Canon Law, and whole paragraphs of the Papal Bulls.

All day long he scribbled away on his knees, on the foot of his bed, dipping away at ink, soot, coffee grounds, with stumps of quills worn down to barbs, covering candle-wraps, parcel paper, newspapers, dust-jackets of books, old letters, old bills, playing cards, with illegible writing, and planning to get his shirt starched and use that too. He was piling sheet upon sheet, and he would point to that indecipherable mountain of scribble and say: "When I come before my judges, I shall flood them with light."

And, one day, with a look of contentment at his defence, which had grown endlessly, and thinking of those judges he was burning to confront, he cried: "I shouldn't like to be in their place!"

The prisoners whom fate had brought together in this cell were either royalist or federalist; there was even a Jacobin among them; they failed to find common ground concerning the conduct of the business of State, but not one of them had the slightest trace of Christian faith left. Feuillants, Constitutionalists and Girondists agreed with Brotteaux in finding the concept of a beneficent God inimical to themselves though excellent for the common herd. In place of Jehovah the Jacobins would instal a Jacobin God, so that Jacobinism should descend from above upon the world; but as neither one lot nor the other could even conceive of being so silly as to believe in any revealed religion, they took Father Longuemarre —since he was clearly no fool—for a rogue. No doubt as preparation for his martyrdom, he professed his faith to all and sundry and so the more sincerity he showed, the more like an impostor he looked.

In vain did Brotteaux vouch for the good faith of the monk; Brotteaux himself was considered not to believe but a fraction of what he said. His notions were too individual not to appear rather sham, and convinced nobody entirely. He would speak of Rousseau as an uninteresting charlatan. On the other hand, he deified Voltaire, though still without considering him the equal of Helvétius, Diderot or Baron d'Holbach. In his view the greatest genius of the age was Boulanger. He also put the astronomer Lalande, and Dupuis, author of a *Memoir on the Origin of the Constellations,* rather high. The inmates of this barrack bedroom teased the poor Barnabite with a thousand quips, which however he never saw—his candour cut through all traps.

To ward off the cares which gnawed at them and escape from the tortures of idleness, the prisoners played draughts, cards and backgammon. No musical instruments were allowed. After supper they sang or recited poetry. Voltaire's *Maid* (*La Pucelle*) brought a touch of gladness to the hearts of these unfortunates, who never tired of listening to the good passages. But since they could never really entirely disperse the terrible thought planted in their innermost hearts, they would on occasion try to turn it into a source of fun and in that eighteen-bedded dormitory act the Revolutionary Tribunal before going to sleep. Parts were distributed according to taste or aptitude. Some played judges and public prosecutor; others, the accused and the witnesses; still others, the executioner and his henchmen. The trials invariably ended by the execution of the condemned, who were stretched out on a bed with their necks under a plank. The next scene was in hell. The more nimble would wrap themselves in sheets and pretend to be spirits. And a young lawyer from Bordeaux, named Dubos, short, swarthy, one-eyed, humpbacked, the personification of the *Diable boiteux,* would come with horns on his head to drag Father Longuemarre out of bed, telling him he had been condemned to eternal fire for having made the Creator of the Universe out to be an envious, stupid and malicious creature, an enemy of pleasure and of love.

"Hah! Hah! Hah!" the devil would shout, eerily, "you old mumbo-jumbo merchant, you have taught that God likes to see his creatures languish in contrition and abstain from his greatest gifts, you impostor, you hypocrite, you sneak, you shall squat on nails and eat egg-shells for eternity!"

Father Longuemarre would merely observe that in such language the philosopher showed through the devil and the minutest demon of hell having a nodding acquaintance with theology, would have uttered fewer stupidities, without question being better informed than an encyclopædist.

But when on one occasion the Girondist lawyer called him a Capuchin, he saw red and said that a man incapable of telling the difference between a Barnabite and a Franciscan wouldn't be able to see a pikestaff.

The Revolutionary Tribunal was emptying the prisons, which the committees incessantly filled again; in three months the dormitory of eighteen saw half new faces. Father Longuemarre lost his pestering devil. Dubos the lawyer, charged before the Revolutionary Tribunal, was condemned to death as a federalist and also for plotting against the unity of the Republic. As he left the court, like so many others before him, he passed down a corridor which led right through the prison and on to which opened the room which for three months he had enlivened with his good spirits. Bidding his companions farewell, he maintained his easy manner and the cheerful mood which were habitual to him. "Sir," he said to Father Longuemarre, "will you please forgive me for having pulled you feet first out of bed. You will see no more of me."

Then, turning to old Brotteaux, he said: "Farewell, I precede you into nothingness. I gladly bequeath to Nature the elements of which I am composed, hoping that in the future she makes better use of them, for one must admit she made a mess of it in me."

He then went down to the gaoler, leaving Brotteaux in grief and Father Longuemarre trembling and green as a leaf, more dead than alive to see this impious man laugh on the edge of the abyss.

When Germinal brought bright days, Brotteaux, sensuous by nature, would make a number of trips every day into the courtyard on to which the women's quarters gave, near the fountain where every morning they came to wash their underwear. The two parts of the prison were separated by an iron grill, but the bars were not too close to prevent hands touching—and lips uniting. During kindly darkness couples pressed together there. Then Brotteaux would take discreet refuge up the stairs and, seated on a step, draw his little Lucretius from his puce surtout and in the light of a lantern read a number of restraining yet consoling maxims: *"Sic ubi non erimus . . .* When we are no more, nothing will move us, not even the mingled confusion of broken earth, sea, and sky . . ."* Yet even as he took enjoyment from this lofty wisdom, Brotteaux envied the Barnabite that madness which concealed the universe from him.

Month by month the terror increased. Every night drunken gaolers, with their watch-dogs, went from cell to cell with their indictments, shouting out names they mutilated, wakening prisoners and terrifying two hundred for every twenty they picked out. Down the corridors, with their bleeding shades, there passed, every day, without a murmur, twenty, thirty, fifty condemned persons, old men, women, youths, and so various in standing, character and beliefs that one wondered whether they had not been chosen at random.

All the time, they played cards, they drank Burgundy, they made plans, they had their trysts, at night, through the rails. This community, almost completely renewed in content, was now largely composed of "extremists" and "irreconcilables." Nevertheless the dormitory of the eighteen still kept up its atmosphere of elegance and good breeding; apart from two prisoners named Navette and Bellier, who had been put there after transference from the Luxembourg to the Conciergeries, and whom the others suspected of being stool-pigeons, they were all decent folk, who all trusted one another. Glass in hand, the victories of the

Republic were celebrated. There were a number of poets among them, as there are in any collection of idle men. The most skilled of these composed odes on the triumphs of the Rhine Army and recited them in the grand style. The odes were met with vociferous applause. Only Brotteaux was faint in his praise of the victors and their bards.

"Ever since Homer," he said one day, "it has been the strange mania of poets to laud soldiers. War is not an art, and battles are decided by luck. Of two generals facing each other and both stupid, one or other must necessarily win. You look out, one fine day one of these sword-brandishers you venerate will swallow you all up like the stork in the fable with the frogs. Then he really will be divine. For the test of a dog is his appetite."

Brotteaux had never been moved by the glory of arms. He was not in the least pleased by the victories of the Republic, which he had foreseen. He had no love for the new régime which those triumphs were consolidating. He was unhappy. It would have needed much less to make anyone else so depressed.

One morning it was noised through the prison that Committee of General Security commissars were going to carry through a search of all under arrest, and that treasury notes, anything of gold or silver, knives, and scissors were being taken and that searches of this sort had already been made at the Luxembourg prison, when letters, documents, and books had also been taken.

Every man then set his brains to work to devise some kind of hiding-place for what he most treasured. Father Longuemarre carried off armfuls of his defence to a culvert. Brotteaux slipped his Lucretius into the fireplace ash.

When the commissars, with tricolour ribbons round their necks, came to carry out their search they found little more than had been thought wise to leave for them. After they had gone, Father Longuemarre ran to his culvert and recovered as much of his defence as wind and rain had spared. Brotteaux drew out his Lucretius covered with soot.

"Let us make the most of every moment now," he said to himself, "for by certain signs I prophesy that the time left us is strictly limited."

One soft Prairial night, while in the paling sky the moon showed its two silver horns above the prison yard, the old financier who, as was his wont, was reading Lucretius on a stone step, heard a voice call him, a woman's voice, an enchanting voice, which he could not recognise. He went down into the yard, and on the other side of the railings saw a form which was no more familiar to him than the voice, but the hazy, entrancing outline of which recalled all the women he had ever loved. The heavens bathed her in azure and silver. Then all at once Brotteaux recognised—the lovely actress of the Rue Feydeau, Rose Thévenin.

"My child, you here! What cruel delight, to see you. Since when have you been here, and why?"

"Since yesterday."

She then added, in a whisper, "I have been denounced as a Royalist. I am charged with plotting to rescue the Queen. Knowing you were here, I immediately tried to see you. Listen, dear friend . . . for you do not mind me calling you that, do you? . . I know some men of standing; I know I have support even right inside the Committee of Public Security. I shall get my friends to do something; they will get me out, and I shall get you out in turn."

But, in a voice which became pressing, Brotteaux said:

"By all that is dear to you, my child, do nothing of the sort! Write to nobody, solicit nothing; ask nothing of anybody, I beg you, let yourself be forgotten."

As she did not seem to take in what he

said, he became more entreating still: "Maintain silence, Rose, let yourself be forgotten; that is your salvation. Anything any friend did would merely hasten your end. Gain time. Very little, I assure you, very little is needed to save you . . . Above all, make no attempt to move judges, or jurors, or any Gamelin. They are not men, but things: you cannot reason with things. Let yourself be forgotten. If you follow my advice, my dear, I shall die happy for having saved your life."

She replied "I shall do what you say . . . But do not speak of dying."

He shrugged his shoulders. "My child, my life is done. You live on and be happy."

She took his hands and put them on her bosom: "Listen, dear friend . . . I only saw you one day, yet for all that I am not indifferent to you. And if what I am going to tell you can give you new hold on life, believe it: I shall be for you . . . all you may wish."

And their lips joined through the rails.

## XX

Évariste Gamelin, during a long-drawn-out trial, sat in his place on the jury, in the heated atmosphere, closed his eyes and reflected:

"By compelling Marat to hide in holes hostile elements turned him into a bird of night, a Minerva-bird, whose eye was able to penetrate to plotters in the obscurity in which they cloaked themselves. Now it is calm, cold blue eyes that see through the enemies of the State and denounce traitors, with a finesse that even the Friend of the People never achieved, who now sleeps for ever in the Cordeliers Gardens. The new saviour, equally zealous but more penetrating than the first, perceives things others never saw, and his upraised

finger sends Terror far and wide. He distinguishes those fine, imperceptible shades which separate good from evil, vice from virtue, which without him were confused, to the detriment of the Fatherland and of Liberty; he reaches out and draws that fine, inflexible line beyond which, either on left or right, is nothing but error, crime and rascality. The Incorruptible teaches what service it is to the Alien to go too far or be too weak, to persecute religions in the name of reason, or in the name of religion to oppose the laws of the Republic. Those who do Le Peltier and Marat divine honour, compromising their memory, serve the Alien no less than those villains who made them their sacrifice. Whoever rejects the notions of order, common-sense and what is opportune, are foreign agents; whoever flouts morals, outrages decency and in the disorder of his heart denies God is a foreign agent. Fanatical priests deserve death; yet there is a counter-revolutionary way of combatting fanaticism; it is possible to abjure criminally. If too moderate, one destroys the Republic; if extreme, one destroys it.

Oh, how formidable the duties of a judge, laid down by the wisest of all men! It is not merely in aristocrats, federalists, or scoundrels of the Orléans faction one should see declared enemies of the country, to be struck down. Your plotter, your foreign agent is a Proteus, he assumes all shapes. He invests himself with the outward form of a patriot, of a revolutionary, of any enemy of kings; he assumes that daring heart which beats but for liberty; he swells his throat and cries so that the enemies of the Republic shake in their shoes: such is Danton, but his extremism is a poor mask for his detestable moderation and at last one sees his corruption. It is that fluent stutterer, the man who was the first to put the revolutionary cockade on his hat, the pamphleteer who in his ironical, cruel patriotism, called himself 'prosecutor lynch-man,' Camille Desmoulins, it is he who is a plotter and enemy agent: he unmasked himself by defending the traitor generals and calling for a verdict which would have been most untimely in clemency. It is Philippeaux, it is Hérault, it is that despicable Lacroix. It's that Father Duchesne who abased liberty by his common demogogy and whose shocking calumnies made even Antoinette interesting, who is a plotter and foreign agent. Or Chaumette, who for all that he seemed gentle, popular, moderate, decent and upright in the Commune administration was all the same an atheist. It is all these red-capped sansculottes with their red coats and clogs, striving to outbid the Jacobins in patriotism, who are plotters and enemy agents. It is your Anarchist Cloots, orator of the human species, condemned to death by all the monarchies in the world, who is a plotter and enemy agent, for one should fear anything of that man, he was a Prussian.

Today, extreme or moderate, all these rascals, all these traitors, Danton, Desmoulins, Hébert, Chaumette, have perished under the axe. The Republic is saved; a symphony of praise for Robespierre and the Mountain is rising from all committees and all popular assemblies. Good citizens cry: 'Worthy representatives of a free people, in vain the children of the Titans raised their lordly heads: Oh beneficent Mountain, oh protecting Sinai, from thy seething bosom came the cleansing thunder . . . .'

In this symphony the Tribunal has its measure of praise. How sweet it is to be stern in virtue and how dear to the heart of a meticulous judge is public recognition!

Yet, for any patriotic heart, what cause for astonishment and reason for concern! Why, were Mirabeau, La Fayette, Bailly, Pétion and Brissot not sufficient traitors of the cause of the people? Why! did all the men who made the Revolution do so but to destroy it? Those great makers of the grand days were together with Pitt and Cobourg, plotting an Orléans monarchy or the regency of Louis VII. Why, Danton was a Monk. Why, Chaumette and the Hébertists were more perfidious than the federalists who they thrust under the knife, they plotted the ruin of the Empire. Yet will not Robespierre's blue eye discover men even more perfidious still among those who cast the Danton traitors and the Chaumette traitors to their death? Where is this hateful chain of traitors betrayed, and where the perspicacity of the Incorruptible, going to end?"

## XXI

All this time, Julie Gamelin, wearing her bottle green box-coat, went every single day to the Luxembourg Gardens and there, on a bench at the end of a walk, waited for the moment when her lover would appear at one of the gratings of the prison. They made signs to each other and exchanged their thoughts in a mute language they had invented. By these means she knew that the prisoner had a fairly good room, enjoyed pleasant company, needed a coverlet or a kettle and loved his mistress tenderly.

She was not the only one whose eyes searched to see a beloved countenance in that palace transformed into prison. Near her a young mother kept her eyes fastened to a closed window, then, the moment she saw it open, held her baby up over her head. An old lady, veiled in lace, spent long hours motionless on a folding chair, hoping in vain to glimpse for an instant her son, who, to keep a hard face on it, played quoits in the prison yard till the gardens were closed.

During these long waits under skies grey or blue, a man of ripe years, heavily built, very neat, remained stationed on a neighbouring seat, playing with his snuff-box and the charms on his watch-chain, in his hands an open newspaper, which he never read. In the old bourgeois fashion, he wore a gold-braided cocked hat, a violet coat and a blue waistcoat with silver edgings. He looked very decent; he was a musician, to judge from the flute sticking from his pocket. Never for a moment did he take his eyes off the supposed youth, or cease to smile at him, and when Julie rose he rose too and followed at a distance. In her unhappiness and loneliness, Julie was touched by the discreet sympathy that kind person showed her.

One day, as she was leaving the garden, it began to rain, and the kind person then went up to her and, opening his enormous red umbrella, asked if he might protect her. In her limpid voice, she told him gently, that he might. But at the sound of that voice—and, possibly, a subtle feminine odour—he made off at high speed, leaving the young woman exposed to the storm; she understood, and despite her worries, could not help smiling.

Julie was lodging in an attic in the Rue du Cherche-Midi, and had given herself out as a draper's assistant looking for work; her mother, finally convinced that Julie ran less risk anywhere but staying with her, had got her away from the Place de Thionville and the Pont-Neuf Ward, and was keeping her in provisions and linen as best she could. Julie did a little cooking, went to the Luxembourg Gardens to see her dear lover, and then back to her burrow; the dull routine of this life soothed her anxieties, and as she was young and strong, she slept soundly at night. Being daring by nature, used to adventures and possibly excited a little by the coat she wore, sometimes of an evening she would go to a lemonade bar in the Rue du Four, at the sign of the *Croix Rouge,* a place frequented by all sorts of men and light women. There, she read the newspapers and played backgammon with some shop assistant or soldier who puffed at his pipe in her face. It was a place for drinking, smoking, gaming and making love, and there were frequent fights. One evening, a customer, hearing horses' hoofs on the paving stones, raised the curtain and, seeing it was Citizen Hanriot, Commander in Chief of the National Guard, galloping by with his staff, muttered: "There goes Robespierre's nark."

The remark made Julie burst out laughing. But a moustached patriot was quick to snatch at the words: "Anybody who says that," he cried, "is a f—— aristocrat, whom I'd like to see gurk into Samson's basket. Let me tell you, General Hanriot is a good patriot, who if need be will be able to defend Paris and the Convention. That's what the Royalists can never forgive him."

Then the moustached patriot, glaring at Julie, who could not stop laughing, said: "And you, greenhorn, take care you don't get my boot up your arse, to teach you to respect a patriot."

Meanwhile there were other cries: "Hanriot is a drunkard and an idiot!" "Hanriot is a good Jacobin! Long live Hanriot!"

Two sides formed. They got to blows, fists came down, hats were battered in, tables overturned, glasses smashed, lights put out, women shrieked. Attacked by a number of patriots, Julie seized a small bench; she was brought down, she scratched and bit her assailants. Her panting bosom burst from her opened box-coat and torn neckerchief. A patrol hearing the din came running up, and the aristocrat girl escaped between the gendarmes' legs.

Every day, the tumbrils were full of condemned persons.

"But I simply cannot let my lover die," Julie told her mother.

She made up her mind to plead for him, to get something done, to go to the committees, to public offices, to go to see magistrates—whomever was necessary. She had no gown. Her mother lent her a striped gown, a shawl, and a lace coif belonging to Citizeness Blaise, and Julie, dressed like a woman and patriot, called on Judge Renaudin, in a dark, damp house in the Rue Mazarin.

Trembling, she mounted the wooden, tiled stairs, and was received by the judge in his wretched study, furnished with a deal table and two straw-bottomed chairs. The wallpaper hung in ribbons. Renaudin, with matted black hair, glowering eyes, flabby lips curled back and prominent jaw, motioned to her to speak, and heard her without a word.

She told him she was the sister of Citizen Chassagne, who had been imprisoned in the Luxembourg Prison, related as clever a story as she could of the circumstances of the arrest, made him out to be an innocent unfortunate, and spoke persuasively.

He remained insensitive and hard.

Begging him, falling to her knees at his feet, she burst into tears.

The moment he saw the tears, his countenance changed; his pupils, of reddish black hue, became inflamed, and his huge bluish jaw moved up and down as if to bring saliva to a dry throat.

"Citizeness, we'll do what's required. Don't worry."

And, opening a door, he pushed his applicant into a little pink sitting-room, with painted panels, Dresden figurines, a cartel clock, gilt candelabrae, deep armchairs, a tapestry sofa with a Boucher pastorale scene. Julie was ready for anything, if only to save her lover.

Renaudin was coarse and quick. When she got up, straightening Citizeness Élodie's pretty gown, she met the cruel, mocking eyes of the creature, and immediately sensed that she had made a sacrifice in vain.

"You have promised me my brother's liberty," she said.

He guffawed.

"I said, Citizeness, that we would do what was required, that means, we shall apply the law, neither more, nor less. I told you not to worry, and why should you? The Revolutionary Tribunal is always just."

Her impulse was to rush at him, bite him, tear out his eyes. But, feeling that this would certainly be fateful for Fortuné Chassagne, she fled and rushed back to her attic to take off Élodie's desecrated gown. And there, alone, she howled all night with anger and sorrow.

The next day, back at the Luxembourg Gardens, she found them full of gendarmes, chasing women and children away. Guards placed in all the walks prevented people communicating with the prisoners. The young mother who came every day with her baby in her arms told Julie there was talk of a plot in the prisons and the womenfolk were reproached with collecting in the Gardens to stir up the populace in favour of the aristocrats and traitors.

## XXII

A "mountain" had suddenly sprung up in the Tuileries Gardens. There was not a cloud to be seen. Robespierre strode in front of all his colleagues, wearing blue coat, yellow breeches, in one hand a bunch of wheat-ears, cornflowers and poppies. He mounted the structure, and to a deeply-moved Republic announced the existence of Rousseau's Deity. How pure! How kindly! What faith! What classic simplicity! What emotional tears! Oh fertilising dew, oh mercy, of human brotherhood!

Vainly atheism still reared its monstrous countenance; Robespierre was handed a torch, and flames devoured the monster, revealing Wisdom, with one hand pointing heavenward, the other holding a crown of stars.

Évariste, on the tribunes erected against the Tuileries wall, surrounded by an excited crowd, shed kindly tears and rendered thanks to the Almighty! He could see an era of happiness begin.

He sighed—at last men were to be happy, pure, innocent—if the villains would but allow it.

Alas! The villains did not allow it. Still more executions were needed, still more foul blood to drench the soil. Three days after this festival to celebrate the new alliance and the reconciliation of heaven and earth, the Convention passed that Law of Prairial which with what amounted to an awful joviality abrogated all the traditional judicial procedure, every safeguard evolved since the days of Rome to ensure that the innocent should not be condemned. An end to preliminary investigation, an end to cross-examination, an end to witnesses, and an end to defending counsel: love of the Fatherland was to take the place of everything. The accused man, with his guilt or innocence locked within him, was to appear before the patriotic juror without uttering a word. In these few moments the case, however difficult, was to be assessed, however complex or hard to get at. How was one to pronounce now? How in a brief moment distinguish the honest man from the villain, the patriot from the enemy of the Fatherland? . . .

After some brief dismay, however, Gamelin grasped his new duties and was reconciled to his new function. In this curtailment of procedure he perceived the real nature of such frightful but salutary justice, for the administrators of it were not togged-up monkeys leisurely weighing split hairs in Gothic scales, but sansculottes, who judged by patriotic light, able to see everything in a flash. One had to be guided by one's innate impulses—kindly nature, never wrong. One had to judge with one's heart, and Gamelin invoked the spirit of Rousseau, breathing: "Oh righteous being, you inspire me, by love of man and fervour to have them born again!"

On the whole his colleagues agreed. They were mostly simple fellows, and now that procedure was simplified too, they felt more at home. Justice abridged suited them. Nothing in this speed-up worried them. They merely enquired about the views of the accused, for they could not see how one could differ without evil intent. Since they were sure they possessed truth, wisdom and the sovereign good, they attributed error and evil to their adversaries. They felt strong, and they could see God.

They could see God, these jurors of the Revolutionary Tribunal. The Supreme Being whom Robespierre recognised poured his burning light over them. They adored, they were believers.

The armchair for the defendant now had substituted for it a broad platform capable of holding fifty at a time; the court only dealt with batches now. The public prosecutor now often assembled and accused of the same crime people who met for the first time in court. The Tribunal dealt with these alleged prison plots with all the frightful ease supplied by the Prairial Law, and as they came next in order to the Dantonist and Commune plots, could, by exercise of artful logic, prove they were connected with these latter. On one occasion, to expose the two essential characteristics of a plot fomented by foreign gold, against the Republic—untimely moderation and calculated extremism, and also to show both

Dantonism and Hébertism, in it all, two polar types had been included, two female polls, that charming creature Lucile, Desmoulins' widow, and Hébertist Momoro's widow, goddess of a day and otherwise hearty domestic dame. To keep the balance, both women had been in the same prison, where they had wept together on the same stone bench; both, again to keep the balance, mounted the scaffold together. An exceedingly cunning piece of symbolism, a masterpiece of equilibrium, conjured no doubt in some prosecutor's heart, with Robespierre getting all the praise. Every event in the Republic, happy or unhappy, was reported to that voice of the nation—laws, morals, seasons, harvests, sicknesses, a merited injustice, for this petty, spruce, weedy, cat-faced man was all-powerful over the nation. . . .

On this particular occasion the Tribunal was despatching a batch of the great prison plot, about thirty plotters from the Luxembourg prison, very docile prisoners, but violent royalists or federalists. The charge was based on the evidence of one single informer. The jurors were unacquainted with a word of the whole case; they did not even know the names of the conspirators. Gamelin, casting a glance over the dockful of prisoners, recognised among them Fortuné Chassagne. Julie's lover, emaciated by long captivity, pale, with lines hardened by the harsh light flooding the courtroom, still maintained a degree of fine bearing and pride. His eyes met those of Gamelin, and flared with scorn.

Gamelin became possessed of icy rage; he rose and demanded the right to speak. Then, his eyes fixed on the bust of Brutus of Ancient Rome, dominating the court, he said: "Citizen President, although there may exist between me and one of the defendants a connection which, if declared, would be one of marriage, I wish to say I do not withdraw. Neither Brutus

did so when, for the salvation of the Republic or the cause of liberty, they had to condemn a son and strike an adopted father."

He sat down again.

"What a scoundrel!" Chassagne muttered, through clenched teeth.

The public present remained unmoved, either because it was sick of sublimities of character, or because Gamelin's victory over natural human impulses had seemed too easy.

"Citizen Gamelin," the President replied, "the law requires any withdrawal to be made in writing, twenty-four hours before the commencement of the hearing. Though as far as that goes, you have no valid reason; a patriotic juror is above sentiment."

Each defendant was interrogated for three or four minutes. The examination in each case terminated in the death sentence. The jurors voted by a word, a nod or other sign. When it was Gamelin's turn to speak he said: "All the accused are guilty, and the law is precise."

As he went down the stairs from the Law-courts, a young man in a bottle-green box-coat, in appearance about seventeen or eighteen, stopped him suddenly. The youth was wearing a round hat, tipped back, the brim forming a black halo for his lovely, pale head. Upright, facing the juror, and frightening in his rage and desperation, he cried: "You foul beast! You murderer! Strike me, you coward! I am a woman! Have me arrested, have me guillotined, Cain! I am your sister!"

And Julie spat in his face.

The crowd of knitting-women and sansculottes on this occasion fell short in revolutionary vigilance; their patriotic fervour must have become most lukewarm; there was merely undecided, pointless movement round Gamelin, and Julie broke through the crowd and vanished into the dusk.

## XXIII

Évariste Gamelin was tired, but could get no rest; twenty times in the night he started from a sleep full of nightmares. It was only in the blue room, in Élodie's arms, that he could sleep for an hour or two. He would talk and shout in his sleep, and then she would waken him; but she could never make out what he said.

One morning, after a night in which he saw the Eumenides, he woke up, shattered, with terror and weak as a child. Daybreak with its sharp arrows was finding its way through the curtains into the room. Évariste's hair, tangled, on his forehead, covered his eyes with a black veil; Élodie, at the head of the bed, was gently separating the wild locks of it. She was watching him now with the tenderness of a sister and with her handkerchief wiping the cold sweat from the unhappy man's brow. That reminded him of that lovely scene of Euripides' *Orestes,* of which he had begun a picture, such that, had he ever finished, it would have been his greatest work—that scene in which luckless Electra wipes away the froth which sullies her brother's lips. It even seemed to him that he could hear Élodie saying softly: "Hear me, dearest brother, while the Furies still leave you master of your reason . . . ."

And he said to himself: "Yet I am not a parricide. On the contrary, it has been by filial love that I have shed the foul blood of the enemies of my country."

## XXIV

There was no end to trying men for the prison conspiracy. There were forty-nine defendants in the dock. Maurice Brotteaux was on the right of the top row, the place of honour. He was wearing his plum-coloured surtout, which the pre-

vious evening he had painstakingly brushed, mended too, outside the pocket where his little Lucretius had at last worn a hole. By his side was the Rochemaure woman, painted, plastered, dazzling, detestable. They had put Father Longuemarre between her and the prostitute Athénais who in the Madelonnettes prison had recovered her adolescent freshness.

The gendarmes filled the tiers of benches with people whom these four did not know, and who may not even have known each other, yet were all conspirators, members of the old parliament, day-labourers, ex-nobles, middle-class men and women. Citizeness Rochemaure had picked out Gamelin on the jury bench. Though he had made no response to her pressing letters and repeated messages, still she had hoped of him, sent him a pleading glance, and tried hard to look beautiful and touching. But the young law-administrator's cold eyes robbed her of any illusions.

The Court Clerk read the indictment which, though brief regarding each individual, was lengthy, because there were so many of them. In broad outline he described the plot hatched in the prisons with the aim of drowning the Republic in the blood of the representatives of the people and of the populace of Paris, and then, dealing with each in turn, he said:

"One of the most pernicious authors of this abominable plot is the defendant Brotteaux, formerly known as des Ilettes, a tax collector under the tyrant. This person, outstanding even in the days of tyranny, in the profligacy of his conduct, is clear proof that libertinage and evil living are the greatest enemies of the liberty and happiness of peoples; in point, having robbed the public exchequer and squandered a considerable portion of the national substance, this creature came into association with a former mistress of his, a woman named Rochemaure, to correspond with émigrés and traitorously keep our alien foes informed of the state of our finances, the movements of our troops and the fluctuations of public opinion.

Brotteaux who, at this period of his wretched existence, was living in intimacy with a prostitute he had picked out of the filth of the Rue Fromenteau, a girl named Athénais, had no difficulty in winning her over to his purposes, and using her to stir up counter-revolution by shameless cries and outrageous acts of provocation.

Certain observations made by this fateful person will show you clearly enough how base his views were and how detrimental his aim. Speaking of this patriotic court, he had the impudence to say: 'The Revolutionary Tribunal is like a play of William Shakespeare, who mixes the most trivial clowning into the most sanguinary scenes.' He has never ceased to preach atheism, as the most certain means of bringing the people low and abasing it to immorality. In the Conciergerie prison, where he has been detained, he lamented the victories of our brave armies, as equivalent to the worst calamities, and strove to cast suspicion on the most patriotic generals, imputing tyrannical purposes to them. 'You just wait,' he once said, in language so shocking that the pen hesitates to reproduce it, 'you just wait, till one day one of these who bear the sword and to whom you owe your salvation, will swallow you up like the stork in the fable did the frogs'."

And so it went on.

"The woman Rochemaure, of noble birth, Brotteaux's mistress, is no less guilty then he. Not merely did she correspond with abroad and was paid by Pitt himself, but, associated with corrupted persons, such as Julien (of Toulouse) and Chabot, and in contact with the former Baron de Batz, together with that scoundrel she schemed all kinds of machinations to bring down the India Company shares, so as to buy them up for a song and then enhance them by machinations in the opposite sense, thereby robbing both private purses and the public purse. Under arrest, in the Bourbe and Madelonnettes prisons, she has never once ceased plotting, speculating and making efforts to corrupt judges and jury alike.

Louis Longuemarre, former noble and a former Capuchin monk, had long since tried his hand at crime before the treasonable acts for which he stands here. Living in shameful promiscuity with the prostitute Gorcut, known as Athénais, under the roof of the same Brotteaux, he was an accomplice of this prostitute and this former noble. During imprisonment in the Conciergerie prison, he never one day ceased writing libels against public liberty and peace.

It is but right, à propos of Marthe Gorcut, known as Athénais, to say that public prostitutes are the greatest scourge of public morals, which they outrage, and the obloquy of the society they harm. But what good would be served by dealing at length with disgusting crimes which the accused has admitted without a trace of shame . . . ?"

The indictment then dealt with the fifty-four other defendants, whom neither Brotteaux, nor Father Longuemarre, nor Citizeness Rochemaure had ever heard of, except that they had seen a number of them in one prison or another, and who were mixed with the preceding in "this shocking plot, the like of which had never before been seen in the history of mankind."

The indictment concluded by demanding the penalty of death against all the accused.

Brotteaux was interrogated first.

"Have you plotted?"

"No, I have not. Not a word of the indictment I have just heard is true."

"See, you are plotting at this very instant, against this Tribunal."

And the President passed to the Rochemaure woman, who replied by desperate assurances, tears and quibbling argument.

Father Longuemarre placed himself entirely in the hands of God. He had not even brought his written defence with him.

To all the questions put him, he replied in a spirit of renunciation. All the same, when the President called him a Capuchin monk, the old Adam woke in him again. "I am not a Capuchin," he said, "I am a priest and monk of the Order of Barnabites."

"The same thing," the President rejoined, good-naturedly.

"A more extraordinary error could not be imagined," Longuemarre insisted, "than to take a monk of the Order of Barnabites, which owes its constitution to Saint Paul himself, for a Capuchin."

Roars of laughter and hooting rang through the court.

Then Father Longuemarre, taking this mockery for a sign of rejection, proclaimed that he would die a member of precisely the Order of Barnabites, the robes of which he bore in his heart.

"Do you admit," the President demanded, "to plotting with the prostitute Gorcut, called Athénais, who gave you her wretched favours?"

At this question, Father Longuemarre raised painful eyes to Heaven and replied by a silence expressive of the astonishment of an honest soul, and the gravity of a monk loth to waste his breath on empty speech.

"Prostitute Gorcut," the President demanded of young Athénais, "do you admit to plotting with Brotteaux?"

She replied gently: "Monsieur Brotteaux, as far as I know, has only done good. It's a pity there aren't more like him and there isn't a better man. Anyone

who says the contrary is wrong. That is all I have to say."

The President asked her if she admitted living in concubinage with Brotteaux. He had to explain the term to her; she did not understand what it meant. But the moment she grasped what was intended, she replied that it would have only depended on him, but he asked nothing of her.

There was laughter in the public gallery, and the President threatened the prostitute Gorcut with being expelled from the hearing if she answered again with such cynicism.

Then she called him an old cockroach, a cuckold, and drenched him with jerryfulls of insults, before the gendarmes could drag her from her place and get her out of the court.

The President then interrogated the remaining accused briefly, in the order in which they were arranged in the dock. A man named Navette replied that he could not have plotted in prison, being there only four days. The President observed that this answer would be taken into consideration and asked the citizen jurors to take note of it. A man named Bellier replied the same, and the President made an identical observation in his favour to the jury. This benevolence on the part of the judge was taken by some to result from a praiseworthy fairness, by others to be a reward to informers.

The Deputy Public Prosecutor then addressed the court. He merely amplified what the indictment had already stated, and then demanded: "Is it established that Maurice Brotteaux, Louise Rochemaure, Louis Longuemarre, Marthe Gorcut, known as Athénais, Eusèbe Rocher, Pierre Guyton-Fabulet, Marcelline Descourtis, etcetera, etcetera, concocted a plot to use assassination, famine, forgery of false treasury notes and coins, depravation of morals and public morale, and an uprising in the prisons, with the aim of causing civil war, the dissolution of the national assembly and re-establishment of the Monarchy?"

The jurors withdrew to the jury room. They were unanimous about all the accused, excepting those who indicated, namely, Navette and Bellier, whom the President and after him the Public Prosecutor had to some extent separated from the rest. Gamelin gave the following motivation of his verdict:

"The guilt of these persons hits you in the face; their punishment is essential to the well-being of the Country and they themselves should desire their execution as the sole means of expiating their crimes."

The President declared the sentence without the presence of those whom it concerned. During these great days, whatever the law might require, they never brought back the accused to read the sentence to them, no doubt because they feared the desperation of such large batches of victims. Foolish fears, so great and so common was the submissiveness of the victims. The Clerk went down below to read the verdict, which was then heard in that silence and calm which produced the comparison of the victims of the month of Prairial to forest trees selected for cutting.

Citizeness Rochemaure declared she was pregnant. A surgeon, who was also a juror, was instructed to examine her. She was carried to her dungeon in a faint.

"Oh," sighed Father Longuemarre, "how worthy of pity these judges are; they really are in a shocking state of spirit. They confuse everything and cannot distinguish between a Barnabite and a Franciscan."

The execution was to take place that very day, at the turnpike bar known as "the Overturned Throne." The condemned, their toilet made, their hair cut, their shirts yoked out, awaited the executioner herded like beasts in the little room

separated from the prison office by a glass partition.

When the executioner and his men arrived, Brotteaux, who was calmly reading his Lucretius, slipped the bookmark in at the page just begun, closed the book, thrust it into his surtout pocket and said to the Barnabite:

"My dear Reverend Father, what makes me mad is that I shall never be able to convince you. We are both of us now going to sleep our final sleep, and I shall be unable to pluck at your sleeve and say: 'See, you are now devoid of feeling and devoid of cognizance; you are inanimate. What follows life is just the same as what preceded it'."

He would have smiled, but a terrible anguish gripped his heart and his bowels and he nearly lost consciousness.

Nevertheless, he went on: "Father, I have let you see my weakness. I love life and it is not without regret that I leave it."

"Monsieur," the man replied, "take note that you are pluckier than I am and yet death worries you more. What is the meaning of that, if not that I see the light, while you still do not."

"It might just as well be," said Brotteaux, "that I regret life because I have got more enjoyment out of it than you, who made it as much like death as you could."

"Monsieur," said Father Longuemarre, turning white, "this is a serious moment. May God be my succour! It is clear that we are going to die unassisted. I must have taken the sacraments in days gone by too lukewarmly and with a thankless heart, for Heaven to refuse them me today, when I have such pressing need."

The tumbrils were waiting. The condemned were huddled in, their hands bound. The Rochemaure woman, whose pregnancy had not been admitted by the surgeon, was hoisted into the tumbril. She rallied a little of her energy, to look about her at the crowd of onlookers, hoping against hope to see among them men who would rescue her. Her eyes were beseeching. The crowd was less dense than it used to be and there was less show of violence. A few women merely cried "Death!" or mocked at those about to perish. The men shrugged their shoulders, turned their heads away, and, whether from caution or respect of the law, remained silent.

A shudder ran through the crowd when Athénais emerged through the narrow gate. She looked like a child.

She bowed to the monk: "Dear Reverend," she said to him, "please absolve me."

Solemnly, Father Longuemarre murmured the sacramental words, saying: "My daughter, you have fallen into very bad ways, but what would I not give to be able to bring to Our Lord a heart as pure as yours!"

She mounted her tumbril lightly, and there, her bosom erect and her child's head on high, she yelled: "Long live the King!"

She gave Brotteaux a little nod to tell him there was room for him next to her. Brotteaux helped the Barnabite climb in, then took his place between the monk and the innocent prostitute.

"Monsieur," Father Longuemarre now said to the epicurean philosopher, "I beg one thing of you: please pray for me to that God whom you do not know yet. There is no certainty that you will not be nearer to him than I shall; very soon we shall know. Any instant now, you may become the privileged son of the Lord; Monsieur, pray for me."

While the wheels ground over the endless cobbles of the suburb, the monk recited the prayers of the dying, in his heart and on his lips.

Brotteaux in thought passed over again those lines of the poet of Nature—*Sic ubi non erimus* . . . Bound tight, as he was,

and jolted in the tumbril of shame, still he maintained his attitude of calm and some concern to show no concern. At his side Athénais, proud to be dying as the Queen of France had died, swept the crowd with haughty eyes, and the old financier, as his connoisseur's eyes fell on the white bosom of the young woman, wished it were not daylight.

## XXV

While the tumbrils rolled on, surrounded by gendarmerie, towards the scene of execution, taking to their death Brotteaux and his co-plotters, Évariste sat, lost in thought, on a seat in the Tuileries Gardens. He was waiting for Élodie. The sun, slanting towards the horizon, riddled the rich foliage of the chestnuts with its arrows of fire. By the gates, Fame, on her winged steed, blew her eternal trumpet. Newsboys were crying the great victory of Fleurus.

"Yes," Gamelin said to himself, "victory is ours. It has cost us something."

He could see the bad generals' executed ghosts shuffling through the bloodstained dust of this Revolution Square where they perished. And he smiled with pride at the thought that, without those harsh deeds in which he had played some part himself, the bark of these trees would still be nibbled by Austrian horses.

Within his heart he cried: "Oh saving Terror, sacred power. A year ago, at this time, our only defenders were defeated heroes, in rags; the enemy was on the soil of our country and two thirds of the country had risen against us. Now our armies are well equipped, well trained, under the command of skilful generals; they have taken the offensive, they are ready to carry liberty throughout the world. Peace reigns over all the territory of the Republic . . . Oh saving Terror, sacred power! O beloved guillotine! A year ago, at this time, the Republic was torn into factions, the hydra of federalism threatened to consume it. Now Jacobin unity extends its power and wisdom throughout the realm. . . ."

And yet he was gloomy. His forehead was deeply furrowed; his lips were bitter. He said to himself: "We used to say *win or perish*. We were wrong, we should have said *win* and *perish*."

He looked about him. Children were making sand castles. Women citizens, on wooden stools, under the trees, were embroidering or sewing. Pedestrians in coat and breeches of peculiar elegance, thoughtful about business or pleasure, were going homewards. And Gamelin felt isolated among them; he was not the compatriot or the contemporary of these men. Whatever had happened? How was it that indifference, weariness and possibly even disgust had taken the place of the fire of the grand years? It was quite plain that these people he saw were sick of hearing about the Revolutionary Tribunal and had turned their backs on the guillotine. It had become too disturbing on the Revolution Square, and so had been moved to the outskirts of the suburb of St. Antoine. Even there people muttered when the tumbrils came along. He had even heard that people had shouted "Enough!"

Enough, when there were still traitors and plotters? Enough, when they would have to form new committees and purge the Assembly? Enough, when there were rogues who dishonoured the people's parliament? Enough, when there were even men inside the Revolutionary Tribunal who were contemplating bringing down Robespierre the Just? For, dreadful thought, yet true, Fouquier himself was plotting, and it was to ruin Robespierre that he had had fifty-seven victims dragged to death in the red shirts of parricides, and publicly executed. What criminal pity was this to which France was beginning to yield? The country had to be saved, in spite of itself, and when it cried for mercy, one would have to stop one's ears and strike and strike! Alas, that Fate should have ruled that the Fatherland should curse those who were saving it; let it curse, but let it be saved!

"The public execution of obscure victims, aristocrats, financiers, publicists, poets—a Lavoisier, a Roucher, an André Chénier, is not nearly enough. We must strike at these all-powerful malefactors who, hands full of gold and dripping with blood, are plotting the downfall of the Mountain—the Fouchers, Talliens, Rovères, Carriers, Bourdons. We must deliver the State from all its enemies. If Hébert had triumphed, the Assembly would have been overthrown and the Republic would have gone pell-mell into the abyss; if Desmoulins and Danton had triumphed, the Assembly would have lost its rigour, ready to surrender the Republic to aristocrats, money-jobbers and generals. If men like Tallien and Foucher, monsters gorged with blood and rapine, triumph, France will be drowned in crime and infamy . . . You sleep, Robespierre, while criminals intoxicated with rage and fear propose your death and to bury liberty. Couthon, Saint-Just, why so slow to denounce these plottings?

Why, the old régime, that monarchic monster, assured its power by imprisoning four hundred thousand men a year, hanging fifteen thousand, breaking three thousand on the wheel, so can the Republic still shrink from sacrificing a few hundred heads to its security and power? Let us drench ourselves in blood and save the Fatherland!"

He was meditating in this fashion, when suddenly Élodie came running, beside herself.

"Évariste, what have you to tell me? Why did you not come to the *Amour*

*Peintre,* to the blue room? Why have you made me come here?"

"To bid you farewell for ever."

She stammered that he was mad, that she could not understand . . .

With an almost imperceptible movement of his hand he stopped her: "Élodie, I can no longer accept your love."

"Silence, Évariste, silence!"

She begged him to go on farther with her; where they were, they could be seen, people were listening.

He moved a score of paces, then, very calm, continued: "I have sacrificed my life and my honour to my country, I shall die execrated, and shall have nothing to leave you, unhappy woman, but an infamous memory . . . Love each other? Can anybody love me any more? Am I capable of loving?"

She told him he was mad; that she loved him and would always love him. She was passionate and sincere; yet she could feel, just as he did, even better than he did, that he was right. So she struggled against the obvious.

He resumed:

"I have nothing to reproach myself with. What I have done, I should do again. I have made myself hateful for the country's sake. I am cursed. I have placed myself outside the pale of humanity, and shall never return. No, the great task is still incomplete. What, clemency, pardon? . . . Do traitors pardon? Are plotters clement? There are more and more parricidal villains; they are rising from the soil, coming in from every frontier; young men who would have done better to give their lives in our armies, old men, children, women, with masks of innocence, purity, and charm. And when they are immolated, one finds still more . . . Can't you see plainly that I must renounce love, happiness, all that is gentle in life, even life itself?"

He was silent. Made for peaceable delights, Élodie had for some time been appalled to find sanguinary forms mingling with her sense of enjoyment of the kisses of her tragic lover; she now made no reply. Évariste drank in the young woman's silence, like a bitter draught.

"You see it clearly, Élodie; we cannot halt; our task devours us. Our days, our hours are years. I shall soon have lived a century. See this forehead—is it the forehead of a lover . . . ?"

"Évariste, you are mine, I shall keep you, I will not let you go from me."

There was a tone of self-sacrifice in her voice. He sensed it; so did she.

"Élodie, some day will you bear witness that I lived faithful to my duty, that my heart was straight and my spirit pure, that I had no other passion but the public good; that I had been born sensitive and gentle? Will you say: 'He did his duty'? Of course not, you won't say that. Nor do I ask you to. Let my memory perish! My glory is in my own heart; I am surrounded by shame. If you love me, never breathe a word about me."

A child of eight or nine years, playing with its hoop, came racing between Gamelin's legs at that moment.

Gamelin swept it up impulsively into his arms. "Child," he cried, "You shall grow up free, happy, and you will owe it to the hateful Gamelin. I am monstrous for you to be happy. I am cruel for you to be good, I am merciless for all Frenchmen to embrace tomorrow and shed tears of delight."

He crushed the child to him.

"Little child, when you are a man, you will owe me your happiness and your innocence; and yet, if you ever hear my name, you will execrate it."

Then he set the child down, and it raced terrified to the skirts of its mother, who had run up to rescue it.

The young mother, who was pretty and in her white lawn frock had an aristocratic charm, led her little boy away with haughty air.

Gamelin turned his wild eyes on Élodie: "I embrace the child—and might well have the mother guillotined."

And he strode swiftly away down the avenue.

For some instants, Élodie did not move, staring at the ground before her. Then she suddenly rushed after her lover, and, maddened, her hair all awry, like a mænad, seized him as if she was about to tear him limb from limb and in tones stifled with blood and tears, cried: "Then me, me too, my beloved, send me to the guillotine too; have my head cut off too!"

And, at thought of the knife on her neck, her whole body grew soft with terror and sensuous delight.

## XXVI

While the Thermidor sun sank horizonwards through bloodstained purple, Évariste, gloomy and worried, made his way through the Marbeuf Gardens, which had become national property and were frequented by Parisian idlers. People took their lemonade or ices there; there were hobby-horses and shooting-galleries for young patriots. Under a tree there was a little Savoyard in rags with a black cap on his head, making a marmot dance to the astringent music of his hurdy-gurdy. A man, still young, slim, in blue coat with powdered hair and a huge dog, had paused to listen to the rustic tunes. It was Robespierre. Évariste, recognising him, thought him more pale, thinner too, his features hardened and crisscrossed with painful folds. And he wondered what exhausting labours, what suffering had made that imprint on Robespierre's forehead. How hard to work for the good of mankind! What was in his mind at the moment? Did the sound of the old hill song distract him from his cares? Was he

thinking that he had made a pact with Death and the time had come to keep it? Was he proposing to re-enter that Committee of Public Security from which he had just resigned, and do so as conqueror tired of being held back, with Couthon and Saint-Just, by a seditious majority? What hopes were stirring, he asked himself, or what fears, behind those impassive features?

Meanwhile, Robespierre gave the lad a smile, and put him a few kindly questions about his native vale, his cottage, the parents the poor young fellow had left, then tossed him a small silver piece and resumed his stroll. After a few paces, he turned round to call his dog which, smelling the rodent, had its bristles up and was baring its teeth.

"Brount! Brount!"

He plunged down a dark tree-lined path.

From respect, Gamelin kept his distance from the lonely stroller, but while he gazed at that slender form, vanishing into the darkness, he addressed the following inward prayer to him:

"Maximilien Robespierre, I see your unhappiness, and I understand your thoughts. Your sadness, your weariness and I would even say that expression of apprehensiveness in your eyes all join to say: 'Let the Terror end and Fraternity begin! Frenchmen, be united, be stern in conduct, be good. Love one another . . .' Very well, then, I shall serve your purpose, so that you with your wisdom and goodness may bring this internal strife to an end, extinguish fratricidal hatred, turn the executioner into a gardener who henceforth will cut no more than cabbage heads and lettuces, I with my colleagues of the Tribunal shall open the road to clemency by exterminating every plotter, every traitor. We shall double our vigilance and our harshness. No guilty person shall escape us. And when the head of the last of the enemies of the Republic falls under the knife, it will be possible for you to be indulgent without transgressing and, oh Father of France, make innocence and virtue reign over our country!"

The Incorruptible was already some distance away. Two men wearing round hats and nankeen breeches, one of whom, lanky and thin, had a cataract on one eye and was like Tallien, came round a corner, the other way, cast a sidelong glance at him and then, pretending not to have recognised him, continued their way. When they were far enough away not to be overheard, they muttered: "And there he is, king, pope and god. For he is God. And Catherine Théot is his prophetess."

"Dictator, traitor, tyrant! there is still to be found a Brutus!"

"Tremble, villain! The Tarpeian rock is not far from the Capitol."

Brount the dog went up to them. They shut their mouths and quickened their pace.


## XXVII

You sleep, Robespierre! Time passes, precious hours are flying . . .

At last, on Thermidor 8th, the Incorruptible rose in the Assembly and was to speak. Sun of May 31st are you rising for the second time? Gamelin is on tenterhooks. So Robespierre really is going to tear them from seats they dishonour, these lawmakers more guilty than any federalist and more dangerous than Danton . . . No, not yet! "I cannot," he declared, "I cannot bring myself to rend away entirely the veil covering this profound mystery of iniquity." And the lightning merely terrified them all, without striking a single one of those who plotted. There were a whole sixty who for the past fortnight had not dared sleep at home. Now, Marat denounced traitors outright and pointed his finger at them. But the Incorruptible hesitated. From that instant he himself was the accused.

That evening the Jacobin gathering was suffocating, in the hall, in the corridors, in the courtyard.

There were all of them there, chattering friends and taciturn enemies. In a devastating silence, Robespierre read them the speech he had made in the Assembly, and it was followed by emotional applause.

"This is my last testament," he declared, "you will see me drink the hemlock undismayed."

"I shall drink it with you," replied David.

"We all shall, all of us," the Jacobins cried—and went their ways, nothing decided.

While the death of the Just One was prepared, Évariste slept like the disciples in the Garden of Olives. The following day, he went to the Tribunal, where two Wards were sitting. His Ward was trying twenty-one plotters of the Lazare prison plot. During the trial the news came in that: "The Assembly, after a six hour sitting, has voted the arraignment of Maximilien Robespierre, Couthon, Saint-Just, together with Augustin Robespierre and Lebas, who requested permission to share the fate of the other accused. The five proscribed men have gone to the bar of the house."

They learned that the President of the Ward sitting in the neighbouring court, Citizen Dumas, had been arrested on the bench—but the trial was continuing. They then heard a general alarm being drummed and the tocsin rung.

At his seat on the jury bench Évariste received orders from the Commune to report at the Town Hall to take his place on the General Council. At the sound of those bells and drums, he gave his verdict, together with his fellow-jurors, and ran home to kiss his mother and get his sash of office. The Place de Thionville was deserted. The Ward was afraid to pronounce either for or against the Assembly. People hugged close to walls, scurried through side-streets, hurried home. The summons of the tocsin and the general alarm was responded to by the clatter of shutters closing and sound of locks turning. Citizen Dupont senior hid in his shop; Remacle the porter barricaded himself in his lodge. Little Joséphine shrank in a corner, hugging Mouton in her arms. Citizeness widow Gamelin complained of the cost of provisions, which was the source of all evil. At the foot of the stairs, Évariste met Élodie; she was breathless, her hair clinging in wet locks to her perspiring neck.

"I tried to find you at the Court. You had just gone. Where are you going?"

"To the Town Hall."

"Do not go! You'll be lost: Hanriot has been arrested . . . The Wards refuse to stir. The Piques Ward, the Robespierre Ward, are passive. I know it; my father's a member. If you go to the Town Hall, you'll be giving your life, to no point."

"You want me to be a coward?"

"If you want to be courageous you should be true to the Assembly and obey the law."

"The law is dead when rogues triumph."

"Évariste, do listen to your Élodie; listen to your sister; come, sit by her, and let her soothe your troubled mind."

He shot her a glance; never had she seemed so lovable to him; never had that voice rang so voluptuous or so persuasive in his ears.

"Two paces, only two paces, my dearest one."

She drew him towards the enclosure which contained the pedestal of the overturned statue. It was surrounded by benches full of strollers and their loves. A woman selling knick-knacks was offering lace; there was a lime-tea seller, with his brass urn slung on his back, jingling his little bell; some little girls were playing the three Graces. At the water's edge there were fishermen, motionless, each holding his line. The weather was stormy, the sky overcast. Gamelin, leaning over the parapet, stared at the islet, with its point like a ship's bows, hearkened to the murmur of the wind in the treetops, and he could feel his spirit overcome with infinite longing for peace and solitude.

Then, like a wonderful echo to his own thought, came the sigh of Élodie's voice: "Do you remember when at sight of the open fields you wanted to be a country magistrate in a tiny village? That would be happiness."

Yet, through that rustle of the trees and beyond the woman's voice, he could hear the tocsin, the general alert, the distant clatter of horses' hooves and cannon over the cobbles.

Two paces away, a young man, in conversation with a stylish woman, said: "Have you heard the news? . . . The Opera has moved to the Rue de la Loi."

Yet it was getting known; Robespierre's name was whispered, though timorously, for he was still feared. And when they heard whispers of his fall, women concealed their smiles.

Évariste Gamelin seized Élodie's hand and the next instant rejected it, violently. "Farewell!" he said, "I have mixed you in my frightful fortune, I have damaged your life for ever. Farewell. May you forget me!"

"Whatever you do," she said to him, "do not go home tonight; come to the *Amour Peintre*. Do not ring; throw a stone at my shutter. I will come and open the door myself and hide you in the attic."

"If you see me again, it will be victorious, or never. Farewell!"

As he drew near the Town Hall, he caught the mutter of the grand days rising into the lowering sky. In the Place de Grève there was a rattle of armament, and the square was bright with sashes and uniforms, with Hanriot's cannon drawn up in a battery. He mounted the grand staircase and, entering the Council Chamber, signed himself in. The General Council of the Assembly, by unanimous vote of the four hundred and ninety-one members present, declared for the proscribed men.

The Mayor called for the Table of the Rights of Man, and read out the Clause which ran: "If the Government violates the rights of the people, insurrection is for the people the most holy and indispensable of duties," and the first magistrate of Paris announced that the Municipal Commune would oppose the coup d'État of the Assembly by a popular insurrection.

The members of the General Council took the oath to die at their posts. Two municipal officers were instructed to proceed to the Place de Grève and call on the populace to join with its magistrates, to save the people and liberty.

Man sought man, exchanged information, proffered advice. There were few artisans among the magistrates. The Municipality here assembled was that which resulted from the Jacobin purge: judges and jurors of the Revolutionary Tribunal, artists like Beauvillet and Gamelin, dividend-drawers and professors, cosy bourgeois, big business men, powdered heads and corporations with fobs; wooden clogs, trousers, carmagnole red coats and red caps were rare. But they were many, these middle-class men, and determined. Yet, when one came to think of it, this was practically all that was truly republican in Paris. As they stood there, in the Town Hall, as on a rock of liberty, there was an ocean of indifference all round them.

Yet still favourable reports did come in. Every prison in which a proscribed man was imprisoned, opened its doors and let him out again. Augustin Robespierre, coming from La Force prison, was the first to enter the Town Hall, to be acclaimed. At eight it was learned that, after opposing the idea for some time, Maximilien Robespierre was on his way to the Municipality. They waited for him; he was to come, he was on his way; a tremendous ovation shook the vaulted roof of the old Town Hall. He entered, borne on a score of arms. There he was, that dainty, natty little man, in blue coat and yellow breeches, that was Robespierre. He took his place. He spoke.

Now he had come, the Council ordered the front of the municipal building to be illuminated at once. He embodied the Republic. He spoke, spoke in that frail voice, elegantly. His discourse was limpid and abundant. Those present, who had now staked their heads on this man, suddenly perceived, and were astounded thereby, that it was but a man of verbiage, a man for committee or platform, incapable of swift decision or revolutionary act.

He was borne to the Inner Chamber. Now they were all there, all the illustrious proscribed men: Lebas, Saint-Just, Couthon. Robespierre spoke. It was a half after midnight; he was still speaking. Meantime, Gamelin, in the Council Chamber, his forehead pressed to a window-pane, watched with anxious eye; through the black night he could see the smoky lanterns. Hanriot's cannon, in battery formation, faced the Town Hall.

There was an undecided, restless crowd surging to and fro in the square. At half-past-twelve torches appeared at the corner of the Rue de la Vannerie; encircled by them, an emissary from the Assembly, all decked in signs of office, who unfolded a paper and in the red glow read out the Assembly Decree, outlawing the insurrected members of the Municipality, as well as the members of the General

Council present, and any citizen who should respond to their appeal.

Outlawry! Death without trial! The mere notion made the most determined blench. Gamelin felt his forehead icy. He watched the crowd hurry away from the Place de Grève.

Then, turning his head, he could see that the council room, where so recently one could not breathe, was nearly empty.

But they had fled in vain; they had signed.

It was two. The Incorruptible was still in deliberation with the Municipality and the proscribed representatives.

In desperation, Gamelin plunged his glance into the blackened square. The light given out by the lanterns revealed the candles dangling from the eaves of a grocer's shop, with a sound like skittles falling; the street lights were swaying and quivering; a high wind had begun to blow. A moment later, the storm broke; the square emptied to the last man; those whom the terrible Decree had not frightened away had been dispersed by a few drops of rain. Hanriot's cannon were abandoned. And when in the illumination of a flash of lightning he saw Convention troops pour into the square simultaneously from the Rue Antoine and the Embankment, he also saw that the approaches of the Town Hall were deserted.

At last Maximilien Robespierre made up his mind—to appeal to the Piques Wards against the Assembly Decree!

The General Council had sabres, pistols and muskets brought in. But a din of arms, trampling and broken glass suddenly filled the building. The Assembly troops poured like an avalanche through the deliberation chamber and flooded in the Council Chamber. There was a shot, and Gamelin saw Robespierre fall, his jaw shattered. He himself drew his knife, that sixpenny knife with which one day during the famine he had cut a piece of bread for a poor mother, and which, one

lovely evening, at that farm at Orangis, Élodie had kept in her lap when they drew forfeits; he opened it and tried to thrust it into his heart; the blade came up against a rib, then the catch slipped and the blade folded back and caught two fingers. Gamelin fell, bleeding. He lay motionless, but felt terribly cold, and then, kicked from all sides in the chaos of a frightful struggle, he distinctly heard the voice of young Dragoon Henry shouting: "The tyrant is no more; his satellites are smashed. The Revolution will now resume its majestic, awful course." Gamelin had lost consciousness.

At six in the morning, a surgeon sent by the Assembly dressed his wounds. The Assembly was most solicitous about the accomplices of Robespierre; it did not want a single one of them to escape the guillotine. The artist, sometime juror, sometime member of the General Council of the Municipality, was taken to the Conciergerie prison on a stretcher.

## XXVIII

On the 10th, while on a dungeon bank Évariste was just waking in a surge of indescribable horror from a fevered sleep, Paris, in all its charm and immensity, was smiling with sunshine; hope was reborn in the prisoners' hearts; shopkeepers gaily took down their shutters, the bourgeoisie felt richer, young men happier, women more beautiful, now Robespierre had fallen. Only a handful of Jacobins, a few constitutional priests and some old women were aghast to see rule pass to evil, corrupt men. A delegation of the Revolutionary Tribunal, consisting of the public prosecutor and two judges, called on the Assembly, to offer congratulations for putting an end to the conspiracies. The National Convention had decided

that the scaffold should once again be erected in Revolution Square. They wanted the wealthy, the smart, and all pretty women to be able to see Robespierre beheaded without putting themselves to much trouble, and it was to be this very day. The dictator and his accomplices were outlaws; all that was needed was for their identity to be certified by two members of the Commune, for the Tribunal to hand them straight to the executioner. But a difficulty arose: since it was the Commune as a whole that was outlawed, strictly legal identification was impossible. The Assembly then authorised the Tribunal to have identity determined by common witnesses.

The triumvirs were dragged to their death, together with their principal accomplices, amid cries of delight and rage, oaths, laughter, dancing.

The following day, Évariste, who had regained a little strength and could almost stand on his feet, was dragged from his cell, brought to the Tribunal, and placed on that platform which he had so many a time seen crowded with accused men, and where throughout it all, so many a victim, illustrious or obscure, had sat. Today it was groaning under the weight of seventy persons, mainly members of the Municipality, some of them, too, jurors like Gamelin, outlawed like him. Now he saw again his former seat, the back-rest against which he used to lean, the place whence he had terrorised luckless persons, the place where he had had to bear the eyes of Jacques Maubel, Fortuné Chassagne, Maurice Brotteaux, and those pleading eyes of Citizeness Rochemaure, who had had him made juror in the first place, only to be rewarded by a death sentence. Again, dominating the platform, where the judges sat on their mahogany thrones upholstered in Utrecht red velvet, he could see the busts of Chalier and Marat and that bust of Brutus which on one occasion he had

called upon as witness. Nothing had altered, neither axes nor fasces, nor the red bonnets of the wallpaper, neither the insults which the knitting women hurled down from their upper seats on those who were to die, nor the soul of Fouquier-Tinville, stubborn, painstaking, carefully sorting his homicidal papers, and, like a capable magistrate, sending his friends of yesterday to the scaffold.

Citizens Remacle, porter and tailor, and Dupont *senior,* cabinet-maker of Place de Thionville, member of the Watch Committee, recognised Gamelin (Évariste) painter, sometime juror of the Revolutionary Tribunal, sometime member of the General Council of the Municipality. They identified him for a hundred sols treasury bill, chargeable to the Ward; but, having been a neighbour and sort of friend of the outlaw, they were embarrassed about meeting his eyes. For that matter, it was hot; they were thirsty and in a hurry to go and drink a glass of wine.

Gamelin made a great effort and managed to get up into the tumbril; he had lost a lot of blood and his wound pained him terribly. The driver lashed out at his hack and the procession set out, amid hooting.

Some women, recognising Gamelin, yelled: "Off with you, blood drinker! Murderer at eighteen francs a day . . . Now he's not laughing. See how pale the coward is!"

These were the same women who had once insulted conspirators and aristocrats, extremists and moderates, sent to the guillotine by Gamelin and his fellowjurors.

The tumbril turned on to the Morfondus Embankment, drew slowly near to the Pont-Neuf bridge and Rue de la Monnaie; they were going to the Place de la Révolution, to Robespierre's scaffold. The horse limped; the driver kept lashing it about the ears. The overjoyed, excited crowd of spectators slowed the convoy down. The public congratulated the gendarmes, who held their horses in. Young people at their mezzanine tables in the fashionable restaurants, crowded to the windows, napkin in hand, and yelled: "Cannibals, man-eaters, vampires!"

When the tumbril plunged into a heap of filth which had not been removed during these two days of disorder, the gilded youth roared with delight: "The tumbril's bogged . . . The Jacobins are in the shit!"

Gamelin reflected, and thought he could understand.

"It is just for me to die," he told himself. "It is just we should receive these insults cast at the Republic, against which we should have known how to defend it. We were weak; we became guilty of indulgence. We betrayed the Republic. We have merited our fate. Even Robespierre, pure, saint-like, sinned by gentleness, by meekness; his errors have been wiped away by his martyrdom. Following his example, I betrayed the Republic; it has perished; it is just that I should die with it. I spared bloodshed; let my blood flow! Let me perish; I have deserved it . . ."

While he reflected thus, he suddenly noticed the sign of the *Amour Peintre,* and floods of bitterness and sweetness poured into his heart.

The shop was closed, the sun-blinds of the three mezzanine windows right down. When the tumbril passed by the left-hand one, the window of the blue room, a woman's hand, with a silver ring on the ring finger, pushed the edge of the blind aside and tossed towards Gamelin a red carnation, which his pinioned hands could not catch, yet which he adored as symbol and sign of those scented red lips by which his lips had been refreshed. His eyes swelled with tears, and when he saw the bloodstained knife rise over Revolution Square he was completely imbued with the grace of that farewell.

## XXIX

The seine waters swirled with the ice-floes of Nivôse. The Tuileries Gardens ponds, the streams and fountains were solid. The North wind eddied clouds of fine frozen snow. Horses expelled jets of white vapour from their nostrils; pedestrians paused at opticians' to look at the thermometer. A shop assistant was wiping the steam from the windows of the *Amour Peintre* and inquisitive eyes glanced at the prints fashionable at the moment: Robespierre squeezing a heart, like a lemon, over a goblet, to drink blood, and huge allegories such as *Robespierre's Tigocracy*—a confusion of hydras, snakes and terrible monsters let loose by the tyrant against France. There were also: *Robespierre's Outrageous Plot, Arrest of Robespierre* and *Robespierre on the Scaffold.*

On this particular day, after his midday dinner, Philippe Desmahis came in, portfolio under arm, to bring Citizen Blaise a stippled engraving he had just done, entitled *Robespierre's Suicide.* The artist's flamboyant burin had made Robespierre as hideous as possible. The people of France were still not satiated of all these monuments to the disgust and loathing felt for this man, now charged of all the crimes of the Revolution. All the same, the dealer, knowing his public, intimated to Desmahis that in future he would only have military subjects done.

"What we're going to need is victories and conquests, sabres, plumes, generals. We're on the road for glory now. I feel it in my bones; my heart leaps when I hear what our gallant forces are doing. And when I feel a thing, it's a rare thing if the world doesn't feel it too. What we want are soldiers and women, Mars and Venus."

"Citizen Blaise, I still have one or two of Gamelin's drawings at my place, those you asked me to engrave. Are they urgent?"

"Not in the least."

"Apropos of Gamelin: yesterday, as I cut through the Temple boulevard, I saw all the poor fellow's canvases, on a dealer's stall, man who stands opposite the Beaumarchais mansion. His *Orestes and Electra* was among them. The Orestes head, which is just like Gamelin himself, is really fine, I assure you . . . the head and the arm are superb . . . The old dealer told me he had nothing against selling the canvases to artists, to paint on . . . Poor Gamelin! Perhaps there was a first-rate talent there, if he hadn't meddled in politics."

"He was a criminal at heart," replied Citizen Blaise. "I saw through the fellow, on this very spot, while his bloodthirsty instincts were still on the leash. He never forgave me . . . Oh, he was a dirty piece of work, right enough!"

"Poor boy! The fanatics ruined him. He was genuine."

"You surely aren't taking his part, Desmahis? . . . There's no defence of that man."

"No, Citizen Blaise, perhaps you're right."

Then, with a pat on handsome Desmahis' shoulder: "Times have changed," he said. "Now the Assembly is recalling the outlaws, you can be called *Barbaroux* . . . I've been wondering, Desmahis—how would it be if you engraved me a portrait of Charlotte Corday."

A tall, good-looking dark woman, wrapped in a fur coat, entered the shop and gave Citizen Blaise an intimate, secret little nod. It was Julie Gamelin; but she no longer bore that dishonoured name; she had herself called "Citizeness widow Chassagne," and under her cloak wore a red tunic, in honour of the red shirts of the Terror.

Julie had at first felt an aversion from Évariste's mistress, for everything connected with her brother was hateful to her. But Citizeness Blaise, after Éva-

riste's death, made a home for the unhappy mother in the *Amour Peintre* attics. Julie too took refuge there, then found a place at her old work in a gown shop of the Rue des Lombards. Her shortcut hair, "victim style," her aristocratic manner, and her mourning brought her the sympathy of gilded youth. Jean Blaise, whom Rose Thévenin had more or less abandoned, paid his court, and was accepted. But Julie still liked to wear men's clothing, as she had done in those wretched days; she had had a fine suit of male clothing made her and, stick in hand, often went to dine like that in a Sèvres or Meudon bar, with a young milliner. Inconsolable for the loss of the former young noble, whose name she bore, this masculine Julie could only find some solace for her melancholy in a sort of mania, and whenever she met a Jacobin, she would stir up a crowd against him, with cries of "Death!" She had little time left to give her mother, who, alone in her room, spent the whole day telling her beads, too overcome by the tragic end of her son to feel real grief. Rose had now become Élodie's constant companion; Élodie certainly got on well with her mothers-in-law.

"Where is Élodie?" Citizeness Chassagne demanded.

Jean Blaise indicated that he did not know. He never did; he made that a principle of conduct.

Julie had come to fetch Élodie to go with her to see Rose Thévenin at Monceaux, where the actress had a little house with an English garden.

In the Conciergerie prison, Rose knew a man named Montfort, who was an army contractor in a big way. Getting out of prison first, through Jean Blaise's intervention, she secured the release of Citizen Montfort, who, the moment he was free, was supplying the army with provisions and speculating in land in the la Pépinière district. Ledoux, Olivier and

Wailly built a number of lovely houses there, and in three months the land trebled its value. After some time in the Luxembourg prison, Montfort became Rose's lover; he gave her this little house near the Tivoli and the Rue du Rocher, worth a lot, but costing him nothing, the sale of the adjoining parcels already having recompensed him many times over. Jean Blaise was a great gentleman; he believed one should put up with what one cannot prevent, and he let Montfort take Rose over, without quarrelling with her.

Soon after Julie's arrival at the *Amour Peintre*, Élodie came down into the shop, all dressed up. Under her cloak, despite the harsh weather she had nothing on but a white gown; her cheeks were paler, she was thinner, her eyes melted ravishingly, and her whole being was expressive of sensual love.

The two women went to see Rose, who was expecting them. Desmahis went with them; the actress was consulting him on the interior decoration of her house, and he was much taken up with Élodie, who just at the moment was more than half determined not to keep him on tenterhooks any longer. When the two women passed near Monceaux, where those executed on the Place de la Révolution were buried in a bed of quicklime, Julie said: "It's alright now it's cold, but in the Spring the air rising from this plot of ground will poison half the city."

Rose received her two friends in a classical *salon*, the sofas and armchairs of which were designed by David. Roman bas-reliefs, copied in camayeu, dominated the walls, with statues, busts and candelabrae painted bronze beneath them. Rose was wearing a curled wig, straw colour. Wigs were just the rage—a bride's trousseau would contain six, or a dozen, or eighteen of them. A gown in Cypriot style wrapped round Rose's figure like a sheath.

Sweeping a cloak over her shoulders, she took her friends and the engraver out into the garden, which Ledoux had planned for her, but which so far was only a medley of leafless trees and plaster. All the same, she could show them her Fingal's Cave, Gothic Chapel and belltower and a stream.

"There," she said, pointing to a bunch of pines, "I should like to have a cenotaph to the memory of poor Brotteaux des Ilettes. I had a weakness for that man. He was a darling. The wretches slaughtered him; I wept. Desmahis, can you design me an urn on a column?"

Then, immediately, she added: "Such a nuisance . . . I did so want to give a ball this week, but all the violinists are booked up three weeks ahead. Citizeness Tallière is giving a dance every evening."

After dinner, Rose's carriage took the three women and Desmahis to the Feydeau Theatre. Here all the elegant world of Paris was to be seen. The women, their hair done in *classic* or *victim* style, with very décolleté gowns, purple, or white, spangled with gold; the men in very high black collars, their chins lost under enormous white cravats.

The placard announced *Phèdre* and *The Gardener's Dog*. There was a general call for the song which at the moment was dear to dandies and gilded youth, namely, the *Nation's Awakening*.

The curtain rose and a stumpy, stout little man entered—the famous Lays. In his lovely tenor he sang:

"*People of France, people of
brothers . . .*"

The applause was so tremendous that the crystals of the candelabrae rang. Then there was some muttering, and a citizen in round hat in the stalls replied with the *Marseillaise*—

"*Come, Children of the Fatherland!*"

His voice was drowned in booing; there were shouts: "Down with the terrorists! Death to the Jacobins!"

Lays was now recalled, and for the second time sang the Thermidorians' hymn:

*"People of France, people of*
*brothers . . ."*

In every theatre you could see the bust of Marat raised on a column or a pedestal; at the Feydeau, the bust stood on a low pillar, on the prompt side, against a masonry upright at the edge of the stage.

While the orchestra was playing the *Phèdre et Hippolyte* overture, a young dandy pointed his cane at the bust, and shouted, "Down with Marat!"

The whole audience repeated: "Down with Marat! Down with Marat!"

Then clearer voices rose above the din: "It's a shame that thing should still be there!"

"That scoundrel Marat reigns everywhere, to our shame! There are as many busts of him as he had heads cut off."

"Poisonous reptile!"

"Tiger!"

"Black snake!"

Suddenly a well-dressed member of the audience climbed on to the front of his box, gave the bust a push, and upset it. The plaster head fell in fragments over the orchestra, to the general applause of the audience, now on their feet, intoning the *Réveil du Peuple:*

*"People of France, people of brothers!"*

Amid the most enthusiastic singers, Élodie suddenly recognised the handsome dragoon, that little prosecutor's clerk, Henry, her first love.

After the show, handsome Desmahis hailed a cab, and took Citizeness Blaise to the *Amour Peintre.*

In the cab, the artist took Élodie's hands in his. "Élodie, don't you believe I love you?"

"I do, because you love every woman."

"In you, yes."

She smiled:

"I should have to take on a great deal, despite all your black, blond and Titian wigs which are the rage, if I were to be all kinds of women to you."

"Élodie, I swear . . ."

"Not oaths, Citizen Desmahis? Either you are very naïve, or you think I am."

Desmahis could not think what to reply, and she congratulated herself on this triumph of baffling his wit.

At the corner of the Rue de la Loi, they heard singing and shouting and saw the silhouettes of some people milling round a brasier. It was a band of fashionable young men who had just come out of the Théâtre Français, and were burning an effigy of the Friend of the People.

In the Rue Honoré, the coachman drove right into a comic effigy of Marat, dangling from a lamp-post, so that it knocked his cocked hat off.

This delighted the man. He turned to his bourgeois passengers and told them how yesterday evening a tripe-butcher in the Rue Montorgueil had smeared blood all over Marat's head. "That's what he liked." And little boys of ten had tipped the bust down the drain. And wasn't it to the point, how some people who saw it shouted: "That's the Pantheon he wants!"

As they rode, they could hear people in all restaurants and cafés singing:

*"People of France, people of brothers!"*

When they reached the *Amour Peintre,* Élodie jumped down. "Farewell!" she cried.

But Desmahis begged her very tenderly, and was so nice and so pressing that she had not the heart to say goodbye at the door.

"It's late," she said, "You can only stay a moment."

In the blue room, she took off her cloak and there she was in her classical white gown, with all her ample warmth of outline.

"Perhaps you are cold," she said, "I'll light a fire; it's all ready."

She struck the flint and stuck her lighted match-stick into the hearth.

Philippe took her in his arms with that gentleness which tells of strength, and this gave her a strange sense of sweetness. She was in fact just yielding under his kisses, when she pulled herself free. "Stop!" she said.

Slowly, before the mirror over the mantel, she undid her hair, then gave a sad glance at the ring she wore on the ring finger of her left hand, a little silver ring on which the features of Marat, now much scratched and worn, could no longer be seen. She gazed at this till tears blinded her, then took it tenderly off and threw it into the fire.

After this, dazzling with tears and smiles, beautiful with tenderness and passion, she threw herself into Philippe's arms.

The night was far advanced when Citizeness Blaise opened the flat door for her lover and, in the darkness, whispered:

"Farewell, my love . . . This is the hour when my father comes home; if you hear any noise on the stairs, go up quickly to the floor above and don't come down till there is no more danger of his seeing you. To have the street door opened, give three taps on the window of the porter's room. Farewell, my life! Farewell, dear sweet!"

The last coals were glowing in the hearth. Élodie's head, happy and wearied, sank into her pillow.

# THE LIFE AND WORKS OF
# ANATOLE FRANCE

*By JACQUES CHASTENET DE CATAING*

---

ANATOLE FRANCE's considerable influence was felt not only through his books but also through his conversation, his lectures, and—more generally—through the example he offered of a perfectly free and humane spirit in a society already dominated by the machine and threatened by conformity.

His real name was not France but Thibault, and although the pseudonym may seem a trifle presumptuous, it is not entirely so. He did not express every aspect of the French genius—far from it—but he presented some of its most characteristic features. The marriage of skepticism and idealism, the traditionalism of the property owner combined with a taste for subversive ideas, a distrust of the metaphysical, a passion for clarity, an ability to retain a light touch in dealing with serious matters, sensuality without coarseness, and the art of saying things well: all these traits are, or were until recently, specifically French.

Anatole Thibault was born in Paris on April 16, 1844, in an apartment on Quai Voltaire. Though he was a keen traveler, he remained a Parisian all his life; and a Parisian, moreover, from the very heart of the capital. How lovingly he wrote of "those noble old quays" and "that glorious river" of his childhood! "It seems impossible to be just ordinary if one has been brought up on the quays of Paris . . . Trees, books, women strolling by —it is the most beautiful place on earth."

His father, François-Noël Thibault, a native of Anjou, ran a bookstall on Quai Malaquais. It was known as the *Librairie de France* and this, rather than conceit, was probably the source of his son's pseudonym. The *Librairie* specialized in second-hand books, caricatures, and manuscripts dealing with the Revolution, and it was there that Anatole developed his taste for old papers and learned conversation.

"My father," he wrote, "had a sublime notion of the human soul and its destiny: he believed it was made for heaven. Where he was pessimistic and melancholy, I was pessimistic and joyful. I was instinctively opposed to him on every subject. I came to love the decorative reason and beautiful order of classical art." His mother, who came from the Beauce, was an intelligent, charitable, and pious woman whom he always remembered with tenderness.

Anatole's love of "the decorative reason and beautiful order of classical art" was slow to show itself. As a schoolboy, first at the Institution de Sainte-Marie and then at the Collège Stanislas, he was inattentive, free-and-easy, and undisciplined. Although he completely neglected the exact sciences, he gained a good knowledge of Latin and a smattering of Greek, while his wide, if somewhat random, reading—novels, poetry, history, philosophy—filled his mind with valuable odds and ends on which he continually drew.

He was very deeply influenced by Sainte-Beuve and especially by Renan, for whom he had a lifelong admiration. He soon—and apparently painlessly—shook off his religious faith and became a pure rationalist, like most young intellectuals of his day. But his rationalism was always tinged with a respect for "holy things"—albeit a respect heavily laced with irony. The elegant but slightly hypocritical manner in which he linked the sacred with the profane, sometimes associating the religious with the scabrous, gives much of his writing a certain piquancy, although it is not always in the best of taste. He was not a disciple of the scientific positivism dear to the nineteenth century; instead, he seemed to be a man of the eighteenth century.

After his education he had to start earning his living immediately; his parents were not rich, and in 1862 he became a reader for Alphonse Lemerre, publisher of several leading lights and young hopefuls among the French poets of the day such as Leconte de Lisle, Théophile Gautier, Théodore de Banville, Catulle Mendès, José-Maria de Hérédia, François Coppée, and many others. Their works, varied in inspiration and far removed from the outpourings of the Romantics, were published by Lemerre in successive issues of the periodical *Parnasse contemporain.* In this milieu, Anatole Thibault, with his long nose, jutting chin, hesitant speech, and unsure gestures, at first seemed rather out of place; but his intelligence, friendliness, and pleasant manner soon won him a number of friends. Gradually he became an accepted Parnassian, and he held a

fairly solid position in the firm, reading manuscripts, annotating them, reporting on them to his employer, and correcting them if necessary. At the same time, he was doing some writing on the side, and in 1873 he published his first collection of verse, *Les Poèmes dorés* (The Gilded Poems): poems with an easy grace, and, if a little languid, exhibiting an unusual technical skill. The connoisseurs applauded, and France—he had now adopted the name—became a figure of some authority at Lemerre's. He used his new influence to remove poems by Mallarmé ("We'll be a laughing-stock") and by Verlaine ("The author is unworthy") from an issue of the *Parnasse contemporain.* In 1875, such exclusions seemed less absurd than they would later on, but nevertheless, they account for the fact that on succeeding Anatole France at the Academy, Paul Valéry refused to refer directly to his predecessor in his inaugural address.

The young writer published his second collection of poetry in 1876, *Les Noces corinthiennes* (*The Corinthian Weddings*), a much more sustained effort than his first. The book is dominated by a nostalgia for a somewhat conventional Hellenism and a hostility toward the Christianity that submerged it. This was the last poetry France ever published. In the same year, thanks to Leconte de Lisle, Librarian to the Senate, Anatole France was appointed curator at the Luxembourg Library. This near-sinecure enabled him to marry Valérie Guerin de Sauville, a pleasant, fair-haired girl of twenty, and also to write a series of prefaces to editions of the classics and to contribute two stories to the periodical *Le Temps:* "Jocaste" (*Jocasta*) and "Le Chat maigre" (*The Thin Cat*). These are lightweight works, rather confused in plot, but they contain some amusing characters sketched with rare skill.

When Anatole France was in his thirty-seventh year he was little known outside his own narrow circle. Then, in April of 1881, *Le Crime de Silvestre Bonnard, membre de l'Institut* (*The Crime of Sylvestre Bonnard*) was published, and overnight he became famous. The Académie Française awarded it a prize, and, in a letter to the author, Maurice Barrès announced "I am a young disciple of yours."

*The Crime* is the juxtaposition of two long stories whose central figure is the erudite Sylvestre Bonnard, old in years but young in heart, eloquent, generous, witty—in fact, delightful. The double plot is rather thin, and improbabilities abound. The style is lucid and lively, refined yet unpretentious; the successive episodes—amusing, touching, but never dull—and settings—the quays of Paris, Sicilian landscapes, picturesque interiors —are handled with great assurance, as are the secondary characters and their doings. There is none of the bitter laughter that echoes through so many of France's later works, only an indulgent smile.

With the passing of the years, the book remains almost as fresh as ever, indisputably a small masterpiece, deserving to survive as a feast for the discriminating.

With its publication Anatole France became, if not a standard author, at least an established one. Between 1882 and 1885, he produced another novel, *Les Désirs de Jean Servien* (*The Desires of Jean Servien*), and various stories and travel sketches. He began to frequent the literary salons, became a member of the Legion of Honor, and published a barely fictionalized account of his own childhood in *Le livre de mon ami* (1885) (*My Friend's Book*, 1885), a work of lasting charm.

In 1886, Adrien Hébrard—a noted wit and a figure of some consequence in his day—paid Anatole France the supreme compliment of entrusting him with the editorship of the literary section of *Le Temps*. For the next seven years, he was able to lay down the law from this august platform once a week. He did so without harshness or pedantry, as a stroller in the garden of the Muses, lingering over vistas that attracted him, turning away from corners that were not to his taste, stopping now and then to pluck a flower and savor its perfume. He was less concerned with dissecting a work than with conveying the impression it made on him, its appeal to his emotions. As a critic, his approach was impressionistic and subjective: "The good critic," he wrote, "is one who relates the adventures of his soul among masterpieces." This method can be irritating when the adventures happen to be of little interest, but it was Montaigne's method and France employed it almost as felicitously.

His critical articles, collected under the title *La Vie littéraire* (1888–1892) (*On Life and Letters,* 1888–1892), hardly shed much light on the literary movements of the time, but they are crammed with subtle ideas and acute insights. Eclectic, interested in all forms of thought, endowed with prodigious intellectual agility, France is not in the least unbending and renders justice even to works that do not appeal to his taste. Nevertheless, his own tastes always show through: the taste for "classical order," for "nature tamed by the hand of man," for measure and for reason. For France, Racine was "the sovereign master in whom all truth and all beauty reside," La Fontaine was "the most French of our poets," and Voltaire shone with an incomparable brilliance. Anyone who turns his back on these great models may be remarkable or amusing, but is none the less a freak. France could not stand Rousseau because he was the father of romanticism and, among the Romantics, he put Lamartine and Vigny above Hugo because they were not so far removed from Classicism. As for his contemporaries, beneath his surface courtesy they were repugnant to him (apart from Maupassant whom he admired for his restraint).

In 1888, something happened that was to have a far-reaching influence on France's life, thought, and work: he became the lover of Madame Arman de Caillavet. Léontine Lippmann was born into a rich family of Jewish bankers. In 1867, she married Albert Arman de Caillavet—a good-hearted if obstreperous man with a taste for gambling. The marriage soon failed and Léontine, who was as active as she was ambitious, sought consolation by plunging into the literary, artistic, and political life of the time. After adorning Madame Aubernon's famous salon for a while, she set up one of her own in her town house on Avenue Roche.

Anatole France soon became an assiduous visitor. His own marriage was an unhappy one, and the birth of a daughter had not succeeded in patching it up. Piquant rather than beautiful, no longer young but sparkling and vivacious, Madame Arman captivated the rather timid forty-year-old writer, who began to confide in her, telling her all his plans, hopes, and fears. Reserved at first, she soon yielded to him and their long liaison began—a liaison that was both ardent and stormy.

Though France divorced his wife in 1893, Léontine did not follow suit. Her husband, for all his bluster, had proved easy to deal with, and while being careful to respect the proprieties (though nobody was taken in), the writer often worked in the house on Avenue Roche, stayed there from time to time, and accompanied his mistress on her travels and holidays whenever possible. She very quickly gained complete ascendancy over him, for France, without being exactly lazy, was easy-going: she obliged him to work, gave him ideas for stories, carried out research for him in the libraries, and re-

vised his manuscripts. In fact it was thanks to her that France, rather inclined to fritter away his time, became an unusually prolific author with an ever expanding public.

While he had very definite ideas, France preferred to conceal them behind a mask of conventional skepticism. Madame Arman, a much more ardent spirit, encouraged him to bring them out into the open. Without her he would probably have gone on being no more than a delightful story-teller, an artist-critic, and a delicate connoisseur of the flowers of rhetoric. In spite of his hesitations and misgivings, she turned him into a political controversialist and the standard-bearer of a great political party.

At first Madame Arman's influence was exercised only on the level of literary output. Then, in 1889, France published the novel *Thaïs* in *La Revue des Deux Mondes*. It was a reworking in prose of a verse narrative he had written in his youth. The tone, however, was quite changed. The basic story remained, the courtesan converted by a hermit, who is then consumed by love for her. But it was not used as the pretext for a gentle pastiche of the Alexandrian poets as earlier. This time it was a means of setting forth the author's philosophy or, if that is too strong a word, his attitude to existence—his horror of the cult of gloom, his denial of the supernatural, and his passion for "the banquet of life." It is a succession of brilliant scenes, sprinkled with subtle dialogue and written in a style that, even if it seems somewhat self-conscious at times, deserves the highest admiration for its flowing clarity. *Thaïs* is far from being Anatole France's best novel, but it is the first in which he reveals himself completely.

During the next few years he continued his work for *Le Temps* and prepared a collection of stories *L'Etui de nacre* (*Mother of Pearl*) and a novel *La*

*Rôtisserie de la reine Pédauque* (*At the Sign of the Reine Pédauque*), both of which appeared in 1893. The short-story form was particularly congenial to France, who did not have a great deal of imagination, but who was a meticulous craftsman. Written in the same spirit as *Thaïs, Mother of Pearl* is a work of infinite charm and playfulness.

*At the Sign of the Reine Pédauque* is not exactly a novel, but rather a series of colorful episodes and ingenious digressions woven around a few selected themes. In it, France created an unforgettable character: Jérôme Coignard, an eighteenth-century priest, doctor of theology, bachelor of arts, eloquent scholar, a bit of a bohemian and a free-liver, fond of the bottle, but with a rare freshness of mind and heart. The circle of people surrounding this picturesque ecclesiastic, who often serves as a spokesman for the author, comprises a variety of lightly drawn but colorful figures.

In the same year, 1893, France published in a Paris paper a serial entitled *Les Opinions de M. Jérôme Coignard sur les affaires du temps* (*The Opinions of Jérôme Coignard*). It develops, without any plot but with a number of allusions to contemporary events, the sensual, compassionate, and lightly pessimistic ideas of the novel that preceded it. "Never," he wrote of his hero Jérôme, "was there a mind at once so bold and so peace-loving . . . While he despised men, he did so with gentleness. He tried to teach them . . . that, being accustomed only to desire and suffering, they should create for themselves virtues of an indulgent and pleasureable kind."

Here—at least as far as that particular period of his life is concerned—we have the gist of France's philosophy.

Both the *Opinions* and *At the Sign of the Reine Pédauque* had a dazzling reception. At the end of the nineteenth century, anarchy was the fashion in worldly and intellectual circles—perhaps because society appeared to be solidly based and not subject to any pressing internal or external threat—and Jérôme Coignard, an erudite and lovable anarchist, had every chance of finding favor, and his creator was launched on the road to fame and fortune.

In 1894, Massenet's opera based on *Thaïs* was produced, and France published *Le Lys rouge* (*The Red Lily*), a novel written at the urging of Madame Arman with the aim of eclipsing the immensely popular works of Paul Bourget.

It is not a very good novel, and while it includes charming glimpses of the Florentine countryside, some amusing *genre* pieces, and a few spirited love scenes, it gives the impression that the author was not entirely in his element. Even the style, though it is nicely handled, becomes tiresome in the end, particularly as all the characters employ it uniformly. Nevertheless, *The Red Lily* was a great success. With his royalties, France was able to buy the Villa Saïd, a small private house near the Avenue du Bois. There, every Sunday and Wednesday, he presided over a small circle of friends and admirers.

This was an extremely active period of the author's life. Articles, prefaces, and lectures poured from his pen, he traveled widely with Madame Arman, scouring the antique shops of France and Italy, and published *Le Jardin d'Epicure* (*The Garden of Epicurus*, 1894), in which M. Coignard's philosophy reappears in rather more melancholy guise, and *Le Puits de Sainte-Claire* (*The Well of Saint Claire*, 1895), a collection of stories. The following passage from *The Garden of Epicurus* is quite a good summing-up of the work: "The more I think of human life, the more I believe that it should be assigned Irony and Pity as witnesses and judges, just as the Egyptians called the goddesses Isis and Nepthes to their dead.

Irony and Pity are two excellent counselors: the first makes life agreeable with her smiles, the other makes it sacred with her tears. The Irony I refer to is not cruel. She does not laugh at either love or beauty. She is gentle and kindly. Her laugh appeases anger, and it is she who teaches us to make fun of the wicked and stupid, whom we might otherwise have the weakness to hate."

France's reputation as a writer and thinker was now firmly established. Only one honor was missing: membership in the Académie Française. This finally came in 1896 when he was elected to the seat left vacant by the death of Ferdinand de Lesseps, the creator of the Suez Canal.

By the end of the nineteenth century—perhaps because of over-prosperity—the French nation was in a perpetual state of turmoil. The Panama scandal had thrown discredit on the opportunist, bourgeois Republic; there was a clamor for social justice; Jaurès proclaimed "the awakening of human misery"; strikes, violence, and anarchist attacks proliferated. At the same time, the Church (which had not yet resigned itself to the growth of secularism) became the ally of the monarchists in the struggle against an abhorrent régime. Finally, in 1897, certain circles began to denounce a legal injustice: the unjust condemnation of Captain Dreyfus as a traitor. Thus was born the affair that was to divide the French into two equally vehement and hostile camps.

*The Opinions of Jérôme Coignard* had given the impression that France was a man of mildly anarchist leanings, completely opposed to religion and decidedly contemptuous of what had become known as "social forces." But his art and his irony involved a certain ambiguity. Did he really identify himself with his leading character, or was the character simply a pretext for perpetrating outrageous paradoxes? France himself had been content to leave the matter in doubt.

Now, however, France finally showed where he stood. The four volumes of his *Histoire contemporaine* (*Contemporary History*)—*L'Orme du mail* (*The Elm-Tree on the Mall,* 1897), *Le Mannequin d'osier* (*The Wicker-Work Woman,* 1897), *L'Anneau d'améthyste* (*The Amethyst Ring,* 1899), and *M. Bergeret à Paris* (*Bergeret in Paris,* 1901)—are not only portrayals of the life of his time, they are also professions of faith.

France's style, however, remained unchanged. Like his earlier works, the *History,* whose hero is a Latin scholar in a provincial university, is full of harmoniously balanced speeches and erudite dissertations, of comic episodes and racy anecdotes. But the author's position is clear: he is against the Church, against the army, against capitalism, and against the established order in general; he is on the side of the humble, of those who are crushed by the social machine, of criticism based on reason, and of irreverence.

The pitch rises with each volume. When *The Elm-Tree on the Mall* appeared, the Dreyfus affair had not even begun, and the writer's main target was the opportunism of the Republic: "My father told me that the Republic represented justice. But he was ignorant of its real nature. It does not represent justice but facility . . . As long as one makes no attempt on its life and attacks only its virtue, it remains unruffled." By the time we come to *Bergeret in Paris,* we find an Anatole France who, horrified by "the crimes of the general staff," has become a confirmed Socialist and condemns the whole of bourgeois society. Madame Arman de Caillavet, who was Jewish, had ardently supported Dreyfus, and she undoubtedly influenced the development of her lover's opinions; in fact, France never ceased to be himself—he was simply more clearly and honestly himself than ever before.

In spite of everything, however, France

remained basically an intellectual, coddled bourgeois and, although there can be little doubt of his sincerity, there is something suspect about his revolutionary fervor.

It is significant that the first three volumes of the *Contemporary History* consist of endless variations on an ecclesiastical theme: the rivalry between the unctuous Abbé Guitrel and the uncompromising Abbé Lantaigne, both candidates for the same episcopal see. Like Renan, his model, France always had a certain nostalgia for the Church and some affection for its ministers. His work swarms with clerical characters, not all of them detestable or ridiculous. "I am not religious," says M. Bergeret, "but I am a theologian." France himself loved to quote the fathers and doctors of the Church, usually doing so to contradict them, but his irony is often tempered by a sort of respect.

When *Contemporary History* was being written, the French Church was still living under the Concordat, whereby its bishops were nominated by the government. Needless to say, France takes the greatest pleasure in mingling the odors of the sacristy and the fusty atmosphere of the government office. *The Amethyst Ring* is almost entirely concerned with the amorous intrigues of a number of ladies who wish—for various profane reasons—to see the mitre bestowed on Abbé Guitrel.

Though much of it is caricature, *Contemporary History* is a valuable document on the political, administrative, and fashionable French world of the period. It will always be a useful source for the social historian, and the ordinary reader will find it lively entertainment.

In 1898, France signed the so-called Petition of the Intellectuals demanding a revision of the Dreyfus case and over this issue he broke with some of his best and oldest friends. In 1899, he stopped attending the meetings of the Académie Française, which contained for him too many who were anti-Dreyfus ("I should find it embarrassing to see people there whose conduct strikes me as despicable and revolting"). In 1901, after the publication of *Bergeret in Paris,* he brought out "L'Affaire Crainquebille" (*The Fearful Affair*), a bitter and very witty pamphlet directed against the administration. In 1902, on the occasion of Zola's funeral, he made a fighting speech in which—forgetting that he had at one time inveighed against the naturalism of the author of *Germinal*—he declared that Zola had been "a moment of human conscience."

France gave his full support to the anticlerical policy of the "Bloc," joined its Socialist left wing, and became friendly with the eloquent people's champion, Jaurès. This was a sincere and understandable friendship for, like France, Jaurès was a lover of good French and good Latin. France diligently attended the party congresses, became a prolific public speaker, and even went so far as to write the preface for a collection of speeches by Émile Combes, the "little father." This preface was reprinted in a pamphlet significantly entitled "Le Parti noir" (The Black Party). In short, he had finally become—at least on the surface—a militant.

This earned him the enthusiastic admiration not only of the left-wing intellectuals but of a working-class public that was hardly capable of appreciating his subtleties. The workers who flocked to trade-union meetings were flattered to see in their midst a writer who, they had been told, was one of the greatest their country had ever produced, and he was always greeted with an ovation. France himself remained ever courteous, gracious, and bland, and if these contacts with the people sometimes offended his susceptibilities he was careful not to show it. His new friends had not estranged him from all his old ones, and Maurice Barrès, although he had become an active nationalist, could still write about him: "There is no Dreyfus, dead or alive, who could make me offend a master I have loved more than anyone on earth for fifteen years." In fact, however much his ideas may have developed, France's manner remained unchanged: he maintained the same considerate politeness, unfailing courtesy, and even temper, was always ready with a well-turned epigram, an erudite anecdote, or a racy story. Those who enjoyed a playful wit, whatever their political allegiance, succumbed to his disarming charm.

France was now approaching his sixties. His trim beard and bristling moustache had turned white, but there was still a twinkle in his fine eyes. At home in the Villa Saïd, or at Madame Arman's, he reigned over an incongruous band of disciples: men of letters, painters and sculptors of both sexes, socialites, art lovers, rich financiers, beautiful actresses, celebrities of all kinds from every country, an ecclesiastic or two, leaders of international socialism, Russian nihilists, Spanish anarchists, Hindu mystics, and a large number of young people who had no special vocation but who were united in their admiration of the great man. One of the most assiduous and enthusiastic of these was Marcel Proust.

But the incense rising to his nostrils did not turn Anatole France's head. After a moment of exaltation at what he took to be the triumph of his political ideals, he realized that this triumph was illusory and that, under their various labels, people's passions, selfishness, and prejudices remained unchanged.

As a distraction, he wrote *L'Histoire comique* (*Comic History*), a pleasantly licentious tale about actors. But this was not what the fervent advocates of social revolution expected of him. To retain their support, he joined the committee of the League of Human Rights, signed manifestoes, took the chair at public meetings, inveighed against Czarism and the French politicians who were "accomplices of the murderous autocrat," and predicted the coming of better days. But he no longer had much faith in these better days, and his innate pessimism rose to the surface again.

The crowd that thronged around him began to be a nuisance, and he turned to travel as a means of escape, always with Madame Arman along with him. Gradually the constant presence of this ever devoted, overeager mistress became irksome. What he really wanted to escape from was the contemporary world. Accordingly he returned to a work he had long since abandoned—a life of Joan of Arc. In 1906 and 1907, he spent a great deal of time on it, consulting specialists, rummaging through archives, visiting places connected with his heroine. At the beginning of 1908, the book was published in two volumes. It had a poor reception.

It disappointed the right wing because Anatole France's Joan was not at all the saint entrusted by heaven with the mission of saving her country. It disappointed the left wing because she was not an incarnation of the people or a forerunner of Jacobin patriotism.

France had tried to be not only as well documented as possible but extremely objective. He did, however, start from a premise—it was not in his nature to do otherwise. This premise was the rationalist one: the supernatural did not exist, and the voices heard by Joan were obviously a sensory illusion. In other words, she was a hysterical neurotic. France took great pains to show that anything that might seem extraordinary in her career could be explained in a perfectly natural way. As for her historical role, he reduced it to that of a mascot. It was a priest who suggested her mission to the pious Joan, and a powerful party made use of her to carry out a long prepared plan. Without her, the war might have lasted longer, but in the end the English would inevitably have been "kicked out" of France. All this he accompanied by great protestations of sympathy, respect, and even affection. Although the book contains some fine passages and is of genuine historical value, it must be admitted that, with its constant digressions and uniformly limpid style, it is rather boring and ultimately unconvincing.

In the following year, 1908, France produced a book that could also be called historical, but was in a much more lively and scathing vein: *L'Île des Pingouins* (*Penguin Island*). These penguins were the French people, who, through the intercession of the good St. Maël, were changed from birds into men. With this metamorphosis they acquired all the human failings: pride, cowardice, licentiousness, selfishness. Their history, which is briefly summarized, is little more than a succession of stupidities, betrayals, and slaughters for which "superstition" is largely responsible. The author dwells at length on certain contemporary events— Boulangism, the Dreyfus affair—and it is easy to guess with what satirical relish he presents them, intermingling sordid intrigue and bedroom comedy.

France has little hope for the future. Men cannot change. With apocalpytic foresight, he predicts that the capitalist civilization of the penguins will become exorbitantly rich to the benefit of a handful of exploiters, that a revolt of the exploited will overthrow them, that general poverty will follow this upheaval, and the land that had nourished so many millions of men will become no more than a desert. Then the story will start all over again with the same follies, the same crimes, and so on *ad infinitum*. Never was Anatole France's irony so bitter, so corrosive, and so uncompromising.

But France's unhappiness continued: the world seemed increasingly absurd to him, and Madame Arman de Caillavet was decidedly too much for him. To escape from her, and from himself, he agreed to give a series of lectures on Rabelais in South America. On the boat he made the acquaintance of an actress, Jeanne Brindeau, who became his mistress. On hearing of this affair, Madame Arman wrote him a series of despairing letters and tried to kill herself. On his return, France repented and broke with his new mistress, but his long-time mistress was unable to regain her peace of mind, fell seriously ill, lingered on for a few months, and died at the beginning of 1910.

France was deeply distressed, but his tears were probably for himself. For such a sensual man, a woman's presence was indispensable. He soon took up with Emma Laprévotte, an amiable woman who had been his late mistress's chambermaid. Before long, he was running several affairs simultaneously, notably one with Laura MacAdoo, an American brunette. It may seem somewhat surprising that a man who had reached his sixty-eighth year should have been so preoccupied with sex. But, as he once wrote: "Life would really be sad if a swarm of randy thoughts did not arise to comfort us from time to time in our old age."

He did not content himself with mere thoughts, however, for his vitality, like his talent, was undiminished. In 1912 he published *Les Dieux ont soif* (*The Gods Are Athirst*), the most vivid and concentrated of his books. This was not so much a novel as a chronicle of the time of the Terror. As a child in his father's bookshop, France had acquired a solid knowledge of the French Revolution, and he was well acquainted with its causes and not insensitive to its grandeur. But he was far from admiring it unreservedly, and the fanaticism of the Jacobins—like all fanaticism—was utterly repugnant to him.

The central figure of the book is a young painter, Évariste Gamelin, a pupil of David's, honest, decent, enthusiastic, but narrow-minded. On his appointment as a juror to the Revolutionary Tribunal, Évariste's patriotism takes the form of a blind, implacable severity. A slavish supporter of Robespierre's, he is finally led to the scaffold to which he himself has sent so many innocent victims, but he remains a blinkered fanatic to the end.

The savage attack on Jacobin excesses in *The Gods Are Athirst* might suggest that France had given up his subversive opinions, but this was not the case. At the beginning of 1914, after a year spent mainly in travel, he brought out *La Révolte des anges (The Revolt of the Angels)*, a philosophical novel in which his anarchistic pessimism is more violently apparent than ever. In this book we find the whole of France's stock-in-trade: a somewhat superficial erudition, pseudo-theological discussions, a nostalgia for the pagan world of the past, sketches of morals and manners (more often bad than good), a freedom often bordering on the salacious, social satire, restrained indignation, and a contemptuous pity for humanity. All this is set down in musical and varied prose, combining an irresistible comic force with an epic sweep.

Like *Penguin Island, The Revolt of the Angels* has an apocalyptic ending. The rebellious angels (several of whom have had love affairs on earth) are on the point of capturing the citadel in which Iadalbaoth, the old God of the Jews and Christians, is enthroned. Victory seems in their grasp when their leader, Lucifer, the most beautiful of the seraphim, realizes that it would not change human nature. "No," he cries, "we shall not conquer the heavens—it is enough to know that we can do it. War engenders war, and victory defeat . . . It is within ourselves, and only within ourselves, that we must attack and destroy Iadalbaoth."

The book appeared at a time when this disillusioned wisdom was far from being shared by other Europeans. World War I broke out in August; the most civilized peoples were caught up in a paroxysm of violence, and all the destructive forces that Anatole France hated most—nationalism, fanaticism, pugnacity, deliberate blindness—were unleashed. In his preface to *The Life of Joan of Arc,* the author had written: "We have no assurance that France will not one day be involved in a European and even worldwide conflagration." Nevertheless, faced with the actual event, he was plunged into a state of helplessness and near despair.

When the Germans advanced on Paris, he fled with Emma Laprévotte to the Manor of La Bechellerie near Tours. From there, he still tried to influence public opinion. In a message published by the newspaper *La Guerre sociale,* he stigmatized German barbarity, but also expressed his longing for the time "when the French people can extend the hand of friendship to the vanquished enemy." This phrase was received with almost universal disapproval and Anatole France felt so appallingly isolated that, for a moment, he contemplated suicide.

But as the months passed and rivers of blood continued to flow, some of his faithful disciples and certain statesmen, such as Caillaux and Léon Blum, made their way to La Bechellerie. In 1917, the aging master judged that the time was ripe to raise the voice of reason once again. In an open letter, he advocated a peace without victory. This time his courage—for it certainly took courage to express such a view just then—did not go unappreciated. Nevertheless, the slaughter continued unabated, and in January of 1918, Anatole France—pessimistic and clearsighted as ever—wrote to a friend: "I am afraid that, no matter what happens, the end of this war will not be the end of the age of violence. It contains the seeds of three or four equally horrible wars, and that is the ghastly truth."

When at long last the dearly bought victory came, he resumed his place in the left wing of the Socialist party, later joining the breakaway Communist Party. He became a regular contributor of *L'Humanité,* took the chair at trade-union meetings, and made pacifist speeches, but this did not prevent him from occasionally occupying his place at the Académie Française or from writing *Le petit Pierre* (*Little Pierre,* 1919), a book in which politics play no part. Finally, he decided to marry his mistress Emma Laprévotte.

In 1921, he was seventy-seven. His beard had grown longer and was a snowy white, his furrowed features had gained nobility, and he had come to be regarded as a grand old man of literature, almost a national monument. In November, the Academy at Stockholm conferred the supreme distinction on him: the Nobel Prize for Literature.

Alas, as sometimes happens, the Prize rewarded the achievements of the past rather than the present. Although still famous and respected even by his opponents, Anatole France had been left behind by the times. His positivism had been successfully discredited by Bergson's philosophy, his agnosticism ran counter to the revival of Christianity among a whole group of the younger intellectuals, his skepticism clashed with a widespread thirst for faith, his rationalism was out of tune with a growing taste for fantasy, dreams, and escapism, and even his classicism seemed dated to a rising literary generation intent on finding new ways of expression. Even his political comrades had begun to view him with suspicion: in 1922 it was with Anatole France in mind that the Fourth International Communist Congress demanded the exclusion of those intellectuals "so numerous in France, who join the party as amateurs." His contributions to the newspapers of the extreme left ceased from that moment.

On May 24, 1924, he was granted a final homage: his eightieth birthday was celebrated at the Trocadéro in a ceremony reminiscent of the apotheosis enjoyed by Voltaire shortly before his death.

But an even swifter end lay in wait for Anatole France. For a long time he had been suffering from arteriosclerosis. Two months after the ceremony at the Trocadéro he was confined to bed. After a painful struggle, he died on October 12, 1924. On his deathbed he was heard to murmur the word "Mother."

The Assembly voted him a state burial. Red flags fluttered over the crowd that thronged to the funeral procession. Almost all the papers published articles in praise of his work. But a few months later, André Breton, the young and irreverent promoter of surrealism, wrote of the three great writers who had died in 1924: "Loti, Barrès, France: we should be eternally grateful for the year that got rid of those three shady characters: the idiot, the traitor, and the policeman." If he could have foreseen such an epitaph, Anatole France—who could appreciate a sick joke—might have smiled with indulgent irony.

Jacques Chastenet de Cataing, journalist, historian, and diplomat, is a member of the Académie Française.

Translated by Helga Harrison.

# THE 1921 PRIZE

## By GUNNAR AHLSTRÖM

By 1921 twenty-five years had passed since the celebrated inventor, Nobel, had died in Italy, leaving his wealth to humanity. Anniversaries invariably encourage meditations on the past, and such considerations set the tone for the address given by the president of the Nobel Foundation as he opened the 1921 ceremonies. The speaker was Professor Henrik Schück of Uppsala University, the erudite patriarch of Swedish literary history. His solemn address was delivered in a style characterized by a majestic unfurling of images worthy of an Old Testament prophet. The question Schück asked was, how well had the Foundation carried out the program of the great humanitarian?

"Alas!" he commented, "the answer which we would be inclined to give to this question could only be discouraging. His aim seems farther off today than ever before in this quarter century. So far as the establishment of peace on earth is concerned, our efforts have been lighter than a feather; we should have to go far back into the dark night of history to meet conditions of life as distressing as those in which we struggle today. Even an optimist must admit that the civilization of our century is built on a volcano which may lie quiescent for a while, but which may just as well erupt at any time and spew out the lava and fire of anarchy.

The world struggles today either in its death agony or in pains of labor—which, we cannot tell. The only thing we understand is humanity's cry of anguish."

The old Europe no longer existed. The once proud eagles of three empires had been wiped from the political map. Exiled princes and grand dukes discussed the enigmatic Russia of Lenin and the Soviets. The Austria of the Hapsburgs had exploded into a Balkan clutter of new and unknown nations. From his exile at Doorn, in Holland, Kaiser Wilhelm II followed the trials of the young Weimar Republic. Inflation spiraled skyward in a grotesque nightmare, while the rubble of defeat fertilized the soil where the myth of poor Germany cruelly oppressed by the Versailles Treaty was blossoming. Beyond any doubt, the new century held more things than had been dreamt of in the idealistic philosophy of the late Alfred Nobel.

If the ceremony in 1921 was one of the most impressive in Nobel history, it was for less prosaic reasons. As always, the Prize for Literature attracted the most attention, and this time the winner was an authentic prince of letters with unquestionable qualifications. For a number of years the Prize had gone to writers whose worth was open to question—writers more or less devalued abroad, more or less Nordic and neutral; now, at one stroke the Prize was restored to its pristine international prestige under the sign of the great French tradition. To this was added the attraction that the laureate proposed to travel to Stockholm to receive the Prize in person. Never before had a French Prizewinner honored the Swedish Academy with his presence. Sully-Prudhomme at sixty and Frédéric Mistral at seventy had both had to refuse because of old age. But Anatole France, although he was nearly eighty, defied the discomforts of travel and was soon off to Sweden for the Prize ceremonies.

This singularly successful Nobel celebration took place only after a series of trials and errors that had endured from almost the beginning of the Nobel awards. Anatole France had been one of the first to submit a nomination on behalf of a fellow writer. His own name had been proposed several times, but the Academy had remained deaf both to the arguments he marshaled in defense of his friend Georg Brandes and to the pleas offered on behalf of France himself. His name had first been submitted in 1904, by Marcelin Berthelot, and his case had first been discussed in a special report drawn up by a Swedish expert who had been a professor of romance languages at the University of Lund and was famous as translator of Dante and Cervantes.

Nominated again in 1910 and 1911 by Paul Hervieu, France continued to meet with invincible opposition. When the World War I finally broke out, the world of Sylvestre Bonnard was blotted out by the murky clouds of battle. There was neither time nor place for the garden of Epicurus.

In 1921, the eighteen candidates proposed included George Bernard Shaw, H. G. Wells, William Butler Yeats, Henri Bergson, and Grazia Deledda. As a candidate, Anatole France had aroused little interest. More than a third of all the nominations had been submitted by the Swedish, most of whom were members of the Academy, and France's candidacy was also sponsored by Swedes, with the three leading professors of romance languages supporting him *en bloc*. It was also well known that he had an enthusiastic promoter in Professor Schück, who had pleaded his cause in vain on a previous occasion.

At the crucial meeting of the Academy, Professor Schück let an imprudent remark escape his lips, to the effect that Anatole France was undeniably a licentious writer. At these words an imposing 84-year-old bishop who had been in the Academy since 1900 leaped from his seat. Licentiousness and the idealistic Nobel Prize were irreconcilable, he argued. But behind his white beard, like a grand vizier, Henrik Schück concealed a goodly streak of France's own Abbé Coignard. He gently suggested that his clerical colleague show a trifle more Christian charity. His appeals to the theological virtues, to tolerance and broad-mindedness in regard to a brother who had gone astray on the permissive highway of literature, bore fruit when the vote was taken and the Prize went to France.

The day came when, Anatole France, disregarding his doctor's warnings, started out with his wife, his publisher Gaston Calmann-Lévy, and his grandson, Lucien Psichari. It was a memorable expedition, with the world press following its progress. The magazine *L'Illustration* sent out a special correspondent-photographer with the group.

The august traveler was not always in a good humor. The party passed through Berlin and then went on to Sassnitz, where they were to take the ferry to Sweden. At the sight of the Baltic everyone was delighted except the author. Shivering, he exclaimed, "I once met an astonishing fish. Whenever I went to visit him, he would say, 'Ah, the land! The land! I love the land.' And you are all quite as mad as that fish!"

Nor was he pacified by the icebound stretches he found on the other shore. "What am I doing here in all this snow— I, who can stand only three countries in the world—France, Greece, and Italy!"

Bundled up in an accumulation of furs, blankets, scarves, and other more or less improvised woolen insulators, Anatole France, made his triumphal entry into Stockholm one December morning. The weather brightened in greeting. On the dock they found the charming Prime Minister, Karl Hjalmar Branting, a Social-Democrat and a fervent European who was also one of the most outstanding delegates to the League of Nations. His presence was the first of many honors paid to the new laureate. Many others followed, equally flattering, culminating in the solemn ceremony when the awards were made in the concert hall of the Academy of Music. Those who accused France of nodding during the address were quite wrong. Questioned about it later he replied, "Not at all—I wasn't sleeping. Even if they were talking about

me in a language I didn't understand, I was embarrassed by so much attention and simply cast my eyes down for modesty's sake."

He didn't lower his gaze, however, in the scene that followed. On the platform he was seated next to Professor Walter Nernst of Berlin, the winner of the Nobel Prize for Chemistry. The official record reported the incident:

"After Anatole France received his Prize from the hands of the King, there occurred an incident which left a strong impression on all present. When the venerable writer had gone up to the rostrum again, he turned to Professor Walter Nernst, Prizewinner for Chemistry, and exchanged a long and cordial handshake with him. The Frenchman, the 'last of the classics,' and the German, the great scientist and representative of intellectual sobriety, the citizens of two countries which had for a long time been enemies, were united in a handshake—a profoundly symbolic gesture. The audience applauded, feeling that the two nations, which for years had fought against one another, had just met in reconciliation."

---

Translated by Dale McAdoo.

# John Galsworthy

## 1932

---

"For his distinguished art of narration,

which takes its highest form in

*The Forsyte Saga*"

---

*Illustrated by MICHEL NO*

# PRESENTATION ADDRESS

## By ANDERS ÖSTERLING

MEMBER OF THE NOBEL COMMITTEE
OF THE SWEDISH ACADEMY

---

WHEN WE SURVEY John Galsworthy's authorship, it seems to develop unusually smoothly, pushed on by a conscientious and indefatigable creative impulse. Yet he is not one of those who have turned to the literary career rapidly and without resistance. Born, as the English put it, with a silver spoon in his mouth, that is, economically independent, he studied at Harrow and Oxford, chose the law without practicing it, and traveled all over the world. When, at the age of twenty-eight, he began writing for the first time, the immediate reason was the exhortation of a woman friend, and it was to Galsworthy a mere recreation, evidently not without the inherent prejudices of the gentleman against the vocation of writing. His first two collections of tales were published under the pen name of John Sinjohn, and the editions were soon withdrawn by the self-critical beginner. Not until he was thirty-seven did he begin his real authorship by publishing the novel *The Island Pharisees* (1904), and two years later appeared *The Man of Property,* the origin of his fame and at the same time of his monumental chief work, *The Forsyte Saga.*

In Galsworthy's satire against the Island Pharisees, the fundamental feature that was to mark all his subsequent works was already apparent. The book deals with an English gentleman's having stayed abroad long enough to forget his conventional sphere of thoughts and feelings; he criticizes the national surroundings severely, and in doing so he is assisted by a Belgian vagabond, who casually makes his acquaintance in an English railway compartment and who becomes his fate. At that time Galsworthy was himself a cosmopolite returned home, prepared to fight against the old capitalistic aristocratic society with about the same program as Bernard Shaw, although the Englishman, contrary to the Irishman who fought with intellectual arms, above all aimed at capturing feeling and imagination. The pharisaical egoism of England's ruling classes, the subject of Galsworthy's debut, remained his program for the future, only specialized in his particular works. He never tired of fighting against all that seemed narrow and harsh in the national character, and the persistence of his attacks on social evil indicates his strong impressions and deeply wounded feeling of justice.

With the Forsyte type he now aimed at the upper middle class, the rich businessmen, a group not yet having reached real gentility, but striving with its sympathies and instincts toward the well-known ideal of the gentleman of rigid, imperturbable, and imposing correctness. These people are particularly on their guard against dangerous feelings, a fact which, however, does not exclude accidental lapses, when passion intrudes upon their life, and liberty claims its rights in a world of property instincts. Beauty, here represented by Irene, does not like to live with *The Man of Property;* in his bitter indignation at this, Soames Forsyte becomes almost a tragic figure. It seems uncertain if in the beginning Galsworthy thought of a sequel to that first Forsyte novel, which is a masterpiece of an energetic, firm, and independent account of human nature.

At any rate, it was not until fifteen years later that he again took up his Forsytes, and at this time the effects of the World War had radically changed the perspective. But now this work expanded; *In Chancery* (1920) and *To Let* (1921) and two short story interludes were added, and thus *The Forsyte Saga* proper was completed. Not finished with the younger members of the family, Galsworthy wrote *A Modern Comedy,* a new trilogy whose structure is exactly like that of its predecessor and consists of the three novels, *The White Monkey* (1924), *The Silver Spoon* (1926), and *Swan Song* (1928), united by two short story interludes. These two trilogies together form an unusual literary accomplishment.

The novelist has carried the history of his time through three generations, and his success in mastering so excellently his enormously difficult material, both in its scope and in its depth, remains an extremely memorable feat in English literature—doubly remarkable, if we consider that it was performed in a field in which the European continent had already produced some of its best works.

In the foreground of this chronicle is everyday reality, as experienced by the Forsytes, all personal fortunes, conflicts, and tragicomedies. But in the background is visible the dark fabric of historical events. Every reader is sure to remember the chapter describing how Soames with his second wife witnesses the funeral of Queen Victoria in gray weather at the Hyde Park fence, and the rapid survey of the age from her accession to the throne: "Morals had changed, manners had changed, men had become monkeys twice removed, God had become Mammon—Mammon so respectable as to deceive himself." In the Forsyte novels we observe the transformation and the dissolution of the Victorian age up to our days. In the first trilogy comes to life the period that in England effected the fusion of nobility and plutocracy with the accompanying change of the notion of a "gentleman," a kind of Indian summer of wealth before the days of the storm. The second trilogy, no longer called "saga" but "comedy," describes the profound crisis of the new England whose task is to change the ruins of the past and the improvised barracks of wartime into its future home. The gallery of types is admirably complete. Robust businessmen, spoiled society ladies, aunts touching in an old-fashioned way, rebellious young girls, gentlemen of the clubs, politicians, artists, children, and even dogs—these last-mentioned especially favored by Galsworthy—emerge in the London panorama in a concrete form, alive before our eyes and ears.

The situations recur as a curious documentation of the oscillation and the undulation in a family of given hereditary dispositions. The individual portraits are distinguished, and the law of social life is at work.

It is also instructive, however, to observe in these novels how Galsworthy's view gradually changes. The radical critic of culture rises by degrees to a greater objectivity in his appreciation and to a more liberal view of the purely human. An often cited example of this is his treatment of Soames, this standard national type, at first satirized, but then described with a respect that, reluctantly growing, finally changes into a genuine sympathy. Galsworthy has seized upon this sympathy; his characterization of Soames's personality thoroughly worked out becomes the most memorable feature of the Forsyte saga and the comedy of the descendants. One easily remembers one of those masterly final episodes of *Swan Song,* in which Old Soames, having driven to his ancestors' village on the west coast, finds with the help of an old census map the place where the Forsytes' farm had been situated, where only a single stone marks the site. Something like the ghost of a path leads him down into a valley of grass and furze. He breathes in the fresh, rough sea air which goes a little to his head; he puts on his overcoat and sits musing, his back against the stone. Had his ancestors built the house themselves at this lonely place, had they been the first to settle down here? he wonders. Their England rises before him, an England "of pack horses and very little smoke, of peat and wood fires, and wives who never left you, because they couldn't probably." He sits there a long time, absorbed in his feeling for the birthplace.

"And something moved in him, as if the salty independence of that lonely spot were still in his bones. Old Jolyon and his own father and the rest of his uncles—no wonder they'd been independent, with this air and loneliness in their blood; and crabbed with the pickling of it—unable to give up, to let go, to die. For a moment he seemed to understand even himself."

To Galsworthy, Soames thus becomes one of the last representatives of static old England. There was no humbug in him, we are told; he had his trying ways, but he was genuine. The sober prosaic respectability is in this manner duly honored in Galsworthy's realism, and this has been pointed out as the essential factor in his judgment of human nature. As time passed, and the weary, cynical laxity grew more and more visibly modern, the chronicler found that several traits, which under other circumstances had been little appreciated, perhaps really constituted the secret of the British power of resistance. On the whole, Galsworthy's later novels are permeated with a patriotic feeling of self-defense that appears also in his descriptions of the home and studies of nature. Even these last-mentioned are rendered with a more tender and more anxious poetry, with the feeling of protecting something precious yet already shadowed by certain loss. It may be old chambers where people have established themselves as if to remain there forever. Or it may be an English garden park, where the September sun is shining beautifully on bronze-colored beech leaves and centenary hedges of yew.

Time does not permit me to dwell in the same detail upon others of Galsworthy's works, often quite comparable in quality to the Forsyte series, which surpasses them by virtue of its epic dimensions. It is above all in *The Country House* (1907), in *Fraternity* (1901), and in *The Dark Flower* (1913) that his mature essential character is to be sought. In the novel of the manor he created perhaps his most exquisite female portrait, Mrs. Pendyce, the type of the perfect, unaffected lady with all the modest tragedy which surrounds a truly noble nature, condemned to be restrained if not destroyed by the fetters of tradition. In *Fraternity* he represented, with a discreet mixture of pity and irony, the unfulfilled martyr of social conscience, the esthete who is tortured by the shadows of the proletarian masses in London, but is not able to take the decisive step and carry out his altruistic impulse of action. There we also meet the old original Mr. Stone, the utopian dreamer with his eternal monologues beneath the night sky, indeed one of Galsworthy's most memorable types. Nor do we forget *The Dark Flower,* which may be called a psychological sonata, played with a masterly hand and based on the variations of passion and resignation in the ages of man. Even in the form of the short story Galsworthy has often been able to evoke an emotional response through contrasts of shadow and light which work rather graphically. He can do this in only a few pages which become animated by his personal style, for example, when he tells about such a simple case as that of the German shoemaker in "Quality," the story of the hopeless struggle of good craftsmanship against low-price industry.

By appealing to education and the sense of justice, his narrative art has always gently influenced contemporary notions of life and habits of thought. The same is true of his dramatic works, which were often direct contributions to social discussion and led to definite reforms at least in one area, the administration of public prisons in England. His dramas show an unusual richness of ideas combined with great ingenuity and technical skill in the working out of scenic effect. When certain inclinations are found, they are always just and humane. In *The Forest* (1924), for example, he brands the inconsiderate spirit of greed that, for crass purposes, exploits the heroism of the British world-conquering mind. *The Show* (1925) represents the defenselessness of the individual against the press in a family tragedy where brutal newspaper curiosity functions like a deaf and unchecked machine, removing the possibility of any one being held responsible for the resultant evil.

*Loyalties* depicts a matter of honor in which loyalty is tested and impartially examined in the different circles where it is at work, that is, the family, the corporation, the profession, and the nation. The force of these and other plays is in their logical structure and their concentrated action; sometimes they also possess an atmosphere of poetic feeling that is far from trivial. I am thinking especially of *A Pigeon* (1912) and *A Bit o'*

*Love* (1915) which, however, did not meet with such brilliant success on the stage. Although on the whole Galsworthy's plays cannot be rated artistically with his novels, they confirm quite as plainly how strongly he sticks to his early ideal of liberty, that which in Shelley put on the wings and flames of dawn. Even in his rather cool dramatic works we meet a steady enemy of all oppression, spiritual as well as material, a sensitive man who with all his heart reacts against lack of consideration and never gives way in his demand for fair play.

In technique Turgenev is one of his first teachers. As in the charming Russian narrator, we find in Galsworthy a definite musical charm catching and keeping the hidden feelings. His intuition is so infallible that he can content himself with a slight allusion and a broken hint. But then there is Galsworthy's irony, such a singular instrument that even the tone separates him from any other writer. There are many different kinds of irony. One principle kind is negative and can be compared to the hoar-frost of the windows in a house where there is no fire, where the hearth has grown cold long ago. But there is also an irony friendly to life, spring-ing from warmth, interest, and humanity; such is Galsworthy's. His is an irony that, in the presence of tragicomic evil, seems to question why it must be so, why it is necessary, and whether there is nothing to remedy it. Sometimes Galsworthy makes nature herself take part in that ironic play about human beings, to underline the bitterness or sweetness of the incidents with the help of winds, clouds, fragrances, and bird cries. Assisted by this irony he successfully appeals to the psychological imagination, always the best ally of understanding and sympathy.

Galsworthy once formulated his artistic motto in words such as harmony, proportion, balance. They mark his natural turn of mind, a spiritual ideal, now often suspect, perhaps because it is so difficult to reach. We soon discover that this poet who so severely and persistently attacked the typical gentleman of self-sufficiency, himself indisputably succeeded in filling the old notion with new life, so that it preserved its contact with both the immediately human and the unrestricted aesthetic instinct. In the artist Galsworthy flourish exactly those qualities of temper that in English are comprehended in this word: *gentleness.* These qualities are expressed in his works, and in this way they have become a cultural contribution to our own times.

As Mr. Galsworthy has unfortunately been prevented by illness from being here today, as he had wished, to receive personally the Nobel

Prize for Literature for 1932, it will now be delivered to the representative of Great Britain here present, Minister Clark Kerr.

Your Excellency—May I ask you to receive from His Majesty's hands the Nobel Prize for Literature, awarded to your famous countryman.

There was no formal Acceptance Speech by Galsworthy.

# SALVATION OF A FORSYTE

## By JOHN GALSWORTHY

Swithin Forsyte lay in bed. The corners of his mouth under his white moustache drooped towards his double chin. He panted: "My doctor says I'm in a bad way, James."

His twin-brother placed his hand behind his ear. "I can't hear you. They tell me I ought to take a cure. There's always a cure wanted for something. Emily had a cure."

Swithin replied: "You mumble so. I hear my man, Adolph. I trained him. . . . You ought to have an ear-trumpet. You're getting very shaky, James."

There was silence; then James Forsyte, as if galvanized, remarked: "I s'pose you've made your will. I s'pose you've left your money to the family; you've nobody else to leave it to. There was Danson died the other day, and left his money to a hospital."

The hairs of Swithin's white moustache bristled. "My fool of a doctor told me to make my will," he said; "I hate a fellow who tells you to make your will. My appetite's good; I ate a partridge last night. I'm all the better for eating. He told me to leave off champagne! I eat a good breakfast. I'm not eighty. You're the same age, James. You look very shaky."

James Forsyte said: "You ought to have another opinion. Have Blank; he's the first man now. I had him for Emily; cost me two hundred guineas. He sent her to Homburg; that's the first place now. The prince was there—everybody goes there."

Swithin Forsyte answered: "I don't get any sleep at night, now I can't get out; and I've bought a new carriage—gave a pot of money for it. D'you ever have bronchitis? They tell me champagne's dangerous; it's my belief I couldn't take a better thing."

James Forsyte rose.

"You ought to have another opinion. Emily sent her love; she would have come in, but she had to go to Niagara. Everybody goes there; it's *the* place now. Rachael goes every morning; she overdoes it—she'll be laid up one of these days. There's a fancy ball there to-night; the Duke gives the prizes."

Swithin Forsyte said angrily: "I can't get things properly cooked here; at the club I get spinach decently done." The bed-clothes jerked at the tremor of his legs.

James Forsyte replied: "You must have done well with Tintos; you must have made a lot of money by them. Your ground-rents must be falling in, too. You must have any amount you don't know what to do with." He mouthed at the words, as if his lips were watering.

Swithin Forsyte glared. "Money!" he said; "my doctor's bill's enormous."

James Forsyte stretched out a cold, damp hand. "Good-bye! You ought to have another opinion. I can't keep the horses waiting: they're a new pair—stood me in three hundred. You ought to take care of yourself. I shall speak to Blank about you. You ought to have him—

[ 235 ]

everybody says he's the first man. Good-bye!"

Swithin Forsyte continued to stare at the ceiling. He thought: 'A poor thing, James! a selfish beggar! Must be worth a couple of hundred thousand!' He wheezed, meditating on life. . . .

He was ill and lonely. For many years he had been lonely, and for two years ill; but as he had smoked his first cigar, so he would live his life—stoutly, to its predestined end. Every day he was driven to the club; sitting forward on the spring cushions of a single brougham, his hands on his knees, swaying a little, strangely solemn. He ascended the steps into that marble hall—the folds of his chin wedged into the aperture of his collar—walking squarely with a stick. Later he would dine, eating majestically, and savouring his food, behind a bottle of champagne set in an ice-pail—his waistcoat defended by a napkin, his eyes rolling a little or glued in a stare on the waiter. Never did he suffer his head or back to droop, for it was not distinguished so to do.

Because he was old and deaf, he spoke to no one; and no one spoke to him. The club gossip, an Irishman, said to each newcomer: "Old Forsyte! Look at 'um! Must ha' had something in his life to sour 'um!" But Swithin had had nothing in his life to sour him.

For many days now he had lain in bed in a room exuding silver, crimson, and electric light, and smelling of opopanax and of cigars. The curtains were drawn, the firelight gleamed: on a table by his bed were a jug of barley-water and *The Times*. He had made an attempt to read, failed, and fell again to thinking. His face with its square chin looked like a block of pale leather bedded in the pillow. It was lonely! A woman in the room would have made all the difference! Why had he never married? He breathed hard, staring frog-like at the ceiling; a memory had come into his mind. It was a long time ago—forty odd years—but it seemed like yesterday. . . .

It happened when he was thirty-eight, for the first and only time in his life travelling on the Continent, with his twin-brother James and a man named Traquair. On the way from Germany to Venice, he had found himself at the Hôtel Goldene Alp at Salzburg. It was late August, and weather for the gods: sunshine on the walls and the shadows of the vine-leaves, and at night, the moonlight, and again on the walls the shadows of the vine-leaves. Averse to the suggestions of other people, Swithin had refused to visit the Citadel; he had spent the day alone in the window of his bedroom, smoking a succession of cigars, and disparaging the appearance of the passers-by. After dinner he was driven by boredom into the streets. His chest puffed out like a pigeon's, and with something of a pigeon's cold and inquiring eye, he strutted, annoyed at the frequency of uniforms, which seemed to him both needless and offensive. His spleen rose at this crowd of foreigners who spoke an unintelligible language, wore hair on their faces, and smoked bad tobacco. 'A queer lot!' he thought. The sound of music from a café attracted him, he walked in, vaguely moved by a wish for the distinction of adventure, without the trouble which adventure usually brought with it; spurred too, perhaps, by an after dinner demon. The café was the *bier-halle* of the 'Fifties, with a door at either end, and lighted by a large wooden lantern. On a small dais three musicians were fiddling. Solitary men, or groups, sat at some dozen tables, and the waiters hurried about replenishing glasses; the air was thick with smoke. Swithin sat down. "Wine!" he said sternly. The astonished waiter brought him wine. Swithin pointed to a beer-glass on the table. "Here!" he said, with the same ferocity. The waiter poured out the wine. 'Ah!' thought Swithin, 'they can understand if they like.' A group of officers close by were laughing; Swithin stared at them uneasily. A hollow cough sounded almost in his ear. To his left a man sat reading, with his elbows on the corners of a journal, and his gaunt shoulders raised almost to his eyes. He had a thin, long nose, broadening suddenly at the nostrils; a black-brown beard, spread in a savage fan over his chest; what was visible of the face was the colour of old parchment. A strange, wild, haughty-looking creature! Swithin observed his clothes with some displeasure—they were the clothes of a journalist or strolling actor. And yet he was impressed. This was singular. How could he be impressed by a fellow in such clothes! The man reached out a hand, covered with black hairs, and took up a tumbler that contained a dark-coloured fluid: 'Brandy!' thought Swithin. The crash of a falling chair startled him—his neighbour had risen. He was of immense height, and very thin; his great beard seemed to splash away from his mouth; he was glaring at the group of officers, and speaking. Swithin made out two words: *"Hunde! Deutsche Hunde!"* 'Hounds! Dutch hounds!' he thought: 'Rather strong!' One of the officers had jumped up, and now drew his sword. The tall man swung his chair up, and brought it down with a thud. Everybody round started up and closed on him. The tall man cried out: "to me, Magyars!"

Swithin grinned. The tall man fighting such odds excited his unwilling admiration; he had a momentary impulse to go to his assistance. 'Only get a broken nose!' he thought, and looked for a safe corner. But at that moment a thrown lemon struck him on the jaw. He jumped out of his chair and rushed at the officers. The Hungarian, swinging his chair, threw him a look of gratitude—Swithin glowed with momentary admiration of himself.

A sword blade grazed his arm: he felt a sudden dislike of the Hungarian. 'This is too much,' he thought, and, catching up a chair, flung it at the wooden lantern. There was a crash—faces and swords vanished. He struck a match, and by the light of it bolted for the door. A second later he was in the street.

## II

A voice said in English, "God bless you, brother!"

Swithin looked round, and saw the tall Hungarian holding out his hand. He took it, thinking, 'What a fool I've been!' There was something in the Hungarian's gesture which said, "You are worthy of me!" It was annoying, but rather impressive. The man seemed even taller than before; there was a cut on his cheek, the blood from which was trickling down his beard. "You English!" he said. "I saw you stone Haynau—I saw you cheer Kossuth. The free blood of your people cries out to us." He looked at Swithin. "You are a big man, you have a big soul—and strong, how you flung them down! Ha!" Swithin had an impulse to take to his heels. "My name," said the Hungarian, "is Boleskey. You are my friend." His English was good.

'Bulsh-kai-ee, Burlsh-kai-ee,' thought Swithin; 'what a devil of a name!' "Mine," he said sulkily, "is Forsyte."

The Hungarian repeated it.

"You've had a nasty jab on the cheek," said Swithin; the sight of the matted beard was making him feel sick. The Hungarian put his fingers to his cheek, brought them away wet, stared at them, then with an indifferent air gathered a wisp of his beard and crammed it against the cut.

"Ugh!" said Swithin. "Here! Take my handkerchief!"

The Hungarian bowed. "Thank you!"

he said; "I couldn't think of it! Thank you a thousand times!"

"Take it!" growled Swithin; it seemed to him suddenly of the first importance. He thrust the handkerchief into the Hungarian's hand, and felt a pain in his arm. 'There!' he thought, 'I've strained a muscle.'

The Hungarian kept muttering, regardless of passers-by, "Swine! How you threw them over! Two or three cracked heads, anyway—the cowardly swine!"

"Look here!" said Swithin suddenly; "which is my way to the Goldene Alp?"

The Hungarian replied, "But you are coming with me, for a glass of wine?"

Swithin looked at the ground. 'Not if I know it!' he thought.

"Ah!" said the Hungarian with dignity, "you do not wish for my friendship!"

'Touchy beggar!' thought Swithin. "Of course," he stammered, "if you put it in that way——"

The Hungarian bowed, murmuring, "Forgive me!"

They had not gone a dozen steps before a youth, with a beardless face and hollow cheeks, accosted them. "For the love of Christ, gentlemen," he said, "help me!"

"Are you a German?" asked Boleskey.

"Yes," said the youth.

"Then you may rot!"

"Master, look here!" Tearing open his coat, the youth displayed his skin, and a leather belt drawn tight round it. Again Swithin felt that desire to take to his heels. He was filled with horrid forebodings—a sense of perpending intimacy with things such as no gentleman had dealings with.

The Hungarian crossed himself. "Brother," he said to the youth, "come you in!"

Swithin looked at them askance, and followed. By a dim light they groped their way up some stairs into a large room, into which the moon was shining through a window bulging over the street. A lamp burned low; there was a smell of spirits and tobacco, with a faint, peculiar scent, as of rose leaves. In one corner stood a czymbal, in another a great pile of newspapers. On the wall hung some old-fashioned pistols, and a rosary of yellow beads. Everything was tidily arranged, but dusty. Near an open fireplace was a table with the remains of a meal. The ceiling, floor, and walls were all of dark wood. In spite of the strange disharmony, the room had a sort of refinement.

The Hungarian took a bottle out of a cupboard and, filling some glasses, handed one to Swithin. Swithin put it gingerly to his nose. 'You never know your luck! Come!' he thought, tilting it slowly into his mouth. It was thick, too sweet, but of a fine flavour.

"Brothers!" said the Hungarian, refilling, "your healths!"

The youth tossed off his wine. And Swithin this time did the same; he pitied this poor devil of a youth now. "Come round to-morrow!" he said, "I'll give you a shirt or two." When the youth was gone, however, he remembered with relief that he had not given his address.

'Better so,' he reflected. 'A humbug, no doubt.'

"What was that you said to him?" he asked of the Hungarian.

"I said," answered Boleskey, " 'You have eaten and drunk; and now you are my enemy!' "

"Quite right!" said Swithin, "quite right! A beggar is every man's enemy."

"You do not understand," the Hungarian replied politely. "While he was a beggar—I, too, have had to beg" (Swithin thought, 'Good God! this is awful!'), "but now that he is no longer hungry, what is he but a German? No Austrian dog soils my floors!"

His nostrils, as it seemed to Swithin, had distended in an unpleasant fashion; and a wholly unnecesary raucousness invaded his voice. "I am an exile—all of my blood are exiles. Those Godless dogs!" Swithin hurriedly assented.

As he spoke, a face peeped in at the door.

"Rozsi!" said the Hungarian. A young girl came in. She was rather short, with a deliciously round figure and a thick plait of hair. She smiled, and showed her even teeth; her little, bright, wide-set grey eyes glanced from one man to the other. Her face was round, too, high in the cheek-bones, the colour of wild roses, with brows that had a twist-up at the corners. With a gesture of alarm, she put her hand to her cheek, and called, "Margit!" An older girl appeared, taller, with fine shoulders, large eyes, a pretty mouth, and what Swithin described to himself after-wards as a "pudding" nose. Both girls, with little cooing sounds, began attending to their father's face. Swithin turned his back to them. His arm pained him.

'This is what comes of interfering,' he thought sulkily; 'I might have had my neck broken!' Suddenly a soft palm was placed in his, two eyes, half-fascinated, half-shy, looked at him; then a voice called, "Rozsi!" the door was slammed, he was alone again with the Hungarian, harassed by a sense of soft disturbance.

"Your daughter's name is Rosy?" he said; "we have it in England—from rose, a flower."

"Rozsi (Rozgi)," the Hungarian re-plied; "your English is a hard tongue, harder than French, German, or Czech-ish, harder than Russian, or Rouma-nian—I know no more."

"What?" said Swithin, "six languages?" Privately he thought, 'He knows how to lie, anyway.'

"If you lived in a country like mine," muttered the Hungarian, "with all men's hands against you! A free people—dying —but not dead!"

Swithin could not imagine what he was talking of. This man's face, with its linen bandage, gloomy eyes, and great black wisps of beard, his fierce mutterings, and hollow cough, were all most unpleasant. He seemed to be suffering from some kind of mental dog-bite. His emotion in-deed appeared so indecent, so uncon-trolled and open, that its obvious sincer-ity produced a sort of awe in Swithin. It was like being forced to look into a fur-nace. Boleskcy stopped roaming up and down. "You think it's over?" he said; "I tell you, in the breast of each one of us Magyars there is a hell. What is sweeter than life? What is more sacred than each breath we draw? Ah! my country!" These words were uttered so slowly, with such intense mournfulness, that Swithin's jaw relaxed; he converted the movement to a yawn.

"Tell me," said Boleskey, "what would you do if the French conquered you?"

Swithin smiled. Then suddenly, as though something had hurt him, he grunted, "The 'Froggies'? Let 'em try!"

"Drink!" said Boleskey—"there is nothing like it"; he filled Swithin's glass. "I will tell you my story."

Swithin rose hurriedly. "It's late," he said. "This is good stuff, though; have you much of it?"

"It is the last bottle."

"What?" said Swithin; "and you gave it to a beggar?"

"My name is Boleskey-Stefan," the Hungarian said, raising his head; "of the Komorn Boleskeys." The simplicity of this phrase—as who shall say: What need of further description?—made an impres-sion on Swithin; he stopped to listen. Boleskey's story went on and on. "There were many abuses," boomed his deep voice, "much wrong done—much cow-ardice. I could see clouds gathering—roll-ing over our plains. The Austrian wished to strangle the breath of our mouths—to take from us the shadow of our liberty— the shadow—all we had. Two years ago —the year of '48, when every man and boy answered the great voice—brother, a dog's life!—to use a pen when all of your blood are fighting, but it was decreed for me! My son was killed; my brothers taken—and myself was thrown out like a dog—I had written out my heart, I had written out all the blood that was in my body!" He seemed to tower, a gaunt shadow of a man, with gloomy, flickering eyes staring at the wall.

Swithin rose, and stammered, "Much obliged—very interesting." Boleskey made no effort to detain him, but continued staring at the wall. "Good-night!" said Swithin, and stamped heavily downstairs.

### III

When at last Swithin reached the Goldene Alp, he found his brother and friend standing uneasily at the door. Traquair, a prematurely dried-up man, with whiskers and a Scotch accent, remarked, "Ye're airly, man!" Swithin growled something unintelligible, and swung up to bed. He discovered a slight cut on his arm. He was in a savage temper—the elements had conspired to show him things he did not want to see; yet now and then a memory of Rozsi, of her soft palm in his, a sense of having been stroked and flattered, came over him. During breakfast next morning his brother and Traquair announced their intention of moving on. James Forsyte, indeed, remarked that it was no place for a "collector," since all the "old" shops were in the hands of Jews or very grasping persons—he had discovered this at once. Swithin pushed his cup aside. *"You* may do what you like," he said, *"I'm* staying here."

James Forsyte replied, tumbling over his own words: "Why! what do you want to stay here for? There's nothing for you to do here—there's nothing to see here, unless you go up the Citadel, an' you won't do that."

Swithin growled, "Who says so?" Having gratified his perversity, he felt in a better temper. He had slung his arm in a silk sash, and accounted for it by saying he had slipped. Later he went out and walked on to the bridge. In the brilliant sunshine spires were glistening against the pearly background of the hills; the town had a clean, joyous air. Swithin glanced at the Citadel and thought, "Looks like a strong place! Shouldn't wonder if it were impregnable!" And this for some occult reason gave him pleasure. It occurred to him suddenly to go and look for the Hungarian's house.

About noon, after a hunt of two hours, he was gazing about him blankly, pale with heat, but more obstinate than ever, when a voice above him called "Mister!" He looked up and saw Rozsi. She was leaning her round chin on her round hand, gazing down at him with her deepset, clever eyes. When Swithin removed his hat, she clapped her hands. Again he had the sense of being admired, caressed. With a careless air, that sat grotesquely on his tall square person, he walked up to the door; both girls stood in the passage. Swithin felt a confused desire to speak in some foreign tongue. "Maam'selles," he began, "er—*bong jour*—er your father—*père, comment?*"

"We also speak English," said the elder girl; "will you come in, please?"

Swithin swallowed a misgiving and entered. The room had a worn appearance by daylight, as if it had always been the nest of tragic or vivid lives. He sat down, and his eyes said: "I am a stranger, but don't try to get the better of me, please—that is impossible." The girls looked at him in silence. Rozsi wore a rather short skirt of black stuff, a white shirt, and across her shoulders an embroidered yoke; her sister was dressed in dark green, with a coral necklace; both girls had their hair in plaits. After a minute Rozsi touched the sleeve of his hurt arm.

"It's nothing!" muttered Swithin.

"Father fought with a chair, but you had no chair," she said in a wondering voice.

He doubled the fist of his sound arm and struck a blow at space. To his amazement she began to laugh. Nettled at this, he put his hand beneath the heavy table and lifted it. Rozsi clapped her hands. "Ah! now I see—how strong you are!" She made him a curtsey and whisked round to the window. He found the quick intelligence of her eyes confusing; sometimes they seemed to look beyond him at something invisible—this, too, confused him. From Margit he learned that they had been two years in England, where their father had made his living by teaching languages; they had now been a year in Salzburg.

"We wait," suddenly with Rozsi; and Margit, with a solemn face, repeated, "We wait."

Swithin's eyes swelled a little with his desire to see what they were waiting for. How queer they were, with their eyes that gazed beyond him! He looked at their figures. "She would pay for dressing," he thought, and tried to imagine Rozsi in a skirt with proper flounces, a thin waist, and hair drawn back over her ears. She would pay for dressing, with that supple figure, fluffy hair, and little hands! And instantly his own hands, face, and clothes disturbed him. He got up, examined the pistols on the wall, and felt resentment at the faded, dusty room. 'Smells like a pothouse!' he thought. He sat down again close to Rozsi.

"Do you love to dance?" she asked: "to dance is to live. First you hear the music—how your feet itch! It is wonderful! You begin slow, quick—quicker; you fly—you know nothing—your feet are in the air. It is wonderful!"

A slow flush had mounted into Swithin's face.

"Ah!" continued Rozsi, her eyes fixed on him, "when I am dancing—out there I see the plains—your feet go one—two—three—quick, quick, quick, quicker—you fly."

She stretched herself, a shiver seemed to pass all down her. "Margit! dance!" and, to Swithin's consternation, the two girls—their hands on each other's shoulders—began shuffling their feet and swaying to and fro. Their heads were thrown back, their eyes half-closed; suddenly the step quickened, they swung to one side, then to the other, and began whirling round in front of him. The sudden fragrance of rose leaves enveloped him. Round they flew again. While they were still dancing, Boleskey came into the room. He caught Swithin by both hands.

"Brother, welcome! Ah! your arm is hurt! I do not forget." His yellow face and deep-set eyes expressed a dignified gratitude. "Let me introduce to you my friend Baron Kasteliz."

Swithin bowed to a man with a small forehead, who had appeared softly, and stood with his gloved hands touching his waist. Swithin conceived a sudden aversion for this cat-like man. About Boleskey there was that which made contempt impossible—the sense of comradeship begotten in the fight; the man's height; something lofty and savage in his face; and an obscure instinct that it would not pay to show distaste; but this Kasteliz, with his neat jaw, low brow, and velvety, volcanic look, excited his proper English animosity. "Your friends are mine," murmured Kasteliz. He spoke with suavity, and hissed his s's. A long, vibrating twang quavered through the room. Swithin turned and saw Rozsi sitting at the czymbal; the notes rang under the little hammers in her hands, incessant, metallic, rising and falling with that strange melody. Kasteliz had fixed his glowing eyes on her; Boleskey, nodding his head, was staring at the floor; Margit, with a pale face, stood like a statue.

'What can they see in it?' thought Swithin; 'it's not a tune.' He took up his hat. Rozsi saw him and stopped; her lips had parted with a faintly dismayed expression. His sense of personal injury diminished; he even felt a little sorry for her. She jumped up from her seat and twirled round with a pout. An inspiration seized on Swithin. "Come and dine with me," he said to Boleskey, "to-morrow—the Goldene Alp—bring your friend." He felt the eyes of the whole room on him—the Hungarian's fine eyes; Margit's wide glance; the narrow, hot gaze of Kasteliz; and lastly—Rozsi's. A glow of satisfaction ran down his spine. When he emerged into the street he thought gloomily, 'Now, I've done it!' And not for some paces did he look round; then, with a forced smile, turned and removed his hat to the faces at the window.

Notwithstanding this moment of gloom, however, he was in an exalted state all day, and at dinner kept looking at his brother and Traquair enigmatically. 'What do they know of life?' he thought; 'they might be here a year and get no farther.' He made jokes, and pinned the menu to the waiter's coat-tails. "I like this place," he said, "I shall spend three weeks here." James, whose lips were on the point of taking in a plum, looked at him uneasily.

### IV

On the day of the dinner Swithin suffered a good deal. He reflected gloomily on Boleskey's clothes. He had fixed an early hour—there would be fewer people to see them. When the time approached he attired himself with a certain neat splendour, and though his arm was still sore, left off the sling. . . .

Nearly three hours afterwards he left the Goldene Alp between his guests. It was sunset, and along the river-bank the houses stood out, unsoftened by the dusk; the streets were full of people hurrying home. Swithin had a hazy vision of empty bottles, of the ground before his feet, and the accessibility of all the world. Dim recollections of the good things he had said, of his brother and Traquair seated in the background eating ordinary meals with inquiring, acid visages, caused perpetual smiles to break out on his face, and he steered himself stubbornly, to prove that he was a better man than either of his guests. He knew, vaguely, that he was going somewhere with an object; Rozsi's face kept dancing before him, like a promise. Once or twice he gave Kasteliz a glassy stare. Towards Boleskey, on the other hand, he felt quite warm, and recalled with admiration the way he had set his glass down empty, time after time. 'I like to see him take his liquor,' he thought; 'the fellow's a gentleman, after all.'

Boleskey strode on, savagely inattentive to everything; and Kasteliz had become more like a cat than ever. It was nearly dark when they reached a narrow street close to the cathedral. They stopped at a door held open by an old woman. The change from the fresh air to a heated corridor, the noise of the door closed behind him, the old woman's anxious glances sobered Swithin.

"I tell her," said Boleskey, "that I reply for you as for my son."

Swithin was angry. What business had this man to reply for him!

They passed into a large room, crowded with men and women; Swithin noticed that they all looked at him. He stared at them in turn—they seemed of all classes, some in black coats or silk dresses, others in the clothes of workpeople; one man, a cobbler, still wore his leather apron, as if he had rushed there straight from his work. Laying his hand on Swithin's arm, Boleskey evidently began explaining who he was; hands were extended, people beyond reach bowed to him. Swithin acknowledged the greetings with a stiff motion of his head; then seeing other people dropping into seats, he, too, sat down. Some one whispered his name—Margit and Rozsi were just behind him.

"Welcome!" said Margit; but Swithin was looking at Rozsi. Her face was so alive and quivering! 'What's the excitement all about?' he thought. 'How pretty she looks!' She blushed, drew in her hands with a quick tense movement, and gazed again beyond him in the room. 'What is it?' thought Swithin; he had a longing to lean back and kiss her lips. He tried angrily to see what she was seeing in those faces turned all one way.

Boleskey rose to speak. No one moved; not a sound could be heard but the tone of his deep voice. On and on he went, fierce and solemn, and with the rise of his voice, all those faces—fair or swarthy—seemed to be glowing with one and the same feeling. Swithin felt the white heat in those faces—it was not decent! In that whole speech he only understood the one word—"Magyar"—which came again and again. He almost dozed off at last. The twang of a czymbal woke him. 'What?' he thought, 'more of that infernal music!' Margit, leaning over him, whispered: "Listen! Racoczy! it is forbidden!" Swithin saw that Rozsi was no longer in her seat; it was she who was striking those forbidden notes. He looked round —everywhere the same unmoving faces, the same entrancement, and fierce stillness. The music sounded muffled, as if it, too, were bursting its heart in silence. Swithin felt within him a touch of panic. Was this a den of tigers? The way these people listened, the ferocity of their stillness, was frightful! . . . He gripped his chair and broke into a perspiration; was there no chance to get away? 'When it stops,' he thought, 'there'll be a rush!' But there was only a greater silence. It flashed across him that any hostile person coming in then would be torn to pieces. A woman sobbed. The whole thing was beyond words unpleasant. He rose, and edged his way furtively towards the doorway. There was a cry of "Police!" The whole crowd came pressing after him. Swithin would soon have been out, but a little behind he caught sight of Rozsi swept off her feet. Her frightened eyes angered him. 'She doesn't deserve it,' he thought sulkily; 'letting all this loose!' and forced his way back to her. She clung to him, and a fever went stealing through his veins; he butted forward at the crowd, holding her tight. When they were outside he let her go.

"I was afraid," she said.

"Afraid!" muttered Swithin; "I should think so." No longer touching her, he felt his grievance revive.

"But you are so strong," she murmured.

"This is no place for you," growled Swithin. "I'm going to see you home."

"Oh!" cried Rozsi; "but papa and—Margit!"

"That's their lookout!" and he hurried her away.

She slid her hand under his arm; the soft curves of her form brushed him gently, each touch only augmented his ill-humour. He burned with a perverse rage, as if all the passions in him were simmering and ready to boil over; it was as if a poison were trying to work its way out of him through the layers of his stolid flesh. He maintained a dogged silence; Rozsi, too, said nothing, but when they reached the door, she drew her hand away.

"You are angry!" she said.

"Angry," muttered Swithin; "no! How d'you make that out?" He had a torturing desire to kiss her.

"Yes, you are angry," she repeated; "I wait here for papa and Margit."

Swithin also waited, wedged against the wall. Once or twice, for his sight was sharp, he saw her steal a look at him, a beseeching look, and hardened his heart with a kind of pleasure. After five minutes Boleskey, Margit, and Kasteliz appeared. Seeing Rozsi they broke into exclamations of relief, and Kasteliz, with a glance at Swithin, put his lips to her hand. Rozsi's look said, "Wouldn't you like to do that?" Swithin turned short on his heel, and walked away.

V

All night he hardly slept, suffering from fever, for the first time in his life. Once he jumped out of bed, lighted a candle, and going to the glass, scrutinised himself long and anxiously. After this he fell asleep, but had frightful dreams. His first thought when he woke was, 'My liver's out of order!' and, thrusting his head into cold water, he dressed hastily and went out. He soon left the house behind. Dew covered everything; blackbirds whistled in the bushes, the air was fresh and sweet. He had not been up so early since he was a boy. Why was he walking through a damp wood at this hour of the morning? Something intolerable and unfamiliar must have sent him out. No fellow in his senses would do such a thing! He came to a dead stop, and began unsteadily to walk back. Regaining the hotel, he went to bed again, and dreamed that in some wild country he was living in a room full of insects, where a housemaid—Rozsi— holding a broom, looked at him with mournful eyes. There seemed an unexplained need for immediate departure; he begged her to forward his things, and shake them out carefully before she put them into the trunk. He understood that the charge for sending would be twenty-two shillings, thought it a great deal, and had the horrors of indecision. "No," he muttered, "pack, and take them myself." The housemaid turned suddenly into a lean creature; and he awoke with a sore feeling in his heart.

His eye fell on his wet boots. The whole thing was scaring, and jumping up, he began to throw his clothes into his trunks. It was twelve o'clock before he went down, and found his brother and Traquair still at the table arranging an itinerary; he surprised them by saying that he too was coming; and without further explanation set to work to eat. James had heard that there were salt-mines in the neighbourhood—his proposal was to start, and halt an hour or so on the road for their inspection: he said: "Everybody'll ask you if you've seen the salt-mines: I shouldn't like to say I hadn't seen the salt-mines. What's the good, they'd say, of your going there if you haven't seen the salt-mines?" He wondered, too, if they need fee the second waiter—an idle chap!

A discussion followed; but Swithin ate on glumly, conscious that his mind was set on larger affairs. Suddenly on the far side of the street Rozsi and her sister passed, with little baskets on their arms. He started up, and at that moment Rozsi looked round—her face was the incarnation of enticement, the chin tilted, the lower lip thrust a little forward, her round neck curving back over her shoulder. Swithin muttered, "Make your own arrangements—leave me out!" and hurried from the room, leaving James beside himself with interest and alarm.

When he reached the street, however, the girls had disappeared. He hailed a carriage. "Drive!" he called to the man, with a flourish of his stick, and as soon as the wheels had begun to clatter on the stones he leaned back, looking sharply to right and left. He soon had to give up thought of finding them, but made the coachman turn round and round again. All day he drove about, far into the country, and kept urging the driver to use greater speed. He was in a strange state of hurry and elation. Finally, he dined at a little country inn; and this gave the measure of his disturbance—the dinner was atrocious.

Returning late in the evening he found a note written by Traquair. "Are you in your senses, man?" it asked; "we have no more time to waste idling about here. If you want to rejoin us, come on to Danielli's Hotel, Venice." Swithin chuckled when he read it, and feeling frightfully tired, went to bed and slept like a log.

## VI

Three weeks later he was still in Salzburg, no longer at the Goldene Alp, but in rooms over a shop near the Boleskeys'. He had spent a small fortune in the purchase of flowers. Margit would croon over them, but Rozsi, with a sober "Many tanks!" as if they were her right, would look long at herself in the glass, and pin one into her hair. Swithin ceased to wonder; he ceased to wonder at anything they did. One evening he found Boleskey deep in conversation with a pale, dishevelled-looking person.

"Our friend Mr. Forsyte—Count D——," said Boleskey.

Swithin experienced a faint, unavoidable emotion; but looking at the Count's trousers, he thought: 'Doesn't look much like one!' And with an ironic bow to the silent girls, he turned, and took his hat. But when he had reached the bottom of the dark stairs he heard footsteps. Rozsi came running down, looked out at the door, and put her hands up to her breast as if disappointed: suddenly with a quick glance round she saw him. Swithin caught her arm. She slipped away, and her face seemed to bubble with defiance or laughter; she ran up three steps, looked at him across her shoulder, and fled on up the stairs. Swithin went out bewildered and annoyed.

'What was she going to say to me?' he kept thinking. During these three weeks he had asked himself all sorts of questions: whether he were being made a fool of; whether she were in love with him; what he was doing there, and sometimes at night, with all his candles burning as if he wanted light, the breeze blowing on him through the window, his cigar, half-smoked, in his hand, he sat, an hour or more, staring at the wall. 'Enough of this!' he thought every morning. Twice he packed fully—once he ordered his travelling carriage, but countermanded it the following day. What definitely he hoped, intended, resolved, he could not have said. He was always thinking of Rozsi, he could not read the riddle in her face—she held him in a vice, notwithstanding that everything about her threatened the very fetishes of his existence. And Boleskey! Whenever he looked at him he thought, 'If he were only clean?' and mechanically fingered his own well-tied cravat. To talk with the fellow, too, was like being forced to look at things which had no place in the light of day. Freedom, equality, self-sacrifice!

'Why can't he settle down at some business,' he thought, 'instead of all this talk?' Boleskey's sudden diffidences, self-depreciation, fits of despair, irritated him. "Morbid beggar!" he would mutter; "thank God *I* haven't a thin skin." And proud too! Extraordinary! An impecunious fellow like that! One evening, moreover, Boleskey had returned home drunk. Swithin had hustled him away into his bedroom, helped him to undress, and stayed until he was asleep. 'Too much of a good thing!' he thought, 'before his own daughters, too!' It was after this that he ordered his travelling carriage. The other occasion on which he packed was one evening, when not only Boleskey, but Rozsi herself had picked chicken bones with her fingers.

Often in the mornings he would go to the Mirabell Garden to smoke his cigar; there, in stolid contemplation of the statues—rows of half-heroic men carrying off half-distressed females—he would spend an hour pleasantly, his hat tilted to keep the sun off his nose. The day after Rozsi had fled from him on the stairs, he came there as usual. It was a morning of blue sky and sunlight glowing on the old prim garden, on its yew-trees, and serio-comic statues, and walls covered with apricots and plums. When Swithin approached his usual seat, who should be sitting there but Rozsi!

"Good-morning," he stammered; "you knew this was my seat then?"

Rozsi looked at the ground. "Yes," she answered.

Swithin felt bewildered. "Do you know," he said, "you treat me very funnily?"

To his surprise Rozsi put her little soft hand down and touched his; then, without a word, sprang up and rushed away. It took him a minute to recover. There were people present; he did not like to run, but overtook her on the bridge, and slipped her hand beneath his arm.

"You shouldn't have done that," he said; "you shouldn't have run away from me, you know."

Rozsi laughed. Swithin withdrew his arm; a desire to shake her seized him. He walked some way before he said, "Will you have the goodness to tell me what you came to that seat for?"

Rozsi flashed a look at him. "To-morrow is the *fête*," she answered.

Swithin muttered, "Is that all?"

"If you do not take us, we cannot go."

"Suppose I refuse," he said sullenly, "there are plenty of others."

Rozsi bent her head, scurrying along. "No," she murmured, "if *you* do not go —I do not wish."

Swithin drew her hand back within his arm. How round and soft it was! He tried to see her face. When she was nearly home he said good-bye, not wishing, for some dark reason, to be seen with her. He watched till she had disappeared; then slowly retraced his steps to the Mirabell Garden. When he came to where she had been sitting, he slowly lighted his cigar, and for a long time after it was smoked out remained there in the silent presence of the statues.

## VII

A crowd of people wandered round the booths, and Swithin found himself obliged to give the girls his arms. 'Like a little Cockney clerk!' he thought. His indignation passed unnoticed; they talked, they laughed, each sight and sound in all the hurly-burly seemed to go straight into their hearts. He eyed them ironically— their eager voices, and little coos of sympathy seemed to him vulgar. In the thick of the crowd he slipped his arm out of Margit's, but, just as he thought that he was free, the unwelcome hand slid up again. He tried again, but again Margit reappeared, serene, and full of pleasant humour; and his failure this time appeared to him in a comic light. But when Rozsi leaned across him, the glow of her round cheek, her curving lip, the inscrutable grey gleam of her eyes, sent a thrill of longing through him. He was obliged to stand by while they parleyed with a gipsy, whose matted locks and skinny hands inspired him with a not unwarranted disgust. "Folly!" he muttered, as Rozsi held out her palm. The old woman mumbled, and shot a malignant look at him. Rozsi drew back her hand, and crossed herself. 'Folly!' Swithin thought again; and seizing the girls' arms, he hurried them away.

"What did the old hag say?" he asked. Rozsi shook her head.

"You don't mean that you believe?"

Her eyes were full of tears. "The gipsies are wise," she murmured.

"Come, what did she tell you?"

This time Rozsi looked hurriedly round, and slipped away into the crowd. After a hunt they found her, and Swithin, who was scared, growled: "You shouldn't do such things—it's not respectable."

On higher ground, in the centre of a clear space, a military band was playing. For the privilege of entering this charmed circle Swithin paid three *kronen,* choosing naturally the best seats. He ordered wine, too, watching Rozsi out of the corner of his eye as he poured it out. The protecting tenderness of yesterday was all lost in this medley. It was every man for himself, after all! The colour had deepened again in her cheeks, she laughed, pouting her lips. Suddenly she put her glass aside. "Thank you, very much," she said, "it is enough!"

Margit, whose pretty mouth was all smiles, cried, *"Lieber Gott!* is it not good —life?" It was not a question Swithin could undertake to answer. The band began to play a waltz. "Now they will dance. *Lieber Gott!* and are the lights not wonderful?" Lamps were flickering beneath the trees like a swarm of fireflies. There was a hum as from a gigantic beehive. Passers-by lifted their faces, then vanished into the crowd; Rozsi stood gazing at them spellbound, as if their very going and coming were a delight.

The space was soon full of whirling couples. Rozsi's head began to beat time. "O Margit!" she whispered.

Swithin's face had assumed a solemn, uneasy expression. A man, raising his hat, offered his arm to Margit. She glanced back across her shoulder to reassure Swithin. "It is a friend," she said.

Swithin looked at Rozsi—her eyes were bright, her lips tremulous. He slipped his hand along the table and touched her fingers. Then she flashed a look at him—appeal, reproach, tenderness, all were expressed in it. Was she expecting him to dance? Did she want to mix with the riff-raff there; with *him* to make an exhibition of himself in this hurly-burly? A voice said, "Good-evening!" Before them stood Kasteliz, in a dark coat tightly buttoned at the waist.

"You are not dancing, *Rozsi Kozsanony?"* (Miss Rozsi). "Let me, then, have the pleasure." He held out his arm. Swithin stared in front of him. In the very act of going she gave him a look that said as plain as words: "Will you not?" But for answer he turned his eyes away, and when he looked again she was gone. He paid the score and made his way into the crowd. But as he went she danced by close to him, all flushed and panting. She hung back as if to stop him, and he caught the glistening of tears. Then he lost sight of her again. To be deserted the first minute he was alone with her, and for that jackanapes with the small head and volcanic glances! It was too much! And suddenly it occurred to him that she was alone with Kasteliz—alone at night, and far from home. 'Well,' he thought, 'what do I care?' and shouldered his way on through the crowd. It served him right for mixing with such people here. He left the fair, but the further he went, the more he nursed his rage, the more heinous seemed her offence, the sharper grew his jealousy. 'A beggarly baron!' was his thought.

A figure came alongside—it was Boleskey. One look showed Swithin his condition. Drunk again! This was the last straw!

Unfortunately Boleskey had recognised him. He seemed violently excited. "Where—where are my daughters?" he began.

Swithin brushed past, but Boleskey caught his arm. "Listen—brother!" he said; "news of my country! After to-morrow——"

"Keep it to yourself!" growled Swithin, wrenching his arm free. He went straight to his lodgings, and, lying on the hard sofa of his unlighted sitting-room, gave himself up to bitter thought. But in spite of all his anger, Rozsi's supply-moving figure, with its pouting lips, and roguish appealing eyes, still haunted him.

## VIII

Next morning there was not a carriage to be had, and Swithin was compelled to put off his departure till the morrow. The day was grey and misty; he wandered about with the strained, inquiring look of a lost dog in his eyes.

Late in the afternoon he went back to his lodgings. In a corner of the sitting-room stood Rozsi. The thrill of triumph, the sense of appeasement, the emotion, that seized on him, crept through to his lips in a faint smile. Rozsi made no sound, her face was hidden by her hands. And this silence of hers weighed on Swithin. She was forcing him to break it. What was behind her hands? His own face was visible! Why didn't she speak? Why was she here? Alone? That was not right surely.

Suddenly Rozsi dropped her hands; her flushed face was quivering—it seemed as though a word, a sign, even, might bring a burst of tears.

He walked over to the window. 'I must give her time!' he thought; then seized by unreasoning terror at this silence, spun round, and caught her by the arms. Rozsi held back from him, swayed forward and buried her face on his breast. . . .

Half an hour later Swithin was pacing up and down his room. The scent of rose leaves had not yet died away. A glove lay on the floor; he picked it up, and for a long time stood weighing it in his hand. All sorts of confused thoughts and feelings haunted him. It was the purest and least selfish moment of his life, this moment after she had yielded. But that pure gratitude at her fiery, simple abnegation did not last; it was followed by a petty sense of triumph, and by uneasiness. He was still weighing the little glove in his hand, when he had another visitor. It was Kasteliz.

"What can I do for you?" Swithin asked ironically.

The Hungarian seemed suffering from excitement. Why had Swithin left his charges the night before? What excuse had he to make? What sort of conduct did he call this?

Swithin, very like a bull-dog at that moment, answered: What business was it of his?

The business of a gentleman! What right had the Englishman to pursue a young girl?

"Pursue?" said Swithin; "you've been spying, then?"

"Spying—I—Kasteliz—Maurus Johann—an insult!"

"Insult!" sneered Swithin; "d'you mean to tell me you weren't in the street just now?"

Kasteliz answered with a hiss, "If you do not leave the city I will make you, with my sword—do you understand?"

"And if you do not leave my room I will throw you out of the window!"

For some minutes Kasteliz spoke in pure Hungarian while Swithin waited, with a forced smile and a fixed look in his eye. He did not understand Hungarian.

"If you are still in the city to-morrow evening," said Kasteliz at last in English, "I will spit you in the street."

Swithin turned to the window and watched his visitor's retiring back with a queer mixture of amusement, stubbornness, and anxiety. 'Well,' he thought, 'I suppose he'll run me through!' The thought was unpleasant; and it kept recurring, but it only served to harden his determination. His head was busy with plans for seeing Rozsi; his blood on fire with the kisses she had given him.

## IX

Swithin was long in deciding to go forth next day. He had made up his mind not to go to Rozsi till five o'clock. 'Mustn't make myself too cheap,' he thought. It was a little past that hour when he at last sallied out, and with a beating heart walked towards Boleskey's. He looked up at the window, more than half expecting to see Rozsi there; but she was not, and he noticed with faint surprise that the window was not open; the plants, too, outside, looked singularly arid. He knocked. No one came. He beat a fierce tattoo. At last the door was opened by a man with a reddish beard, and one of those sardonic faces only to be seen on shoemakers of Teutonic origin.

"What do you want, making all this noise?" he asked in German.

Swithin pointed up the stairs. The man grinned, and shook his head.

"I want to go up," said Swithin.

The cobbler shrugged his shoulders, and Swithin rushed upstairs. The rooms were empty. The furniture remained, but all signs of life were gone. One of his own bouquets, faded, stood in a glass; the ashes of a fire were barely cold; little scraps of paper strewed the hearth; already the room smelt musty. He went into the bedrooms, and with a feeling of stupefaction stood staring at the girls' beds, side by side against the wall. A bit of ribbon caught his eye; he picked it up and put it in his pocket—it was a piece of evidence that she had once existed. By the mirror some pins were dropped about; a little powder had been spilled. He looked at his own disquiet face and thought, 'I've been cheated!'

The shoemaker's voice aroused him. "*Tausend Teufel! Eilen Sie, nur! Zeit is Geld! Kann nich' länger warten!*" Slowly he descended.

"Where have they gone?" asked Swithin painfully. "A pound for every English word you speak. A pound!" and he made an O with his fingers.

The corners of the shoemaker's lips curled. "*Geld! Mff! Eilen Sie, nur!*"

But in Swithin a sullen anger had begun to burn. "If you don't tell me," he said, "it'll be the worse for you."

"*Sind ein komischer Kerl!*" remarked the shoemaker. "*Hier ist meine Frau!*"

A battered-looking woman came hurrying down the passage, calling out in German, "Don't let him go!"

With a snarling sound the shoemaker turned his back, and shambled off.

The woman furtively thrust a letter into Swithin's hand, and furtively waited.

The letter was from Rozsi.

"Forgive me"—it ran—"that I leave you and do not say good-bye. To-day our father had the call from our dear Father-town so long awaited. In two hours we are ready. I pray to the Virgin to keep you ever safe, and that you do not quite forget me.—Your unforgetting good friend

ROZSI."

When Swithin read it his first sensation was that of a man sinking in a bog; then his obstinacy stiffened. 'I won't be done,' he thought. Taking out a sovereign he tried to make the woman comprehend that she could earn it, by telling him where they had gone. He got her finally to write the words out in his pocket-book, gave her the sovereign, and hurried to the Goldene Alp, where there was a waiter who spoke English.

The translation given him was this:

"At three o'clock they start in a carriage on the road to Linz—they have bad horses—the Herr also rides a white horse."

Swithin at once hailed a carriage and started at full gallop on the road to Linz.

Outside the Mirabell Garden he caught sight of Kasteliz and grinned at him. 'I've sold *him* anyway,' he thought; 'for all their talk, they're no good, these foreigners!'

His spirits rose, but soon fell again. What chance had he of catching them? They had three hours' start! Still, the roads were heavy from the rain of the last two nights—they had luggage and bad horses; his own were good, his driver bribed—he might overtake them by ten o'clock! But did he want to? What a fool he had been not to bring his luggage; he would then have had a respectable position. What a brute he would look without a change of shirt, or anything to shave with! He saw himself with horror, all bristly, and in soiled linen. People would think him mad. 'I've given myself away,' flashed across him, 'what the devil can I say to them?' and he stared sullenly at the driver's back. He read Rozsi's letter again; it had a scent of her. And in the growing darkness, jolted by the swinging of the carriage, he suffered tortures from his prudence, tortures from his passion.

It grew colder and dark. He turned the collar of his coat up to his ears. He had visions of Piccadilly. This wild-goose chase appeared suddenly a dangerous, unfathomable business. Lights, fellowship, security! 'Never again!' he brooded; 'why won't they let me alone?' But it was not clear whether by 'they' he meant the conventions, the Boleskeys, his passions, or those haunting memories of Rozsi. If he had only had a bag with him! What was he going to say? What was he going to get by this? He received no answer to these questions. The darkness itself was less obscure than his sensations. From time to time he took out his watch. At each village the driver made inquiries. It was past ten when he stopped the carriage with a jerk. The stars were bright as steel, and by the side of the road a reedy lake showed in the moonlight. Swithin shiv-

ered. A man on a horse had halted in the centre of the road. "Drive on!" called Swithin, with a stolid face. It turned out to be Boleskey, who, on a gaunt white horse, looked like some winged creature. He stood where he could bar the progress of the carriage, holding out a pistol.

'Theatrical beggar!' thought Swithin, with a nervous smile. He made no sign of recognition. Slowly Boleskey brought his lean horse up to the carriage. When he saw who was within he showed astonishment and joy.

"You?" he cried, slapping his hand on his attenuated thigh, and leaning over till his beard touched Swithin. "You have come? You followed us?"

"It seems so," Swithin grunted out.

"You throw in your lot with us. Is it possible? You—you are a knight-errant then!"

"Good God!" said Swithin. Boleskey, flogging his dejected steed, cantered forward in the moonlight. He came back, bringing an old cloak, which he insisted on wrapping round Swithin's shoulders. He handed him, too, a capacious flask.

"How cold you look!" he said. "Wonderful! Wonderful! you English!" His grateful eyes never left Swithin for a moment. They had come up to the heels of the other carriage now, but Swithin, hunched in the cloak, did not try to see what was in front of him. To the bottom of his soul he resented the Hungarian's gratitude. He remarked at last, with wasted irony:

"You're in a hurry, it seems!"

"If we had wings," Boleskey answered, "we would use them."

"Wings!" muttered Swithin thickly; "legs are good enough for me."

X

Arrived at the inn where they were to pass the night, Swithin waited, hoping to get into the house without a "scene," but when at last he alighted the girls were in the doorway, and Margit greeted him with an admiring murmur, in which, however, he seemed to detect irony. Rozsi, pale and tremulous, with a half-scared look, gave him her hand, and, quickly withdrawing it, shrank behind her sister. When they had gone up to their room Swithin sought Boleskey. His spirits had risen remarkably. "Tell the landlord to get us supper," he said; "we'll crack a bottle to our luck." He hurried on the landlord's preparations. The window of the room faced a wood, so near that he could almost touch the trees. The scent from the pines blew in on him. He turned away from that scented darkness, and began to draw the corks of wine-bottles. The sound seemed to conjure up Boleskey. He came in, splashed all over, smelling slightly of stables; soon after, Margit appeared, fresh and serene, but Rozsi did not come.

"Where is your sister?" Swithin said. Rozsi, it seemed, was tired. "It will do her good to eat," said Swithin. And Boleskey, murmuring, "She must drink to our country," went out to summon her, Margit followed him, while Swithin cut up a chicken. They came back without her. She had "a megrim of the spirit."

Swithin's face fell. "Look here!" he said, *"I'll* go and try. Don't wait for me."

"Yes," answered Boleskey, sinking mournfully into a chair; "try, brother, try —by all means, try."

Swithin walked down the corridor with an odd, sweet, sinking sensation in his chest; and tapped on Rozsi's door. In a minute, she peeped forth, with her hair loose, and wondering eyes.

"Rozsi," he stammered, "what makes you afraid of me, *now?"*

She stared at him, but did not answer. "Why won't you come?"

Still she did not speak, but suddenly stretched out to him her bare arm.

Swithin pressed his face to it. With a shiver, she whispered above him, "I will come," and gently shut the door.

Swithin stealthily retraced his steps, and paused a minute outside the sitting-room to regain his self-control.

The sight of Boleskey with a bottle in his hand steadied him.

"She is coming," he said. And very soon she did come, her thick hair roughly twisted in a plait.

Swithin sat between the girls; but did not talk, for he was really hungry. Boleskey too was silent, plunged in gloom; Rozsi was dumb; Margit alone chattered.

"You will come to our Father-town? We shall have things to show you. Rozsi, what things we will show him!" Rozsi, with a little appealing movement of her hands, repeated, "What things we will show you!" She seemed suddenly to find her voice, and with glowing cheeks, mouth full, and eyes bright as squirrels, they chattered reminiscences of the "dear Father-town," of "dear friends," of the "dear home."

'A poor place!' Swithin could not help thinking. This enthusiasm seemed to him common; but he was careful to assume a look of interest, feeding on the glances flashed at him from Rozsi's restless eyes.

As the wine waned Boleskey grew more and more gloomy, but now and then a sort of gleaming flicker passed over his face. He rose to his feet at last.

"Let us not forget," he said, "that we go perhaps to ruin, to death; in the face of all this we go, because our country needs—in this there is no credit, neither to me nor to you, my daughters; but for this noble Englishman, what shall we say? Give thanks to God for a great heart. He comes—not for country, not for fame, not for money, but to help the weak and the oppressed. Let us drink, then, to him; let us drink again and again to heroic Forsyte!" In the midst of the dead silence, Swithin caught the look of suppliant mockery in Rozsi's eyes. He glanced at the Hungarian. Was he laughing at him? But Boleskey, after drinking up his wine, had sunk again into his seat; and there suddenly, to the surprise of all, he began to snore. Margit rose and, bending over him like a mother, murmured: "He is tired—it is the ride!" She raised him in her strong arms, and leaning on her shoulder Boleskey staggered from the room. Swithin and Rozsi were left alone. He slid his hand towards her hand that lay so close, on the rough tablecloth. It seemed to await his touch. Something gave way in him, and words came welling up; for the moment he forgot himself, forgot everything but that he was near her. Her head dropped on his shoulder, he breathed the perfume of her hair. "Good-night!" she whispered, and the whisper was like a kiss; yet before he could stop her she was gone. Her footsteps died away in the passage, but Swithin sat gazing intently at a single bright drop of spilt wine quivering on the table's edge. In that moment she, in her helplessness and emotion, was all in all to him—his life nothing; all the real things —his conventions, convictions, training, and himself—all seemed remote, behind a mist of passion and strange chivalry. Carefully with a bit of bread he soaked up the bright drop; and suddenly, he thought: 'This is tremendous!' For a long time he stood there in the window, close to the dark pine-trees.

## XI

In the early morning he awoke, full of the discomfort of this strange place and the medley of his dreams. Lying, with his nose peeping over the quilt, he was visited by a horrible suspicion. When he could bear it no longer, he started up in bed. What if it were all a plot to get him to marry her? The thought was treacherous,

and inspired in him a faint disgust. Still, *she* might be ignorant of it! But was she so innocent? What innocent girl would have come to his room like that? What innocent girl? Her father, who pretended to be caring only for his country? It was not probable that any man was such a fool; it was all part of the game—a scheming rascal! Kasteliz, too—his threats! They intended him to marry her? And the horrid idea was strengthened by his reverence for marriage. It was the proper, the respectable condition; he was genuinely afraid of this other sort of *liaison*—it was somehow too primitive! And yet the thought of that marriage made his blood run cold. Considering that she had already yielded, it would be all the more monstrous! With the cold, fatal clearness of the morning light he now for the first time saw his position in its full bearings. And, like a fish pulled out of water, he gasped at what was disclosed. Sullen resentment against this attempt to force him settled deep into his soul.

He seated himself on the bed, holding his head in his hands, solemnly thinking out what such marriage meant. In the first place it meant ridicule, in the next place ridicule, in the last place ridicule. She would eat chicken bones with her fingers—those fingers his lips still burned to kiss. She would dance wildly with other men. She would talk of her "dear Fathertown," and all the time her eyes would look beyond him, somewhere or other into some d——d place he knew nothing of. He sprang up and paced the room, and for a moment thought he would go mad.

They meant him to marry her! Even she—she meant him to marry her! Her tantalising inscrutability; her sudden little tendernesses; her quick laughter; her swift, burning kisses; even the movements of her hands; her tears—all were evidence against her. Not one of these things that Nature made her do counted on her side, but how they fanned his longing, his desire, and distress. He went to the glass and tried to part his hair with his fingers, but being rather fine, it fell into lank streaks. There was no comfort to be got from it. He drew his muddy boots on. Suddenly he thought: 'If I could see her alone, I could arrive at some arrangement!' Then, with a sense of stupefaction, he made the discovery that no arrangement could possibly be made that would not be dangerous, even desperate. He seized his hat, and, like a rabbit that has been fired at, bolted from the room. He plodded along amongst the damp woods with his head down, and resentment and dismay in his heart. But, as the sun rose, and the air grew sweet with pine scent, he slowly regained a sort of equability. After all, she had already yielded; it was not as if—! And the tramp of his own footsteps lulled him into feeling that it would all come right. 'Look at the thing practically,' he thought. The faster he walked the firmer became his conviction that he could still see it through. He took out his watch—it was past seven—he began to hasten back. In the yard of the inn his driver was harnessing the horses; Swithin went up to him.

"Who told you to put them in?" he asked.

The driver answered, *"Der Herr."*

Swithin turned away. 'In ten minutes,' he thought, 'I shall be in that carriage again, with this going on in my head! Driving away from England, from all I'm used to—driving to—what?' Could he face it? Could he face all that he had been through that morning; face it day after day, night after night? Looking up, he saw Rozsi at her open window gazing down at him; never had she looked sweeter, more roguish. An inexplicable terror seized on him; he ran across the yard and jumped into his carriage. "To Salzburg!" he cried; "drive on!" And rattling out of the yard without a look behind, he flung a sovereign at the hostler.

Flying back along the road faster even than he had come, with pale face, and eyes blank and staring like a pug-dog's, Swithin spoke no single word; nor, till he had reached the door of his lodgings, did he suffer the driver to draw rein.

## XII

Towards evening, five days later, Swithin, yellow and travel-worn, was ferried in a gondola to Danielli's Hotel. His brother, who was on the steps, looked at him with an apprehensive curiosity.

"Why, it's you!" he mumbled. "So you've got here safe?"

"Safe?" growled Swithin.

James replied, "I thought you wouldn't leave your friends!" Then, with a jerk of suspicion, "You haven't brought your friends?"

"What friends?" growled Swithin.

James changed the subject. "You don't look the thing," he said.

"Really!" muttered Swithin: "what's that to you?"

He appeared at dinner that night, but fell asleep over his coffee. Neither Traquair nor James asked him any further question, nor did they allude to Salzburg; and during the four days which concluded the stay in Venice Swithin went about with his head up, but his eyes half-closed like a dazed man. Only after they had taken ship at Genoa did he show signs of any healthy interest in life, when, finding that a man on board was perpetually strumming, he locked the piano up and pitched the key into the sea.

That winter in London he behaved much as usual, but fits of moroseness would seize on him, during which he was not pleasant to approach.

One evening when he was walking with a friend in Piccadilly, a girl coming from a side-street accosted him in German. Swithin, after staring at her in silence for some seconds, handed her a five-pound note, to the great amazement of his friend; nor could he himself have explained the meaning of this freak of generosity.

Of Rozsi he never heard again. . . .

This, then, was the substance of what he remembered as he lay ill in bed. Stretching out his hand he pressed the bell. His valet appeared, crossing the room like a cat; a Swede, who had been with Swithin many years; a little man with a dried face and fierce moustache, morbidly sharp nerves, and a queer devotion to his master.

Swithin made a feeble gesture. "Adolf," he said, "I'm very bad."

"Yes, sir!"

"Why do you stand there like a cow?" asked Swithin; "can't you see I'm very bad?"

"Yes, sir!" The valet's face twitched as though it masked the dance of obscure emotions.

"I shall feel better after dinner. What time is it?"

"Five o'clock."

"I thought it was more. The afternoons are very long."

"Yes, sir!"

Swithin sighed, as though he had expected the consolation of denial.

"Very likely I shall have a nap. Bring up hot water at half-past six and shave me before dinner."

The valet moved towards the door. Swithin raised himself.

"What did Mr. James say to you!"

"He said you ought to have another doctor; two doctors, he said, better than one. He said, also, he would look in again on his way 'home.' "

Swithin grunted, "Umph! What else did he say?"

"He said you didn't take care of yourself."

Swithin glared.

"Has anybody else been to see me?"

The valet turned away his eyes. "Mrs. Thomas Forsyte came last Monday fortnight."

"How long have I been ill?"

"Five weeks on Saturday."

"Do you think I'm very bad?"

Adolf's face was covered suddenly with crow's-feet. "You have no business to ask me question like that! I am not paid, sir, to answer question like that."

Swithin said faintly: "You're a peppery fool! Open a bottle of champagne!"

Adolf took a bottle of champagne from a cupboard and held nippers to it. He fixed his eyes on Swithin. "The doctor said——"

"Open the bottle!"

"It is not——"

"Open the bottle—or I give you warning."

Adolf removed the cork. He wiped a glass elaborately, filled it, and bore it scrupulously to the bedside. Suddenly twirling his moustaches, he wrung his hands, and burst out: "It is poison."

Swithin grinned faintly. "You foreign fool!" he said. "Get out!"

The valet vanished.

'He forgot himself!' thought Swithin. Slowly he raised the glass, slowly put it back, and sank gasping on his pillows. Almost at once he fell asleep.

He dreamed that he was at his club, sitting after dinner in the crowded smoking-room, with its bright walls and trefoils of light. It was there that he sat every evening, patient, solemn, lonely, and sometimes fell asleep, his square, pale old face nodding to one side. He dreamed that he was gazing at the picture over the fireplace, of an old statesman with a high collar, supremely finished face, and sceptical eyebrows—the picture, smooth, and reticent as sealing-wax, of one who seemed for ever exhaling the narrow wisdom of final judgments. All round him, his fellow-members were chattering. Only he himself, the old sick member, was silent. If fellows only knew what it was like to sit by yourself and feel ill all the time! What they were saying he had heard a hundred times. They were talking of investments, of cigars, horses, actresses, machinery. What was that? A foreign patent for cleaning boilers? There was no such thing; boilers couldn't be cleaned, any fool knew that! If an Englishman couldn't clean a boiler, no foreigner could clean one. He appealed to the old statesman's eyes. But for once those eyes seemed hesitating, blurred, wanting in finality. They vanished. In their place were Rozsi's little deep-set eyes, with their wide and far-off look; and as he gazed they seemed to grow bright as steel, and to speak to him. Slowly the whole face grew to be there, floating on the dark background of the picture; it was pink, aloof, unfathomable, enticing, with its fluffy hair and quick lips, just as he had last seen it. "Are you looking for something?" she seemed to say: "I could show you."

"I have everything safe enough," answered Swithin, and in his sleep he groaned.

He felt the touch of fingers on his forehead. 'I'm dreaming,' he thought in his dream.

She had vanished; and far away, from behind the picture, came a sound of footsteps.

Aloud, in his sleep, Swithin muttered: "I've missed it."

Again he heard the rustling of those light footsteps, and close in his ear a sound, like a sob. He awoke; the sob was his own. Great drops of perspiration stood on his forehead. 'What is it?' he thought; 'what have I lost?' Slowly his mind travelled over his investments; he could not think of any single one that was unsafe. What was it, then, that he had lost? Struggling on his pillows, he clutched the wine-glass. His lips touched the wine. 'This isn't the "Heidseck"!' he thought angrily, and before the reality of that displeasure all the dim vision passed away. But as he bent to drink, something snapped, and with a sigh, Swithin Forsyte died above the bubbles. . . .

When James Forsyte came in again on his way home, the valet, trembling, took his hat and stick.

"How's your master?"

"My master is dead, sir!"

"Dead! He can't be! I left him safe an hour ago!"

On the bed Swithin's body was doubled like a sack; his hand still grasped the glass.

James Forsyte paused. "Swithin!" he said, and with his hand to his ear he waited for an answer; but none came, and slowly in the glass a last bubble rose and burst.

# AWAKENING

## By JOHN GALSWORTHY

Through the massive skylight illuminating the hall at Robin Hill, the July sunlight at five o'clock fell just where the broad stairway turned; and in that radiant streak little Jon Forsyte stood, blue-linen-suited. His hair was shining, and his eyes, from beneath a frown, for he was considering how to go down-stairs, this last of innumerable times before the car brought his father and mother home. Four at a time, and five at the bottom? Stale! Down the banisters? But in which fashion? On his face, feet foremost? Very stale! On his stomach, sideways? Paltry! On his back, with his arms stretched down on both sides? Forbidden! Or on his face, head foremost, in a manner unknown as yet to any but himself? Such was the cause of the frown on the illuminated face of little Jon. . . .

In that summer of 1909 the simple souls who even then desired to simplify the English tongue, had, of course, no cognizance of little Jon, or they would have claimed him for a disciple. But one can be too simple in this life, for his real name was Jolyon, and his living father and dead half-brother had usurped of old the other shortenings, Jo and Jolly. As a fact little Jon had done his best to conform to convention and spell himself first Jonh, then John; not till his father had explained the sheer necessity, had he spelled his name Jon.

Up till now that father had possessed what was left of his heart by the groom, Bob, who played the concertina, and his nurse "Da," who wore the violet dress on Sundays, and enjoyed the name of Spraggins in that private life lived at odd moments even by domestic servants. His mother had only appeared to him, as it were in dreams, smelling delicious, smoothing his forehead just before he fell asleep, and sometimes docking his hair, of a golden brown colour. When he cut his head open against the nursery fender she was there to be bled over; and when he had nightmare she would sit on his bed and cuddle his head against her neck. She was precious but remote, because "Da" was so near, and there is hardly room for more than one woman at a time in a man's heart. With his father, too, of course, he had special bonds of union; for little Jon also meant to be a painter when he grew up—with the one small difference that his father painted pictures, and little Jon intended to paint ceilings and walls, standing on a board between two step ladders, in a dirty-white apron, and a lovely smell of whitewash. His father also took him riding in Richmond Park, on his pony, Mouse, so-called because it was so-coloured.

Little Jon had been born with a silver spoon in a mouth which was rather curly and large. He had never heard his father or his mother speak in an angry voice, either to each other, himself, or anybody else; the groom, Bob, Cook, Jane, Bela and the other servants; even "Da," who alone restrained him in his courses, had special voices when they talked to him. He was therefore of opinion that the world was a place of perfect and perpetual gentility and freedom.

A child of 1901, he had come to consciousness when his country, just over that bad attack of scarlet fever, the Boer War, was preparing for the Liberal revival of 1906. Coercion was unpopular, parents had exalted notions of giving their offspring a good time. They spoiled their rods, spared their children, and anticipated the results with enthusiasm. In choosing, moreover, for his father an amiable man of fifty-two who had already lost an only son, and for his mother a woman of thirty-eight, whose first and only child he was, little Jon had done well and wisely. What had saved him from becoming a cross between a lap dog and a little prig, had been his father's adoration of his mother, for even little Jon could see that she was not merely just his mother, and that he played second fiddle to her in his father's heart. What he played in his mother's heart he knew not yet. As for "Auntie" June, his half-sister (but so old that she had grown out of the relationship), she loved him, of course, but was too sudden. His devoted "Da," too, had a Spartan touch. His bath was cold and his knees were bare; he was not encouraged to be sorry for himself. As to the vexed question of his education, little Jon shared the theory of those who considered that children should not be forced. He rather liked the Mademoiselle who came for two hours every morning to teach him her language, together with history, geography and sums; nor were the piano lessons which his mother gave him disagreeable, for she had a way of luring him from tune to tune, never making him practise one which did not give him pleasure, so that he remained eager to convert ten thumbs into eight fingers. Under his father he learned to draw

pleasure-pigs and other animals. He was not a highly educated little boy. Yet, on the whole, the silver spoon stayed in his mouth without spoiling it, though "Da" sometimes said that other children would do him a "world of good."

It was a disillusionment, then, when at the age of nearly seven she held him down on his back, because he wanted to do something of which she did not approve. This first interference with the free individualism of a Forsyte drove him almost frantic. There was something appalling in the utter helplessness of that position, and the uncertainty as to whether it would ever come to an end. Suppose she never let him get up any more! He suffered torture at the top of his voice for fifty seconds. Worse than anything was his perception that "Da" had taken all that time to realise the agony of fear he was enduring. Thus, dreadfully, was revealed to him the lack of imagination in the human being! When he was let up he remained convinced that "Da" had done a dreadful thing. Though he did not wish to bear witness against her, he had been compelled, by fear of repetition, to seek his mother and say: "Mum, don't let 'Da' hold me down on my back again."

His mother, her hands held up over her head, and in them two plaits of hair— *"couleur de feuille morte,"* as little Jon had not yet learned to call it—had looked at him with eyes like little bits of his brown velvet tunic, and answered:

"No, darling, I won't."

She, being in the nature of a goddess, little Jon was satisfied; especially when, from under the dining-table at breakfast, where he happened to be waiting for a mushroom, he had overheard her say to his father:

"Then, will *you* tell 'Da,' dear, or shall I? She's *so* devoted to him"; and his father's answer:

"Well, she mustn't show it that way. I know exactly what it feels like to be held down on one's back. No Forsyte can stand it for a minute."

Conscious that they did not know him to be under the table, little Jon was visited by the quite new feeling of embarrassment, and stayed where he was, ravaged by desire for the mushroom.

Such had been his first dip into the dark abysses of existence. Nothing much had been revealed to him after that, till one day, having gone down to the cowhouse for his drink of milk fresh from the cow, after Garratt had finished milking, he had seen Clover's calf, dead. Inconsolable, and followed by an upset Garratt, he had sought "Da"; but suddenly aware that she was not the person he wanted, had rushed away to find his father and had run into the arms of his mother.

"Clover's calf's dead! Oh! Oh! It looked so soft!"

His mother's clasp, and her:

"Yes, darling, there, there" had stayed his sobbing. But if Clover's calf could die, anything could—not only bees, flies, beetles and chickens—and look soft like that! This was appalling—and soon forgotten!

The next thing had been to sit on a bumble bee, a poignant experience, which his mother had understood much better than "Da"; and nothing of vital importance had happened after that till the year turned; when, following a day of utter wretchedness, he had enjoyed a disease composed of little spots, bed, honey in a spoon, and many tangerine oranges. It was then that the world had flowered. To "Auntie" June he owed that flowering, for no sooner was he a little lame duck than she came rushing down from London, bringing with her the books which had nurtured her own Berserker spirit, born in the noted year of 1869. Aged, and of many colours, they were stored with the most formidable happenings. Of these she read to little Jon, till he was allowed to read to himself; whereupon she

whisked back to London and left them with him in a heap. Those books cooked his fancy, till he thought and dreamed of nothing but midshipmen and dhows, pirates, rafts, sandal-wood traders, iron horses, sharks, battles, Tartars, Red Indians, balloons, North Poles and other extravagant delights. The moment he was suffered to get up, he rigged his bed fore and aft, and set out from it in a narrow bath across green seas of carpet, to a rock, which he climbed by means of its mahogany drawer knobs, to sweep the horizon with his drinking tumbler screwed to his eye, in search of rescuing sails. He made a daily raft out of the towel stand, the tea tray, and his pillows. He saved the juice from his French plums, bottled it in an empty medicine bottle, and provisioned the raft with the rum that it became; also with pemmican made out of little saved-up bits of chicken sat on and dried at the fire; and with lime juice against scurvy, extracted from the peel of his oranges and a little economised juice. He made a North Pole one morning from the whole of his bedclothes except the bolster, and reached it in a birch-bark canoe (in private life the fender), after a terrible encounter with a polar bear fashioned from the bolster and four skittles dressed up in "Da's" nightgown. After that, his father, seeking to steady his imagination, brought him *Ivanhoe, Bevis,* a book about King Arthur, and *Tom Brown's Schooldays.* He read the first, and for three days built, defended and stormed Front de Bœuf's castle, taking every part in the piece except those of Rebecca and Rowena; with piercing cries of: *"En avant, de Bracy!"* and similar utterances. After reading the book about King Arthur he became almost exclusively Sir Lamorac de Galis, because, though there was very little about him, he preferred his name to that of any other knight; and he rode his old rocking-horse to death, armed with a long bamboo. *Bevis* he found tame; besides, it required woods and animals, of which he had none in his nursery, except his two cats, Fitz and Puck Forsyte, who permitted no liberties. For *Tom Brown* he was as yet too young. There was relief in the house when, after the fourth week, he was permitted to go down and out.

The month being March the trees were exceptionally like the masts of ships, and for little Jon that was a wonderful Spring, extremely hard on his knees, suits, and the patience of "Da," who had the washing and reparation of his clothes. Every morning the moment his breakfast was over, he could be viewed by his mother and father, whose windows looked out that way, coming from the study, crossing the terrace, climbing the old oak tree, his face resolute and his hair bright. He began the day thus because there was not time to go far afield before his lessons. The old tree's variety never staled; it had mainmast, foremast, top-gallant mast, and he could always come down by the halyards—or ropes of the swing. After his lessons, completed by eleven, he would go to the kitchen for a thin piece of cheese, a biscuit and two French plums—provision enough for a jolly-boat at least—and eat it in some imaginative way; then, armed to the teeth with gun, pistols, and sword, he would begin the serious climbing of the morning, encountering by the way innumerable slavers, Indians, pirates, leopards, and bears. He was seldom seen at that hour of the day without a cutlass in his teeth (like Dick Needham) amid the rapid explosion of copper caps. And many were the gardeners he brought down with yellow peas shot out of his little gun. He lived a life of the most violent action.

"Jon," said his father to his mother, under the oak tree, "is terrible. I'm afraid he's going to turn out a sailor, or something hopeless. Do you see any sign of his appreciating beauty?"

"Not the faintest."

"Well, thank heaven he's no turn for wheels or engines! I can bear anything but that. But I wish he'd take more interest in Nature."

"He's imaginative, Jolyon."

"Yes, in a sanguinary way. Does he love anyone just now?"

"No; only everyone. There never was anyone born more loving or more lovable than Jon."

"Being your boy, Irene."

At this moment little Jon, lying along a branch high above them, brought them down with two peas; but that fragment of talk lodged, thick, in his small gizzard. Loving, lovable, imaginative, sanguinary!

The leaves also were thick by now and it was time for his birthday, which, occupying every year on the twelfth of May, was always memorable for his chosen dinner of sweetbread, mushrooms, macaroons, and ginger beer.

Between that eighth birthday, however, and the afternoon when he stood in the July radiance at the turning of the stairway, several important things had happened.

"Da," worn out by washing his knees, or moved by that mysterious instinct which forces even nurses to desert their nurslings, left the very day after his birthday in floods of tears "to be married"—of all things—"to a man." Little Jon, from whom it had been kept, was inconsolable for an afternoon. It ought not to have been kept from him! Two large boxes of soldiers and some artillery, together with *The Young Buglers,* which had been among his birthday presents, cooperated with his grief in a sort of conversion, and instead of seeking adventures in person and risking his own life, he began to play imaginative games, in which he risked the lives of countless tin soldiers, marbles, stones and beans. Of these forms of *"chair á canon"* he made collections, and, using them alternately, fought the Peninsular, the Seven Years, the Thirty Years, and other wars, about which he had been reading of late in a big *History of Europe* which had been his grandfather's. He altered them to suit his genius and fought them all over the floor in his day nursery, so that nobody could come in, for fear of disturbing Gustavus Adolphus, King of Sweden, or treading on an army of Austrians. Because of the sound of the word he was passionately addicted to the Austrians, and finding there were so few battles in which they were successful he had to invent them in his games. His favourite generals were Prince Eugène, the Archduke Charles and Wallenstein. Tilly and Mack ("music-hall turns" he heard his father call them one day, whatever that might mean) one really could not love very much, Austrian though they were. For euphonic reasons, too, he doted on Turenne.

This phase, which caused his parents anxiety, because it kept him indoors when he ought to have been out, lasted through May and half of June, till his father killed it by bringing home to him *Tom Sawyer* and *Huckleberry Finn*. When he read those books something happened in him, and he went out of doors again in passionate quest of a river. There being none on the premises at Robin Hill, he had to make one out of the pond, which fortunately had water lilies, dragon-flies, gnats, bullrushes, and three small willow trees. On this pond, after his father and Garratt had ascertained by sounding that it had a reliable bottom and was nowhere more than two feet deep, he was allowed a little collapsible canoe, in which he spent hours and hours paddling, and lying down out of sight of Indian Joe and other enemies. On the shore of the pond too, he built him-self a wigwam about four feet square, of old biscuit tins, roofed in by boughs. In this he would make little fires, and cook the birds he had not shot with his gun

hunting in the coppice and fields, or the fish he did not catch in the pond because there were none. This occupied the rest of June and that July, when his father and mother were away in Ireland. He led a lonely life of "make believe" during those five weeks of summer weather, with gun, wigwam, water and canoe; and, however hard his active little brain tried to keep the sense of beauty away, she did creep in on him for a second now and then, perching on the wing of a dragonfly, glistening on the water lilies, or brushing his eyes with her blue as he lay on his back in ambush.

"Auntie" June, who had been left in charge, had a "grown-up" in the house, with a cough and a large piece of putty which he was making into a face; so she hardly ever came down to see him in the pond. Once, however, she brought with her two other "grown-ups." Little Jon, who happened to have painted his naked self bright blue and yellow in stripes out of his father's water-colour box, and put some duck's feathers in his hair, saw them coming, and ambushed himself among the willows. As he had foreseen, they came at once to his wigwam and knelt down to look inside, so that with a blood-curdling yell he was able to take the scalps of "Auntie" June and the woman "grown-up" in an almost complete manner before they kissed him. The names of the two grown-ups were "Auntie" Holly and "Uncle" Val, who had a brown face and a little limp, and laughed at him terribly. He took a fancy to "Auntie" Holly, who seemed to be a sister too; but they both went away the same afternoon and he did not see them again. Three days before his father and mother were to come home "Auntie" June also went off in a great hurry, taking the "grown-up" who coughed and his piece of putty; and Mademoiselle said: "Poor man, he was veree ill. I forbid you to go into his room, Jon." Little Jon, who rarely did things merely because he was told not to, refrained from going, though he was bored and lonely. In truth the day of the pond was past and he was filled to the brim of his soul with restlessness and the want of something—not a tree, not a gun—something soft. Those last two days had seemed like months in spite of *Cast Up by the Sea,* wherein he was reading about Mother Lee and her terrible wrecking bonfire. He had gone up and down the stairs perhaps a hundred times in those two days, and often from the day nursery, where he slept now, had stolen into his mother's room, looked at everything, without touching, and on into the dressing-room; and standing on one leg beside the bath, like Slingsby, had whispered—

"Ho, ho, ho! Dog my cats!" mysteriously, to bring luck. Then, stealing back, he had opened his mother's wardrobe, and taken a long sniff which seemed to bring him nearer to—he didn't know what.

He had done this just before he stood in the streak of sunlight, debating in which of the several ways he should slide down the banisters. They all seemed silly, and in a sudden languor he began descending the steps one by one. During that descent he could remember his father quite distinctly—the short grey beard, the deep eyes twinkling, the furrow between them, the funny smile, the thin figure which always seemed so tall to little Jon; but his mother he couldn't see. All that represented her was something swaying with two dark eyes looking back at him; and the scent of her wardrobe.

Bella was in the hall, drawing aside the big curtains, and opening the front door. Little Jon said, wheedling:

"Bella!"

"Yes, Master Jon."

"Do let's have tea under the oak tree when they come; I *know* they'd like it best."

"You mean *you'd* like it best."

Little John considered.

"No, *they* would, to please me."

Bella smiled. "Very well, I'll take it out if you'll stay quiet here and not get into mischief before they come."

Little Jon sat down on the bottom step, and nodded. Bella came close, and looked him over.

"Get up!" she said.

Little Jon got up. She scrutinized him behind; he was not green, and his knees seemed clean.

"All right!" she said. "My! Aren't you brown? Give me a kiss!"

And little Jon received a peck on his hair.

"What jam?" he asked. "I'm *so* tired of waiting."

"Gooseberry and strawberry."

Num! They were his favourites!

When she was gone he sat still for quite a minute. It was quiet in the big hall open to its East end so that he could see one of his trees, a brig sailing very slowly across the upper lawn. In the outer hall shadows were slanting from the pillars. Little Jon got up, jumped one of them, and walked round the clump of iris plants which filled the pool of grey-white marble in the centre. The flowers were pretty, but only smelled a very little. He stood in the open doorway and looked out. Suppose! —suppose they didn't come! He had waited so long that he felt he could not bear that, and his attention slid at once from such finality to the dust motes in the bluish sunlight coming in. Thrusting his hand up, he tried to catch some. Bella ought to have dusted that piece of air! But perhaps they weren't dust—only what sunlight was made of, and he looked to see whether the sunlight out of doors was the same. It was not. He had said he would stay quiet in the hall, but he simply couldn't any more; and crossing the gravel of the drive he lay down on the grass beyond. Pulling six daisies he named them carefully, Sir Lamorac, Sir Tristram, Sir Lancelot, Sir Palimedes, Sir Bors, Sir Gawain, and fought them in couples till only Sir Lamorac, whom he had selected for a specially stout stalk, had his head on, and even he, after three encounters, looked worn and waggly. A beetle was moving slowly in the grass, which almost wanted cutting. Every blade was a small tree, round whose trunk the beetle had to glide. Little Jon stretched out Sir Lamorac, feet foremost, and stirred the creature up. It scuttled painfully. Little Jon laughed, lost interest, and sighed. His heart felt empty. He turned over and lay on his back. There was a scent of honey from the lime trees in flower, and in the sky the blue was beautiful, with a few white clouds which looked and perhaps tasted like lemon ice. He could hear Bob playing: "Way down upon de Suwannee ribber" on his concertina, and it made him nice and sad. He turned over again and put his ear to the ground—Indians could hear things coming ever so far—but he could hear nothing—only the concertina! And almost instantly he did hear a grinding sound, a faint toot. Yes! it was a car—coming—coming! Up he jumped. Should he wait in the porch, or rush upstairs, and as they came in, shout: "Look!" and slide slowly down the banisters, head foremost? Should he? The car turned in at the drive. It was too late! And he only waited, jumping up and down in his excitement. The car came quickly, whirred, and stopped. His father got out, exactly like life. He bent down and little Jon bobbed up—they bumped. His father said:

"Bless us! Well, old man, you *are* brown!" just as he would; and the sense of expectation—of something wanted—bubbled unextinguished in little Jon. Then, with a long, shy look he saw his mother, in a blue dress, with a blue motor scarf over her cap and hair, smiling. He

jumped as high as ever he could, twined his legs behind her back, and hugged. He heard her gasp, and felt her hugging back. His eyes, very dark blue just then, looked into hers, very dark brown, till her lips closed on his eyebrow, and, squeezing with all his might, he heard her creak and laugh, and say:

"You *are* strong, Jon!"

He slid down at that, and rushed into the hall, dragging her by the hand.

While he was eating his jam beneath the oak tree, he noticed things about his mother that he had never seemed to see before, her cheeks for instance were creamy, there were silver threads in her dark goldy hair, her throat had no knob in it like Bella's, and she went in and out softly. He noticed, too, some little lines running away from the corners of her eyes, and a nice darkness under them. She was ever so beautiful, more beautiful than "Da" or Mademoiselle, or "Auntie" June or even "Auntie" Holly, to whom he had taken a fancy; even more beautiful than Bella, who had pink cheeks and came out too suddenly in places. This new beautifulness of his mother had a kind of particular importance, and he ate less than he had expected to.

When tea was over his father wanted him to walk round the gardens. He had a long conversation with his father about things in general, avoiding his private life —Sir Lamorac, the Austrians, and the emptiness he had felt these last three days, now so suddenly filled up. His father told him of a place called Glensofantrim, where he and his mother had been; and of the little people who came out of the ground there when it was very quiet. Little Jon came to a halt, with his heels apart.

"Do you really believe they do, Daddy?"

"No, Jon, but I thought you might."

"Why?"

"You're younger than I; and they're

fairies." Little Jon squared the dimple in his chin.

"I don't believe in fairies. I never see any."

"Ha!" said his father.

"Does Mum?"

His father smiled his funny smile.

"No; she only sees Pan."

"What's Pan?"

"The Goaty God who skips about in wild and beautiful places."

"Was he in Glensofantrim?"

"Mum said so."

Little Jon took his heels up, and led on.

"Did *you* see him?"

"No; I only saw Venus Anadyomene."

Little Jon reflected; Venus was in his book about the Greeks and Trojans. Then Anna was her Christian and Dynomene her surname?

But it appeared, on inquiry, that it was one word, which meant rising from the foam.

"Did she rise from the foam in Glensofantrim?"

"Yes; every day."

"What is she like, Daddy?"

"Like Mum."

"Oh! Then she must be——" but he stopped at that, rushed at a wall, scrambled up, and promptly scrambled down again. The discovery that his mother was beautiful was one which he felt must absolutely be kept to himself. His father's cigar, however, took so long to smoke, that at last he was compelled to say:

"I want to see what Mum's brought home. Do you mind, Daddy?"

He pitched the motive low, to absolve him from unmanliness, and was a little disconcerted when his father looked at him right through, heaved an important sigh, and answered:

"All right, old man, you go and love her."

He went, with a pretence of slowness, and then rushed, to make up. He entered her bedroom from his own, the door being open. She was still kneeling before a trunk, and he stood close to her, quite still.

She knelt up straight, and said:

"Well, Jon?"

"I thought I'd just come and see."

Having given and received another hug, he mounted the window-seat, and tucking his legs up under him watched her unpack. He derived a pleasure from the operation such as he had not yet known, partly because she was taking out things which looked suspicious, and partly because he liked to look at her. She moved differently from anybody else, especially from Bella; she was certainly the refinedest-looking person he had ever seen. She finished the trunk at last, and knelt down in front of him.

"Have you missed us, Jon?"

Little Jon nodded, and having thus admitted his feelings, continued to nod.

"But you had 'Auntie' June?"

"Oh! she had a man with a cough."

His mother's face changed, and looked almost angry. He added hastily:

"He was a poor man, Mum; he coughed awfully; I—I liked him."

His mother put her hands behind his waist.

"You like everybody, Jon?"

Little Jon considered.

"Up to a point," he said: " 'Auntie' June took me to church one Sunday."

"To church? Oh!"

"She wanted to see how it would affect me."

"And did it?"

"Yes. I came over all funny, so she took me home again very quick. I wasn't sick after all. I went to bed and had hot brandy and water, and read *The Boys of Beechwood*. It was scrumptious."

His mother bit her lip.

"When was that?"

"Oh! about—a long time ago—I wanted her to take me again, but she wouldn't. You and Daddy never go to church, do you?"

"No, we don't."

"Why don't you?"

His mother smiled.

"Well, dear, we both of us went when we were little. Perhaps we went when we were too little."

"I see," said little Jon, "it's dangerous."

"You shall judge for yourself about all those things as you grow up."

Little Jon replied in a calculating manner:

"I don't want to grow up, much. I don't want to go to school." A sudden overwhelming desire to say something more, to say what he really felt, turned him red. "I—I want to stay with you, and be your lover, Mum."

Then with an instinct to improve the situation, he added quickly:

"I don't want to go to bed to-night, either. I'm simply tired of going to bed, every night."

"Have you had any more nightmares?"

"Only about one. May I leave the door open into your room to-night, Mum?"

"Yes, just a little."

Little Jon heaved a sigh of satisfaction.

"What did you see in Glensofantrim?"

"Nothing but beauty, darling."

"What exactly is beauty?"

"What exactly is—— Oh! Jon, that's a poser."

"Can I see it, for instance?"

His mother got up, and sat beside him.

"You do, every day. The sky is beautiful, the stars, and moonlit nights, and then the birds, the flowers, the trees—they're all beautiful. Look out of the window—there's beauty for you, Jon."

"Oh! yes, that's the view. Is that all?"

"All? No. The sea is wonderfully beautiful, and the waves, with their foam flying back."

"Did you rise from it every day, Mum?"

His mother smiled. "Well, we bathed."

Little Jon suddenly reached out and caught her neck in his hands.

"*I know,*" he said mysteriously, "you're it, really, and all the rest is make-believe."

She sighed, laughed, said:

"Oh! Jon!"

Little Jon said critically:

"Do you think Bella beautiful, for instance? I hardly do."

"Bella is young; that's something."

"But you look younger, Mum. If you bump against Bella she hurts. I don't believe 'Da' was beautiful, when I come to think of it; and Mademoiselle's almost ugly."

"Mademoiselle has a very nice face."

"Oh! yes; nice. I love your little rays, Mum."

"Rays?"

Little Jon put his finger to the outer corner of her eye.

"Oh! Those? But they're a sign of age."

"They come when you smile."

"But they usen't to."

"Oh! well, I like them. Do you love me, Mum?"

"I do—I do love you, darling."

"Ever so?"

"Ever so!"

"More than I thought you did?"

"Much—much more."

"Well, so do I; so that makes it even."

Conscious that he had never in his life so given himself away, he felt a sudden reaction to the manliness of Sir Lamorac, Dick Needham, Huck Finn, and other heroes.

"Shall I show you a thing or two?" he said; and slipping out of her arms, he stood on his head. Then, fired by her obvious admiration, he mounted the bed, and threw himself head foremost from his feet on to his back, without touching anything with his hands. He did this several times.

That evening, having inspected what they had brought, he stayed up to dinner, sitting between them at the little round table they used when they were alone. He was extremely excited. His mother wore a French-grey dress, with creamy lace made out of little scriggly roses, round her neck, which was browner than the lace. He kept looking at her, till at last his father's funny smile made him suddenly attentive to his slice of pineapple. It was later than he had ever stayed up, when he went to bed. His mother went up with him, and he undressed very slowly so as to keep her there. When at last he had nothing on but his pyjamas, he said:

"Promise you won't go while I say my prayers!"

"I promise."

Kneeling down and plunging his face into the bed, little Jon hurried up, under his breath, opening one eye now and then, to see her standing perfectly still with a smile on her face. "Our Father"— so went his last prayer, "which art in heaven, hallowed be thy Mum, thy Kingdom Mum—on Earth as it is in heaven, give us this day our daily Mum and forgive us our trespasses on earth as it is in heaven and trespass against us, for thine is the evil the power and the glory for ever and ever. Amum! Look out!" He sprang, and for a long minute remained in her arms. Once in bed, he continued to hold her hand.

"You won't shut the door any more than that, will you? Are you going to be long, Mum?"

"I must go down and play to Daddy."

"Oh! well, I shall hear you."

"I hope not; you must go to sleep."

"I can sleep any night."

"Well, this is just a night like any other."

"Oh! no—it's extra special."

"On extra special nights one always sleeps soundest."

"But if I go to sleep, Mum, I shan't hear you come up."

"Well, when I do, I'll come in and give you a kiss, then if you're awake you'll know, and if you're not you'll still know you've had one."

Little Jon sighed, "All right!" he said: "I suppose I must put up with that. Mum?"

"Yes?"

"What was her name that Daddy believes in? Venus Anna Diomedes?"

"Oh! my angel! Anadyomene."

"Yes! but I like my name for you much better."

"What is yours, Jon?"

Little Jon answered shyly:

"Guinevere! it's out of the Round Table—I've only just thought of it, only of course her hair was down."

His mother's eyes, looking past him, seemed to float.

"You won't forget to come, Mum?"

"Not if you'll go to sleep."

"That's a bargain, then." And little Jon screwed up his eyes.

He felt her lips on his forehead, heard her footsteps; opened his eyes to see her gliding through the doorway, and, sighing, screwed them up again.

Then Time began.

For some ten minutes of it he tried loyally to sleep, counting a great number of thistles in a row, "Da's" old recipe for bringing slumber. He seemed to have been hours counting. It must, he thought, be nearly time for her to come up now. He threw the bedclothes back. "I am hot!" he said, and his voice sounded funny in the darkness, like someone else's. Why didn't she come? He sat up. He must look! He got out of bed, went to the window and pulled the curtain a slice aside. It wasn't dark, but he couldn't tell whether because of daylight or the moon, which was very big. It had a funny, wicked face, as if laughing at him, and he did not want to look at it. Then, remembering that his mother had said moonlit nights were beautiful, he continued to

stare out in a general way. The trees threw thick shadows, the lawn looked like spilt milk, and a long, long way he could see; oh! very far; right over the world, and it all looked different and swimmy. There was a lovely smell, too, in his open window.

'I wish I had a dove like Noah!' he thought.

"The moony moon was round and bright,
It shone and shone and made it light."

After that rhyme, which came into his head all at once, he became conscious of music, very soft—lovely! Mum playing! He bethought himself of a macaroon he had, laid up in his chest of drawers, and, getting it, came back to the window. He leaned out, now munching, now holding his jaws to hear the music better. "Da" used to say that angels played on harps in heaven; but it wasn't half so lovely as Mum playing in the moony night, with him eating a macaroon. A cockchafer buzzed by, a moth flew in his face, the music stopped, and little Jon drew his head in. She must be coming! He didn't want to be found awake. He got back into bed and pulled the clothes nearly over his head; but he had left a streak of moonlight coming in. It fell across the floor, near the foot of the bed, and he watched it moving ever so slowly towards him, as if it were alive. The music began again, but he could only just hear it now; sleepy music, pretty—sleepy—music— sleepy—slee——.

And time slipped by, the music rose, fell, ceased; the moonbeam crept towards his face. Little Jon turned in his sleep till he lay on his back, with one brown fist still grasping the bedclothes. The corners of his eyes twitched—he had begun to dream. He dreamed he was drinking milk out of a pan that was the moon, opposite a great black cat which watched him with a funny smile like his father's. He heard it

whisper: "Don't drink too much!" It was the cat's milk, of course, and he put out his hand amicably to stroke the creature; but it was no longer there; the pan had become a bed, in which he was lying, and when he tried to get out he couldn't find the edge; he couldn't find it—he—he— couldn't get out! It was dreadful!

He whimpered in his sleep. The bed had begun to go round too; it was outside him and inside him; going round and round, and getting fiery, and Mother Lee out of *Cast up by the Sea* was stirring it! Oh! so horrible she looked! Faster and faster!—till he and the bed and Mother Lee and the moon and the cat were all one wheel going round and round and up and up—awful—awful—awful!

He shrieked.

A voice saying: "Darling, darling!" got through the wheel, and he awoke, standing on his bed, with his eyes wide open.

There was his mother, with her hair like Guinevere's, and, clutching her, he buried his face in it: "Oh! oh!"

"It's all right, treasure. You're awake now. There! There! It's nothing!"

But little Jon continued to say: "Oh! oh!"

Her voice went on, velvety in his ear:

"It was the moonlight, sweetheart, coming on your face."

Little Jon burbled into her nightgown:

"You said it was beautiful. Oh!"

"Not to sleep in, Jon. Who let it in? Did you draw the curtains?"

"I wanted to see the time; I—I looked out. I—I heard you playing, Mum; I—I ate my macaroon." But he was growing slowly comforted; and the instinct to excuse his fear revived within him.

"Mother Lee went round in me and got all fiery," he mumbled.

"Well, Jon, what can you expect if you eat macaroons after you've gone to bed?"

"Only one, Mum; it made the music ever so more beautiful. I was waiting for you—I nearly thought it was to-morrow."

"My ducky, it's only just eleven now."

Little Jon was silent, rubbing his nose on her neck.

"Mum, is Daddy in your room?"

"Not to-night."

"Can I come?"

"If you wish, my precious."

Half himself again, little Jon drew back.

"You look different, Mum; ever so younger."

"It's my hair, darling."

Little Jon laid hold of it, thick dark gold, with a few silver threads.

"I like it," he said: "I like you best of all like this."

Taking her hand, he had begun dragging her towards the door. He shut it as they passed, with a sigh of relief.

"Which side of the bed do you like, Mum?"

"The left side."

"All right."

Wasting no time, giving her no chance to change her mind, little Jon got into the bed, which seemed much softer than his own. He heaved another sigh, screwed his head into the pillow and lay examining the battle chariots and swords and spears which always went on outside blankets, where the little hairs stood up against the light.

"It wasn't anything, *really,* was it?" he said.

From before her glass his mother answered:

"Nothing but the moon and your imagination heated up. You mustn't get so excited, Jon."

But, still not quite in possession of his nerves, little Jon answered boastfully:

"I wasn't afraid, really, of course!" And again he lay watching the spears and chariots. It all seemed very long.

"Oh! Mum, do hurry up!"

"Darling, I have to plait my hair."

"Oh! not to-night. You'll only have to unplait it again to-morrow. I'm sleepy now! if you don't come, I shan't be sleepy soon."

His mother stood up white and flowery before the winged mirror: he could see three of her, with her neck turned and her hair bright under the light, and her dark eyes smiling. It was unnecessary, and he said:

"Do come, Mum; I'm waiting."

"Very well, my love, I'll come."

Little Jon closed his eyes. Everything was turning out most satisfactory, only she must hurry up! He felt the bed shake, she was getting in. And, still with his eyes closed, he said sleepily: "It's nice, isn't it?"

He heard her voice say something, felt her lips touching his nose, and, snuggling up beside her who lay awake and loved him with her thoughts, he fell into the dreamless sleep, which rounded off his past.

# INDIAN SUMMER OF A FORSYTE

## By JOHN GALSWORTHY

---

### I

On the last day of May in the early 'nineties, about six o'clock of the evening, old Jolyon Forsyte sat under the oak tree below the terrace of his house at Robin Hill. He was waiting for the midges to bite him, before abandoning the glory of the afternoon. His thin brown hand, where blue veins stood out, held the end of a cigar in its tapering, long-nailed fingers—a pointed polished nail had survived with him from those earlier Victorian days when to touch nothing, even with the tips of the fingers, had been so distinguished. His domed forehead, great white moustache, lean cheeks, and long lean jaw were covered from the westering sunshine by an old brown Panama hat. His legs were crossed; in all his attitude was serenity and a kind of elegance, as of an old man who every morning put eau de Cologne upon his silk handkerchief. At his feet lay a woolly brown-and-white dog trying to be a Pomeranian—the dog Balthasar between whom and old Jolyon primal aversion had changed into attachment with the years. Close to his chair was a swing, and on the swing was seated one of Holly's dolls—called 'Duffer Alice'—with her body fallen over her legs and her doleful nose buried in a black petticoat. She was never out of disgrace, so it did not matter to her how she sat.

Below the oak tree the lawn dipped down a bank, stretched to the fernery, and, beyond that refinement, became fields, dropping to the pond, the coppice, and the prospect—'Fine, remarkable'—at which Swithin Forsyte, from under this very tree, had stared five years ago when he drove down with Irene to look at the house. Old Jolyon had heard of his brother's exploit—that drive which had become quite celebrated on Forsyte 'Change. Swithin! And the fellow had gone and died, last November, at the age of only seventy-nine, renewing the doubt whether Forsytes could live for ever, which had first arisen when Aunt Ann passed away. Died! and left only Jolyon and James, Roger and Nicholas and Timothy, Julia, Hester, Susan! And old Jolyon thought: 'Eighty-five! I don't feel it —except when I get that pain.'

His memory went searching. He had not felt his age since he had bought his nephew Soames's ill-starred house and settled into it here at Robin Hill over three years ago. It was as if he had been getting younger every spring, living in the country with his son and his grandchildren—June, and the little ones of the second marriage, Jolly and Holly; living down here out of the racket of London and the cackle of Forsyte 'Change, free of his boards, in a delicious atmosphere of no work and all play, with plenty of occupation in the perfecting and mellowing of the house and its twenty acres, and in ministering to the whims of Holly and Jolly. All the knots and crankiness, which had gathered in his heart during that long and tragic business of June, Soames, Irene his wife, and poor young Bosinney, had been smoothed out. Even June had thrown off her melancholy at last—witness this travel in Spain she was taking now with her father and her stepmother. Curiously perfect peace was left by their departure; blissful, yet blank, because his son was not there. Jo was never anything but a comfort and a pleasure to him nowadays—an amiable chap; but women, somehow—even the best—got a little on one's nerves, unless of course one admired them.

Far-off a cuckoo called; a wood-pigeon was cooing from the first elm-tree in the field, and how the daisies and buttercups had sprung up after the last mowing! The wind had got into the sou'west, too—a delicious air, sappy! He pushed his hat back and let the sun fall on his chin and cheek. Somehow, to-day, he wanted company—wanted a pretty face to look at. People treated the old as if they wanted nothing. And with the un-Forsytean philosophy which ever intruded on his soul, he thought: 'One's never had enough! With a foot in the grave one'll want something, I shouldn't be surprised!' Down here—away from the exigencies of affairs—his grandchildren, and the flowers, trees, birds of his little domain, to say nothing of sun and moon and stars above them, said, 'Open, sesame,' to him day and night. And sesame had opened—how much, perhaps, he did not know. He had always been responsive to what they had begun to call 'Nature,' genuinely, almost religiously responsive, though he had never lost his habit of calling a sunset a sunset and a view a view, however deeply they might move him. But nowadays Nature actually made him ache, he appreci-

ated it so. Every one of these calm, bright, lengthening days, with Holly's hand in his, and the dog Balthasar in front looking studiously for what he never found, he would stroll, watching the roses open, fruit budding on the walls, sunlight brightening the oak leaves and saplings in the coppice, watching the water-lily leaves unfold and glisten, and the silvery young corn of the one wheatfield; listening to the starlings and skylarks, and the Alderney cows chewing the cud, flicking slow their tufted tails; and every one of these fine days he ached a little from sheer love of it all, feeling perhaps, deep down, that he had not very much longer to enjoy it. The thought that some day—perhaps not ten years hence, perhaps not five—all this world would be taken away from him, before he had exhausted his powers of loving it, seemed to him in the nature of an injustice brooding over his horizon. If anything came after this life, it wouldn't be what he wanted; not Robin Hill, and flowers and birds and pretty faces—too few, even now, of those about him! With the years his dislike of humbug had increased; the orthodoxy he had worn in the 'sixties, as he had worn side-whiskers out of sheer exuberance, had long dropped off, leaving him reverent before three things alone—beauty, upright conduct, and the sense of property; and the greatest of these now was beauty. He had always had wide interests, and, indeed could still read *The Times*, but he was liable at any moment to put it down if he heard a blackbird sing. Upright conduct, property—somehow, they were tiring; the blackbirds and the sunsets never tired him, only gave him an uneasy feeling that he could not get enough of them. Staring into the stilly radiance of the early evening and at the little gold and white flowers on the lawn, a thought came to him: This weather was like the music of 'Orfeo,' which he had recently heard at Covent Garden. A beautiful opera, not like Meyerbeer, nor even quite Mozart, but, in its way, perhaps even more lovely; something classical and of the Golden Age about it, chaste and mellow, and the Ravogli 'almost worthy of the old days'—highest praise he could bestow. The yearning of Orpheus for the beauty he was losing, for his love going down to Hades, as in life love and beauty did go—the yearning which sang and throbbed through the golden music, stirred also in the lingering beauty of the world that evening. And with the tip of his cork-soled, elastic-sided boot he involuntarily stirred the ribs of the dog Balthasar, causing the animal to wake and attack his fleas; for though he was supposed to have none, nothing could persuade him of the fact. When he had finished, he rubbed the place he had been scratching against his master's calf, and settled down again with his chin over the instep of the disturbing boot. And into old Jolyon's mind came a sudden recollection—a face he had seen at that opera three weeks ago—Irene, the wife of his precious nephew Soames, that man of property! Though he had not met her since the day of the 'at home' in his old house at Stanhope Gate, which celebrated his granddaughter June's ill-starred engagement to young Bosinney, he had remembered her at once, for he had always admired her—a very pretty creature. After the death of young Bosinney, whose mistress she had so reprehensibly become, he had heard that she had left Soames at once. Goodness only knew what she had been doing since. That sight of her face—a side view—in the row in front, had been literally the only reminder these three years that she was still alive. No one ever spoke of her. And yet Jo had told him something once—something which had upset him completely. The boy had got it from George Forsyte, he believed, who had seen Bosinney in the fog the day he was run over—some-

thing which explained the young fellow's distress—an act of Soames towards his wife—a shocking act. Jo had seen her, too, that afternoon, after the news was out, seen her for a moment, and his description had always lingered in old Jolyon's mind—'wild and lost' he had called her. And next day June had gone there—bottled up her feelings and gone there, and the maid had cried and told her how her mistress had slipped out in the night and vanished. A tragic business altogether! One thing was certain—Soames had never been able to lay hands on her again. And he was living at Brighton, and journeying up and down—a fitting fate, the man of property! For when he once took a dislike to anyone—as he had to his nephew—old Jolyon never got over it. He remembered still the sense of relief with which he had heard the news of Irene's disappearance. It had been shocking to think of her a prisoner in that house to which she must have wandered back, when Jo saw her, wandered back for a moment—like a wounded animal to its hole after seeing that news, 'Tragic death of an Architect,' in the street. Her face had struck him very much the other night—more beautiful than he had remembered, but like a mask, with something going on beneath it. A young woman still—twenty-eight perhaps. Ah, well! Very likely she had another lover by now. But at this subversive thought—for married women should never love: once, even, had been too much—his instep rose, and with it the dog Balthasar's head. The sagacious animal stood up and looked into old Jolyon's face. 'Walk?' he seemed to say; and old Jolyon answered: "Come on, old chap!"

Slowly, as was their wont, they crossed among the constellations of buttercups and daisies, and entered the fernery. This feature, where very little grew as yet, had been judiciously dropped below the level of the lawn so that it might come up again on the level of the other lawn and give the impression of irregularity, so important in horticulture. Its rocks and earth were beloved of the dog Balthasar, who sometimes found a mole there. Old Jolyon made a point of passing through it because, though it was not beautiful, he intended that it should be, some day, and he would think: 'I must get Varr to come down and look at it; he's better than Beech.' For plants, like houses and human complaints, required the best expert consideration. It was inhabited by snails, and if accompanied by his grandchildren, he would point to one and tell them the story of the little boy who said: 'Have plummers got leggers, Mother?' 'No, sonny.' 'Then darned if I haven't been and swallowed a snileybob.' And when they skipped and clutched his hand, thinking of the snileybob going down the little boy's 'red lane,' his eyes would twinkle. Emerging from the fernery, he opened the wicket gate, which just there led into the first field, a large and park-like area, out of which, within brick walls, the vegetable garden had been carved. Old Jolyon avoided this, which did not suit his mood, and made down the hill towards the pond. Balthasar, who knew a water-rat or two, gambolled in front, at the gait which marks an oldish dog who takes the same walk every day. Arrived at the edge, old Jolyon stood, noting another water-lily opened since yesterday; he would show it to Holly to-morrow, when 'his little sweet' had got over the upset which had followed on her eating a tomato at lunch—her little arrangements were very delicate. Now that Jolly had gone to school—his first term— Holly was with him nearly all day long, and he missed her badly. He felt that pain too, which often bothered him now, a little dragging at his left side. He looked back up the hill. Really, poor young Bosinney had made an uncommonly good job of the house; he would have done

very well for himself if he had lived! And where was he now? Perhaps, still haunting this, the site of his last work, of his tragic love affair. Or was Philip Bosinney's spirit diffused in the general? Who could say? That dog was getting his legs muddy! And he moved towards the coppice. There had been the most delightful lot of bluebells, and he knew where some still lingered like little patches of sky fallen in between the trees, away out of the sun. He passed the cow-houses and the hen-houses there installed, and pursued a path into the thick of the saplings, making for one of the bluebell plots. Balthasar, preceding him once more, uttered a low growl. Old Jolyon stirred him with his foot, but the dog remained motionless, just where there was no room to pass, and the hair rose slowly along the centre of his woolly back. Whether from the growl and the look of the dog's stivered hair, or from the sensation which a man feels in a wood, old Jolyon also felt something move along his spine. And then the path turned, and there was an old mossy log, and on it a woman sitting. Her face was turned away, and he had just time to think: 'She's trespassing—I must have a board put up!' before she turned. Powers above! The face he had seen at the opera—the very woman he had just been thinking of! In that confused moment he saw things blurred, as if a spirit—queer effect—the slant of sunlight perhaps on her violet-grey frock! And then she rose and stood smiling, her head a little to one side. Old Jolyon thought: 'How pretty she is!' She did not speak, neither did he; and he realized why with a certain admiration. She was here no doubt because of some memory, and did not mean to try and get out of it by vulgar explanation.

"Don't let that dog touch your frock," he said; "he's got wet feet. Come here, you!"

But the dog Balthasar went on towards

the visitor, who put her hand down and stroked his head. Old Jolyon said quickly:

"I saw you at the opera the other night; you didn't notice me."

"Oh, yes! I did."

He felt a subtle flattery in that, as though she had added: 'Do you think one could miss seeing you?'

"They're all in Spain," he remarked abruptly. "I'm alone; I drove up for the opera. The Ravogli's good. Have you seen the cow-houses?"

In a situation so charged with mystery and something very like emotion he moved instinctively towards that bit of property, and she moved beside him. Her figure swayed faintly, like the best kind of French figures; her dress, too, was a sort of French grey. He noticed two or three silver threads in her amber-coloured hair, strange hair with those dark eyes of hers, and that creamy-pale face. A sudden side-long look from the velvety brown eyes disturbed him. It seemed to come from deep and far, from another world almost, or at all events from someone not living very much in this. And he said mechanically:

"Where are you living now?"

"I have a little flat in Chelsea."

He did not want to hear what she was doing, did not want to hear anything; but the perverse word came out:

"Alone?"

She nodded. It was a relief to know that. And it came into his mind that, but for a twist of fate, she would have been mistress of this coppice, showing these cow-houses to him, a visitor.

"All Alderneys," he muttered; "they give the best milk. This one's a pretty creature. Woa, Myrtle!"

The fawn-coloured cow, with eyes as soft and brown as Irene's own, was standing absolutely still, not having long been milked. She looked round at them out of the corner of those lustrous, mild, cynical eyes, and from her grey lips a little dribble of saliva threaded its way towards the straw. The scent of hay and vanilla and ammonia rose in the dim light of the cool cow-house; and old Jolyon said:

"You must come up and have some dinner with me. I'll send you home in the carriage."

He perceived a struggle going on within her; natural, no doubt, with her memories. But he wanted her company; a pretty face, a charming figure, beauty! He had been alone all the afternoon. Perhaps his eyes were wistful, for she answered: "Thank you, Uncle Jolyon. I should like to."

He rubbed his hands, and said:

"Capital! Let's go up, then!" And, preceded by the dog Balthasar, they ascended through the field. The sun was almost level in their faces now, and he could see, not only those silver threads, but little lines, just deep enough to stamp her beauty with a coin-like fineness—the special look of life unshared with others. 'I'll take her in by the terrace,' he thought: 'I won't make a common visitor of her.'

"What do you do all day?" he said.

"Teach music; I have another interest, too."

"Work!" said old Jolyon, picking up the doll from off the swing, and smoothing its black petticoat. "Nothing like it, is there? I don't do any now. I'm getting on. What interest is that?"

"Trying to help women who've come to grief." Old Jolyon did not quite understand. "To grief?" he repeated; then realised with a shock that she meant exactly what he would have meant himself if he had used that expression. Assisting the Magdalenes of London! What a weird and terrifying interest! And, curiosity overcoming his natural shrinking, he asked:

"Why? What do you do for them?"

"Not much. I've no money to spare. I

can only give sympathy and food sometimes."

Involuntarily old Jolyon's hand sought
his purse. He said hastily: "How d'you
get hold of them?"

"I go to a hospital."

"A hospital! Phew!"

"What hurts me most is that once they
nearly all had some sort of beauty."

Old Jolyon straightened the doll.
"Beauty!" he ejaculated: "Ha! Yes! A sad
business!" and he moved towards the
house. Through a French window, under
sun-blinds not yet drawn up, he preceded
her into the room where he was wont to
study *The Times* and the sheets of an
agricultural magazine, with huge illustra-
tions of mangold wurzels, and the like,
which provided Holly with material for
her paint brush.

"Dinner's in half an hour. You'd like
to wash your hands! I'll take you to
June's room."

He saw her looking round eagerly;
what changes since she had last visited
this house with her husband, or her lover,
or both perhaps—he did not know, could
not say! All that was dark, and he wished
to leave it so. But what changes! And in
the hall he said:

"My boy Jo's a painter, you know.
He's got a lot of taste. It isn't mine, of
course, but I've let him have his way."

She was standing very still, her eyes
roaming through the hall and music
room, as it now was—all thrown into
one, under the great skylight. Old Jolyon
had an odd impression of her. Was she
trying to conjure somebody from the
shades of that space where the colouring
was all pearl-grey and silver? He would
have had gold himself; more lively and
solid. But Jo had French tastes, and it
had come out shadowy like that, with an
effect as of the fume of cigarettes the
chap was always smoking, broken here
and there by a little blaze of blue or crimson colour. It was not *his* dream! Men-

tally he had hung this space with those
gold-framed masterpieces of still and
stiller life which he had bought in days
when quantity was precious. And now
where were they? Sold for a song! That
something which made him, alone among
Forsytes, move with the times had
warned him against the struggle to retain
them. But in his study he still had 'Dutch
Fishing Boats at Sunset.'

He began to mount the stairs with her,
slowly, for he felt his side.

"These are the bathrooms," he said,
"and other arrangements. I've had them
tiled. The nurseries are along there. And
this is Jo's and his wife's. They all communicate. But you remember, I expect."

Irene nodded. They passed on, up the
gallery and entered a large room with a
small bed, and several windows.

"This is mine," he said. The walls were
covered with the photographs of children
and water-colour sketches, and he added
doubtfully:

"These are Jo's. The view's first-rate.
You can see the Grand Stand at Epsom
in clear weather."

The sun was down now, behind the
house, and over the 'prospect' a luminous
haze had settled, emanation of the long
and prosperous day. Few houses showed,
but fields and trees faintly glistened, away
to a loom of downs.

"The country's changing," he said
abruptly, "but there it'll be when we're all
gone. Look at those thrushes—the birds
are sweet here in the mornings. I'm glad
to have washed my hands of London."

Her face was close to the window
pane, and he was struck by its mournful
look. 'Wish I could make her look
happy!' he thought. 'A pretty face, but
sad!' And taking up his can of hot water
he went out into the gallery.

"This is June's room," he said, opening
the next door and putting the can down;
"I think you'll find everything." And closing the door behind her he went back to

his own room. Brushing his hair with his great ebony brushes, and dabbing his forehead with eau de Cologne, he mused. She had come so strangely—a sort of visitation, mysterious, even romantic, as if his desire for company, for beauty, had been fulfilled by—whatever it was which fulfilled that sort of thing. And before the mirror he straightened his still upright figure, passed the brushes over his great white moustache, touched up his eyebrows with eau de Cologne, and rang the bell.

"I forgot to let them know that I have a lady to dinner with me. Let cook do something extra, and tell Beacon to have the landau and pair at half-past ten to drive her back to Town to-night. Is Miss Holly asleep?"

The maid thought not. And Old Jolyon, passing down the gallery, stole on tiptoe towards the nursery, and opened the door whose hinges he kept specially oiled that he might slip in and out in the evenings without being heard.

But Holly *was* asleep, and lay like a miniature Madonna, of that type which the old painters could not tell from Venus, when they had completed her. Her long dark lashes clung to her cheeks; on her face was perfect peace—her little arrangements were evidently all right again. And old Jolyon, in the twilight of the room, stood adoring her! It was so charming, solemn, and loving—that little face. He had more than his share of the blessed capacity of living again in the young. They were to him his future life— all of a future life—that his fundamental pagan sanity perhaps admitted. There she was with everything before her, and his blood—some of it—in her tiny veins. There she was, his little companion, to be made as happy as ever he could make her, so that she knew nothing but love. His heart swelled, and he went out, stifling the sound of his patent-leather boots. In the corridor an eccentric notion

attacked him: To think that children should come to that which Irene had told him she was helping! Women who were all, once, little things like this one sleeping there! 'I must give her a cheque!' he mused; 'Can't bear to think of them!' They had never borne reflecting on, those poor outcasts; wounding too deeply the core of true refinement hidden under layers of conformity to the sense of property —wounding too grievously the deepest thing in him—a love of beauty which could give him, even now, a flutter of the heart, thinking of his evening in the society of a pretty woman. And he went downstairs, through the swinging doors, to the back regions. There, in the wine-cellar, was a hock worth at least two pounds a bottle, a Steinberg Cabinet, better than any Johannisberg that ever went down throat; a wine of perfect bouquet, sweet as a nectarine—nectar indeed! He got a bottle out, handling it like a baby, and holding it level to the light, to look. Enshrined in its coat of dust, that mellow-coloured, slender-necked bottle gave him deep pleasure. Three years to settle down again since the move from Town—ought to be in prime condition! Thirty-five years ago he had bought it—thank God he had kept his palate, and earned the right to drink it. She would appreciate this; not a spice of acidity in a dozen. He wiped the bottle, drew the cork with his own hands, put his nose down, inhaled its perfume, and went back to the music room.

Irene was standing by the piano; she had taken off her hat and a lace scarf she had been wearing, so that her gold-coloured hair was visible, and the pallor of her neck. In her grey frock she made a pretty picture for old Jolyon, against the rosewood of the piano.

He gave her his arm, and solemnly they went. The room, which had been designed to enable twenty-four people to dine in comfort, held now but a little round table. In his present solitude the big dining-table oppressed old Jolyon; he had caused it to be removed till his son came back. Here in the company of two really good copies of Raphael Madonnas he was wont to dine alone. It was the only disconsolate hour of his day, this summer weather. He had never been a large eater, like that great chap Swithin, or Sylvanus Heythorp, or Anthony Thornworthy, those cronies of past times; and to dine alone, overlooked by the Madonnas, was to him but a sorrowful occupation, which he got through quickly, that he might come to the more spiritual enjoyment of his coffee and cigar. But this evening was a different matter! His eyes twinkled at her across the little table and he spoke of Italy and Switzerland, telling her stories of his travels there, and other experiences which he could no longer recount to his son and granddaughter because they knew them. This fresh audience was precious to him; he had never become one of those old men who ramble round and round the fields of reminiscence. Himself quickly fatigued by the insensitive, he instinctively avoided fatiguing others, and his natural flirtatiousness towards beauty guarded him specially in his relations with a woman. He would have liked to draw her out, but though she murmured and smiled and seemed to be enjoying what he told her, he remained conscious of that mysterious remoteness which constituted half her fascination. He could not bear women who threw their shoulders and eyes at you, and chattered away; or hardmouthed women who laid down the law and knew more than you did. There was only one quality in a woman that appealed to him—charm; and the quieter it was, the more he liked it. And this one had charm, shadowy as afternoon sunlight on those Italian hills and valleys he had loved. The feeling, too, that she was, as it were, apart, cloistered, made her seem nearer to himself, a strangely desir-

able companion. When a man is very old and quite out of the running he loves to feel secure from the rivalries of youth, for he would still be first in the heart of beauty. And he drank his hock, and watched her lips, and felt nearly young. But the dog Balthasar lay watching her lips too, and despising in his heart the interruptions of their talk, and the tilting of those greenish glasses full of a golden fluid which was distasteful to him.

The light was just failing when they went back into the music-room. And, cigar in mouth, old Jolyon said:

"Play me some Chopin."

By the cigars they smoke, and the composers they love, ye shall know the texture of men's souls. Old Jolyon could not bear a strong cigar or Wagner's music. He loved Beethoven and Mozart, Handel and Gluck, and Schumann, and, for some occult reason, the operas of Meyerbeer; but of late years he had been seduced by Chopin, just as in painting he had succumbed to Botticelli. In yielding to these tastes he had been conscious of divergence from the standard of the Golden Age. Their poetry was not that of Milton and Byron and Tennyson; of Raphael and Titian; Mozart and Beethoven. It was, as it were, behind a veil; their poetry hit no one in the face, but slipped its fingers under the ribs and turned and twisted, and melted up the heart. And, never certain that this was healthy, he did not care a rap so long as he could see the pictures of the one or hear the music of the other.

Irene sat down at the piano under the electric lamp festooned with pearl-grey, and old Jolyon, in an armchair, whence he could see her, crossed his legs and drew slowly at his cigar. She sat a few moments with her hands on the keys, evidently searching her mind for what to give him. Then she began and within old Jolyon there arose a sorrowful pleasure, not quite like anything else in the world.

He fell slowly into a trance, interrupted only by the movements of taking the cigar out of his mouth at long intervals, and replacing it. She was there, and the hock within him, and the scent of tobacco; but there, too, was a world of sunshine lingering into moonlight, and pools with storks upon them, and bluish trees above, glowing with blurs of wine-red roses, and fields of lavender where milk-white cows were grazing, and a woman all shadowy, with dark eyes and a white neck, smiled, holding out her arms; and through air which was like music a star dropped and was caught on a cow's horn. He opened his eyes. Beautiful piece; she played well—the touch of an angel! And he closed them again. He felt miraculously sad and happy, as one does, standing under a lime-tree in full honey flower. Not live one's own life again, but just stand there and bask in the smile of a woman's eyes, and enjoy the bouquet! And he jerked his hand; the dog Balthasar had reached up and licked it.

"Beautiful!" He said: "Go on—more Chopin!"

She began to play again. This time the resemblance between her and 'Chopin' struck him. The swaying he had noticed in her walk was in her playing too, and the Nocturne she had chosen and the soft darkness of her eyes, the light on her hair, as of moonlight from a golden moon. Seductive, yes; but nothing of Delilah in her or in that music. A long blue spiral from his cigar ascended and dispersed. 'So we go out!' he thought. 'No more beauty! Nothing?'

Again Irene stopped.

"Would you like some Gluck? He used to write his music in a sunlit garden, with a bottle of Rhine wine beside him."

"Ah! yes. Let's have 'Orfeo.' " Round about him now were fields of gold and silver flowers, white forms swaying in the sunlight, bright birds flying to and fro. All was summer. Lingering waves of sweetness and regret flooded his soul. Some cigar ash dropped, and taking out a silk handkerchief to brush it off, he inhaled a mingled scent as of snuff and eau de Cologne. 'Ah!, he thought, 'Indian summer—that's all!' and he said: "You haven't played me 'Che faro.' "

She did not answer; did not move. He was conscious of something—some strange upset. Suddenly he saw her rise and turn away, and a pang of remorse shot through him. What a clumsy chap! Like Orpheus, she of course—she too was looking for her lost one in the hall of memory! And disturbed to the heart, he got up from his chair. She had gone to the great window at the far end. Gingerly he followed. Her hands were folded over her breast; he could just see her cheek, very white. And, quite emotionalized, he said: "There, there, my love!" The words had escaped him mechanically, for they were those he used to Holly when she had a pain, but their effect was instantaneously distressing. She raised her arms, covered her face with them, and wept.

Old Jolyon stood gazing at her with eyes very deep from age. The passionate shame she seemed feeling at her abandonment, so unlike the control and quietude of her whole presence, was as if she had never before broken down in the presence of another being.

"There, there—there, there!" he murmured, and putting his hand out reverently, touched her. She turned, and leaned the arms which covered her face against him. Old Jolyon stood very still, keeping one thin hand on her shoulder. Let her cry her heart out—it would do her good! And the dog Balthasar, puzzled, sat down on his stern to examine them.

The window was still open, the curtains had not been drawn, the last of daylight from without mingled with faint intrusion from the lamp within; there was a scent of new-mown grass. With the wisdom of a long life old Jolyon did not speak. Even grief sobbed itself out in time; only Time was good for sorrow— Time who saw the passing of each mood, each emotion in turn; Time the layer-to-rest. There came into his mind the words: 'As panteth the hart after cooling streams'—but they were of no use to him. Then, conscious of a scent of violets, he knew she was drying her eyes. He put his chin forward, pressed his moustache against her forehead, and felt her shake with a quivering of her whole body, as of a tree which shakes itself free of rain-drops. She put his hand to her lips, as if saying: "All over now! Forgive me!"

The kiss filled him with a strange comfort; he led her back to where she had been so upset. And the dog Balthasar, following, laid the bone of one of the cutlets they had eaten at their feet.

Anxious to obliterate the memory of that emotion, he could think of nothing better than china; and moving with her slowly from cabinet to cabinet, he kept taking up bits of Dresden and Lowestoft and Chelsea, turning them round and round with his thin, veined hands, whose skin, faintly freckled, had such an aged look.

"I bought this at Jobson's," he would say; "cost me thirty pounds. It's very old. That dog leaves his bones all over the place. This old 'ship-bowl' I picked up at the sale when that precious rip, the Marquis, came to grief. But you don't remember. Here's a nice piece of Chelsea. Now, what would you say *this* was?" And he was comforted, feeling that, with her taste, she was taking a real interest in these things; for, after all, nothing better composes the nerves than a doubtful piece of china.

When the crunch of the carriage wheels was heard at last, he said:

"You must come again; you must come to lunch, then I can show you these by daylight, and my little sweet—she's a dear little thing. This dog seems to have taken a fancy to you."

For Balthasar, feeling that she was about to leave, was rubbing his side against her leg. Going out under the porch with her, he said:

"He'll get you up in an hour and a quarter. Take this for your *protégées*," and he slipped a cheque for fifty pounds into her hand. He saw her brightened eyes, and heard her murmur: "Oh! Uncle Jolyon!" and a real throb of pleasure went through him. That meant one or two poor creatures helped a little, and it meant that she would come again. He put his hand in at the window and grasped hers once more. The carriage rolled away. He stood looking at the moon and the shadows of the trees, and thought: 'A sweet night! She——!'

## II

Two days of rain, and summer set in bland and sunny. Old Jolyon walked and talked with Holly. At first he felt taller and full of a new vigour; then he felt restless. Almost every afternoon they would enter the coppice, and walk as far as the log. 'Well, she's not there!' he would think, 'of course not!' And he would feel a little shorter, and drag his feet walking up the hill home, with his hand clapped to his left side. Now and then the thought would move in him: 'Did she come—or did I dream it?' and he would stare at space, while the dog Balthasar stared at him. Of course she would not come again! He opened the letters from Spain with less excitement. They were not returning till July; he felt, oddly, that he could bear it. Every day at dinner he screwed up his eyes and looked at where she had sat. She was not there, so he unscrewed his eyes again.

On the seventh afternoon he thought: 'I must go up and get some boots.' He ordered Beacon, and set out. Passing from Putney towards Hyde Park he reflected: 'I might as well go to Chelsea and see her.' And he called out: "Just drive me to where you took that lady the other night." The coachman turned his broad red face, and his juicy lips answered: "The lady in grey, sir?"

"Yes, the lady in grey." What other ladies were there! Stodgy chap!

The carriage stopped before a small three-storied block of flats, standing a little back from the river. With a practised eye old Jolyon saw that they were cheap. 'I should think about sixty pound a year,' he mused; and entering, he looked at the name-board. The name 'Forsyte,' was not on it, but against 'First Floor, Flat C' were the words: 'Mrs. Irene Heron.' Ah! She had taken her maiden name again! And somehow this pleased him. He went upstairs slowly, feeling his side a little. He stood a moment, before ringing, to lose the feeling of drag and fluttering there. She would not be in! And then—Boots! The thought was black. What did he want with boots at his age? He could not wear out all those he had.

"Your mistress at home?"

"Yes, sir."

"Say Mr. Jolyon Forsyte."

"Yes, sir, will you come this way?"

Old Jolyon followed a very little maid —not more than sixteen one would say— into a very small dining-room where the sunblinds were drawn. It held a cottage piano and little else save a vague fragrance and good taste. He stood in the middle, with his top hat in his hand, and thought: 'I expect she's very badly off!' There was a mirror above the fireplace, and he saw himself reflected. An old-looking chap! He heard a rustle, and turned round. She was so close that his moustache almost brushed her forehead, just under her hair.

"I was driving up," he said. "Thought I'd look in on you, and ask you how you got up the other night."

And, seeing her smile, he felt suddenly relieved. She was really glad to see him, perhaps.

"Would you like to put on your hat and come for a drive in the Park?"

But while she was gone to put her hat on, he frowned. The Park! James and Emily! Mrs. Nicholas, or some other member of his precious family would be there very likely, prancing up and down. And they would go and wag their tongues about having seen him with her, afterwards. Better not! He did not wish to revive the echoes of the past on Forsyte 'Change. He removed a white hair from the lapel of his closely buttoned-up frock coat, and passed his hand over his cheeks, moustache, and square chin. It felt very hollow there under the cheekbones. He had not been eating much lately—he had better get that little whippersnapper who attended Holly to give him a tonic. But she had come back and when they were in the carriage, he said:

"Suppose we go and sit in Kensington Gardens instead?" and added with a twinkle: "No prancing up and down there," as if she had been in the secret of his thoughts.

Leaving the carriage, they entered those select precincts, and strolled towards the water.

"You've gone back to your maiden name, I see," he said: "I'm not sorry."

She slipped her hand under his arm: "Has June forgiven me, Uncle Jolyon?"

He answered gently: "Yes—yes; of course, why not?"

"And have you?"

"I? I forgave you as soon as I saw how the land really lay." And perhaps he had; his instinct had always been to forgive the beautiful.

She drew a deep breath. "I never regretted—I couldn't. Did you ever love very deeply, Uncle Jolyon?"

At that strange question old Jolyon stared before him. Had he? He did not seem to remember that he ever had. But he did not like to say this to the young woman whose hand was touching his arm, whose life was suspended, as it were, by memory of a tragic love. And he thought: 'If I had met *you* when I was young I—I might have made a fool of myself, perhaps.' And a longing to escape in generalities beset him.

"Love's a queer thing," he said, "fatal thing often. It was the Greeks—wasn't it? —made love into a goddess; they were right, I dare say, but then they lived in the Golden Age."

"Phil adored them."

Phil! The word jarred him, for suddenly—with his power to see all round a thing, he perceived why she was putting up with him like this. She wanted to talk about her lover! Well! If it was any pleasure to her! And he said: "Ah! There was a bit of the sculptor in him, I fancy."

"Yes. He loved balance and symmetry; he loved the wholehearted way the Greeks gave themselves to art."

Balance! The chap had no balance at all, if he remembered; as for symmetry— clean-built enough he was, no doubt; but those queer eyes of his, and high cheek-bones—Symmetry?

"You're of the Golden Age, too, Uncle Jolyon."

Old Jolyon looked round at her. Was she chaffing him? No, her eyes were soft as velvet. Was she flattering him? But if so, why? There was nothing to be had out of an old chap like him.

"Phil thought so. He used to say: 'But I can never tell him that I admire him.' "

Ah! There it was again. Her dead lover; her desire to talk of him! And he pressed her arm, half resentful of those memories, half grateful, as if he recognised what a link they were between herself and him.

"He was a very talented young fellow," he murmured. "It's hot; I feel the heat nowadays. Let's sit down."

They took two chairs beneath a chestnut tree whose broad leaves covered them from the peaceful glory of the afternoon. A pleasure to sit there and watch her, and feel that she liked to be with him. And the wish to increase that liking, if he could, made him go on:

"I expect he showed you a side of him I never saw. He'd be at his best with you. His ideas of art were a little new—to me" —he had stifled the word 'fangled.'

"Yes: but he used to say you had a real sense of beauty." Old Jolyon thought: 'The devil he did!' but answered with a twinkle: "Well, I have, or I shouldn't be sitting here with you." She was fascinating when she smiled with her eyes, like that!

"He thought you had one of those hearts that never grow old. Phil had real insight."

He was not taken in by this flattery spoken out of the past, out of a longing to talk of her dead lover—not a bit; and yet it was precious to hear, because she pleased his eyes and heart which—quite true!—had never grown old. Was that because—unlike her and her dead lover, he had never loved to desperation, had always kept his balance, his sense of symmetry. Well! It had left him power, at eighty-four, to admire beauty. And he thought, 'If I were a painter or a sculptor! But I'm an old chap. Make hay while the sun shines.'

A couple with arms entwined crossed on the grass before them, at the edge of the shadow from their tree. The sunlight fell cruelly on their pale, squashed, unkempt young faces. "We're an ugly lot!" said old Jolyon suddenly. "It amazes me to see how—love triumphs over that."

"Love triumphs over everything!"

"The young think so," he muttered.

"Love has no age, no limit, and no death."

With that glow in her pale face, her breast heaving, her eyes so large and dark and soft, she looked like Venus come to life! But this extravagance brought instant reaction, and, twinkling, he said: "Well, if it had limits, we shouldn't be born; for by George! it's got a lot to put up with."

Then, removing his top hat, he brushed it round with a cuff. The great clumsy thing heated his forehead; in these days he often got a rush of blood to the head —his circulation was not what it had been.

She still sat gazing straight before her, and suddenly she murmured:

"It's strange enough that *I'm* alive."

Those words of Jo's 'Wild and lost' came back to him.

"Ah!" he said: "my son saw you for a moment—that day."

"Was it your son? I heard a voice in the hall; I thought for a second it was— Phil."

Old Jolyon saw her lips tremble. She put her hand over them, took it away again, and went on calmly: "That night I went to the Embankment; a woman caught me by the dress. She told me about herself. When one knows that others suffer, one's ashamed."

"One of *those?*"

She nodded, and horror stirred within old Jolyon, the horror of one who has never known a struggle with desperation. Almost against his will he muttered: "Tell me, won't you?"

"I didn't care whether I lived or died. When you're like that, Fate ceases to want to kill you. She took care of me three days—she never left me. I had no money. That's why I do what I can for them, now."

But old Jolyon was thinking: 'No money!' What fate could compare with that? Every other was involved in it.

"I wish you had come to me," he said. "Why didn't you?" But Irene did not answer.

"Because my name was Forsyte, I suppose? Or was it June who kept you away? How are you getting on now?" His eyes involuntarily swept her body. Perhaps even now she was—! And yet she wasn't thin—not really!

"Oh! with my fifty pounds a year, I make just enough." The answer did not reassure him; he had lost confidence. And that fellow Soames! But his sense of justice stifled condemnation. No, she would certainly have died rather than take another penny from *him*. Soft as she looked, there must be strength in her somewhere—strength and fidelity. But what business had young Bosinney to have got run over and left her stranded like this!

"Well, you must come to me now," he said, "for anything you want, or I shall be quite cut up." And putting on his hat, he rose. "Let's go and get some tea. I told that lazy chap to put the horses up for an hour, and come for me at your place. We'll take a cab presently; I can't walk as I used to."

He enjoyed that stroll to the Kensington end of the gardens—the sound of her voice, the glancing of her eyes, the subtle beauty of a charming form moving beside him. He enjoyed their tea at Ruffel's in the High Street, and came out thence with a great box of chocolates swung on his little finger. He enjoyed the drive back to Chelsea in a hansom, smoking his cigar. She had promised to come down next Sunday and play to him again, and already in thought he was plucking carnations and early roses for her to carry back to town. It was a pleasure to give her a little pleasure, if it *were* pleasure from an old chap like him! The carriage was already there when they arrived. Just like that fellow, who was always late when he was wanted! Old Jolyon went in for a minute to say good-bye. The little dark hall of the flat was impregnated with a disagreeable odour of patchouli, and on a bench against the wall—its only furniture—he saw a figure sitting. He heard Irene say softly: "Just one minute." In the little drawing-room when the door was shut, he asked gravely: "One of your *protégées?*"

"Yes. Now thanks to you, I can do something for her."

He stood, staring and stroking that chin whose strength had frightened so many in its time. The idea of her thus actually in contact with this outcast, grieved and frightened him. What could she do for them? Nothing. Only soil and make trouble for herself, perhaps. And he said: "Take care, my dear! The world puts the worst construction on everything."

"I know that."

He was abashed by her quiet smile. "Well then—Sunday," he murmured: "Good-bye."

She put her cheek forward for him to kiss.

"Good-bye," he said again; "take care of yourself." And he went out, not looking towards the figure on the bench. He drove home by way of Hammersmith, that he might stop at a place he knew of and tell them to send her in two dozen of their best Burgundy. She must want picking-up sometimes! Only in Richmond Park did he remember that he had gone up to order himself some boots, and was surprised that he could have had so paltry an idea.

### III

The little spirits of the past which throng an old man's days had never pushed their faces up to his so seldom as in the seventy hours elapsing before Sunday came. The spirit of the future, with the charm of the unknown, put up her lips instead. Old Jolyon was not restless now, and paid no visits to the log, because she was *coming to lunch*. There is wonderful finality about a meal; it removes a world of doubts, for no one misses meals except for reasons beyond control. He played many games with Holly on the lawn, pitching them up to her who was batting so as to be ready to bowl to Jolly in the holidays. For she was not a Forsyte, but Jolly was—and Forsytes always bat, until they have resigned and reached the age of eighty-five. The dog Balthasar, in attendance, lay on the ball as often as he could, and the page-boy fielded, till his face was like the harvest moon. And because the time was getting shorter, each day was longer and more golden than the last. On Friday night he took a liver pill, his side hurt him rather, and though it was not the liver side, there is no remedy like that. Anyone telling him that he had found a new excitement in life and that excitement was not good for him, would have been met by one of those steady and rather defiant looks of his deep-set iron-grey eyes, which seemed to say: 'I know my own business best.' He always had and always would.

On Sunday morning, when Holly had gone with her governess to church, he visited the strawberry beds. There, accompanied by the dog Balthasar, he examined the plants narrowly and succeeded in finding at least two dozen berries which were really ripe. Stooping was not good for him, and he became very dizzy and red in the forehead. Having placed the strawberries in a dish on the dining-table, he washed his hands and bathed his forehead with eau de Cologne. There, before the mirror, it occurred to him that he was thinner. What a 'threadpaper' he had been when he was young! It was nice to be slim—he could not bear a fat chap; and yet perhaps his cheeks were *too* thin! She was to arrive by train at half-past twelve and walk up, entering from the road past Gage's farm at the far end of the coppice. And, having looked into June's room to see that there was hot water ready, he set forth to meet her, leisurely, for his heart was beating. The air smelled sweet, larks sang, and the Grand Stand at Epsom was visible. A perfect day! On just such a one, no doubt, six years ago, Soames had brought young Bosinney down with him to look at the site before they began to build. It was Bosinney who had pitched on the exact spot for the house—as June had often told him. In these days he was thinking much about that young fellow, as if his spirit were really haunting the field of his last work, on the chance of seeing—her. Bosinney—the one man who had possessed her heart, to whom she had given her whole self with rapture! At his age one could not, of course, imagine such things, but there stirred in him a queer vague aching—as it were the ghost of an impersonal jealousy; and a feeling, too, more generous, of pity for that love so early lost. All over in a few poor months! Well, well! He looked at his watch before entering the coppice—only a quarter past, twenty-five minutes to wait! And then, turning the corner of the path, he saw her exactly where he had seen her the first time, on the log; and realised that she must have come by the earlier train to sit there alone for a couple of hours at least. Two hours of her society—missed! What memory could make that log so dear to her? His face showed what he was thinking, for she said at once:

"Forgive me, Uncle Jolyon; it was here that I first knew."

"Yes, yes; there it is for you whenever you like. You're looking a little Londony; you're giving too many lessons."

That she should have to give lessons worried him. Lessons to a parcel of young girls thumping out scales with their thick fingers!

"Where do you go to give them?" he asked.

"They're mostly Jewish families, luckily."

Old Jolyon stared; to all Forsytes Jews seem strange and doubtful.

"They love music, and they're very kind."

"They had better be, by George!" He took her arm—his side always hurt him a little going uphill—and said:

"Did you ever see anything like those buttercups? They came like that in a night."

Her eyes seemed really to fly over the field, like bees after the flowers and the honey. "I wanted you to see them—wouldn't let them turn the cows in yet." Then, remembering that she had come to talk about Bosinney, he pointed to the clock-tower over the stables:

"I expect *he* wouldn't have let me put that there—had no notion of time, if I remember."

But, pressing his arm to her, she talked of flowers instead, and he knew it was done that he might not feel she came because of her dead lover.

"The best flower I can show you," he said, with a sort of triumph, "is my little sweet. She'll be back from Church directly. There's something about her which reminds me a little of you," and it did not seem to him peculiar that he had put it thus, instead of saying: "There's something about you which reminds me a little of her." Ah! And here she was!

Holly, followed closely by her elderly French governess, whose digestion had been ruined twenty-two years ago in the siege of Strasbourg, came rushing towards them from under the oak tree. She stopped about a dozen yards away, to pat Balthasar and pretend that this was all she had in her mind. Old Jolyon who knew better, said:

"Well, my darling, here's the lady in grey I promised you."

Holly raised herself and looked up. He watched the two of them with a twinkle, Irene smiling, Holly beginning with grave inquiry, passing into a shy smile too, and then to something deeper. She had a sense of beauty, that child—knew what was what! He enjoyed the sight of the kiss between them.

"Mrs. Heron, Mam'zelle Beauce. Well, Mam'zelle—good sermon?"

For, now that he had not much more time before him, the only part of the service connected with this world absorbed what interest in church remained to him. Mam'zelle Beauce stretched out a spidery hand clad in a black kid glove—she had been in the best families—and the rather sad eyes of her lean yellowish face seemed to ask: "Are you well-brrred?" Whenever Holly or Jolly did anything unpleasing to her—a not uncommon occurrence—she would say to them: "The little Tayleurs never did that—they were such well-brred little children." Jolly hated the little Tayleurs; Holly wondered dreadfully how it was she fell so short of them. 'A thin rum little soul,' old Jolyon thought her—Mam'zelle Beauce.

Luncheon was a successful meal, the mushrooms which he himself had picked in the mushroom house, his chosen strawberries, and another bottle of the Steinberg cabinet filled him with a certain aromatic spirituality, and a conviction that he would have a touch of eczema tomorrow. After lunch they sat under the oak tree drinking Turkish coffee. It was no matter of grief to him when Mademoiselle Beauce withdrew to write her Sunday letter to her sister, whose future had been endangered in the past by swallowing a pin—an event held up daily in warning to the children to eat slowly and digest what they had eaten. At the foot of the bank, on a carriage rug, Holly and the dog Balthasar teased and loved each other, and in the shade old Jolyon with his legs crossed and his cigar luxuriously savoured, gazed at Irene sitting in the swing. A light, vaguely swaying, grey figure with a fleck of sunlight here and there upon it, lips just opened, eyes dark and soft under lids a little drooped. She looked content; surely it did her good to come and see him! The selfishness of age had not set its proper grip on him, for he could still feel pleasure in the pleasure of others, realising that what he wanted, though much, was not quite all that mattered.

"It's quiet here," he said; "you mustn't come down if you find it dull. But it's a pleasure to see you. My little sweet's is the only face which gives me any pleasure, except yours."

From her smile he knew that she was not beyond liking to be appreciated, and this reassured him. "That's not humbug," he said. "I never told a woman I admired her when I didn't. In fact I don't know when I've told a woman I admired her, except my wife in the old days; and wives are funny." He was silent, but resumed abruptly:

"She used to expect me to say it more often than I felt it, and there we were." Her face looked mysteriously troubled, and, afraid that he had said something painful, he hurried on:

"When my little sweet marries, I hope she'll find someone who knows what women feel. I shan't be here to see it, but there's too much topsy-turvydom in marriage; I don't want her to pitch up against that." And, aware that he had made bad worse, he added: "That dog *will* scratch."

A silence followed. Of what was she thinking, this pretty creature whose life was spoiled; who had done with love, and yet was made for love? Some day when he was gone, perhaps, she would find another mate—not so disorderly as that young fellow who had got himself run over. Ah! but her husband?

"Does Soames never trouble you?" he asked.

She shook her head. Her face had closed up suddenly. For all her softness there was something irreconcilable about her. And a glimpse of light on the inexorable nature of sex antipathies strayed into a brain which, belonging to early Victorian civilisation—so much older than this of his old age—had never thought about such primitive things.

"That's a comfort," he said. "You can see the Grand Stand to-day. Shall we take a turn round?"

Through the flower and fruit garden, against whose high outer walls peach trees and nectarines were trained to the sun, through the stables, the vinery, the mushroom house, the asparagus beds, the rosery, the summer house, he conducted her—even into the kitchen garden to see the tiny green peas which Holly loved to scoop out of their pods with her finger, and lick up from the palm of her little brown hand. Many delightful things he showed her, while Holly and the dog Balthasar danced ahead, or came to them at intervals for attention. It was one of the happiest afternoons he had ever spent, but it tired him and he was glad to sit down in the music room and let her give him tea. A special little friend of Holly's had come in—a fair child with short hair like a boy's. And the two sported in the distance, under the stairs, on the stairs, and up in the gallery. Old Jolyon begged for Chopin. She played studies, mazurkas, waltzes, till the two children, creeping near, stood at the foot of the piano—their dark and golden heads bent forward, listening. Old Jolyon watched.

"Let's see you dance, you two!"

Shyly, with a false start, they began. Bobbing and circling, earnest, not very adroit, they went past and past his chair to the strains of that waltz. He watched them and the face of her who was playing turned smiling towards those little dancers thinking: 'Sweetest picture I've seen for ages.' A voice said:

"Hollee! *Mais enfin—qu'est-ce que tu fais là—danser, le dimanche! Viens, donc!*"

But the children came close to old Jolyon, knowing that he would save them, and gazed into a face which was decidedly 'caught out.'

"Better the day, better the deed, Mam'zelle. It's all my doing. Trot along, chicks, and have your tea."

And, when they were gone, followed by the dog Balthasar, who took every meal, he looked at Irene with a twinkle and said:

"Well, there we are! Aren't they sweet? Have you any little ones among your pupils?"

"Yes, three—two of them darlings."

"Pretty?"

"Lovely!"

Old Jolyon sighed; he had an insatiable appetite for the very young. "My little sweet," he said, "is devoted to music; she'll be a musician some day. You wouldn't give me your opinion of her playing, I suppose?"

"Of course I will."

"You wouldn't like——" but he stifled the words "to give her lessons." The idea that she gave lessons was unpleasant to him; yet it would mean that he would see her regularly. She left the piano and came over to his chair.

"I would like, very much; but there is —June. When are they coming back?"

Old Jolyon frowned. "Not till the middle of next month. What does that matter?"

"You said June had forgiven me; but she could never forget, Uncle Jolyon."

Forget! She *must* forget, if he wanted her to.

But as if answering, Irene shook her head. "You know she couldn't; one doesn't forget."

Always that wretched past! And he said with a sort of vexed finality:

"Well, we shall see."

He talked to her an hour or more, of the children, and a hundred little things, till the carriage came round to take her home. And when she had gone he went back to his chair, and sat there smoothing his face and chin, dreaming over the day.

That evening after dinner he went to his study and took a sheet of paper. He stayed for some minutes without writing, then rose and stood under the master-piece 'Dutch Fishing Boats at Sunset.' He was not thinking of that picture, but of his life. He was going to leave her some-thing in his Will; nothing could so have stirred the stilly deeps of thought and memory. He was going to leave her a por-tion of his wealth, of his aspirations, deeds, qualities, work—all that had made that wealth; going to leave her, too, a part of all he had missed in life, by his sane and steady pursuit of wealth. Ah! What had he missed? 'Dutch Fishing Boats' re-sponded blankly; he crossed to the French window, and drawing the curtain aside, opened it. A wind had got up, and one of last year's oak leaves which had somehow survived the gardener's brooms, was dragging itself with a tiny clicking rustle along the stone terrace in the twi-light. Except for that it was very quiet out there, and he could smell the heliotrope watered not long since. A bat went by. A bird uttered its last 'cheep.' And right above the oak tree the first star shone. Faust in the opera had bartered his soul for some fresh years of youth. Morbid notion! No such bargain was possible, that was *real* tragedy! No making oneself new again for love or life or anything. Nothing left to do but enjoy beauty afar off while you could, and leave it some-thing in your Will. But how much? And, as if he could not make that calculation looking out into the mild freedom of the country night, he turned back and went up to the chimney-piece. There were his pet bronzes—a Cleopatra with the asp at her breast; a Socrates; a greyhound play-ing with her puppy; a strongman reining in some horses. 'They last!' he thought, and a pang went through his heart. They had a thousand years of life before them!

'How much?' Well! enough at all events to save her getting old before her time, to keep the lines out of her face as long as possible, and grey from soiling that bright hair. He might live another five years. She would be well over thirty by then. 'How much?' She had none of his blood in her! In loyalty to the tenor of his life for forty years and more, ever since he married and founded that myste-rious thing, a family, came this warning thought—None of his blood, no right to anything! It was a luxury then, this no-tion. An extravagance, a petting of an old man's whim, one of those things done in dotage. His real future was vested in those who had his blood, in whom he would live on when he was gone. He turned away from the bronzes and stood looking at the old leather chair in which he had sat and smoked so many hundreds of cigars. And suddenly he seemed to see her sitting there in her grey dress, fra-grant, soft, dark-eyed, graceful, looking up at him. Why! She cared nothing for him, really; all she cared for was that lost lover of hers. But she was there, whether she would or no, giving him pleasure with her beauty and grace. One had no right to inflict an old man's company, no right to ask her down to play to him and let him look at her—for no reward! Pleasure must be paid for in this world. 'How much?' After all, there was plenty; his son and his three grandchildren would never miss that little lump. He had made it himself, nearly every penny; he could leave it where he liked, allow himself this little pleasure. He went back to the bu-reau. 'Well, I'm going to,' he thought, 'let them think what they like. I'm going to!' And he sat down.

'How much?' Ten thousand, twenty thousand—how much? If only with his money he could buy one year, one month of youth. And startled by that thought, he wrote quickly:

"DEAR HERRING,—Draw me a codicil to this effect: 'I leave to my niece Irene Forsyte, born Irene Heron, by which name she now goes, fifteen thousand pounds free of legacy duty.'
                    "Yours faithfully,
                         "JOLYON FORSYTE."

When he had sealed and stamped the envelope, he went back to the window and drew in a long breath. It was dark, but many stars shone now.

## IV

He woke at half-past two, an hour which long experience had taught him brings panic intensity to all awkward thoughts. Experience had also taught him that a further waking at the proper hour of eight showed the folly of such panic. On this particular morning the thought which gathered rapid momentum was that if he became ill, at his age not improbable, he would not see her. From this it was but a step to realisation that he would be cut off, too, when his son and June returned from Spain. How could he justify desire for the company of one who had stolen—early morning does not mince words—June's lover? That lover was dead; but June was a stubborn little thing; warm-hearted, but stubborn as wood, and—quite true—not one who forgot! By the middle of next month they would be back. He had barely five weeks left to enjoy the new interest which had come into what remained of his life. Darkness showed up to him absurdly clear the nature of his feeling. Admiration for beauty—a craving to see that which delighted his eyes. Preposterous, at his age! And yet—what other reason was there for asking June to undergo such painful reminder, and how prevent his son and his son's wife from thinking him very queer? He would be reduced to sneaking up to London, which tired him; and the least indisposition would cut him off even from that. He lay with eyes open, setting his jaw against the prospect, and calling himself an old fool, while his heart beat loudly, and then seemed to stop beating altogether. He had seen the dawn lighting the window chinks, heard the birds chirp and twitter, and the cocks crow, before he fell asleep again, and awoke tired but sane. Five weeks before he need bother, at his age an eternity! But that early morning panic had left its mark, had slightly fevered the will of one who had always had his own way. He would see her as often as he wished! Why not go up to town and make that codicil at his solicitor's instead of writing about it; she might like to go to the opera! But, by train, for he would not have that fat chap Beacon grinning behind his back. Servants were such fools; and, as likely as not, they had known all the past history of Irene and young Bosinney—servants knew everything, and suspected the rest. He wrote to her that morning:

"MY DEAR IRENE,—I have to be up in town to-morrow. If you would like to have a look in at the opera, come and dine with me quietly . . ."

But where? It was decades since he had dined anywhere in London save at his Club or at a private house. Ah! that new-fangled place close to Covent Garden . . .

"Let me have a line to-morrow morning to the Piedmont Hotel whether to expect you there at 7 o'clock.
                    "Yours affectionately,
                         "JOLYON FORSYTE."

She would understand that he just wanted to give her a little pleasure; for the idea that she should guess he had this itch to see her was instinctively unpleasant to him; it was not seemly that one so old should go out of his way to see beauty, especially in a woman.

The journey next day, short though it was, and the visit to his lawyer's, tired him. It was hot too, and after dressing for dinner he lay down on the sofa in his bedroom to rest a little. He must have had a sort of fainting fit, for he came to himself feeling very queer; and with some difficulty rose and rang the bell. Why! it was past seven! And there he was and she would be waiting. But suddenly the dizziness came on again, and he was obliged to relapse on the sofa. He heard the maid's voice say:

"Did you ring, sir?"

"Yes, come here"; he could not see her clearly, for the cloud in front of his eyes. "I'm not well, I want some sal volatile."

"Yes, sir." Her voice sounded frightened.

Old Jolyon made an effort.

"Don't go. Take this message to my niece—a lady waiting in the hall—a lady in grey. Say Mr. Forsyte is not well—the heat. He is very sorry; if he is not down directly, she is not to wait dinner."

When she was gone, he thought feebly: 'Why did I say a lady in grey—she may be in anything. Sal volatile!' He did not go off again, yet was not conscious of how Irene came to be standing beside him, holding smelling salts to his nose, and pushing a pillow up behind his head. He heard her say anxiously: "Dear Uncle Jolyon, what is it?" was dimly conscious of the soft pressure of her lips on his hand; then drew a long breath of smelling salts, suddenly discovered strength in them, and sneezed.

"Ha!" he said, "it's nothing. How did you get here? Go down and dine—the tickets are on the dressing-table. I shall be all right in a minute."

He felt her cool hand on his forehead, smelled violets, and sat divided between a sort of pleasure and a determination to be all right.

"Why! You *are* in grey!" he said. "Help me up." Once on his feet he gave himself a shake.

"What business had I to go off like that!" And he moved very slowly to the glass. What a cadaverous chap! Her voice, behind him, murmured:

"You mustn't come down, Uncle; you must rest."

"Fiddlesticks! A glass of champagne'll soon set me to rights. I can't have you missing the opera."

But the journey down the corridor was troublesome. What carpets they had in these new-fangled places, so thick that you tripped up in them at every step! In the lift he noticed how concerned she looked, and said with the ghost of a twinkle:

"I'm a pretty host."

When the lift stopped he had to hold firmly to the seat to prevent its slipping under him; but after soup and a glass of champagne he felt much better, and began to enjoy an infirmity which had brought such solicitude into her manner towards him.

"I should have liked you for a daughter," he said suddenly; and watching the smile in her eyes, went on:

"You mustn't get wrapped up in the past at your time of life; plenty of that when you get to my age. That's a nice dress—I like the style."

"I made it myself."

Ah! A woman who could make herself a pretty frock had not lost her interest in life.

"Make hay while the sun shines," he said; "and drink that up. I want to see some colour in your cheeks. We mustn't waste life; it doesn't do. There's a new Marguerite to-night; let's hope she won't be fat. And Mephisto—anything more dreadful than a fat chap playing the Devil I can't imagine."

But they did not go to the opera after all, for in getting up from dinner the dizziness came over him again, and she insisted on his staying quiet and going to bed early. When he parted from her at the door of the hotel, having paid the cabman to drive her to Chelsea, he sat down again for a moment to enjoy the memory of her words: "You *are* such a darling to me, Uncle Jolyon!" Why! Who wouldn't be! He would have liked to stay up another day and take her to the Zoo, but two days running of him would bore her to death. No, he must wait till next Sunday; she had promised to come then. They would settle those lessons for Holly, if only for a month. It would be something. That little Mam'zelle Beauce wouldn't like it, but she would have to lump it. And crushing his old opera hat against his chest he sought the lift.

He drove to Waterloo next morning, struggling with a desire to say: 'Drive me to Chelsea.' But his sense of proportion was too strong. Besides, he still felt shaky, and did not want to risk another aberration like that of last night, away from home. Holly, too, was expecting him, and what he had in his bag for her. Not that there was any cupboard love in his little sweet—she was a bundle of affection. Then, with the rather bitter cynicism of the old, he wondered for a second whether it was not cupboard love which made Irene put up with him. No, she was not that sort either. She had, if anything, too little notion of how to butter her bread, no sense of property, poor thing! Besides, he had not breathed a word about that codicil, nor should he— sufficient unto the day was the good thereof.

In the victoria which met him at the station Holly was restraining the dog Balthasar, and their caresses made 'jubey' his drive home. All the rest of that fine hot day and most of the next he was content and peaceful, reposing in the shade, while the long lingering sunshine showered gold on the lawns and the flowers. But on Thursday evening at his lonely dinner he began to count the hours; sixty-five till he would go down to meet her again in the little coppice, and walk up through the fields at her side. He had intended to consult the doctor about his fainting fit, but the fellow would be sure to insist on quiet, no excitement and all that; and he did not mean to be tied by the leg, did not want to be told of an infirmity—if there were one, could not afford to hear of it at his time of life, now that this new interest had come. And he carefully avoided making any mention of it in a letter to his son. It would only bring them back with a run! How far this silence was due to consideration for their pleasure, how far to regard for his own, he did not pause to consider.

That night in his study he had just finished his cigar and was dozing off, when he heard the rustle of a gown, and was conscious of a scent of violets. Opening his eyes he saw her, dressed in grey, standing by the fireplace, holding out her arms. The odd thing was that, though those arms seemed to hold nothing, they were curved as if round someone's neck, and her own neck was bent back, her lips open, her eyes closed. She vanished at once, and there were the mantelpiece and his bronzes. But those bronzes and the mantelpiece had not been there when she was, only the fireplace and the wall! Shaken and troubled, he got up. 'I must take medicine,' he thought; 'I can't be well.' His heart beat too fast, he had an asthmatic feeling in the chest; and going to the window, he opened it to get some air. A dog was barking far away, one of the dogs at Gage's farm no doubt, beyond the coppice. A beautiful still night, but dark. 'I dropped off,' he mused, 'that's it! And yet I'll swear my eyes were open!' A sound like a sigh seemed to answer.

"What's that?" he said sharply, "who's there?"

Putting his hand to his side to still the beating of his heart, he stepped out on the terrace. Something soft scurried by in the dark. "Shoo!" It was that great grey cat. 'Young Bosinney was like a great cat!' he thought. 'It was him in there, that she—that she was—He's got her still!' He walked to the edge of the terrace, and looked down into the darkness; he could just see the powdering of the daisies on the unmown lawn. Here to-day and gone to-morrow! And there came the moon, who saw all, young and old, alive and dead, and didn't care a dump! His own turn soon. For a single day of youth he would give what was left! And he turned again towards the house. He could see the windows of the night nursery up there. His little sweet would be asleep. 'Hope that dog won't wake her!' he thought. 'What is it makes us love, and makes us die! I must go to bed.'

And across the terrace stones, growing grey in the moonlight, he passed back within.

## V

How should an old man live his days if not in dreaming of his well-spent past? In that, at all events, there is no agitating warmth, only pale winter sunshine. The shell can withstand the gentle beating of the dynamos of memory. The present he should distrust; the future shun. From beneath thick shade he should watch the sunlight creeping at his toes. If there be sun of summer, let him not go out into it, mistaking it for the Indian-summer sun! Thus peradventure he shall decline softly, slowly, imperceptibly, until impatient Nature clutches his wind-pipe and he gasps away to death some early morning before the world is aired, and they put on his tombstone: 'In the fulness of years!' yea! If he preserve his principles in perfect order, a Forsyte may live long after he is dead.

Old Jolyon was conscious of all this, and yet there was in him that which transcended Forsyteism. For it is written that a Forsyte shall not love beauty more than reason; nor his own way more than his own health. And something beat within him in these days that with each throb fretted at the thinning shell. His sagacity knew this, but it knew too that he could not stop that beating, nor would if he could. And yet, if you had told him he was living on his capital, he would have stared you down. No, no; a man did not live on his capital; it was not done! The shibboleths of the past are ever more real than the actualities of the present. And he, to whom living on one's capital had always been anathema, could not have borne to have applied so gross a phrase to his own case. Pleasure is healthful; beauty good to see; to live again in the youth of the young—and what else on earth was he doing!

Methodically, as had been the way of his whole life, he now arranged his time. On Tuesdays he journeyed up to town by train; Irene came and dined with him. And they went to the opera. On Thursdays he drove to town, and, putting that fat chap and his horses up, met her in Kensington Gardens, picking up the carriage after he had left her, and driving home again in time for dinner. He threw out the casual formula that he had business in London on those two days. On Wednesdays and Saturdays she came down to give Holly music lessons. The greater the pleasure he took in her society, the more scrupulously fastidious he became, just a matter-of-fact and friendly uncle. Not even in feeling, really, was he more—for, after all, there was his age. And yet, if she were late he fidgeted himself to death. If she missed coming, which happened twice, his eyes grew sad as an old dog's, and he failed to sleep.

And so a month went by—a month of summer in the fields, and in his heart, with summer's heat and the fatigue thereof. Who could have believed a few weeks back that he would have looked forward to his son's and his grand-daughter's return with something like dread! There was such a delicious freedom, such recovery of that independence a man enjoys before he founds a family, about these weeks of lovely weather, and this new companionship with one who demanded nothing, and remained always a little unknown, retaining the fascination of mystery. It was like a draught of wine to him who has been drinking water for so long that he has almost forgotten the stir wine brings to his blood, the narcotic to his brain. The flowers were coloured brighter, scents and music and the sunlight had a living value—were no longer mere reminders of past enjoyment. There was something now to live for which stirred him continually to anticipation. He lived in that, not in retrospection; the difference is considerable to any so old as he. The pleasures of the table, never of much consequence to one naturally abstemious, had lost all value. He ate little, without knowing what he ate; and every day grew thinner and more worn to look at. He was again a 'threadpaper'; and to this thinned form his massive forehead, with hollows at the temples, gave more dignity than ever. He was very well aware that he ought to see the doctor, but liberty was too sweet. He could not afford to pet his frequent shortness of breath and the pain in his side at the expense of liberty. Return to the vegetable existence he had led among the agricultural journals with the life-size mangold wurzels, before this new attraction came into his life—no! He exceeded his allowance of cigars. Two a day had always been his rule. Now he smoked three and sometimes four—a man will when he is filled with the creative spirit. But very often he thought: 'I must give up smoking, and coffee; I must give up rattling up to town.' But he did not; there was no one in any sort of authority to notice him, and this was a priceless boon. The servants perhaps wondered, but they were, naturally, dumb. Mam'zelle Beauce was too concerned with her own digestion, and too 'well-brrred' to make personal allusions. Holly had not as yet an eye for the relative appearance of him who was her plaything and her god. It was left for Irene herself to beg him to eat more, to rest in the hot part of the day, to take a tonic, and so forth. But she did not tell him that she was the cause of his thinness—for one cannot see the havoc oneself is working. A man of eighty-five has no passions, but the Beauty which produces passion works on in the old way, till death closes the eyes which crave the sight of Her.

On the first day of the second week in July he received a letter from his son in Paris to say that they would all be back on Friday. This had always been more sure than Fate; but, with the pathetic improvidence given to the old, that they may endure to the end, he had never quite admitted it. Now he did, and something would have to be done. He had ceased to be able to imagine life without this new interest, but that which is not imagined sometimes exists, as Forsytes are perpetually finding to their cost. He sat in his old leather chair, doubling up the letter, and mumbling with his lips the end of an unlighted cigar. After to-morrow his Tuesday expeditions to town would have to be abandoned. He could still drive up, perhaps, once a week, on the pretext of seeing his man of business. But even that would be dependent on his health, for now they would begin to fuss about him. The lessons! The lessons must go on! She must swallow down her scruples, and June must put her feelings in her pocket. She had done so once, on the day after the news of Bosinney's death; what she had done then, she could surely do again now. Four years since that injury was inflicted on her—not Christian to keep the memory of old sores alive. June's will was strong, but his was stronger, for his sands were running out. Irene was soft, surely she would do this for him, subdue her natural shrinking, sooner than give him pain! The lessons must continue; for if they did, he was secure. And lighting his cigar at last, he began trying to shape out how to put it to them all, and explain this strange intimacy; how to veil and wrap it away from the naked truth—that he could not bear to be deprived of the sight of beauty. Ah! Holly! Holly was fond of her, Holly liked her lessons. She would save him—his little sweet! And with that happy thought he became serene, and wondered what he had been worrying about so fearfully. He must not worry, it left him always curiously weak, and as if but half present in his own body.

That evening after dinner he had a return of the dizziness, though he did not faint. He would not ring the bell, because he knew it would mean a fuss, and make his going-up on the morrow more conspicuous. When one grew old, the whole world was in conspiracy to limit freedom, and for what reason?—just to keep the breath in him a little longer. He did not want it at such cost. Only the dog Balthasar saw his lonely recovery from that weakness; anxiously watched his master go to the sideboard and drink some brandy, instead of giving him a biscuit. When at last old Jolyon felt able to tackle the stairs he went up to bed. And, though still shaky next morning, the thought of the evening sustained and strengthened him. It was always such a pleasure to give her a good dinner—he suspected her of undereating when she was alone; and, at the opera to watch her eyes glow and brighten, the unconscious smiling of her lips. She hadn't much pleasure, and this

was the last time he would be able to give her that treat. But when he was packing his bag he caught himself wishing that he had not the fatigue of dressing for dinner before him, and the exertion, too, of telling her about June's return.

The opera that evening was 'Carmen,' and he chose the last *entr'acte* to break the news, instinctively putting it off till the latest moment. She took it quietly, queerly; in fact, he did not know how she had taken it before the wayward music lifted up again and silence became necessary. The mask was down over her face, that mask behind which so much went on that he could not see. She wanted time to think it over, no doubt! He would not press her, for she would be coming to give her lesson to-morrow afternoon, and he should see her then when she had got used to the idea. In the cab he talked only of the Carmen; he had seen better in the old days, but this one was not bad at all. When he took her hand to say good-night, she bent quickly forward and kissed his forehead.

"Good-bye, dear Uncle Jolyon, you have been so sweet to me."

"To-morrow then," he said. "Good-night. Sleep well." She echoed softly: "Sleep well!" and from the cab window, already moving away, he saw her face screwed round towards him, and her hand put out in a gesture which seemed to linger.

He sought his room slowly. They never gave him the same, and he could not get used to these 'spick-and-spandy' bedrooms with new furniture and grey-green carpets sprinkled all over with pink roses. He was wakeful and that wretched Habanera kept throbbing in his head. His French had never been equal to its words, but its sense he knew, if it had any sense, a gipsy thing—wild and unaccountable. Well, there *was* in life something which upset all your care and plans—something which made men and women dance to its pipes. And he lay staring from deep-sunk eyes into the darkness where the unaccountable held sway. You thought you had hold of life, but it slipped away behind you, took you by the scruff of the neck, forced you here and forced you there, and then, likely as not, squeezed life out of you! It took the very stars like that, he shouldn't wonder, rubbed their noses together and flung them apart; it had never done playing its pranks. Five million people in this great blunderbuss of a town, and all of them at the mercy of that Life-Force, like a lot of little dried peas hopping about on a board when you struck your fist on it. Ah, well! Himself would not hop much longer—a good long sleep would do him good!

How hot it was up here!—how noisy! His forehead burned; she had kissed it just where he always worried! just there—as if she had known the very place and wanted to kiss it all away for him. But, instead, her lips left a patch of grievous uneasiness. She had never spoken in quite that voice, had never before made that lingering gesture or looked back at him as she drove away. He got out of bed and pulled the curtains aside; his room faced down over the river. There was little air, but the sight of that breadth of water flowing by, calm, eternal, soothed him. 'The great thing,' he thought, 'is not to make myself a nuisance. I'll think of my little sweet, and go to sleep.' But it was long before the heat and throbbing of the London night died out into the short slumber of the summer morning. And old Jolyon had but forty winks.

When he reached home next day he went out to the flower garden, and with the help of Holly, who was very delicate with flowers, gathered a great bunch of carnations. They were, he told her, for 'the lady in grey'—a name still bandied between them; and he put them in a bowl in his study where he meant to tackle Irene the moment she came, on the sub-

ject of June and future lessons. Their fragrance and colour would help. After lunch he lay down, for he felt very tired, and the carriage would not bring her from the station till four o'clock. But as the hour approached he grew restless, and sought the schoolroom, which overlooked the drive. The sun-blinds were down, and Holly was there with Mademoiselle Beauce, sheltered from the heat of a stifling July day, attending to their silkworms. Old Jolyon had a natural antipathy to these methodical creatures, whose heads and colour reminded him of elephants; who nibbled such quantities of holes in nice green leaves; and smelled, as he thought, horrid. He sat down on a chintz-covered windowseat whence he could see the drive, and get what air there was; and the dog Balthasar who appreciated chintz on hot days, jumped up beside him. Over the cottage piano a violet dust-sheet, faded almost to grey, was spread, and on it the first lavender, whose scent filled the room. In spite of the coolness here, perhaps because of that coolness the beat of life vehemently impressed his ebbed-down senses. Each sunbeam which came through the chinks had annoying brilliance; that dog smelled very strong; the lavender perfume was overpowering; those silkworms heaving up their grey green backs seemed horribly alive; and Holly's dark head bent over them had a wonderfully silk sheen. A marvellous cruelly strong thing was life when you were old and weak; it seemed to mock you with its multitude of forms and its beating vitality. He had never, till those last few weeks, had this curious feeling of being with one half of him eagerly borne along in the stream of life, and with the other half left on the bank, watching that helpless progress. Only when Irene was with him did he lose this double consciousness.

Holly turned her head, pointed with her little brown fist to the piano—for to

point with a finger was not 'well-brrred'
—and said slyly:

"Look at the 'lady in grey,' Gran; isn't
she pretty to-day?"

Old Jolyon's heart gave a flutter, and
for a second the room was clouded; then
it cleared, and he said with a twinkle:

"Who's been dressing her up?"

"Mam'zelle."

"Hollee! Don't be foolish!"

That prim little Frenchwoman! She
hadn't yet got over the music lessons being taken away from her. That wouldn't
help. His little sweet was the only friend
they had. Well, they were her lessons.
And he shouldn't budge—shouldn't
budge for anything. He stroked the warm
wool on Balthasar's head, and heard
Holly say: "When mother's home, there
won't be any changes, will there? She
doesn't like strangers, you know."

The child's words seemed to bring the
chilly atmosphere of opposition about old
Jolyon, and disclose all the menace to his
newfound freedom. Ah! He would have
to resign himself to being an old man at
the mercy of care and love, or fight to
keep this new and prized companionship;
and to fight tired him to death. But his
thin, worn face hardened into resolution
till it appeared all jaw. This was his
house, and his affair; he should not
budge! He looked at his watch, old and
thin like himself; he had owned it fifty
years. Past four already! And kissing the
top of Holly's head in passing, he went
down to the hall. He wanted to get hold
of her before she went up to give her lesson. At the first sound of wheels he
stepped out into the porch, and saw at
once that the victoria was empty.

"The train's in, sir; but the lady 'asn't
come."

Old Jolyon gave him a sharp upward
look, his eyes seemed to push away that
fat chap's curiosity, and defy him to see
the bitter disappointment he was feeling.

"Very well," he said, and turned back

into the house. He went to his study and
sat down, quivering like a leaf. What did
this mean? She might have lost her train,
but he knew well enough she hadn't.
'Good-bye, dear Uncle Jolyon.' Why
'Good-bye' and not 'Good-night'? And
that hand of hers lingering in the air. And
her kiss. What did it mean? Vehement
alarm and irritation took possession of
him. He got up and began to pace the
Turkey carpet, between window and wall.
She was going to give him up! He felt it
for certain—and he defenceless. An old
man wanting to look on beauty! It was
ridiculous! Age closed his mouth, para-
lysed his power to fight. He had no right
to what was warm and living, no right to
anything but memories and sorrow. He
could not plead with her; even an old
man has his dignity. Defenceless! For an
hour, lost to bodily fatigue, he paced up
and down, past the bowl of carnations he
had plucked, which mocked him with its
scent. Of all things hard to bear, the pros-
tration of will-power is hardest, for one
who has always had his way. Nature had
got him in its net, and like an unhappy
fish he turned and swam at the meshes,
here and there, found no hole, no breaking point. They brought him tea at five
o'clock, and a letter. For a moment hope
beat up in him. He cut the envelope with
the butter knife, and read:

"DEAREST UNCLE JOLYON,—I can't
bear to write anything that may disap-
point you, but I was too cowardly to tell
you last night. I feel I can't come down
and give Holly any more lessons, now
that June is coming back. Some things go
too deep to be forgotten. It has been such
a joy to see you and Holly. Perhaps I
shall still see you sometimes when you
come up, though I'm sure it's not good
for you; I can see you are tiring yourself
too much. I believe you ought to rest
quite quietly all this hot weather, and now
you have your son and June coming back

you will be so happy. Thank you a million times for all your sweetness to me.

"Lovingly your IRENE."

So, there it was! Not good for him to have pleasure and what he chiefly cared about; to try and put off feeling the inevitable end of all things, the approach of death with its stealthy, rustling footsteps. Not good for him! Not even she could see how she was his new lease of interest in life, the incarnation of all the beauty he felt slipping from him!

His tea grew cold, his cigar remained unlit; and up and down he paced, torn between his dignity and his hold on life. Intolerable to be squeezed out slowly, without a say of your own, to live on when your will was in the hands of others bent on weighing you to the ground with care and love. Intolerable! He would see what telling her the truth would do—the truth that he wanted the sight of her more than just a lingering on. He sat down at his old bureau and took a pen. But he could not write. There was something revolting in having to plead like this; plead that she should warm his eyes with her beauty. It was tantamount to confessing dotage. He simply could not. And instead, he wrote:

"I had hoped that the memory of old sores would not be allowed to stand in the way of what is a pleasure and a profit to me and my little grand-daughter. But old men learn to forego their whims; they are obliged to, even the whim to live must be foregone sooner or later; and perhaps the sooner the better.

"My love to you,

"JOLYON FORSYTE."

'Bitter,' he thought, 'but I can't help it. I'm tired.' He sealed and dropped it into the box for the evening post, and hearing it fall to the bottom, thought: 'There goes all I've looked forward to!'

That evening after dinner which he scarcely touched, after his cigar which he left half-smoked for it made him feel faint, he went very slowly upstairs and stole into the night-nursery. He sat down on the window-seat. A night-light was burning, and he could just see Holly's face, with one hand underneath the cheek. An early cockchafer buzzed in the Japanese paper with which they had filled the grate, and one of the horses in the stable stamped restlessly. To sleep like that child! He pressed apart two rungs of the venetian blind and looked out. The moon was rising, blood-red. He had never seen so red a moon. The woods and fields out there were dropping to sleep too, in the last glimmer of the summer light. And beauty, like a spirit, walked. 'I've had a long life,' he thought, 'the best of nearly everything. I'm an ungrateful chap; I've seen a lot of beauty in my time. Poor young Bosinney said I have a sense of beauty. There's a man in the moon to-night!' A moth went by, another, another. 'Ladies in grey!' He closed his eyes. A feeling that he would never open them again beset him; he let it grow, let himself sink; then, with a shiver, dragged the lids up. There was something wrong with him, no doubt, deeply wrong; he would have to have the doctor after all. It didn't much matter now! Into that coppice the moonlight would have crept; there would be shadows, and those shadows would be the only things awake. No birds, beasts, flowers, insects; just the shadows—moving; 'Ladies in grey!' Over that log they would climb; would whisper together. She and Bosinney! Funny thought! And the frogs and little things would whisper too! How the clock ticked, in here! It was all eerie—out there in the light of that red moon; in here with the little steady night-light and the ticking clock and the nurse's dressing-gown hanging from the edge of the screen, tall, like a woman's figure. 'Lady in grey!'

And a very odd thought beset him: Did she exist? Had she ever come at all? Or was she but the emanation of all the beauty he had loved and must leave so soon? The violet-grey spirit with the dark eyes and the crown of amber hair, who walks the dawn and the moonlight, and at blue-bell time? What was she, who was she, did she exist? He rose and stood a moment clutching the window-sill, to give him a sense of reality again; then began tiptoeing towards the door. He stopped at the foot of the bed; and Holly, as if conscious of his eyes fixed on her, stirred, sighed, and curled up closer in defence. He tiptoed on and passed out into the dark passage; reached his room, undressed at once, and stood before a mirror in his night-shirt. What a scarecrow—with temples fallen in, and thin legs! His eyes resisted his own image, and a look of pride came on his face. All was in league to pull him down, even his reflection in the glass, but he was not down—yet! He got into bed, and lay a long time without sleeping, trying to reach resignation, only too well aware that fretting and disappointment were very bad for him.

He woke in the morning so unrefreshed and strengthless that he sent for the doctor. After sounding him, the fellow pulled a face as long as your arm, and ordered him to stay in bed and give up smoking. That was no hardship; there was nothing to get up for, and when he felt ill, tobacco always lost its savour. He spent the morning languidly with the sun-blinds down, turning and re-turning *The Times,* not reading much, the dog Balthasar lying beside his bed. With his lunch they brought him a telegram, running thus: 'Your letter received coming down this afternoon will be with you at four-thirty. Irene.'

Coming down! After all! Then she did exist—and he was not deserted. Coming down! A glow ran through his limbs; his cheeks and forehead felt hot. He drank his soup, and pushed the tray-table away, lying very quiet until they had removed lunch and left him alone; but every now and then his eyes twinkled. Coming down! His heart beat fast, and then did not seem to beat at all. At three o'clock he got up and dressed deliberately, noiselessly. Holly and Mam'zelle would be in the schoolroom, and the servants asleep after their dinner, he shouldn't wonder. He opened his door cautiously, and went downstairs. In the hall the dog Balthasar lay solitary, and, followed by him, old Jolyon passed into his study and out into the burning afternoon. He meant to go down and meet her in the coppice, but felt at once he could not manage that in this heat. He sat down instead under the oak tree by the swing, and the dog Balthasar, who also felt the heat, lay down beside him. He sat there smiling. What a revel of bright minutes! What a hum of insects, and cooing of pigeons! It was the quintessence of a summer day. Lovely! And he was happy—happy as a sand-boy, whatever that might be. She was coming; she had not given him up! He had everything in life he wanted—except a little more breath, and less weight—just here! He would see her when she emerged from the fernery, come swaying just a little, a violet-grey figure passing over the daisies and dandelions and 'soldiers' on the lawn—the soldiers with their flowery crowns. He would not move, but she would come up to him and say: 'Dear Uncle Jolyon, I am sorry!' and sit in the swing and let him look at her and tell her that he had not been very well but was all right now; and that dog would lick her hand. That dog knew his master was fond of her; that dog was a good dog.

It was quite shady under the tree; the sun could not get at him, only make the rest of the world bright so that he could see the Grand Stand at Epsom away out there, very far, and the cows cropping the clover in the field and swishing at the flies with their tails. He smelled the scent of limes, and lavender. Ah! that was why there was such a racket of bees. They were excited—busy, as his heart was busy and excited. Drowsy, too, drowsy and drugged on honey and happiness; as his heart was drugged and drowsy. Summer—summer—they seemed saying; great bees and little bees, and the flies too!

The stable clock struck four; in half an hour she would be here. He would have just one tiny nap, because he had had so little sleep of late; and then he would be fresh for her, fresh for youth and beauty, coming towards him across the sunlit lawn—lady in grey! And settling back in his chair he closed his eyes. Some thistledown came on what little air there was, and pitched on his moustache more white than itself. He did not know; but his breathing stirred it, caught there. A ray

of sunlight struck through and lodged on his boot. A bumble-bee alighted and strolled on the crown of his Panama hat. And the delicious surge of slumber reached the brain beneath that hat, and the head swayed forward and rested on his breast. Summer—summer! So went the hum.

The stable clock struck the quarter past. The dog Balthasar stretched and looked up at his master. The thistledown no longer moved. The dog placed his chin over the sunlit foot. It did not stir. The dog withdrew his chin quickly, rose, and leaped on old Jolyon's lap, looked in his face, whined; then leaping down, sat on his haunches, gazing up. And suddenly he uttered a long, long howl.

But the thistledown was still as death, and the face of his old master.

Summer—summer—summer!

The soundless footsteps on the grass!

# JUSTICE

### A TRAGEDY IN FOUR ACTS

## By JOHN GALSWORTHY

---

## PERSONS OF THE PLAY

JAMES HOW
WALTER HOW, *his son*  } *solicitors*

ROBERT COKESON, *their managing clerk*

WILLIAM FALDER, *their junior clerk*

SWEEDLE, *their office-boy*

WISTER, *a detective*

COWLEY, *a cashier*

MR. JUSTICE FLOYD, *a judge*

HAROLD CLEAVER, *an old advocate*

HECTOR FROME, *a young advocate*

CAPTAIN DANSON, V.C., *a prison governor*

THE REV. HUGH MILLER, *a prison chaplain*

EDWARD CLEMENTS, *a prison doctor*

WOODER, *a chief warder*

MOANEY
CLIPTON  } *convicts*
O'CLEARY

RUTH HONEYWILL, *a woman*

A NUMBER OF BARRISTERS, SOLICITORS, SPECTATORS, USHERS, REPORTERS, JURY-MEN, WARDERS, AND PRISONERS

TIME: The present.

ACT I. The office of James and Walter How. Morning. July.

ACT II. Assizes. Afternoon. October.

ACT III. A prison. December.
    SCENE I. The Governor's office.
    SCENE II. A corridor.
    SCENE III. A cell.

ACT IV. The office of James and Walter How. Morning. March, two years later.

# ACT 1

*The scene is the managing clerk's room, at the offices of* JAMES AND WALTER HOW, *on a July morning. The room is old-fashioned, furnished with well-worn mahogany and leather, and lined with tin boxes and estate plans. It has three doors. Two of them are close together in the centre of a wall. One of these two doors leads to the outer office, which is only divided from the managing clerk's room by a partition of wood and clear glass; and when the door into this outer office is opened there can be seen the wide outer door leading out on to the stone stairway of the building. The other of these two centre doors leads to the junior clerk's room. The third door is that leading to the partners' room.*

*The managing clerk,* COKESON, *is sitting at his table adding up figures in a pass-book, and murmuring their numbers to himself. He is a man of sixty, wearing spectacles; rather short, with a bald head, and an honest, pug-dog face. He is dressed in a well-worn black frock-coat and pepper-and-salt trousers.*

COKESON. And five's twelve, and three —fifteen, nineteen, twenty-three, thirty-two, forty-one—and carry four. [*He ticks the page, and goes on murmuring*] Five, seven, twelve, seventeen, twenty-four and nine, thirty-three, thirteen and carry one.

*He again makes a tick. The outer office door is opened and* SWEEDLE, *the office-boy, appears, closing the door behind him. He is a pale youth of sixteen, with spiky hair.*

COKESON. [*With grumpy expectation*] And carry one.

SWEEDLE. There's a party wants to see Falder, Mr. Cokeson.

COKESON. Five, nine, sixteen, twenty-

one, twenty-nine—and carry two. Sent him to Morris's. What name?

SWEEDLE. Honeywill.

COKESON. What's his business?

SWEEDLE. It's a woman.

COKESON. A lady?

SWEEDLE. No, a person.

COKESON. Ask her in. Take this pass-book to Mr. James.

[*He closes the pass-book.*

SWEEDLE. [*Reopening the door*] Will you come in, please?

RUTH HONEYWILL *comes in. She is a tall woman, twenty-six years old, unpretentiously dressed, with black hair and eyes, and an ivory-white, clear-cut face. She stands very still, having a natural dignity of pose and gesture.*

SWEEDLE *goes out into the partners' room with the pass-book.*

COKESON. [*Looking round at* RUTH] The young man's out. [*Suspiciously*] State your business, please.

RUTH. [*Who speaks in a matter-of-fact voice, and with a slight West-Country accent*] It's a personal matter, sir.

COKESON. We don't allow private callers here. Will you leave a message?

RUTH. I'd rather see him, please.

[*She narrows her dark eyes and gives him a honeyed look.*

COKESON. [*Expanding*] It's all against the rules. Suppose I had *my* friends here to see me! It'd never do!

RUTH. No, sir.

COKESON. [*A little taken aback*] Exactly! And here you are wanting to see a *junior* clerk!

RUTH. Yes, sir; I must see him.

COKESON. [*Turning full round to her with a sort of outraged interest*] But this is a lawyer's office. Go to his private address.

RUTH. He's not there.

COKESON. [*Uneasy*] Are you related to the party?

RUTH. No, sir.

COKESON. [*In real embarrassment*] I don't know what to say. It's no affair of the office.

RUTH. But what am I to do?

COKESON. Dear me! I can't tell you that.

SWEEDLE *comes back. He crosses to the outer office and passes through into it, with a quizzical look at* COKESON, *carefully leaving the door an inch or two open.*

COKESON. [*Fortified by this look*] This won't do, you know, this won't do at all. Suppose one of the partners came in!

*An incoherent knocking and chuckling is heard from the outer door of the outer office.*

SWEEDLE. [*Putting his head in*] There's some children outside here.

RUTH. They're mine, please.

SWEEDLE. Shall I hold them in check?

RUTH. They're quite small, sir.

[*She takes a step towards* COKESON.

COKESON. You mustn't take up his time in office hours; we're a clerk short as it is.

RUTH. It's a matter of life and death.

COKESON. [*Again outraged*] Life and death!

SWEEDLE. Here *is* Falder.

FALDER *has entered through the outer office. He is a pale, good-looking young man, with quick, rather scared eyes. He moves towards the door of the clerk's office, and stands there irresolute.*

COKESON. Well, I'll give you a minute. It's not regular.

*Taking up a bundle of papers, he goes out into the partners' room.*

RUTH. [*In a low, hurried voice*] He's on the drink again, Will. He tried to cut my throat last night. I came out with the children before he was awake. I went round to you——

FALDER. I've changed my digs.

RUTH. Is it all ready for to-night?

FALDER. I've got the tickets. Meet me 11.45 at the booking office. For God's sake don't forget we're man and wife! [*Looking at her with tragic intensity*] Ruth!

RUTH. You're not afraid of going, are you?

FALDER. Have you got your things, and the children's?

RUTH. Had to leave them, for fear of waking Honeywill, all but one bag. I can't go near home again.

FALDER. [*Wincing*] All that money gone for nothing. How much *must* you have?

RUTH. Six pounds—I could do with that, I think.

FALDER. Don't give away where we're going. [*As if to himself*] When I get out there I mean to forget it all.

RUTH. If you're sorry, say so. I'd sooner he killed me than take you against your will.

FALDER. [*With a queer smile*] We've got to go. I don't care; I'll have *you*.

RUTH. You've just to say; it's not too late.

FALDER. It *is* too late. Here's seven pounds. Booking office—11.45 to-night. If you weren't what you are to me, Ruth——!

RUTH. Kiss me!

*They cling together passionately then fly apart just as* COKESON *re-enters the room.* RUTH *turns and goes out through the outer office.* COKESON *advances deliberately to his chair and seats himself.*

COKESON. This isn't right, Falder.

FALDER. It shan't occur again, sir.

COKESON. It's an improper use of these premises.

FALDER. Yes, sir.

COKESON. You quite understand—the party was in some distress; and, having children with her, I allowed my feelings—[*He opens a drawer and produces from it a tract*] Just take this! "Purity in the Home." It's a well-written thing.

FALDER. [*Taking it, with a peculiar expression*] Thank you, sir.

COKESON. And look here, Falder, before Mr. Walter comes, have you finished up that cataloguing Davis had in hand before he left?

FALDER. I shall have done with it to-morrow, sir—for good.

COKESON. It's over a week since Davis went. Now it won't do, Falder. You're neglecting your work for private life. I shan't mention about the party having called, but——

FALDER. [*Passing into his room*] Thank you, sir.

COKESON *stares at the door through which* FALDER *has gone out; then shakes his head, and is just settling down to write, when* WALTER HOW *comes in through the outer office. He is a rather refined-looking man of thirty-five, with a pleasant, almost apologetic voice.*

WALTER. Good-morning, Cokeson.

COKESON. Morning, Mr. Walter.

WALTER. My father here?

COKESON. [*Always with a certain patronage as to a young man who might be doing better*] Mr. James has been here since eleven o'clock.

WALTER. I've been in to see the pictures, at the Guildhall.

COKESON. [*Looking at him as though this were exactly what was to be expected*] Have you now—ye-es. This lease of Boulter's—am I to send it to counsel?

WALTER. What does my father say?

COKESON. 'Aven't bothered him.

WALTER. Well, we can't be too careful.

COKESON. It's such a little thing—hardly worth the fees. I thought you'd do it yourself.

WALTER. Send it, please. I don't want the responsibility.

COKESON. [*With an indescribable air of compassion*] Just as you like. This "right-of-way" case—we've got 'em on the deeds.

WALTER. I know; but the intention was obviously to exclude that bit of common ground.

COKESON. We needn't worry about that. We're the *right* side of the law.

WALTER. I don't like it.

COKESON. [*With an indulgent smile*] We shan't want to set ourselves up against the law. Your father wouldn't waste his time doing that.

*As he speaks* JAMES HOW *comes in from the partners' room. He is a shortish man, with white side-whiskers, plentiful grey hair, shrewd eyes, and gold pince-nez.*

JAMES. Morning, Walter.

WALTER. How are you, Father?

COKESON. [*Looking down his nose at the papers in his hand as though deprecating their size*] I'll just take Boulter's lease in to young Falder to draft the instructions.

[*He goes out into* FALDER'S *room.*

WALTER. About that right-of-way case?

JAMES. Oh, well, we must go forward there. I thought you told me yesterday the firm's balance was over four hundred.

WALTER. So it is.

JAMES. [*Holding out the pass-book to his son*] Three—five—one, no recent cheques. Just get me out the cheque-book.

WALTER *goes to a cupboard, unlocks a drawer, and produces a cheque-book.*

JAMES. Tick the pounds in the counterfoils. Five, fifty-four, seven, five, twenty-eight, twenty, ninety, eleven, fifty-two, seventy-one. Tally?

WALTER. [*Nodding*] Can't understand. Made sure it was over four hundred.

JAMES. Give me the cheque-book. [*He takes the cheque-book and cons the counterfoils*] What's this ninety?

WALTER. Who drew it?

JAMES. You.

WALTER. [*Taking the cheque-book*] July 7th? That's the day I went down to look over the Trenton Estate—last Friday week; I came back on the Tuesday, you remember. But look here, Father, it was *nine* I drew a cheque for. Five guineas to Smithers and my expenses. It just covered all but half a crown.

JAMES. [*Gravely*] Let's look at that ninety cheque. [*He sorts the cheque out from the bundle in the pocket of the passbook*] Seems all right. There's no nine here. This is bad. Who cashed that nine-pound cheque?

WALTER. [*Puzzled and pained*] Let's see! I was finishing Mrs. Reddy's will—only just had time; yes—I gave it to Cokeson.

JAMES. Look at that t y; that yours?

WALTER. [*After consideration*] My y's curl back a little; this doesn't.

JAMES. [*As* COKESON *re-enters from* FALDER'S *room*] We must ask him. Just come here and carry your mind back a bit, Cokeson. D'you remember cashing a cheque for Mr. Walter last Friday week—the day he went to Trenton?

COKESON. Ye-es. Nine pounds.

JAMES. Look at this. [*Handing him the cheque.*

COKESON. No! Nine pounds. My lunch was just coming in; and of course I *like* it hot; I gave the cheque to Davis to run round to the bank. He brought it back, all notes—you remember, Mr. Walter, you wanted some silver to pay your cab. [*With a certain contemptuous compassion*] Here, let *me* see. You've got the wrong cheque.

[*He takes cheque-book and pass-book from* WALTER.

WALTER. Afraid not.

COKESON. [*Having seen for himself*] It's funny.

JAMES. You gave it to Davis, and Davis sailed for Australia on Monday. Looks black, Cokeson.

COKESON. [*Puzzled and upset*] Why this'd be a felony! No, no! there's some mistake.

JAMES. I hope so.

COKESON. There's never been anything of that sort in the office the twenty-nine years I've been here.

JAMES. [*Looking at cheque and counterfoil*] This is a very clever bit of work; a warning to you not to leave space after your figures, Walter.

WALTER. [*Vexed*] Yes, I know—I was in such a tearing hurry that afternoon.

COKESON. [*Suddenly*] This has upset me.

JAMES. The counterfoil altered too—very deliberate piece of swindling. What was Davis's ship?

WALTER. *City of Rangoon.*

JAMES. We ought to wire and have him arrested at Naples; he can't be there yet.

COKESON. His poor young wife. I liked the young man. Dear, oh dear! In this office!

WALTER. Shall I go to the bank and ask the cashier?

JAMES. [*Grimly*] Bring him round here. And ring up Scotland Yard.

WALTER. Really?

*He goes out through the outer office.* JAMES *paces the room. He stops and looks at* COKESON, *who is disconsolately rubbing the knees of his trousers.*

JAMES. Well, Cokeson! There's something in character, isn't there?

COKESON. [*Looking at him over his spectacles*] I don't quite take you, sir.

JAMES. Your story would sound d——d thin to any one who didn't know you.

COKESON. Ye-es! [*He laughs. Then with sudden gravity*] I'm sorry for that young man. I feel it as if it was my own son, Mr. James.

JAMES. A nasty business!

COKESON. It unsettles you. All goes on regular, and then a thing like this happens. Shan't relish my lunch to-day.

JAMES. As bad as that, Cokeson?

COKESON. It makes you think. [*Confi-*

*dentially*] He must have had temptation.

JAMES. Not so fast. We haven't convicted him yet.

COKESON. I'd sooner have lost a month's salary than had this happen.

[*He broods.*

JAMES. I hope that fellow will hurry up.

COKESON. [*Keeping things pleasant for the cashier*] It isn't fifty yards, Mr. James. He won't be a minute.

JAMES. The idea of dishonesty about this office—it hits me hard, Cokeson.

[*He goes towards the door of the partners' room.*

SWEEDLE. [*Entering quietly, to* COKESON *in a low voice*] She's popped up again, sir—something she forgot to say to Falder.

COKESON. [*Roused from his abstraction*] Eh? Impossible. Send her away!

JAMES. What's that?

COKESON. Nothing, Mr. James. A private matter. Here, I'll come myself. [*He goes into the outer office as* JAMES *passes into the partners' room*] Now, you really mustn't—we can't have anybody just now.

RUTH. Not for a minute, sir?

COKESON. Reely! Reely! I can't have it. If you want him, wait about; he'll be going out for his lunch directly.

RUTH. Yes, sir.

WALTER, *entering with the cashier, passes* RUTH *as she leaves the outer office.*

COKESON. [*To the cashier, who resembles a sedentary dragoon*] Good-morning. [*To* WALTER] Your father's in there.

WALTER *crosses and goes into the partners' room.*

COKESON. It's a nahsty, unpleasant little matter, Mr. Cowley. I'm quite ashamed to have to trouble you.

COWLEY. I remember the cheque quite well. [*As if it were a liver*] Seemed in perfect order.

COKESON. Sit down, won't you? I'm not a sensitive man, but a thing like this about the place—it's not nice. I like people to be open and jolly together.

COWLEY. Quite so.

COKESON. [*Buttonholing him, and glancing towards the partners' room*] Of course he's a young man. I've told him about it before now—leaving space after his figures, but he *will* do it.

COWLEY. I should remember the person's face—quite a youth.

COKESON. I don't think we shall be able to show him to you, as a matter of fact.

JAMES *and* WALTER *have come back from the partners' room.*

JAMES. Good-morning, Mr. Cowley. You've seen my son and myself, you've seen Mr. Cokeson, and you've seen Sweedle, my office-boy. It was none of us, I take it.

*The cashier shakes his head with a smile.*

JAMES. Be so good as to sit there. Cokeson, engage Mr. Cowley in conversation, will you?

[*He goes towards* FALDER'S *room.*

COKESON. Just a word, Mr. James.

JAMES. Well?

COKESON. You don't want to upset the young man in there, do you? He's a nervous young feller.

JAMES. This must be thoroughly cleared up, Cokeson, for the sake of Falder's name, to say nothing of yours.

COKESON. [*With some dignity*] That'll look after itself, sir. He's been upset once this morning; I don't want him startled again.

JAMES. It's a matter of form; but I can't stand upon niceness over a thing like this—too serious. Just talk to Mr. Cowley. [*He opens the door of* FALDER'S *room*] Bring in the papers in Boulter's lease, will you, Falder?

COKESON. [*Bursting into voice*] Do you keep dogs?

*The cashier, with his eyes fixed on the door, does not answer.*

COKESON. You haven't such a thing as a bulldog pup you could spare me, I suppose?

*At the look on the cashier's face his jaw drops, and he turns to see* FALDER *standing in the doorway, with his eyes fixed on* COWLEY, *like the eyes of a rabbit fastened on a snake.*

FALDER. [*Advancing with the papers*] Here they are, sir!

JAMES. [*Taking them*] Thank you.

FALDER. Do you want me, sir?

JAMES. No, thanks.

FALDER *turns and goes back into his own room. As he shuts the door* JAMES *gives the cashier an interrogative look, and the cashier nods.*

JAMES. Sure? This isn't as we suspected.

COWLEY. Quite. He knew me. I suppose he can't slip out of that room?

COKESON. [*Gloomily*] There's only the window—a whole floor and a basement.

*The door of* FALDER'S *room is quietly opened, and* FALDER, *with his hat in his hand, moves towards the door of the outer office.*

JAMES. [*Quietly*] Where are you going, Falder?

FALDER. To have my lunch, sir.

JAMES. Wait a few minutes, would you? I want to speak to you about this lease.

FALDER. Yes, sir. [*He goes back into his room.*

COWLEY. If I'm wanted, I can swear that's the young man who cashed the cheque. It was the last cheque I handled that morning before my lunch. These are the numbers of the notes he had. [*He puts a slip of paper on the table; then, brushing his hat round*] Good-morning!

JAMES. Good-morning, Mr. Cowley!

COWLEY. [*To* COKESON] Good-morning.

COKESON. [*With stupefaction*] Good-morning.

*The cashier goes out through the outer office.* COKESON *sits down in his chair, as though it were the only place left in the morass of his feelings.*

WALTER. What are you going to do?

JAMES. Have him in. Give me the cheque and the counterfoil.

COKESON. I don't understand. I thought young Davis——

JAMES. We shall see.

WALTER. One moment, Father—have you thought it out?

JAMES. Call him in!

COKESON. [*Rising with difficulty and opening* FALDER'S *door; hoarsely*] Step in here a minute.

FALDER *comes in.*

FALDER. [*Impressively*] Yes, sir?

JAMES. [*Turning to him suddenly with the cheque held out*] You know this cheque, Falder?

FALDER. No, sir.

JAMES. Look at it. You cashed it last Friday week.

FALDER. Oh! yes, sir; that one—Davis gave it me.

JAMES. I know. And you gave Davis the cash?

FALDER. Yes, sir.

JAMES. When Davis gave you the cheque was it exactly like this?

FALDER. Yes, I think so, sir.

JAMES. You know that Mr. Walter drew that cheque for *nine* pounds?

FALDER. No, sir—ninety.

JAMES. Nine, Falder.

FALDER. [*Faintly*] I don't understand, sir.

JAMES. The suggestion, of course, is that the cheque was altered; whether by you or Davis is the question.

FALDER. I—I——

COKESON. Take your time, take your time.

FALDER. [*Regaining his impassivity*] Not by me, sir.

JAMES. The cheque was handed to Cokeson by Mr. Walter at one o'clock, we know that because Mr. Cokeson's lunch had just arrived.

COKESON. I couldn't leave it.

JAMES. Exactly; he therefore gave the cheque to Davis. It was cashed by you at 1.15. We know that because the cashier recollects it for the last cheque he handled before *his* lunch.

FALDER. Yes, sir, Davis gave it to me because some friends were giving him a farewell luncheon.

JAMES. [*Puzzled*] You accuse Davis, then?

FALDER. I don't know, sir—it's very funny.

WALTER, *who has come close to his father, says something to him in a low voice.*

JAMES. Davis was not here again after that Saturday, was he?

COKESON. [*Anxious to be of assistance to the young man, and seeing faint signs of their all being jolly once more*] No, he sailed on the Monday.

JAMES. Was he, Falder?

FALDER. [*Very faintly*] No, sir.

JAMES. Very well, then, how do you account for the fact that this nought was added to the nine in the counterfoil on or after *Tuesday?*

COKESON. [*Surprised*] How's that?

FALDER *gives a sort of lurch; he tries to pull himself together, but he has gone all to pieces.*

JAMES. [*Very grimly*] Out, I'm afraid, Cokeson. The cheque-book remained in Mr. Walter's pocket till he came back from Trenton on Tuesday morning. In the face of this, Falder, do you still deny that you altered both cheque and counterfoil?

FALDER. No, sir—no, Mr. How. I did it, sir; I did it.

COKESON. [*Succumbing to his feelings*] Dear, dear! what a thing to do!

FALDER. I wanted the money so badly,

sir. I didn't know what I was doing.

COKESON. However such a thing could have come into your head!

FALDER. [*Grasping at the words*] I can't think, sir, really! It was just a minute of madness.

JAMES. A long minute, Falder. [*Tapping the counterfoil*] Four days at least.

FALDER. Sir, I swear I didn't know what I'd done till afterwards, and then I hadn't the pluck. Oh! sir, look over it! I'll pay the money back—I will, I promise.

JAMES. Go into your room.

FALDER, *with a swift imploring look, goes back into his room. There is silence.*

JAMES. About as bad a case as there could be.

COKESON. To break the law like that —in here!

WALTER. What's to be done?

JAMES. Nothing for it. Prosecute.

WALTER. It's his first offence.

JAMES. [*Shaking his head*] I've grave doubts of that. Too neat a piece of swindling altogether.

COKESON. I shouldn't be surprised if he was tempted.

JAMES. Life's one long temptation, Cokeson.

COKESON. Ye-es, but I'm speaking of the flesh and the devil, Mr. James. There was a woman come to see him this morning.

WALTER. The woman we passed as we came in just now. Is it his wife?

COKESON. No, no relation. [*Restraining what in jollier circumstances would have been a wink*] A married person, though.

WALTER. How do you know?

COKESON. Brought her children. [*Scandalized*] There they were outside the office.

JAMES. A real bad egg.

WALTER. I should like to give him a chance.

JAMES. I can't forgive him for the sneaky way he went to work—counting on our suspecting young Davis if the matter came to light. It was the merest accident the cheque-book stayed in your pocket.

WALTER. It *must* have been the temptation of a moment. He hadn't time.

JAMES. A man doesn't succumb like that in a moment, if he's a clean mind and habits. He's rotten; got the eyes of a man who can't keep his hands off when there's money about.

WALTER. [*Dryly*] We hadn't noticed that before.

JAMES. [*Brushing the remark aside*] I've seen lots of those fellows in my time. No doing anything with them except to keep 'em out of harm's way. They've got a blind spot.

WALTER. It's penal servitude.

COKESON. They're *nahsty* places— prisons.

JAMES. [*Hesitating*] I don't see how it's possible to spare him. Out of the question to keep him in this office—honesty's the *sine qua non*.

COKESON. [*Hypnotized*] Of course it is.

JAMES. Equally out of the question to send him out amongst people who've no knowledge of his character. One must think of society.

WALTER. But to brand him like this?

JAMES. If it had been a straightforward case I'd give him another chance. It's far from that. He has dissolute habits.

COKESON. I didn't say that—extenuating circumstances.

JAMES. Same thing. He's gone to work in the most cold-blooded way to defraud his employers, and cast the blame on an innocent man. If that's not a case for the law to take its course, I don't know what is.

WALTER. For the sake of his future, though.

JAMES. [*Sarcastically*] According to you, no one would ever prosecute.

WALTER. [*Nettled*] I hate the idea of it.

COKESON. We must have protection.

JAMES. This is degenerating into talk.

[*He moves towards the partners' room.*

WALTER. Put yourself in his place, Father.

JAMES. You ask too much of me.

WALTER. We can't possibly tell the pressure there was on him.

JAMES. You may depend on it, my boy, if a man is going to do this sort of thing he'll do it, pressure or no pressure; if he isn't nothing'll make him.

WALTER. He'll never do it again.

COKESON. [*Fatuously*] S'pose I were to have a talk with him. We don't want to be hard on the young man.

JAMES. That'll do, Cokeson. I've made up my mind.

[*He passes into the partners' room.*

COKESON. [*After a doubtful moment*] We must excuse your father. I don't want to go against your father; if he thinks it right.

WALTER. Confound it, Cokeson! why don't you back me up? You know you feel——

COKESON. [*On his dignity*] I really can't say what I feel.

WALTER. We shall regret it.

COKESON. He must have known what he was doing.

WALTER. [*Bitterly*] "The quality of mercy is not strained."

COKESON. [*Looking at him askance*] Come, come, Mr. Walter. We must try and see it sensible.

SWEEDLE. [*Entering with a tray*] Your lunch, sir.

COKESON. Put it down!

*While* SWEEDLE *is putting it down on* COKESON'S *table, the detective,* WISTER, *enters the outer office, and, finding no one there, comes to the inner doorway. He is a square, medium-sized man, clean-shaved, in a serviceable blue serge suit and strong boots.*

WISTER. [*To* WALTER] From Scotland Yard, sir. Dectective-Sergeant Wister.

WALTER. [*Askance*] Very well! I'll speak to my father.

[*He goes into the partners' room.* JAMES *enters.*

JAMES. Morning! [*In answer to an appealing gesture from* COKESON] I'm sorry; I'd stop short of this if I felt I could. Open that door.

SWEEDLE, *wondering and scared, opens it.*

JAMES. Come here, Mr. Falder.

As FALDER *comes shrinkingly out, the detective, in obedience to a sign from* JAMES, *slips his hand out and grasps his arm.*

FALDER. [*Recoiling*] Oh! no,—oh! no!

WISTER. Come, come, there's a good lad.

JAMES. I charge him with felony.

FALDER. Oh, sir! There's some one—I did it for her. Let me be till to-morrow.

JAMES *motions with his hand. At that sign of hardness,* FALDER *becomes rigid. Then, turning, he goes out quietly in the detective's grip.* JAMES *follows, stiff and erect.* SWEEDLE, *rushing to the door with open mouth, pursues them through the outer office into the corridor. When they have all disappeared* COKESON *spins completely around and makes a rush for the outer office.*

COKESON. [*Hoarsely*] Here! Here! What are we doing?

*There is silence. He takes out his handkerchief and mops the sweat from his face. Going back blindly to his table, he sits down, and stares blankly at his lunch.*

*The curtain falls.*

## ACT II

*A Court of Justice, on a foggy October afternoon—crowded with barristers, solicitors, reporters, ushers, and jurymen. Sitting in the large, solid dock is* FALDER, *with a warder on either side of him, placed there for his safe custody, but seemingly indifferent to and unconscious of his presence.* FALDER *is sitting exactly opposite to the* JUDGE, *who, raised above the clamor of the court, also seems unconscious of and indifferent to everything.* HAROLD CLEAVER, *the counsel for the Crown, is a dried, yellowish man, of more than middle age, in a wig worn almost to the color of his face.* HECTOR FROME, *the counsel for the defense, is a young, tall man, clean-shaven, in a very white wig. Among the spectators, having already given their evidence, are* JAMES *and* WALTER HOW, *and* COWLEY, *the cashier.* WISTER, *the detective, is just leaving the witness-box.*

CLEAVER. That is the case for the Crown, me lud!

[*Gathering his robes together, he sits down.*

FROME. [*Rising and bowing to the* JUDGE] If it please your lordship and members of the jury. I am not going to dispute the fact that the prisoner altered this cheque, but I am going to put before you evidence as to the condition of his mind, and to submit that you would not be justified in finding that he was responsible for his actions at the time. I am going to show you, in fact, that he did this in a moment of aberration, amounting to temporary insanity, caused by the violent distress under which he was laboring. Gentlemen, the prisoner is only twenty-three years old. I shall call before you a woman from whom you will learn the events that led up to this act. You will hear from her own lips the tragic circumstances of her life, the still more tragic infatuation with which she has inspired the prisoner. This woman, gentlemen, has been leading a miserable existence with a husband who habitually ill-uses her, from whom she actually goes in terror of her life. I am not, of course, saying that it's either right or desirable for a young man to fall in love with a married woman or that it's his business to rescue her from an ogre-like husband. I'm not saying anything of the sort. But we all know the power of the passion of love; and I would ask you to remember, gentlemen, in listening to her evidence, that, married to a drunken and violent husband, she has no power to get rid of him; for, as you know, another offense besides violence is necessary to enable a woman to obtain a divorce; and of this offense it does not appear that her husband is guilty.

THE JUDGE. Is this relevant, Mr. Frome?

FROME. My lord, I submit, extremely—I shall be able to show your lordship that directly.

THE JUDGE. Very well.

FROME. In these circumstances, what alternatives were left to her? She could either go on living with this drunkard, in terror of her life; or she could apply to the Court for a separation order. Well, gentlemen, my experience of such cases assures me that this would have given her very insufficient protection from the violence of such a man; and even if effectual would very likely have reduced her either to the workhouse or the streets—for it's not easy, as she is now finding, for an unskilled woman without means of livelihood to support herself and her children without resorting either to the Poor Law or—to speak quite plainly—to the sale of her body.

THE JUDGE. You are ranging rather far, Mr. Frome.

FROME. I shall fire point-blank in a minute, my lord.

THE JUDGE. Let us hope so.

FROME. Now, gentlemen, mark—and this is what I have been leading up to—this woman will tell you, and the prisoner will confirm her, that, confronted with such alternatives, she set her whole hopes on himself, knowing the feeling with which she had inspired him. She saw a way out of her misery by going with him

to a new country, where they would both be unknown, and might pass as husband and wife. This was a desperate and, as my friend Mr. Cleaver will no doubt call it, an immoral resolution; but, as a fact, the minds of both of them were constantly turned towards it. One wrong is no excuse for another, and those who are never likely to be faced by such a situation possibly have the right to hold up their hands —as to that I prefer to say nothing. But whatever view you take, gentlemen, of this part of the prisoner's story—whatever opinion you form of the right of these two young people under such circumstances to take the law into their own hands—the fact remains that this young woman in her distress, and this young man, little more than a boy, who was so devotedly attached to her, *did* conceive this—if you like—reprehensible design of going away together. Now, for that, of course, they required money, and—they had none. As to the actual events of the morning of July 7th, on which this cheque was altered, the events on which I rely to prove the defendant's irresponsibility—I shall allow those events to speak for themselves, through the lips of my witnesses, Robert Cokeson.

[*He turns, looks round, takes up a sheet of paper, and waits.*

COKESON *is summoned into court, and goes into the witness-box, holding his hat before him. The oath is administered to him.*

FROME. What is your name?

COKESON. Robert Cokeson.

FROME. Are you managing clerk to the firm of solicitors who employ the prisoner?

COKESON. Ye-es.

FROME. How long had the prisoner been in their employ?

COKESON. Two years. No, I'm wrong there—all but seventeen days.

FROME. Had you him under your eye all that time?

COKESON. Except Sundays and holidays.

FROME. Quite so. Let us hear, please, what you have to say about his general character during those two years.

COKESON. [*Confidentially to the jury, and as if a little surprised at being asked*] He was a nice, pleasant-spoken young man. I'd no fault to find with him—quite the contrary. It was a *great* surprise to me when he did a thing like that.

FROME. Did he ever give you reason to suspect his honesty?

COKESON. No! To have dishonesty in our office, that'd never do.

FROME. I'm sure the jury fully appreciate that, Mr. Cokeson.

COKESON. Every man of business knows that honesty's the sign qua nonne.

FROME. Do you give him a good character all round, or do you not?

COKESON. [*Turning to the* JUDGE] Certainly. We were all very jolly and pleasant together, until this happened. Quite upset me.

FROME. Now, coming to the morning of the 7th of July, the morning on which the cheque was altered. What have you to say about his demeanor that morning?

COKESON. [*To the jury*] If you ask me, I don't think he was quite compos when he did it.

THE JUDGE. [*Sharply*] Are you suggesting that he was insane?

COKESON. Not compos.

THE JUDGE. A little more precision, please.

FROME. [*Smoothly*] Just tell us, Mr. Cokeson.

COKESON. [*Somewhat outraged*] Well, in my opinion—[*looking at the* JUDGE] such as it is—he was jumpy at the time. The jury will understand my meaning.

FROME. Will you tell us how you came to that conclusion?

COKESON. Ye-es, I will. I have my lunch in from the restaurant, a chop and a potato—saves times. That day it happened to come just as Mr. Walter How handed me the cheque. Well, I like it hot; so I went into the clerks' office and I handed the cheque to Davis, the other clerk, and told him to get change. I noticed young Falder walking up and down. I said to him: "This is not the Zoological Gardens, Falder."

FROME. Do you remember what he answered?

COKESON. Ye-es: "I wish to God it were!" Struck me as funny.

FROME. Did you notice anything else peculiar?

COKESON. I did.

FROME. What was that?

COKESON. His collar was unbuttoned. Now, I like a young man to be neat. I said to him: "Your collar's unbuttoned."

FROME. And what did he answer?

COKESON. Stared at me. It wasn't nice.

THE JUDGE. Stared at you? Isn't that a very common practice?

COKESON. Ye-es, but it was the look in his eyes. I can't explain my meaning—it was funny.

FROME. Had you ever seen such a look in his eyes before?

COKESON. No. If I had I should have spoken to the partners. We can't have anything eccentric in our profession.

THE JUDGE. Did you speak to them on that occasion?

COKESON. [*Confidentially*] Well, I didn't like to trouble them without prime facey evidence.

FROME. But it made a very distinct impression on your mind.

COKESON. Ye-es. The clerk Davis could have told you the same.

FROME. Quite so. It's very unfortunate that we've not got him here. Now can you tell me of the morning on which the discovery of the forgery was made? That would be the 18th. Did anything happen that morning?

COKESON. [*With his hand to his ear*] I'm a little deaf.

FROME. Was there anything in the course of that morning—I mean before the discovery—that caught your attention?

COKESON. Ye-es—a woman.

THE JUDGE. How is *this* relevant, Mr. Frome?

FROME. I am trying to establish the state of mind in which the prisoner committed this act, my lord.

THE JUDGE. I quite appreciate that. But this was long after the act.

FROME. Yes, my lord, but it contributes to my contention.

THE JUDGE. Well!

FROME. You say a woman. Do you mean that she came to the office?

COKESON. Ye-es.

FROME. What for?

COKESON. Asked to see young Falder; he was out at the moment.

FROME. Did you see her?

COKESON. I did.

FROME. Did she come alone?

COKESON. [*Confidentially*] Well, there you put me in a difficulty. I mustn't tell you what the office-boy told me.

FROME. Quite so, Mr. Cokeson, quite so——

COKESON. [*Breaking in with an air of "You are young—leave it to me"*] But I think we can get round it. In answer to a question put to her by a third party the woman said to me: "They're mine, sir."

THE JUDGE. What are? What were?

COKESON. Her children. They were outside.

THE JUDGE. How do you know?

COKESON. Your lordship mustn't ask me that, or I shall have to tell you what I was told—and that'd never do.

THE JUDGE. [*Smiling*] The office-boy made a statement.

COKESON. Egg-zactly.

FROME. What I want to ask you, Mr. Cokeson, is this. In the course of her appeal to see Falder, did the woman say anything that you specially remember?

COKESON. [*Looking at him as if to encourage him to complete the sentence*] A leetle more, sir.

FROME. Or did she not?

COKESON. She did. I shouldn't like you to have led me to the answer.

FROME. [*With an irritated smile*] Will you tell the jury what it was?

COKESON. "It's a matter of life and death."

FOREMAN OF THE JURY. Do you mean the woman said that?

COKESON. [*Nodding*] It's not the sort of thing you like to have said to you.

FROME. [*A little impatiently*] Did Falder come in while she was there?

[COKESON *nods.*

FROME. And she saw him, and went away?

COKESON. Ah! there I can't follow you. I didn't see her go.

FROME. Well, is she there now?

COKESON. [*With an indulgent smile*] No!

FROME. Thank you, Mr. Cokeson.

[*He sits down.*

CLEAVER. [*Rising*] You say that on the morning of the forgery the prisoner was jumpy. Well, now, sir, what precisely do you mean by that word?

COKESON. [*Indulgently*] I *want* you to understand. Have you ever seen a dog that's lost its master? He was kind of everywhere at once with his eyes.

CLEAVER. Thank you; I was coming to his eyes. You called them "funny." What are we to understand by that? Strange, or what?

COKESON. Ye-es, funny.

CLEAVER. [*Sharply*] Yes, sir, but what may be funny to you may not be funny to me, or to the jury. Did they look frightened, or shy, or fierce, or what?

COKESON. You make it very hard for me. I give you the word, and you want me to give you another.

CLEAVER. [*Rapping his desk*] Does "funny" mean mad?

COKESON. Not mad, fun——

CLEAVER. Very well! Now you say he had his collar unbuttoned? Was it a hot day?

COKESON. Ye-es; I think it was.

CLEAVER. And did he button it when you called his attention to it?

COKESON. Ye-es, I think he did.

CLEAVER. Would you say that that denoted insanity?

*He sits down.* COKESON, *who has opened his mouth to reply, is left gaping.*

FROME. [*Rising hastily*] Have you ever caught him in that dishevelled state before?

COKESON. No! He was *always* clean and quiet.

FROME. That will do, thank you.

COKESON *turns blandly to the* JUDGE, *as though to rebuke counsel for not remembering that the* JUDGE *might wish to have a chance; arriving at the conclusion that he is to be asked nothing further, he turns and descends from the box, and sits down next to* JAMES *and* WALTER.

FROME. Ruth Honeywill.

RUTH *comes into court, and takes her stand stoically in the witness-box. She is sworn.*

FROME. What is your name, please?

RUTH. Ruth Honeywill.

FROME. How old are you?

RUTH. Twenty-six.

FROME. You are a married woman, living with your husband? A little louder.

RUTH. No, sir; not since July.

FROME. Have you any children?

RUTH. Yes, sir, two.

FROME. Are they living with you?

RUTH. Yes, sir.

FROME. You know the prisoner?

RUTH. [*Looking at him*] Yes.

FROME. What was the nature of your relations with him?

RUTH. We were friends.

THE JUDGE. Friends?

RUTH. [*Simply*] Lovers, sir.

THE JUDGE. [*Sharply*] In what sense do you use that word?

RUTH. We love each other.

THE JUDGE. Yes, but——

RUTH. [*Shaking her head*] No, your lordship—not yet.

THE JUDGE. Not yet! H'm! [*He looks from* RUTH *to* FALDER] Well!

FROME. What is your husband?

RUTH. Traveller.

FROME. And what was the nature of your married life?

RUTH. [*Shaking her head*] It don't bear talking about.

FROME. Did he ill-treat you, or what?

RUTH. Ever since my first was born.

FROME. In what way?

RUTH. I'd rather not say. All sorts of ways.

THE JUDGE. I am afraid I must stop this, you know.

RUTH. [*Pointing to* FALDER] *He* offered to take me out of it, sir. We were going to South America.

FROME. [*Hastily*] Yes, quite—and what prevented you?

RUTH. I was outside his office when he was taken away. It nearly broke my heart.

FROME. You knew, then, that he had been arrested?

RUTH. Yes, sir. I called at his office afterwards, and [*pointing to* COKESON] that gentleman told me all about it.

FROME. Now, do you remember the morning of Friday, July 7th?

RUTH. Yes.

FROME. Why?

RUTH. My husband nearly strangled me that morning.

THE JUDGE. Nearly strangled you!

RUTH. [*Bowing her head*] Yes, my lord.

FROME. With his hands, or——?

RUTH. Yes, I just managed to get away from him. I went straight to my friend. It was eight o'clock.

THE JUDGE. In the morning? Your

husband was not under the influence of liquor then?

RUTH. It wasn't always that.

FROME. In what condition were you?

RUTH. In very bad condition, sir. My dress was torn, and I was half choking.

FROME. Did you tell your friend what had happened?

RUTH. Yes. I wish I never had.

FROME. It upset him?

RUTH. Dreadfully.

FROME. Did he ever speak to you about a cheque?

RUTH. Never.

FROME. Did he ever give you any money?

RUTH. Yes.

FROME. When was that?

RUTH. On Saturday.

FROME. The 8th?

RUTH. To buy an outfit for me and the children, and get all ready to start.

FROME. Did that surprise you, or not?

RUTH. What, sir?

FROME. That he had money to give you.

RUTH. Yes, because on the morning when my husband nearly killed me my friend cried because he hadn't the money to get me away. He told me afterwards he'd come into a windfall.

FROME. And when did you last see him?

RUTH. The day he was taken away, sir. It was the day we were to have started.

FROME. Oh, yes, the morning of the arrest. Well, did you see him at all between the Friday and that morning?

RUTH *nods*.

FROME. What was his manner then?

RUTH. Dumb-like—sometimes he didn't seem able to say a word.

FROME. As if something unusual had happened to him?

RUTH. Yes.

FROME. Painful, or pleasant, or what?

RUTH. Like a fate hanging over him.

FROME. [*Hesitating*] Tell me, did you love the defendant very much?

RUTH. [*Bowing her head*] Yes.

FROME. And had he a very great affection for you?

RUTH. [*Looking at* FALDER] Yes, sir.

FROME. Now, ma'am, do you or do you not think that your danger and unhappiness would seriously affect his balance, his control over his actions?

RUTH. Yes.

FROME. His reason, even?

RUTH. For a moment like, I think it would.

FROME. Was he very much upset that Friday morning, or was he fairly calm?

RUTH. Dreadfully upset. I could hardly bear to let him go from me.

FROME. Do you still love him?

RUTH. [*With her eyes on* FALDER] He's ruined himself for me.

FROME. Thank you.

[*He sits down.* RUTH *remains stoically upright in the witness-box.*

CLEAVER. [*In a considerate voice*] When you left him on the morning of Friday the 7th you would not say that he was out of his mind, I suppose?

RUTH. No, sir.

CLEAVER. Thank you; I've no further questions to ask you.

RUTH. [*Bending a little forward to the jury*] I would have done the same for him; I would indeed.

THE JUDGE. Please, please! You say your married life is an unhappy one? Faults on both sides?

RUTH. Only that I never bowed down to him. I don't see why I should, sir, not to a man like that.

THE JUDGE. You refused to obey him?

RUTH. [*Avoiding the question*] I've always studied him to keep things nice.

THE JUDGE. Until you met the prisoner—was that it?

RUTH. No; even after that.

THE JUDGE. I ask, you know, because you seem to me to glory in this affection of yours for the prisoner.

RUTH. [*Hesitating*] I—I do. It's the only thing in my life now.

THE JUDGE. [*Staring at her hard*] Well, step down, please.

RUTH *looks at* FALDER, *then passes quietly down and takes her seat among the witnesses.*

FROME. I call the prisoner, my lord.

FALDER *leaves the dock; goes into the witness-box, and is duly sworn.*

FROME. What is your name?

FALDER. William Falder.

FROME. And age?

FALDER. Twenty-three.

FROME. You are not married?

FALDER *shakes his head.*

FROME. How long have you known the last witness?

FALDER. Six months.

FROME. Is her account of the relationship between you a correct one?

FALDER. Yes.

FROME. You became devotedly attached to her, however?

FALDER. Yes.

THE JUDGE. Though you knew she was a married woman?

FALDER. I couldn't help it, your lordship.

THE JUDGE. Couldn't help it?

FALDER. I didn't seem able to.

*The* JUDGE *slightly shrugs his shoulders.*

FROME. How did you come to know her?

FALDER. Through my married sister.

FROME. Did you know whether she was happy with her husband?

FALDER. It was trouble all the time.

FROME. You knew her husband?

FALDER. Only through her—he's a brute.

THE JUDGE. I can't allow indiscriminate abuse of a person not present.

FROME. [*Bowing*] If your lordship pleases. [*To* FALDER] You admit altering this cheque?

FALDER *bows his head.*

FROME. Carry your mind, please, to the morning of Friday, July the 7th, and tell the jury what happened.

FALDER. [*Turning to the jury*] I was having my breakfast when she came. Her dress was all torn, and she was gasping and couldn't seem to get her breath at all; there were the marks of his fingers round her throat; her arm was bruised, and the blood had got into her eyes dreadfully. It frightened me, and then when she told me, I felt—I felt—well—it was too much for me! [*Hardening suddenly*] If you'd seen it, having the feelings for her that I had, you'd have felt the same, I know.

FROME. Yes?

FALDER. When she left me—because I had to go to the office—I was out of my senses for fear that he'd do it again, and thinking what I could do. I couldn't work—all the morning I was like that—simply couldn't fix my mind on anything. I couldn't think at all. I seemed to have to keep moving. When Davis—the other clerk—gave me the cheque—he said: "It'll do you good, Will, to have a run with this. You seem half off your chump this morning." Then when I had it in my hand—I don't know how it came, but it just flashed across me that if I put the t y and the nought there would be the money to get her away. It just came and went—I never thought of it again. Then Davis went out to his luncheon, and I don't really remember what I did till I'd pushed the cheque through to the cashier under the rail. I remember his saying "Notes?" Then I suppose I knew what I'd done. Anyway, when I got outside I wanted to chuck myself under a 'bus; I wanted to throw the money away; but it seemed I was in for it, so I thought at any rate I'd save her. Of course the tickets I took for the passage and the little I gave her's been wasted, and all, except what I was obliged to spend myself, I've restored. I keep thinking over and over however it was I came to do it, and how I can't have it all again to do differently!

FALDER *is silent, twisting his hands before him.*

FROME. How far is it from your office to the bank?

FALDER. Not more than fifty yards, sir.

FROME. From the time Davis went out to lunch to the time you cashed the cheque, how long do you say it must have been?

FALDER. It couldn't have been four minutes, sir, because I ran all the way.

FROME. During those four minutes you say you remember nothing?

FALDER. No, sir; only that I ran.

FROME. Not even adding the t y and the nought?

FALDER. No, sir. I don't really.

FROME *sits down, and* CLEAVER *rises.*

CLEAVER. But you remember running, do you?

FALDER. I was all out of breath when I got to the bank.

CLEAVER. And you don't remember altering the cheque?

FALDER. [*Faintly*] No, sir.

CLEAVER. Divested of the romantic glamour which my friend is casting over the case, is this anything but an ordinary forgery? Come.

FALDER. I was half frantic all that morning, sir.

CLEAVER. Now, now! You don't deny that the t y and the nought were so like the rest of the handwriting as to thoroughly deceive the cashier?

FALDER. It was an accident.

CLEAVER. [*Cheerfully*] Queer sort of accident, wasn't it? On which day did you alter the counterfoil?

FALDER. [*Hanging his head*] On the Wednesday morning.

CLEAVER. Was that an accident, too?

FALDER. [*Faintly*] No.

CLEAVER. To do that you had to watch your opportunity, I suppose?

FALDER. [*Almost inaudibly*] Yes.

CLEAVER. You don't suggest that you were suffering under great excitement when you did that?

FALDER. I was haunted.

CLEAVER. With the fear of being found out?

FALDER. [*Very low*] Yes.

THE JUDGE. Didn't it occur to you that the only thing for you to do was to confess to your employers, and restore the money?

FALDER. I was afraid.

*There is silence.*

CLEAVER. You desired, too, no doubt to complete your design of taking this woman away?

FALDER. When I found I'd done a thing like that, to do it for nothing seemed so dreadful. I might just as well have chucked myself into the river.

CLEAVER. You knew that the clerk Davis was about to leave England—didn't it occur to you when you altered this cheque that suspicion would fall on him?

FALDER. It was all done in a moment. I thought of it afterwards.

CLEAVER. And that didn't lead you to avow what you'd done?

FALDER. [*Sullenly*] I meant to write when I got out there—I would have repaid the money.

THE JUDGE. But in the meantime your innocent fellow clerk might have been prosecuted.

FALDER. I knew he was a long way off, your lordship. I thought there'd be time. I didn't think they'd find it out so soon.

FROME. I might remind your lordship that as Mr. Walter How had the cheque-book in his pocket till after Davis had sailed, if the discovery had been made only one day later Falder himself would have left, and suspicion would have attached to him, and not to Davis, from the beginning.

THE JUDGE. The question is whether the prisoner knew that suspicion would light on himself, and not on Davis. [*To* FALDER *sharply*] Did you know that Mr. Walter How had the cheque-book till after Davis had sailed?

FALDER. I—I thought—he——

THE JUDGE. Now speak the truth—yes or no!

FALDER. [*Very low*] No, my lord. I had no means of knowing.

THE JUDGE. That disposes of your point, Mr. Frome.

FROME *bows to the* JUDGE.

CLEAVER. Has any aberration of this nature ever attacked you before?

FALDER. [*Faintly*] No, sir.

CLEAVER. You had recovered sufficiently to go back to your work that afternoon?

FALDER. Yes, I had to take the money back.

CLEAVER. You mean the *nine* pounds. Your wits were sufficiently keen for you to remember that? And you still persist in saying you don't remember altering this cheque.

[*He sits down.*

FALDER. If I hadn't been mad I should never have had the courage.

FROME. [*Rising*] Did you have your lunch before going back?

FALDER. I never ate a thing all day; and at night I couldn't sleep.

FROME. Now, as to the four minutes that elapsed between Davis's going out and your cashing the cheque: do you say that you recollect *nothing* during those four minutes?

FALDER. [*After a moment*] I remember thinking of Mr. Cokeson's face.

FROME. Of Mr. Cokeson's face! Had that any connection with what you were doing?

FALDER. No, sir.

FROME. Was that in the office, before you ran out?

FALDER. Yes, and while I was running.

FROME. And that lasted till the cashier said: "Will you have notes?"

FALDER. Yes, and then I seemed to come to myself—and it was too late.

FROME. Thank you. That closes the evidence for the defence, my lord.

*The* JUDGE *nods, and* FALDER *goes back to his seat in the dock.*

FROME. [*Gathering up notes*] If it please your lordship—members of the jury,—My friend in cross-examination has shown a disposition to sneer at the defence which has been set up in this case, and I am free to admit that nothing I can say will move you, if the evidence has not already convinced you that the prisoner committed this act in a moment when to all practical intents and purposes he was not responsible for his actions; a moment of such mental and moral vacuity, arising from the violent emotional agitation under which he had been suffering, as to amount to temporary madness. My friend has alluded to the "romantic glamour" with which I have sought to invest this case. Gentlemen, I have done nothing of the kind. I have merely shown you the background of "life"—that palpitating life which, believe me—whatever my friend may say—always lies behind the commission of a crime. Now, gentlemen, we live in a highly civilised age, and the sight of brutal violence disturbs us in a very strange way, even when we have no personal interest in the matter. But when we see it inflicted on a woman whom we love—what then? Just think of what your own feelings would have been, each of you, at the prisoner's age; and then look at him. Well! he is hardly the comfortable, shall we say bucolic, person likely to contemplate with equanimity marks of gross violence on a woman to whom he was devotedly attached. Yes, gentlemen, look at him! He has not a strong face; but neither has he a vicious face. He is just the sort of man who would easily become the prey of his emotions. You have heard the description of his eyes. My friend may laugh at the word "funny"—*I* think it better describes the peculiar uncanny look of those who are strained to breaking-point than any other word which could have been used. I don't pretend, mind you, that his mental irresponsibility was more than a flash of darkness, in which all sense of proportion became lost; but I do contend, that, just as a man who destroys himself at such a moment may be, and often is, absolved from the stigma attaching to the crime of self-murder, so he may, and frequently does, commit other crimes while in this irresponsible condition, and that he may as justly be acquitted of criminal intent and treated as a patient. I admit that this is a plea which might well be abused. It is a matter for discretion. But here you have a case in which there is every reason to give the benefit of the doubt. You heard me ask the prisoner what he thought of during those four fatal minutes. What was his answer? "I thought of Mr. Cokeson's face!" Gentlemen, no man could invent an answer like that; it is absolutely stamped with truth. You have seen the great affection (legitimate or not) existing between him and this woman, who came here to give evidence for him at the risk of her life. It is impossible for you to doubt his distress on the morning when he committed this act. We well know what terrible havoc such distress can make in weak and highly nervous people. It was all the work of a moment. The rest has followed, as death follows a stab to the heart, or water drops if you hold up a jug to empty it. Believe me, gentlemen, there is nothing more tragic in life than the utter impossibility of changing what you have done. Once this cheque was altered and presented, the work of four

minutes—four mad minutes—the rest has been silence. But in those four minutes the boy before you has slipped through a door, hardly opened, into that great cage which never again quite lets a man go—the cage of the Law. His further acts, his failure to confess, the alteration of the counterfoil, his preparations for flight, are all evidence—not of deliberate and guilty intention when he committed the prime act from which these subsequent acts arose; no—they are merely evidence of the weak character which is clearly enough his misfortune. But is a man to be lost because he is bred and born with a weak character? Gentlemen, men like the prisoner are destroyed daily under our law for want of that human insight which sees them as they are, patients, and not criminals. If the prisoner be found guilty, and treated as though he were a criminal type, he will, as all experience shows, in all probability become one. I beg you not to return a verdict that may thrust him back into prison and brand him for ever. Gentlemen, Justice is a machine that, when some one has once given it the starting push, rolls on of itself. Is this young man to be ground to pieces under this machine for an act which at the worst was one of weakness? Is he to become a member of the luckless crews that man those dark, ill-starred ships called prisons? Is that to be his voyage—from which so few return? Or is he to have another chance, to be still looked on as one who has gone a little astray, but who will come back? I urge you, gentlemen, do not ruin this young man! For, as a result of those four minutes, ruin, utter and irretrievable, stares him in the face. He can be saved now. Imprison him as a criminal, and I affirm to you that he will be lost. He has neither the face nor the manner of one who can survive that terrible ordeal. Weigh in the scales his criminality and the suffering he has undergone. The latter is ten times heavier already. He has lain in prison under this charge for more than two months. Is he likely ever to forget that? Imagine the anguish of his mind during that time. He has had his punishment, gentlemen, you may depend. The rolling of the chariot-wheels of Justice over this boy began when it was decided to prosecute him. We are now already at the second stage. If you permit it to go on to the third I would not give—that for him.

*He holds up finger and thumb in the form of a circle, drops his hand, and sits down.*

*The jury stir, and consult each other's faces; then they turn towards the counsel for the Crown, who rises, and, fixing his eyes on a spot that seems to give him satisfaction, slides them every now and then towards the jury.*

CLEAVER. May it please your lordship. [*Rising on his toes*] Gentlemen of the jury,—The facts in this case are not disputed, and the defence, if my friend will allow me to say so, is so thin that I don't propose to waste the time of the Court by taking you over the evidence. The plea is one of temporary insanity. Well, gentlemen, I daresay it is clearer to me than it is to you why this rather—what shall we call it?—bizarre defence has been set up. The alternative would have been to plead guilty. Now, gentlemen, if the prisoner had pleaded guilty my friend would have had to rely on a simple appeal to his lordship. Instead of that, he has gone into the byways and hedges and found this—er—peculiar plea, which has enabled him to show you the proverbial woman, to put her in the box—to give, in fact, a romantic glow to this affair. I compliment my friend; I think it highly ingenious of him. By these means, he has—to a certain extent—got round the Law. He has brought the whole story of motive and stress out in court, at first hand, in a way that he would not otherwise have been able to

do. But when you have once grasped that fact, gentlemen, you have grasped everything. [*With good-humoured contempt*] For look at this plea of insanity; we can't put it lower than that. You have heard the woman. She has every reason to favour the prisoner, but what did she say? She said that the prisoner was *not* insane when she left him in the morning. If he were going out of his mind through distress, that was obviously the moment when insanity would have shown itself. You have heard the managing clerk, another witness for the defence. With some difficulty I elicited from him the admission that the prisoner, though jumpy (a word that he seemed to think you would understand, gentlemen, and I'm sure I hope you do), was *not* mad when the cheque was handed to Davis. I agree with my friend that it's unfortunate that we have not got Davis here, but the prisoner has told you the words with which Davis in turn handed him the cheque; he obviously, therefore, was *not* mad when he received it, or he would not have remembered those words. The cashier has told you that he was certainly in his senses when he cashed it. We have therefore the plea that a man who is sane at ten minutes past one, and sane at fifteen minutes past, may, for the purposes of avoiding the consequences of a crime, call himself insane between those points of time. Really, gentlemen, this is so peculiar a proposition that I am not disposed to weary you with further argument. You will form your own opinion of its value. My friend has adopted this way of saying a great deal to you—and very eloquently —on the score of youth, temptation, and the like. I might point out, however, that the offence with which the prisoner is charged is one of the most serious known to our law; and there are certain features in this case, such as the suspicion which he allowed to rest on his innocent fellow clerk, and his relations with this married woman, which will render it difficult for you to attach too much importance to such pleading. I ask you, in short, for that verdict of guilty which, in the circumstances, I regard you as, unfortunately, bound to record.

*Letting his eyes travel from the* JUDGE *and the jury to* FROME, *he sits down.*

THE JUDGE. [*Bending a little towards the jury, and speaking in a businesslike voice*] Members of the jury, you have heard the evidence, and the comments on it. My only business is to make clear to you the issues you have to try. The facts are admitted, so far as the alteration of this cheque and counterfoil by the prisoner. The defence set up is that he was not in a responsible condition when he committed the crime. Well, you have heard the prisoner's story, and the evidence of the other witnesses—so far as it bears on the point of insanity. If you think that what you have heard establishes the fact that the prisoner was insane at the time of the forgery, you will find him guilty but insane. If, on the other hand, you conclude from what you have seen and heard that the prisoner was sane—and nothing short of insanity will count—you will find him guilty. In reviewing the testimony as to his mental condition you must bear in mind very carefully the evidence as to his demeanour and conduct both before and after the act of forgery— the evidence of the prisoner himself, of the woman, of the witness—er—Cokeson, and—er—of the cashier. And in regard to that I especially direct your attention to the prisoner's admission that the idea of adding the t y and the nought did come into his mind at the moment when the cheque was handed to him; and also to the alteration of the counterfoil, and to his subsequent conduct generally. The bearing of all this on the question of premeditation (and premeditation will imply sanity) is very obvious. You must not allow any considerations of age or tempta-

tion to weigh with you in the finding of your verdict. Before you can come to a verdict guilty but insane, you must be well and thoroughly convinced that the condition of his mind was such as would have qualified him at the moment for a lunatic asylum. [*He pauses; then, seeing that the jury are doubtful whether to retire or no, adds*] You may retire, if you wish to do so.

*The jury retire by a door behind the* JUDGE. *The* JUDGE *bends over his notes.* FALDER, *leaning from the dock speaks excitedly to his solicitor, pointing down at* RUTH. *The solicitor in turn speaks to* FROME.

FROME. [*Rising*] My lord. The prisoner is very anxious that I should ask you if your lordship would kindly request the reporters not to disclose the name of the woman witness in the Press reports of these proceedings. Your lordship will understand that the consequences might be extremely serious to her.

THE JUDGE. [*Pointedly—with the suspicion of a smile*] Well, Mr. Frome, you deliberately took this course which involved bringing her here.

FROME. [*With an ironic bow*] If your lordship thinks I could have brought out the full facts in any other way?

THE JUDGE. H'm! Well.

FROME. There is very real danger to her, your lordship.

THE JUDGE. You see, I have to take your word for all that.

FROME. If your lordship would be so kind. I can assure your lordship that I am not exaggerating.

THE JUDGE. It goes very much against the grain with me that the name of a witness should ever be suppressed. [*With a glance at* FALDER, *who is gripping and clasping his hands before him, and then at* RUTH, *who is sitting perfectly rigid with her eyes fixed on* FALDER] I'll consider your application. It must depend. I have to remember that she may have come here to commit perjury on the prisoner's behalf.

FROME. Your lordship, I really——

THE JUDGE. Yes, yes—I don't suggest anything of the sort, Mr. Frome. Leave it at that for the moment.

*As he finishes speaking, the jury return, and file back into the box.*

CLERK OF ASSIZE. Members of the jury, are you agreed on your verdict?

FOREMAN. We are.

CLERK OF ASSIZE. Is it Guilty, or Guilty, but insane?

FOREMAN. Guilty.

*The* JUDGE *nods; then, gathering up his notes, he looks at* FALDER, *who sits motionless.*

FROME. [*Rising*] If your lordship would allow me to address you in mitigation of sentence. I don't know if your lordship thinks I can add anything to what I have said to the jury on the score of the prisoner's youth, and the great stress under which he acted.

THE JUDGE. I don't think you can, Mr. Frome.

FROME. If your lordship says so—I do most earnestly beg your lordship to give the utmost weight to my plea.

[*He sits down.*

THE JUDGE. [*To the Clerk*] Call upon him.

THE CLERK. Prisoner at the bar, you stand convicted of felony. Have you anything to say for yourself why the Court should not give you judgment according to Law?

FALDER *shakes his head.*

THE JUDGE. William Falder, you have been given fair trial and found guilty, in my opinion rightly found guilty, of forgery. [*He pauses; then, consulting his notes, goes on*] The defence was set up that you were not responsible for your actions at the moment of committing this crime. There is no doubt, I think, that this was a device to bring out at first hand the nature of the temptation to which you

succumbed. For throughout the trial your counsel was in reality making an appeal for mercy. The setting up of this defence of course enabled him to put in some evidence that might weigh in that direction. Whether he was well advised to do so is another matter. He claimed that you should be treated rather as a patient than as a criminal. And this plea of his, which in the end amounted to a passionate appeal, he based in effect on an indictment of the march of Justice, which he practically accused of confirming and completing the process of criminality. Now, in considering how far I should allow weight to his appeal, I have a number of factors to take into account. I have to consider on the one hand the grave nature of your offence, the deliberate way in which you subsequently altered the counterfoil, the danger you caused to an innocent man—and that, to my mind, is a very grave point—and finally I have to consider the necessity of deterring others from following your example. On the other hand, I bear in mind that you are young, that you have hitherto borne a good character, that you were, if I am to believe your evidence and that of your witnesses, in a state of some emotional excitement when you committed this crime. I have every wish, consistently with my duty—not only to you, but to the community, to treat you with leniency. And this brings me to what are the determining factors in my mind in my consideration of your case. You are a clerk in a lawyer's office—that is a very serious aggravation in this case; no possible excuse can be made for you on the ground that you were not fully conversant with the nature of the crime you were committing and the penalties that attach to it. It is said, however, that you were carried away by your emotions. The story has been told here to-day of your relations with this—er—Mrs. Honeywill; on that story both the defence and the plea for mercy were in effect based. Now what is that story? It is that you, a young man, and she, a young woman unhappily married, had formed an attachment, which you both say—with what truth I am unable to gauge—had not yet resulted in immoral relations, but which you both admit was about to result in such relationship. Your counsel has made an attempt to palliate this, on the ground that the woman is in what he describes, I think, as "a hopeless position." As to that I can express no opinion. She is a married woman, and the fact is patent that you committed this crime with the view of furthering an immoral design. Now, however I might wish, I am not able to justify to my conscience a plea for mercy which has a basis inimical to morality. It is vitiated *ab initio*. Your counsel has made an attempt also to show that to punish you with further imprisonment would be unjust. I do not follow him in these flights. *The Law, is what it is*—a majestic edifice, sheltering all of us, each stone of which rests on another. I am concerned only with its administration. The crime you have committed is a very serious one. I cannot feel it in accordance with my duty to society to exercise the powers I have in your favour. You will go to penal servitude for three years.

FALDER, *who throughout the* JUDGE'S *speech has looked at him steadily, lets his head fall forward on his breast.* RUTH *starts up from her seat as he is taken out by the warders. There is a bustle in court.*

THE JUDGE. [*Speaking to the reporters*] Gentlemen of the Press, I think that the name of the female witness should not be reported.

*The reporters bow their acquiescence.*

THE JUDGE. [*To* RUTH, *who is staring in the direction in which* FALDER *has disappeared*] Do you understand, your name will not be mentioned?

COKESON. [*Pulling her sleeve*] The judge is speaking to you.

RUTH *turns, stares at the* JUDGE, *and turns away.*

THE JUDGE. I shall sit rather late today. Call the next case.

CLERK OF ASSIZE. [*To a warder*] Put up John Booley.

*To cries of* "Witnesses in the case of Booley."

*The curtain falls.*

## ACT III

### SCENE I

*A prison. A plainly furnished room, with two large barred windows, overlooking the prisoners' exercise yard, where men, in yellow clothes marked with arrows, and yellow brimless caps, are seen in single file at a distance of four yards from each other, walking rapidly on serpentine white lines traced on the concrete floor of the yard. Two warders in blue uniforms, with peaked caps and swords, are stationed amongst them. The room has distempered walls, a bookcase with numerous official-looking books, a cupboard between the windows, a plan of the prison on the wall, a writing-table covered with documents. It is Christmas Eve.*

*The* GOVERNOR, *a neat, grave-looking man, with a trim, fair moustache, the eyes of a theorist, and grizzled hair, receding from the temples, is standing close to this writing-table looking at a sort of rough saw made out of a piece of metal. The hand in which he holds it is gloved, for two fingers are missing. The chief warder,* WOODER, *a tall, thin, military-looking man of sixty, with grey moustache and melancholy, monkey-like eyes, stands very upright two paces from him.*

THE GOVERNOR. [*With a faint, distracted smile*] Queer-looking affair, Mr. Wooder! Where did you find it?

WOODER. In his mattress, sir. Haven't come across such a thing for two years now.

THE GOVERNOR. [*With curiosity*] Had he any set plan?

WOODER. He'd sawed his window-bar about that much.

[*He holds up his thumb and finger a quarter of an inch apart.*

THE GOVERNOR. I'll see him this afternoon. What's his name? Moaney! An old hand, I think?

WOODER. Yes, sir—four spell of penal. You'd think an old lag like him would have had more sense by now. [*With pitying contempt*] Occupied his mind, he said. Breaking in and breaking out— that's all they think about.

THE GOVERNOR. Who's next him?

WOODER. O'Cleary, sir.

THE GOVERNOR. The Irishman.

WOODER. Next him again there's that young fellow, Falder—star class—and next him old Clipton.

THE GOVERNOR. Ah, yes! "The philosopher." I want to see him about his eyes.

WOODER. Curious thing, sir: they seem to know when there's one of these tries at escape going on. It makes them restive—there's a regular wave going through them just now.

THE GOVERNOR. [*Meditatively*] Odd things—those waves. [*Turning to look at the prisoners exercising*] Seem quiet enough out here!

WOODER. That Irishman, O'Cleary, began banging on his door this morning. Little thing like that's quite enough to upset the whole lot. They're just like dumb animals at times.

THE GOVERNOR. I've seen it with horses before thunder—it'll run right through cavalry lines.

*The prison* CHAPLAIN *has entered. He is a dark-haired, ascetic man, in clerical undress, with a peculiarly steady, tight-lipped face and slow, cultured speech.*

THE GOVERNOR. [*Holding up the saw*] Seen this, Miller?

THE CHAPLAIN. Useful-looking specimen.

THE GOVERNOR. Do for the Museum, eh! [*He goes to the cupboard and opens it, displaying to view a number of quaint ropes, hooks, and metal tools with labels tied on them*] That'll do, thanks, Mr. Wooder.

WOODER. [*Saluting*] Thank you, sir.

[*He goes out.*

THE GOVERNOR. Account for the state of the men last day or two, Miller? Seems going through the whole place.

THE CHAPLAIN. No. I don't know of anything.

THE GOVERNOR. By the way, will you dine with us to-morrow?

THE CHAPLAIN. Christmas Day? Thanks very much.

THE GOVERNOR. Worries me to feel the men discontented. [*Gazing at the saw*] Have to punish this poor devil. Can't help liking a man who tries to escape.

[*He places the saw in his pocket and locks the cupboard again.*

THE CHAPLAIN. Extraordinary perverted will-power—some of them. Nothing to be done till it's broken.

THE GOVERNOR. And not much afterwards, I'm afraid. Ground too hard for golf?

WOODER *comes in again.*

WOODER. Visitor to speak to you, sir. I told him it wasn't usual.

THE GOVERNOR. What about?

WOODER. Shall I put him off, sir?

THE GOVERNOR. [*Resignedly*] No, no. Let's see him. Don't go, Miller.

WOODER *motions to some one without, and as the visitor comes in withdraws.*

*The visitor is* COKESON, *who is attired in a thick overcoat to the knees, woollen gloves, and carries a top hat.*

COKESON. I'm sorry to trouble you.

But it's about a young man you've got here.

THE GOVERNOR. We have a good many.

COKESON. Name of Falder, forgery. [*Producing a card, and handing it to the* GOVERNOR] Firm of James and Walter How. Well known in the law.

THE GOVERNOR. [*Receiving the card —with a faint smile*] What do you want to see me about, sir?

COKESON. [*Suddenly seeing the prisoners at exercise*] Why! what a sight!

THE GOVERNOR. Yes, we have that privilege from here; my office is being done up. [*Sitting down at his table*] Now, please!

COKESON. [*Dragging his eyes with difficulty from the window*] I *wanted* to say a word to you; I shan't keep you long. [*Confidentially*] Fact is, I oughtn't to be here by rights. His sister came to me— he's got no father and mother—and she was in some distress. "My husband won't let me go and see him," she said; "says he's disgraced the family. And his other sister," she said, "is an invalid." And she asked me to come. Well, I take an interest in him. He was our junior—I go to the same chapel—and I didn't like to refuse.

THE GOVERNOR. I'm afraid he's not allowed a visitor yet—he's only here for his one month's separate confinement.

COKESON. You see I saw him while he was shut up waiting for his trial and he was lonely.

THE GOVERNOR. [*With faint amusement*] Ring the bell—would you, Miller. [*To* COKESON] You'd like to hear what the doctor says about him, perhaps.

THE CHAPLAIN. [*Ringing the bell*] You are not accustomed to prisons, it would seem, sir.

COKESON. No. But it's a pitiful sight. He's quite a young fellow. I said to him: "Be patient," I said. "Patient!" he said. "A day," he said, "shut up in your cell

thinking and brooding as I do, it's longer than a year outside. I can't help it," he said, "I try—but I'm built that way, Mr. Cokeson." And he held his hand up to his face. I could see the tears trickling through his fingers. It wasn't nice.

THE CHAPLAIN. He's a young man with rather peculiar eyes, isn't he? Not Church of England, I think?

COKESON. No.

THE CHAPLAIN. I know.

THE GOVERNOR. [*To* WOODER, *who has come in*] Ask the doctor to be good enough to come here for a minute.

WOODER *salutes, and goes out.*

THE GOVERNOR. Let's see, he's not married?

COKESON. No. [*Confidentially*] But there's a party he's very much attached to, not altogether com-il-fo. It's a sad story.

THE CHAPLAIN. If it wasn't for drink and women, sir, this prison might be closed.

COKESON. [*Looking at the* CHAPLAIN *over his spectacles*] Ye-es, but I wanted to tell you about that, special. It preys on his mind.

THE GOVERNOR. Well!

COKESON. Like this. The woman had a nahsty, spiteful feller for a husband, and she'd left him. Fact is, she was going away with our young friend. It's not nice —but I've looked over it. Well, after the trial she said she'd earn her living apart, and wait for him to come out. That was a great consolation to him. But after a month she came to me—I *don't* know her personally—and she said: "I can't earn the children's living, let alone my own— I've got no friends. I'm obliged to keep out of everybody's way, else my husband'd get to know where I was. I'm very much reduced," she said. And she has lost flesh. "I'll have to go to the workhouse!" It's a painful story. I said to her: "No," I said, "not that! I've got a wife an' family, but sooner than you should do that I'll spare you a little myself." "Really," she said—she's a nice creature—"I don't like to take it from you. I think I'd better go back to my husband." Well, I know he's a nahsty, spiteful feller—drinks—but I didn't like to persuade her not to.

THE CHAPLAIN. Surely—no.

COKESON. Ye-es, but I'm sorry now. He's got his three years to serve. I *want* things to be pleasant for him.

THE CHAPLAIN. [*With a touch of impatience*] The Law hardly shares your view, I'm afraid.

COKESON. He's all alone there by himself. I'm afraid it'll turn him silly. And nobody wants that, I s'pose. He cried when I saw him. I don't like to see a man cry.

THE CHAPLAIN. It's a very rare thing for them to give way like that.

COKESON. [*Looking at him—in a tone of sudden dogged hostility*] I keep dogs.

THE CHAPLAIN. Indeed?

COKESON. Ye-es. And I say this: I wouldn't shut one of them up all by himself, week after week, not if he'd bit me all over.

THE CHAPLAIN. Unfortunately, the criminal is not a dog; he has a sense of right and wrong.

COKESON. But that's not the way to make him feel it.

THE CHAPLAIN. Ah! there I'm afraid we must differ.

COKESON. It's the same with dogs. If you treat 'em with kindness they'll do anything for you; but to shut 'em up alone, it only makes 'em savage.

THE CHAPLAIN. Surely you should allow those who have had a little more experience than yourself to know what is best for prisoners.

COKESON. [*Doggedly*] I know this young feller, I've watched him for years. He's eurotic— got no stamina. His father died of consumption. I'm thinking of his future. If he's to be kept there shut up by

himself, without a cat to keep him company, it'll do him harm. I said to him: "Where do you feel it?" "I can't tell you, Mr. Cokeson," he said, "but sometimes I could beat my head against the wall." It's not nice.

*During this speech the* DOCTOR *has entered. He is a medium-sized, rather good-looking man, with a quick eye. He stands leaning against the window.*

THE GOVERNOR. This gentleman thinks the separate is telling on Q 3007—Falder, young thin fellow, star class. What do you say, Doctor Clements?

THE DOCTOR. He doesn't like it, but it's not doing him any harm, it's only a month.

COKESON. But he was weeks before he came in here.

THE DOCTOR. We can always tell. He's lost no weight since he's been here.

COKESON. It's his state of mind I'm speaking of.

THE DOCTOR. His mind's all right so far. He's nervous, rather melancholy. I don't see signs of anything more. I'm watching him carefully.

COKESON. [*Nonplussed*] I'm glad to hear you say that.

THE CHAPLAIN. [*More suavely*] It's just at this period that we are able to make some impression on them, sir. I am speaking from my special standpoint.

COKESON. [*Turning bewildered to the* GOVERNOR] I *don't* want to be unpleasant, but I do feel it's awkward.

THE GOVERNOR. I'll make a point of seeing him to-day.

COKESON. I'm much obliged to you. I thought perhaps seeing him every day you wouldn't notice it.

THE GOVERNOR. [*Rather sharply*] If any sign of injury to his health shows itself his case will be reported at once. That's fully provided for.

[*He rises.*

COKESON. [*Following his own thoughts*] Of course; what you don't see

[ 325 ]

doesn't trouble you; but I don't want to have him on my mind.

THE GOVERNOR. I think you may safely leave it to us, sir.

COKESON. [*Mollified and apologetic*] I thought you'd understand me. I'm a plain man—never set myself up against authority. [*Expanding to the* CHAPLAIN] Nothing personal meant. Good-morning.

*As he goes out the three officials do not look at each other, but their faces wear peculiar expressions.*

THE CHAPLAIN. Our friend seems to think that prison is a hospital.

COKESON. [*Returning suddenly with an apologetic air*] There's just one little thing. This woman—I suppose I mustn't ask you to let him see her. It'd be a rare treat for them both. He'll be thinking about her all the time. Of course she's not his wife. But he's quite safe in here. They're a pitiful couple. You couldn't make an exception?

THE GOVERNOR. [*Wearily*] As you say, my dear sir, I couldn't make an exception; he won't be allowed a visit till he goes to a convict prison.

COKESON. I see. [*Rather coldly*] Sorry to have troubled you.

[*He again goes out.*

THE CHAPLAIN. [*Shrugging his shoulders*] The plain man indeed, poor fellow. Come and have some lunch, Clements?

[*He and the* DOCTOR *go out talking.*

*The* GOVERNOR, *with a sigh, sits down at his table and takes up a pen.*

*The curtain falls.*

## SCENE II

*Part of the ground corridor of the prison. The walls are coloured with greenish distemper up to a stripe of deeper green about the height of a man's shoulder, and above this line are whitewashed. The floor is of blackened stones. Daylight is filtering through a heavily barred window at the end. The doors of four*

*cells are visible. Each cell has a little round peephole at the level of a man's eye, covered by a little round disc, which, raised upwards, affords a view of the cell. On the wall, close to each cell door, hangs a little square board with the prisoner's name, number, and record.*

*Overhead can be seen the iron structures of the first-floor and second-floor corridors.*

*The* WARDER INSTRUCTOR, *a bearded man in blue uniform, with an apron, and some dangling keys, is just emerging from one of the cells.*

INSTRUCTOR. [*Speaking from the door into the cell*] I'll have another bit for you when that's finished.

O'CLEARY. [*Unseen—in an Irish voice*] Little doubt o' that, sirr.

INSTRUCTOR. [*Gossiping*] Well, you'd rather have it than nothing, I s'pose.

O'CLEARY. An' that's the blessed truth.

*Sounds are heard of a cell door being closed and locked, and of approaching footsteps.*

INSTRUCTOR. [*In a sharp, changed voice*] Look alive over it!

*He shuts the cell door, and stands at attention. The* GOVERNOR *comes walking down the corridor, followed by* WOODER.

THE GOVERNOR. Anything to report?

INSTRUCTOR. [*Saluting*] Q 3007 [*he points to a cell*] is behind with his work, sir. He'll lose marks to-day.

*The* GOVERNOR *nods and passes on to the end cell. The* INSTRUCTOR *goes away.*

THE GOVERNOR. This is our maker of saws, isn't it?

*He takes the saw from his pocket as* WOODER *throws open the door of the cell. The convict* MOANEY *is seen lying on his bed, athwart the cell, with his cap on. He springs up and stands in the middle of the cell. He is a raw-boned fellow, about fifty-six years old, with outstanding bat's ears and fierce, staring, steel-coloured eyes.*

WOODER. Cap off!

MOANEY *removes his cap.*

WOODER. Out here!

MOANEY *comes to the door.*

THE GOVERNOR. [*Beckoning him out into the corridor, and holding up the saw—with the manner of an officer speaking to a private*] Anything to say about this, my man?

MOANEY *is silent.*

THE GOVERNOR. Come!

MOANEY. It passed the time.

THE GOVERNOR. [*Pointing into the cell*] Not enough to do, eh?

MOANEY. It don't occupy your mind.

THE GOVERNOR. [*Tapping the saw*] You might find a better way than this.

MOANEY. [*Sullenly*] Well! What way? I must keep my hand in against the time I get out. What's the good of anything else to me at my time of life? [*With a gradual change to civility, as his tongue warms*] Ye know that, sir. I'll be in again within a year or two, after I've done this lot. I don't want to disgrace meself when I'm out. *You've* got your pride keeping the prison smart; well, I've got mine. [*Seeing that the* GOVERNOR *is listening with interest, he goes on, pointing to the saw*] *I must* be doin' a little o' this. It's no harm to any one. I was five weeks makin' that saw—a bit of all right it is, too; now I'll get cells, I suppose, or seven days' bread and water. You can't help it, sir, I know that—I quite put meself in your place.

THE GOVERNOR. Now, look here, Moaney, if I pass it over will you give me your word not to try it on again? Think!

*He goes into the cell, walks to the end of it, mounts the stool, and tries the window-bars.*

THE GOVERNOR. [*Returning*] Well?

MOANEY. [*Who has been reflecting*] I've got another six weeks to do in here, alone. I can't do it and think o' nothing. I must have something to interest me. You've made me a sporting offer, sir, but I can't pass my word about it. I shouldn't like to deceive a gentleman. [*Pointing into the cell*] Another four hours' steady work would have done it.

THE GOVERNOR. Yes, and what then? Caught, brought back, punishment. Five weeks' hard work to make this, and cells at the end of it, while they put a new bar to your window. Is it worth it, Moaney?

MOANEY. [*With a sort of fierceness*] Yes, it is.

THE GOVERNOR. [*Putting his hand to his brow*] Oh, well! Two days' cells—bread and water.

MOANEY. Thank 'e, sir.

[*He turns quickly like an animal and slips into his cell.*

*The* GOVERNOR *looks after him and shakes his head as* WOODER *closes and locks the cell door.*

THE GOVERNOR. Open Clipton's cell.

WOODER *opens the door of* CLIPTON'S *cell.* CLIPTON *is sitting on a stool just inside the door, at work on a pair of trousers. He is a small, thick, oldish man, with an almost shaven head, and smouldering little dark eyes behind smoked spectacles. He gets up and stands motionless in the doorway, peering at his visitors.*

THE GOVERNOR. [*Beckoning*] Come out here a minute, Clipton.

CLIPTON, *with a sort of dreadful quietness, comes into the corridor, the needle and thread in his hand. The* GOVERNOR *signs to* WOODER, *who goes into the cell and inspects it carefully.*

THE GOVERNOR. How are your eyes?

CLIPTON. I don't complain of them. I don't see the sun here. [*He makes a stealthy movement, protruding his neck a little*] There's just one thing, Mr. Governor, as you're speaking to me. I wish you'd ask the cove next door here to keep a bit quieter.

THE GOVERNOR. What's the matter? I don't want any tales, Clipton.

CLIPTON. He keeps me awake. I don't know who he is. [*With contempt*] One of this *star* class, I expect. Oughtn't to be here with *us*.

THE GOVERNOR. [*Quietly*] Quite right, Clipton. He'll be moved when there's a cell vacant.

CLIPTON. He knocks about like a wild beast in the early morning. I'm not used to it—stops me getting my sleep out. In the evening too. It's not fair, Mr. Governor, as you're speaking to me. Sleep's the comfort I've got here; I'm entitled to take it out full.

WOODER *comes out of the cell, and instantly, as though extinguished,* CLIPTON *moves with stealthy suddenness back into his cell.*

WOODER. All right, sir.

*The* GOVERNOR *nods. The door is closed and locked.*

THE GOVERNOR. Which is the man who banged on his door this morning?

WOODER. [*Going towards* O'CLEARY'S *cell*] This one, sir; O'Cleary.

[*He lifts the disc and glances through the peep-hole.*

THE GOVERNOR. Open.

WOODER *throws open the door.* O'CLEARY, *who is seated at a little table by the door as if listening, springs up and stands at attention just inside the doorway. He is a broadfaced, middle-aged man, with a wide, thin, flexible mouth, and little holes under his high cheekbones.*

THE GOVERNOR. Where's the joke, O'Cleary?

O'CLEARY. The joke, your honour? I've not seen one for a long time.

THE GOVERNOR. Banging on your door?

O'CLEARY. Oh! that!

THE GOVERNOR. It's womanish.

O'CLEARY. An' it's that I'm becoming this two months past.

THE GOVERNOR. Anything to complain of?

O'CLEARY. No, sirr.

THE GOVERNOR. You're an old hand; you ought to know better.

O'CLEARY. Yes, I've been through it all.

THE GOVERNOR. You've got a youngster next door; you'll upset him.

O'CLEARY. It cam' over me, your honour. I can't always be the same steady man.

THE GOVERNOR. Work all right?

O'CLEARY. [*Taking up a rush mat he is making*] Oh! I can do it on me head. It's the miserablest stuff—don't take the brains of a mouse. [*Working his mouth*] It's here I feel it—the want of a little noise—a terrible little wud aise me.

THE GOVERNOR. You know as well as I do that if you were out in the shops you wouldn't be allowed to talk.

O'CLEARY. [*With a look of profound meaning*] Not with my mouth.

THE GOVERNOR. Well, then?

O'CLEARY. But it's the great conversation I'd be havin'.

THE GOVERNOR. [*With a smile*] Well, no more conversation on your door.

O'CLEARY. No, sir, I wud not have the little wit to repate meself.

THE GOVERNOR. [*Turning*] Good-night.

O'CLEARY. Good-night, your honour.

[*He turns into his cell. The* GOVERNOR *shuts the door.*

THE GOVERNOR. [*Looking at the record card*] Can't help liking the poor blackguard.

WOODER. He's an amiable man, sir.

THE GOVERNOR. [*Pointing down the corridor*] Ask the doctor to come here, Mr. Wooder.

WOODER *salutes and goes away down the corridor.*

*The* GOVERNOR *goes to the door of* FALDER'S *cell. He raises his uninjured hand to uncover the peephole; but, without uncovering it, shakes his head and drops his hand; then, after scrutinising the record board, he opens the cell door.*

FALDER, *who is standing against it, lurches forward, with a gasp.*

THE GOVERNOR. [*Beckoning him out*] Now tell me: can't you settle down, Falder?

FALDER. [*In a breathless voice*] Yes, sir.

THE GOVERNOR. You know what I mean? It's no good running your head against a stone wall, is it?

FALDER. No, sir.

THE GOVERNOR. Well, come.

FALDER. I try, sir.

THE GOVERNOR. Can't you sleep?

FALDER. Very little. Between two o'clock and getting up's the worst time.

THE GOVERNOR. How's that?

FALDER. [*His lips twitch with a sort of smile*] I don't know, sir. I was always nervous. [*Suddenly voluble*] Everything seems to get such a size then. I feel I'll never get out as long as I live.

THE GOVERNOR. That's morbid, my lad. Pull yourself together.

FALDER. [*With an equally sudden dogged resentment*] Yes—I've got to——

THE GOVERNOR. Think of all these other fellows?

FALDER. They're used to it.

THE GOVERNOR. They all had to go through it once for the first time, just as you're doing now.

FALDER. Yes, sir, I shall get to be like them in time, I suppose.

THE GOVERNOR. [*Rather taken aback*] H'm! Well! That rests with you. Now, come. Set your mind to it, like a good fellow. You're still quite young. A man can make himself what he likes.

FALDER. [*Wistfully*] Yes, sir.

THE GOVERNOR. Take a good hold of yourself. Do you read?

FALDER. I don't take the words in. [*Hanging his head*] I know it's no good; but I can't help thinking of what's going on outside.

THE GOVERNOR. Private trouble?

FALDER. Yes.

THE GOVERNOR. You mustn't think about it.

FALDER. [*Looking back at his cell*] How can I help it, sir?

*He suddenly becomes motionless as* WOODER *and the* DOCTOR *approach. The* GOVERNOR *motions to him to go back into his cell.*

FALDER. [*Quick and low*] I'm quite right in my head, sir.

[*He goes back into his cell.*

THE GOVERNOR. [*To the Doctor*] Just go in and see him, Clements.

*The* DOCTOR *goes into the cell. The* GOVERNOR *pushes the door to, nearly closing it, and walks towards the window.*

WOODER. [*Following*] Sorry you should be troubled like this, sir. Very contented lot of men, on the whole.

THE GOVERNOR. [*Shortly*] You think so?

WOODER. Yes, sir. It's Christmas doing it, in my opinion.

THE GOVERNOR. [*To himself*] Queer, that!

WOODER. Beg, pardon, sir?

THE GOVERNOR. Christmas!

*He turns towards the window, leaving* WOODER *looking at him with a sort of pained anxiety.*

WOODER. [*Suddenly*] Do you think we make show enough sir? If you'd like us to have more holly?

THE GOVERNOR. Not at all, Mr. Wooder.

WOODER. Very good, sir.

*The* DOCTOR *has come out of* FALDER'S *cell, and the* GOVERNOR *beckons to him.*

THE GOVERNOR. Well?

THE DOCTOR. I can't make anything much of him. He's nervous, of course.

THE GOVERNOR. Is there any sort of case to report? Quite frankly, Doctor.

THE DOCTOR. Well, I don't think the separate's doing him any good; but then I could say the same of a lot of them—they'd get on better in the shops, there's no doubt.

THE GOVERNOR. You mean you'd have to recommend others?

THE DOCTOR. A dozen at least. It's on his nerves. There's nothing tangible. This fellow here [*pointing to* O'CLEARY'S *cell*], for instance—feels it just as much, in his way. If I once get away from physical facts—I shan't know where I am. Conscientiously, sir, I don't know how to differentiate him. He hasn't lost weight. Nothing wrong with his eyes. His pulse is good. Talks all right. It's only another week before he goes.

THE GOVERNOR. It doesn't amount to melancholia?

THE DOCTOR. [*Shaking his head*] I can report on him if you like; but if I do I ought to report on others.

THE GOVERNOR. I see. [*Looking towards* FALDER'S *cell*] The poor devil must just stick it then.

[*As he says this he looks absently at* WOODER.

WOODER. Beg pardon, sir?

*For answer the* GOVERNOR *stares at him, turns on his heel, and walks away.*

*There is a sound as of beating on metal.*

THE GOVERNOR. [*Stopping*] Mr. Wooder?

WOODER. Banging on his door, sir. I thought we should have more of that.

[*He hurries forward, passing the* GOVERNOR, *who follows slowly.*

*The curtain falls.*

## SCENE III

FALDER'S *cell, a whitewashed space thirteen feet broad by seven deep, and nine feet high, with a rounded ceiling. The floor is of shiny blackened bricks. The barred window, with a ventilator, is high up in the middle of end wall. In the centre of the opposite end wall is the* narrow door. In a corner are the mattress and bedding rolled up (*two blankets, two sheets, and a coverlet*). Above them is a quarter-circular wooden shelf, on which is a Bible and several little devotional books, piled in a symmetrical pyramid; there are also a black hairbrush, toothbrush, and a bit of soap. In another corner is the wooden frame of a bed, standing on end. There is a dark ventilator under the window, and another over the door. FALDER'S *work (a shirt to which he is putting buttonholes) is hung to a nail on the wall over a small wooden table, on which the novel "Lorna Doone" lies open. Low down in the corner by the door is a thick glass screen, about a foot square, covering the gas-jet let into the wall. There is also a wooden stool, and a pair of shoes beneath it. Three bright round tins are set under the window.*

*In fast-failing daylight,* FALDER, *in his stockings, is seen standing motionless, with his head inclined towards the door, listening. He moves a little closer to the door, his stockinged feet making no noise. He stops at the door. He is trying harder and harder to hear something, any little thing that is going on outside. He springs suddenly upright—as if at a sound—and remains perfectly motionless. Then, with a heavy sigh, he moves to his work, and stands looking at it, with his head down; he does a stitch or two, having the air of a man so lost in sadness that each stitch is, as it were, a coming to life. Then, turning abruptly, he begins pacing the cell, moving his head, like an animal pacing its cage. He stops again at the door, listens, and, placing the palms of his hands against it with his fingers spread out, leans his forehead against the iron. Turning from it presently, he moves slowly back towards the window, tracing his way with his finger along the top line of the distemper that runs round the walls. He stops under the window, and, picking up the lid of one of the tins, peers*

into it, as if trying to make a companion of his own face. It has grown very nearly dark. Suddenly the lid falls out of his hand with a clatter—the only sound that has broken the silence—and he stands staring intently at the wall where the stuff of the shirt is hanging rather white in the darkness—he seems to be seeing somebody or something there. There is a sharp tap and click; the cell light behind the glass screen has been turned up. The cell is brightly lighted. FALDER is seen gasping for breath.

A sound from far away, as of distant, dull beating on thick metal, is suddenly audible. FALDER shrinks back, not able to bear this sudden clamour. But the sound grows, as though some great tumbril were rolling towards the cell. And gradually it seems to hypnotize him. He begins creeping inch by inch nearer to the door. The banging sound, travelling from cell to cell, draws closer and closer; FALDER'S hands are seen moving as if his spirit had already joined in this beating, and the sound swells till it seems to have entered the very cell. He suddenly raises his clenched fists. Panting violently, he flings himself at his door, and beats on it.

The curtain falls.


## ACT IV

The scene is again COKESON'S room, at a few minutes to ten of a March morning, two years later. The doors are all open. SWEEDLE, now blessed with a sprouting moustache, is getting the offices ready. He arranges papers on COKESON'S table; then goes to a covered washstand, raises the lid, and looks at himself in the mirror. While he is gazing his fill RUTH HONEYWILL comes in through the outer office and stands in the doorway. There seems a kind of exultation and excitement behind her habitual impassivity.

SWEEDLE. [Suddenly seeing her, and dropping the lid of the washstand with a bang] Hello! It's you!

RUTH. Yes.

SWEEDLE. There's only me here! They don't waste their time hurrying down in the morning. Why, it must be two years since we had the pleasure of seeing you. [Nervously] What have you been doing with yourself?

RUTH. [Sardonically] Living.

SWEEDLE. [Impressed] If you want to see him [he points to COKESON'S chair], he'll be here directly—never misses—not much. [Delicately] I hope our friend's back from the country. His time's been up these three months, if I remember.

RUTH nods.

SWEEDLE. I was awful sorry about that. The governor made a mistake—if you ask me.

RUTH. He did.

SWEEDLE. He ought to have given him a chanst. And, I say, the judge ought to ha' let him go after that. They've forgot what human nature's like. Whereas we know.

RUTH gives him a honeyed smile.

SWEEDLE. They come down on you like a cartload of bricks, flatten you out, and when you don't swell up again they complain of it. I know 'em—seen a lot of that sort of thing in my time. [He shakes his head in the plenitude of wisdom] Why, only the other day the governor——

But COKESON has come in through the outer office; brisk with east wind, and decidedly greyer.

COKESON. [Drawing off his coat and gloves] Why! it's you! [Then motioning SWEEDLE out, and closing the door] Quite a stranger! Must be two years. D'you want to see me? I can give you a minute. Sit down! Family well?

RUTH. Yes. I'm not living where I was.

COKESON. [Eyeing her askance] I

hope things are more comfortable at home.

RUTH. I couldn't stay with Honeywill, after all.

COKESON. You haven't done anything rash, I hope. I should be sorry if you'd done anything rash.

RUTH. I've kept the children with me.

COKESON. [*Beginning to feel that things are not so jolly as he had hoped*] Well, I'm glad to have seen you. You've not heard from the young man, I suppose, since he came out?

RUTH. Yes, I ran across him yesterday.

COKESON. I hope he's well.

RUTH. [*With sudden fierceness*] He can't get anything to do. It's dreadful to see him. He's just skin and bone.

COKESON. [*With genuine concern*] Dear me! I'm sorry to hear that. [*On his guard again*] Didn't they find him a place when his time was up?

RUTH. He was only there three weeks. It got out.

COKESON. I'm sure I don't know what I can do for you. I don't like to be snubby.

RUTH. I can't bear his being like that.

COKESON. [*Scanning her not unprosperous figure*] I know his relations aren't very forthy about him. Perhaps *you* can do something for him, till he finds his feet.

RUTH. Not now. I could have—but not *now*.

COKESON. I don't understand.

RUTH. [*Proudly*] I've seen *him* again —that's all over.

COKESON. [*Staring at her—disturbed*] I'm a family man—I don't want to hear anything unpleasant. Excuse me—I'm very busy.

RUTH. I'd have gone home to my people in the country long ago, but they've never got over me marrying Honeywill. I never was waywise, Mr. Cokeson, but I'm proud. I was only a girl,

you see, when I married him. I thought the world of him, of course . . . he used to come travelling to our farm.

COKESON. [*Regretfully*] I did hope you'd have got on better, after you saw me.

RUTH. He used me worse than ever. He couldn't break my nerve, but I lost my health; and then he began knocking the children about. . . . I couldn't stand that. I wouldn't go back now, if he were dying.

COKESON. [*Who has risen and is shifting about as though dodging a stream of lava*] We mustn't be violent, must we?

RUTH. [*Smouldering*] A man that can't behave better than that——

*There is silence.*

COKESON. [*Fascinated in spite of himself*] Then there you were! And what did you do then?

RUTH. [*With a shrug*] Tried the same as when I left him before . . . making skirts . . . cheap things. It was the best I could get, but I never made more than ten shillings a week, buying my own cotton and working all day; I hardly ever got to bed till past twelve. I kept at it for nine months. [*Fiercely*] Well, I'm not fit for that; I wasn't made for it. I'd rather die.

COKESON. My dear woman! We musn't talk like that.

RUTH. It was starvation for the children too—after what they'd always had. I soon got not to care. I used to be too tired.

[*She is silent.*

COKESON. [*With fearful curiosity*] And —what happened then?

RUTH. [*With a laugh*] My employer happened then—he's happened ever since.

COKESON. Dear! Oh Dear! I never came across a thing like this.

RUTH. [*Dully*] He's treated me all right. But I've done with that. [*Suddenly her lips begin to quiver, and she hides them with the back of her hand*] I never thought I'd see *him* again, you see. It was just a chance I met him by Hyde Park. We went in there and sat down, and he told me all about himself. Oh! Mr. Cokeson, give him another chance.

COKESON. [*Greatly disturbed*] Then you've both lost your livings! What a horrible position!

RUTH. If he could only get here—where there's nothing to find out about him!

COKESON. We can't have anything derogatory to the firm.

RUTH. I've no one else to go to.

COKESON. I'll speak to the partners, but I don't think they'll take him, under the circumstances. I don't really.

RUTH. He came with me; he's down there in the street.

[*She points to the window.*]

COKESON. [*On his dignity*] He shouldn't have done that until he's sent for. [*Then softening at the look on her face*] We've got a vacancy, as it happens, but I can't promise anything.

RUTH. It would be the saving of him.

COKESON. Well, I'll do what I can, but I'm not sanguine. Now tell him that I don't want him here till I see how things are. Leave your address? [*Repeating her*] 83 Mullingar Street? [*He notes it on blotting-paper*] Good-morning.

RUTH. Thank you.

*She moves towards the door, turns as if to speak, but does not, and goes away.*

COKESON. [*Wiping his head and forehead with a large white cotton handkerchief*] What a business!

*Then, looking amongst his papers, he sounds his bell.* SWEEDLE *answers it.*

COKESON. Was that young Richards coming here to-day after the clerk's place?

SWEEDLE. Yes.

COKESON. Well, keep him in the air; I don't want to see him yet.

SWEEDLE. What shall I tell him, sir?

COKESON. [*With asperity*] Invent some-thing. Use your brains. Don't stump him off altogether.

SWEEDLE. Shall I tell him that we've got illness, sir?

COKESON. No! Nothing untrue. Say I'm not here to-day.

SWEEDLE. Yes, sir. Keep him hankering?

COKESON. Exactly. And look here. You remember Falder? I may be having him round to see me. Now, treat him like you'd have him treat you in a similar position.

SWEEDLE. I naturally should do.

COKESON. That's right. When a man's down never hit 'im. 'Tisn't necessary. Give him a hand up. That's a metaphor I recommend to you in life. It's sound policy.

SWEEDLE. Do you think the governors will take him on again, sir?

COKESON. Can't say anything about that. [*At the sound of some one having entered the outer office*] Who's there?

SWEEDLE. [*Going to the door and looking*] It's Falder, sir.

COKESON. [*Vexed*] Dear me! That's very naughty of her. Tell him to call again. I don't want—

*He breaks off as* FALDER *comes in.* FALDER *is thin, pale, older, his eyes have grown more restless. His clothes are very worn and loose.*

SWEEDLE, *nodding cheerfully, withdraws.*

COKESON. Glad to see you. You're rather previous. [*Trying to keep things pleasant*] Shake hands! She's striking while the iron's hot. [*He wipes his forehead*] I don't blame her. She's anxious.

FALDER *timidly takes* COKESON'S *hand and glances towards the partners' door.*

COKESON. No—not yet! Sit down!

FALDER *sits in the chair at the side of* COKESON'S *table, on which he places his cap.*

COKESON. Now you are here I'd like

you to give me a little account of your-self. [*Looking at him over his spectacles*] How's your health?

FALDER. I'm alive, Mr. Cokeson.

COKESON. [*Preoccupied*] I'm glad to hear that. About this matter. I don't like doing anything out of the ordinary; it's not my habit. I'm a plain man, and I want everything smooth and straight. But I promised your friend to speak to the partners, and I always keep my word.

FALDER. I just want a chance, Mr. Cokeson. I've paid for that job a thou-sand times and more. I have, sir. No one knows. They say I weighed more when I came out than when I went in. They couldn't weigh me here [*he touches his head*] or here [*he touches his heart, and gives a sort of laugh*]. Till last night I'd have thought there was nothing in here at all.

COKESON. [*Concerned*] You've not got heart disease?

FALDER. Oh! they passed me sound enough.

COKESON. But they got you a place, didn't they?

FALDER. Yes; very good people, knew all about it—very kind to me. I thought I was going to get on first rate. But one day, all of a sudden, the other clerks got wind of it. . . . I couldn't stick it, Mr. Cokeson, I couldn't, sir.

COKESON. Easy, my dear fellow, easy.

FALDER. I had one small job after that, but it didn't last.

COKESON. How was that?

FALDER. It's no good deceiving you, Mr. Cokeson. The fact is, I seem to be struggling against a thing that's all round me. I can't explain it. It's as if I was in a net; as fast as I cut it here, it grows up there. I didn't act as I ought to have, about references; but what are you to do? You must have them. And that made me afraid, and I left. In fact, I'm—I'm afraid all the time now.

[*He bows his head and leans deject-edly silent over the table.*

COKESON. I feel for you—I do really. Aren't your sisters going to do anything for you?

FALDER. One's in consumption. And the other——

COKESON. Ye . . . es. She told me her husband wasn't quite pleased with you.

FALDER. When I went there—they were at supper—my sister wanted to give me a kiss—I know. But he just looked at her, and said: "What have you come for?" Well, I pocketed my pride and I said: "Aren't you going to give me your hand, Jim? Cis is, I know," I said. "Look here!" he said, "that's all very well, but we'd better come to an understanding. I've been expecting you, and I've made up my mind. I'll give you twenty-five pounds to go to Canada with." "I see," I said—"good riddance! No, thanks; keep your twenty-five pounds." Friendship's a queer thing when you've been where I have.

COKESON. I understand. Will you take the twenty-five pounds from me? [*Flus-tered, as* FALDER *regards him with a queer smile*] Quite without prejudice; I meant it kindly.

FALDER. They wouldn't let me in.

COKESON. Oh! Ah! No! You aren't looking the thing.

FALDER. I've slept in the Park three nights this week. The dawns aren't all poetry there. But meeting her—I feel a different man this morning. I've often thought the being fond of her's the best thing about me; it's sacred, somehow—and yet it did for me. That's queer, isn't it?

COKESON. I'm sure we're all very sorry for you.

FALDER. That's what I've found, Mr. Cokeson. Awfully sorry for me. [*With quiet bitterness*] But it doesn't do to as-sociate with criminals!

COKESON. Come, come, it's no use calling yourself names. That never did a man any good. Put a face on it.

FALDER. It's easy enough to put a face on it, sir, when you're independent. Try it when you're down like me. They talk about giving you your deserts. Well, I think I've had just a bit over.

COKESON. [*Eyeing him askance over his spectacles*] I hope they haven't made a Socialist of you.

FALDER *is suddenly still, as if brooding over his past self; he utters a peculiar laugh.*

COKESON. You must give them credit for the best intentions. Really you must. Nobody wishes you harm, I'm sure.

FALDER. I believe that, Mr. Cokeson. Nobody wishes you harm, but they down you all the same. This feeling—— [*He stares round him, as though at something closing in*] It's crushing me. [*With sudden impersonality*] I know it is.

COKESON. [*Horribly disturbed*] There's nothing there! We must try and take it quiet. I'm sure I've often had you in my prayers. Now leave it to me. I'll use my gumption and take 'em when they're jolly.

[*As he speaks the two partners come in.*

COKESON. [*Rather disconcerted, but trying to put them all at ease*] I didn't expect you quite so soon. I've just been having a talk with this young man. I think you'll remember him.

JAMES. [*With a grave, keen look*] Quite well. How are you, Falder?

WALTER. [*Holding out his hand almost timidly*] Very glad to see you again, Falder.

FALDER. [*Who has recovered his self-control, takes the hand*] Thank you, sir.

COKESON. Just a word, Mr. James. [*To* FALDER, *pointing to the clerks' office*] You might go in there a minute. You know your way. Our junior won't be coming this morning. His wife's just had a little family.

FALDER *goes uncertainly out into the clerks' office.*

COKESON. [*Confidentially*] I'm bound to tell you all about it. He's quite penitent. But there's a prejudice against him. And you're not seeing him to advantage this morning; he's under-nourished. It's very trying to go without your dinner.

JAMES. Is that so, Cokeson?

COKESON. I wanted to ask you. He's had his lesson. Now *we* know all about him, and we want a clerk. There is a young fellow applying, but I'm keeping him in the air.

JAMES. A gaol-bird in the office, Cokeson? I don't see it.

WALTER. "The rolling of the chariot-wheels of Justice!" I've never got that out of my head.

JAMES. I've nothing to reproach myself with in this affair. What's he been doing since he came out?

COKESON. He's had one or two places, but he hasn't kept them. He's sensitive—quite natural. Seems to fancy everybody's down on him.

JAMES. Bad sign. Don't like the fellow—never did from the first. "Weak character" 's written all over him.

WALTER. I think we owe him a leg up.

JAMES. He brought it all on himself.

WALTER. The doctrine of full responsibility doesn't quite hold in these days.

JAMES. [*Rather grimly*] You'll find it safer to hold it for all that, my boy.

WALTER. For oneself, yes—not for other people, thanks.

JAMES. Well! I don't want to be hard.

COKESON. I'm glad to hear you say that. He seems to see something [*spreading his arms*] round him. 'Tisn't healthy.

JAMES. What about that woman he was mixed up with? I saw some one uncommonly like her outside as we came in.

COKESON. *That!* Well, I can't keep anything from you. He has met her.

[ 335 ]

JAMES. Is she with her husband?

COKESON. No.

JAMES. Falder living with her, I suppose?

COKESON. [*Desperately trying to retain the new-found jollity*] I don't know that of my own knowledge. 'Tisn't my business.

JAMES. It's *our* business, if we're going to engage him, Cokeson.

COKESON. [*Reluctantly*] I ought to tell you, perhaps: I've had the party here this morning.

JAMES. I thought so. [*To* WALTER] No, my dear boy, it won't do. Too shady altogether!

COKESON. The two things together make it very awkward for you—I see that.

WALTER. [*Tentatively*] I don't quite know what we have to do with his private life.

JAMES. No, no! He must make a clean sheet of it, or he can't come here.

WALTER. Poor devil!

COKESON. Will you have him in? [*And as* JAMES *nods*] I think I can get him to see reason.

JAMES. [*Grimly*] You can leave that to me, Cokeson.

WALTER. [*To* JAMES, *in a low voice, while* COKESON *is summoning* FALDER] His whole future may depend on what we do, Dad.

FALDER *comes in. He has pulled himself together, and presents a steady front.*

JAMES. Now look here, Falder. My son and I want to give you another chance; but there are two things I must say to you. In the first place: It's no good coming here as a victim. If you've any notion that you've been unjustly treated —get rid of it. You can't play fast and loose with morality and hope to go scot-free. If society didn't take care of itself, nobody would—the sooner you realise that the better.

FALDER. Yes, sir; but—may I say something?

JAMES. Well?

FALDER. I had a lot of time to think it over in prison.

[*He stops.*

COKESON. [*Encouraging him*] I'm sure you did.

FALDER. There were all sorts there. And what I mean, sir, is, that if we'd been treated differently the first time, and put under somebody that could look after us a bit, and not put in prison, not a quarter of us would ever have got there.

JAMES. [*Shaking his head*] I'm afraid I've very grave doubts of that, Falder.

FALDER. [*With a gleam of malice*] Yes, sir, so I found.

JAMES. My good fellow, don't forget that you began it.

FALDER. I never wanted to do wrong.

JAMES. Perhaps not. But you did.

FALDER. [*With all the bitterness of his past suffering*] It's knocked me out of time. [*Pulling himself up*] That is, I mean, I'm not what I was.

JAMES. This isn't encouraging for us, Falder.

COKESON. He's putting it awkwardly, Mr. James.

FALDER. [*Throwing over his caution from the intensity of his feeling*] I mean it, Mr. Cokeson.

JAMES. Now, lay aside all those thoughts, Falder, and look to the future.

FALDER. [*Almost eagerly*] Yes sir, but you don't understand what prison is. It's here it gets you.

[*He grips his chest.*

COKESON. [*In a whisper to* JAMES] I told you he wanted nourishment.

WALTER. Yes, but, my dear fellow, that'll pass away. Time's merciful.

FALDER. [*With his face twitching*] I hope so, sir.

JAMES. [*Much more gently*] Now, my boy, what you've got to do is to put all the past behind you and build yourself up a steady reputation. And that brings me to the second thing. This woman you were mixed up with—you must give us your word, you know, to have done with that. There's no chance of your keeping straight if you're going to begin your future with such a relationship.

FALDER. [*Looking from one to the other with a hunted expression*] But sir . . . but sir . . . it's the one thing I looked forward to all that time. And she too . . . I couldn't find her before last night.

*During this and what follows* COKESON *becomes more and more uneasy.*

JAMES. This is painful, Falder. But you must see for yourself that it's impossible for a firm like this to close its eyes to everything. Give us this proof of your resolve to keep straight, and you can come back—not otherwise.

FALDER. [*After staring at* JAMES, *suddenly stiffens himself*] I couldn't give her up. I couldn't! Oh, sir. I'm all she's got to look to. And I'm sure she's all I've got.

JAMES. I'm very sorry, Falder, but I must be firm. It's for the benefit of you both in the long run. No good can come of this connection. It was the cause of all your disaster.

FALDER. But, sir, it means—having gone through all that—getting broken up —my nerves are in an awful state—for nothing. I did it for her.

JAMES. Come! If she's anything of a woman she'll see it for herself. She won't want to drag you down further. If there were a prospect of your being able to marry her—it might be another thing.

FALDER. It's not my fault, sir, that she couldn't get rid of him—she would have if she could. That's been the whole trouble from the beginning. [*Looking suddenly at* WALTER] . . . If anybody would help her! It's only money wanted now, I'm sure.

COKESON. [*Breaking in, as* WALTER *hesitates, and is about to speak*] I don't think we need consider that—it's rather far-fetched.

FALDER. [*To* WALTER, *appealing*] He must have given her full cause since; she could prove that he drove her to leave him.

WALTER. I'm inclined to do what you say, Falder, if it can be managed.

FALDER. Oh, sir!

[*He goes to the window and looks down into the street.*

COKESON. [*Hurriedly*] You don't take me, Mr. Walter. I have my reasons.

FALDER. [*From the window*] She's down there, sir. Will you see her? I can beckon to her from here.

WALTER *hesitates, and looks from* COKESON *to* JAMES.

JAMES. [*With a sharp nod*] Yes, let her come.

FALDER *beckons from the window.*

COKESON. [*In a low fluster to* JAMES *and* WALTER] No, Mr. James. She's not quite what she ought to ha' been, while this young man's been away. She's lost her chance. We can't consult how to swindle the Law.

FALDER *has come from the window. The three men look at him in a sort of awed silence.*

FALDER. [*With instinctive apprehension of some change—looking from one to the other*] There's been nothing between us, sir, to prevent it. . . . What I said at the trial was true. And last night we only just sat in the Park.

SWEEDLE *comes in from the outer office.*

COKESON. What is it?

SWEEDLE. Mrs. Honeywill.

*There is silence.*

JAMES. Show her in.

RUTH *comes slowly in, and stands stoically with* FALDER *on one side and the three men on the other. No one speaks.* COKESON *turns to his table, bending over his papers as though the burden of the*

*situation were forcing him back into his
accustomed groove.*

JAMES. [*Sharply*] Shut the door.

SWEEDLE *shuts the door.*

JAMES. We've asked you to come up
because there are certain facts to be faced
in this matter. I understand you have
only just met Falder again.

RUTH. Yes—only yesterday.

JAMES. He's told us about himself, and
we're very sorry for him. I've promised to
take him back here if he'll make a fresh
start. [*Looking steadily at* RUTH] This is
a matter that requires courage, ma'am.

RUTH, *who is looking at* FALDER, *begins to twist her hands in front of her as
though prescient of disaster.*

FALDER. Mr. Walter How is good
enough to say that he'll help us to get you
a divorce.

RUTH *flashes a startled glance at*
JAMES *and* WALTER.

JAMES. I don't think that's practicable,
Falder.

FALDER. But, sir——!

JAMES. [*Steadily*] Now, Mrs. Honeywill. You're fond of him.

RUTH. Yes, sir; I love him.

[*She looks miserably at* FALDER.

JAMES. Then you don't want to stand
in his way, do you?

RUTH. [*In a faint voice*] I could take
care of him.

JAMES. The best way you can take
care of him will be to give him up.

FALDER. Nothing shall make me give
you up. You can get a divorce. There's
been nothing between us, has there?

RUTH. [*Mournfully shaking her head
—without looking at him*] No.

FALDER. We'll keep apart till it's over,
sir; if you'll only help us—we promise.

JAMES. [*To* RUTH] You see the thing
plainly, don't you? You see what I mean?

RUTH. [*Just above a whisper*] Yes.

COKESON. [*To himself*] There's a dear
woman.

JAMES. The situation is impossible.

RUTH. Must I, sir?

JAMES. [*Forcing himself to look at
her*] I put it to you, ma'am. His future is
in your hands.

RUTH. [*Miserably*] I want to do the
best for him.

JAMES. [*A little huskily*] That's right,
that's right!

FALDER. I don't understand. You're
not going to give me up—after all this?
There's something—— [*Starting forward
to* JAMES] Sir, I swear solemnly there's
been nothing between us.

JAMES. I believe you, Falder. Come,
my lad, be as plucky as she is.

FALDER. Just now you were going to
help us. [*He stares at* RUTH, *who is
standing absolutely still; his face and
hands twitch and quiver as the truth
dawns on him*] What is it? You've not
been——

WALTER. Father!

JAMES. [*Hurriedly*] There, there! That'll
do, that'll do! I'll give you your chance,
Falder. Don't let me know what you do
with yourselves, that's all.

FALDER. [*As if he has not heard*]
Ruth?

RUTH *looks at him; and* FALDER *covers
his face with his hands. There is silence.*

COKESON. [*Suddenly*] There's some
one out there. [*To* RUTH] Go in here.
You'll feel better by yourself for a
minute.

*He points to the clerks' room and
moves towards the outer office.* FALDER
*does not move.* RUTH *puts out her hand
timidly. He shrinks back from the touch.
She turns and goes miserably into the
clerks' room. With a brusque movement
he follows, seizing her by the shoulder
just inside the doorway.* COKESON *shuts
the door.*

JAMES. [*Pointing to the outer office*]
Get rid of that, whoever it is.

SWEEDLE. [*Opening the office door, in
a scared voice*] Detective-Sergeant Wister.

*The detective enters, and closes the door behind him.*

WISTER. Sorry to disturb you, sir. A clerk you had here, two years and a half ago. I arrested him in this room.

JAMES. What about him?

WISTER. I thought perhaps I might get his whereabouts from you.

*There is an awkward silence.*

COKESON. [*Pleasantly, coming to the rescue*] We're not responsible for his movements; you know that.

JAMES. What do you want with him?

WISTER. He's failed to report himself lately.

WALTER. Has he to keep in touch with the police then?

WISTER. We're bound to know his whereabouts. I dare say we shouldn't interfere, sir, but we've just heard there's a serious matter of obtaining employment with a forged reference. What with the two things together—we must have him.

*Again there is silence.* WALTER *and* COKESON *steal glances at* JAMES, *who stands staring steadily at the detective.*

COKESON. [*Expansively*] We're very busy at the moment. If you could make it convenient to call again we might be able to tell you then.

JAMES. [*Decisively*] I'm a servant of the Law, but I dislike peaching. In fact, I can't do such a thing. If you want him you must find him without us.

*As he speaks his eye falls on* FALDER'S *cap, still lying on the table, and his face contracts.*

WISTER. [*Noting the gesture—quietly*] Very good, sir: I ought to warn you that sheltering——

JAMES. I shelter no one. But you mustn't come here and ask questions which it's not my business to answer.

WISTER. [*Dryly*] I won't trouble you further then, gentlemen.

COKESON. I'm sorry we couldn't give you the information. You quite understand, don't you? Good morning!

WISTER *turns to go, but instead of going to the door of the outer office he goes to the door of the clerks' room.*

COKESON. The other door . . . the other door!

WISTER *opens the clerks' door.* RUTH'S *voice is heard: "Oh, do!" and* FALDER'S: *"I can't!" There is a little pause; then, with sharp fright,* RUTH *says: "Who's that?"* WISTER *has gone in.*

*The three men look aghast at the door.*

WISTER. [*From within*] Keep back, please!

*He comes swiftly out with his arm twisted in* FALDER'S. *The latter gives a white, staring look at the three men.*

WALTER. Let him go this time, for God's sake!

WISTER. I couldn't take the responsibility, sir.

FALDER. [*With a queer, desperate laugh*] Good!

*Flinging a look back at* RUTH, *he throws up his head, and goes out through the outer office, half dragging* WISTER *after him.*

WALTER. [*With despair*] That finishes him. It'll go on for ever now.

SWEEDLE *can be seen staring through the outer door. There are sounds of footsteps descending the stone stairs; suddenly a dull thud, a faint "My God!" in* WISTER'S *voice.*

JAMES. What's that?

SWEEDLE *dashes forward. The door swings to behind him. There is dead silence.*

WALTER. [*Starting forward to the inner room*] The woman—she's fainting!

*He and* COKESON *support the fainting* RUTH *from the doorway of the clerks' room.*

COKESON. [*Distracted*] Here, my dear! There, there!

WALTER. Have you any brandy?

COKESON. I've got sherry.

WALTER. Get it, then. Quick!

[*He places* RUTH *in a chair—which* JAMES *has dragged forward.*

COKESON. [*With sherry*] Here! It's good strong sherry.

*They try to force the sherry between her lips.*

*There is the sound of feet, and they stop to listen. The outer door is reopened—*WISTER *and* SWEEDLE *are seen carrying some burden.*

JAMES. [*Hurrying forward*] What is it?

*They lay the burden down in the outer office, out of sight, and all but* RUTH *cluster round it, speaking in hushed voices.*

WISTER. He jumped—neck's broken.

WALTER. Good God!

WISTER. He must have been mad to think he could give me the slip like that. And what was it—just a few months!

WALTER. [*Bitterly*] Was that all?

JAMES. What a desperate thing! [*Then, in a voice unlike his own*] Run for a doctor—you!

SWEEDLE *rushes from the outer office.*

JAMES. An ambulance!

WISTER *goes out. On* RUTH'S *face an expression of fear and horror has been seen growing, as if she dared not turn towards the voices. She now rises and steals towards them.*

WALTER. [*Turning suddenly*] Look!

*The three men shrink back out of her way.*

RUTH *drops on her knees by the body.*

RUTH. [*In a whisper*] What is it? He's not breathing. [*She crouches over him*] My dear! My pretty!

*In the outer office doorway the figures of men are seen standing.*

RUTH. [*Leaping to her feet*] No, no! No, no! He's dead!

*The figures of the men shrink back.*

COKESON. [*Stealing forward. In a hoarse voice*] There, there, poor dear woman!

*At the sound behind her* RUTH *faces round at him.*

COKESON. No one'll touch him now! Never again! He's safe with gentle Jesus!

RUTH *stands as though turned to stone in the doorway staring at* COKESON, *who, bending humbly before her, holds out his hand as one would to a lost dog.*

*The curtain falls.*

# THE JURYMAN

## By JOHN GALSWORTHY

### I

"Don't you see, brother, I was reading yesterday the Gospel about Christ, the little Father; how He suffered, how He walked on the earth. I suppose you have heard about it?"

"Indeed, I have," replied Stepanuitch; "but we are people in darkness; we can't read."—TOLSTOI.

Mr. HENRY BOSENGATE, of the London Stock Exchange, seated himself in his car that morning during the Great War with a sense of injury. Major in a Volunteer Corps; member of all the local committees; lending this very car to the neighbouring hospital, at times even driving it himself for their benefit; subscribing to funds, so far as his diminished income permitted—he was conscious of being an asset to the country, and one whose time could not be wasted with impunity. To be summoned to sit on a jury at the local assizes, and not even the grand jury at that! It was in the nature of an outrage.

Strong and upright, with hazel eyes and dark eyebrows, pinkish-brown cheeks, a forehead white, well-shaped, and getting high, with greyish hair glossy and well-brushed, and a trim moustache, he might have been taken for that colonel of Volunteers which indeed he was in a fair way of becoming.

His wife had followed him out under the porch, and stood bracing her supple body clothed in lilac linen. Red rambler roses formed a sort of crown to her dark head; her ivory-coloured face had in it just a suggestion of the Japanese.

Mr. Bosengate spoke through the whirr of the engine:

"I don't expect to be late, dear. This business is ridiculous. There oughtn't to *be* any crime in these days."

His wife—her name was Kathleen—smiled. She looked very pretty and cool, Mr. Bosengate thought. To one bound on this dull and stuffy business everything he owned seemed pleasant—the geranium beds beside the gravel drive, his long, red-brick house mellowing decorously in its creepers and ivy, the little clock-tower over stables now converted to a garage, the dovecote, masking at the other end the conservatory which adjoined the billiard-room. Close to the red-brick lodge his two children, Kate and Harry, ran out from under the acacia trees, and waved to him, scrambling bare-legged on to the low, red, ivy-covered wall which guarded his domain of eleven acres. Mr. Bosengate waved back, thinking: 'Jolly couple—by Jove, they are!' Above their heads, through the trees, he could see right away to some Downs, faint in the July heat haze. And he thought: 'Pretty a spot as one could have got, so close to town!'

Despite the war he had enjoyed these last two years more than any of the ten since he built "Charmleigh" and settled down to semi-rural domesticity with his young wife. There had been a certain piquancy, a savour added to existence, by the country's peril, and all the public service and sacrifice it demanded. His chauffeur was gone, and one gardener did the work of three. He enjoyed—positively enjoyed—his committee work; even the serious decline of business and increase of taxation had not much worried one continually conscious of the national crisis and his own part therein. The country had wanted waking up, wanted a lesson in effort and economy; and the feeling that he had not spared himself in these strenuous times had given a zest to those quiet pleasures of bed and board which, at his age, even the most patriotic could retain with a good conscience. He had denied himself many things—new clothes, presents for Kathleen and the children, travel, and that pine-apple house which he had been on the point of building when the war broke out; new wine, too, and cigars, and membership of the two Clubs which he had never used in the old days. The hours had seemed fuller and longer, sleep better earned—wonderful, the things one could do without when put to it! He turned the car into the high road, driving dreamily, for he was in plenty of time. The war was going pretty well now; he was no fool optimist, but now that conscription was in force, one might reasonably hope for its end within a year. Then there would be a boom, and one might let oneself go a little. Visions of theatres and supper with his wife at the Savoy afterwards, and cosy night drives back into the sweet-smelling country behind your own chauffeur once more teased a fancy which even now did not soar beyond the confines of domestic pleasures. He pictured his wife in new dresses by Jay—she was fifteen years younger than himself, and "paid for dressing" as they said. He had always delighted—as men older than their wives will—in the admiration she excited from others not privileged to enjoy her charms. Her rather queer and ironical beauty, her

cool irreproachable wifeliness, was a constant balm to him. They would give dinner parties again, have their friends down from town, and he would once more enjoy sitting at the foot of the dinner table while Kathleen sat at the head, with the light soft on her ivory shoulders, behind flowers she had arranged in that original way of hers, and fruit which he had grown in his hothouses; once more he would take legitimate interest in the wine he offered to his guests—once more stock that Chinese cabinet wherein he kept cigars. Yes—there was a certain satisfaction in these days of privation, if only from the anticipation they created.

The sprinkling of villas had become continuous on either side of the high road; and women going to shop, tradesmen's boys delivering victuals, young men in khaki, began to abound. Now and then a limping or bandaged form would pass—some bit of human wreckage! and Mr. Bosengate would think mechanically: 'Another of those poor devils! Wonder if we've had his case before us!'

Running his car into the best hotel garage of the little town, he made his way leisurely over to the court. It stood back from the market-place, and was already lapped by a sea of persons having, as in the outer ring at race meetings, an air of business at which one must not be caught out, together with a soaked or flushed appearance. Mr. Bosengate could not resist putting his handkerchief to his nose. He had carefully drenched it with lavender water, and to this fact owed, perhaps, his immunity from the post of foreman on the jury—for, say what you will about the English, they have a deep instinct for affairs.

He found himself second in the front row of the jury box, and through the odour of "Sanitas" gazed at the judge's face expressionless up there, for all the world like a be-wigged bust. His fellows in the box had that appearance of falling between two classes characteristic of jurymen. Mr. Bosengate was not impressed. On one side of him the foreman sat, a prominent upholsterer, known in the town as "Gentleman Fox." His dark and beautifully brushed and oiled hair and moustache, his radiant linen, gold watch and chain, the white piping to his waistcoat, and a habit of never saying "Sir" had long marked him out from commoner men; he undertook to bury people too, to save them trouble; and was altogether superior. On the other side Mr. Bosengate had one of those men who, except when they sit on juries, are never seen without a little brown bag, and the appearance of having been interrupted in a drink. Pale and shiny, with large loose eyes shifting from side to side, he had an underdone voice and uneasy, flabby hands. Mr. Bosengate disliked sitting next to him. Beyond this commercial traveller sat a dark pale young man with spectacles; beyond him again, a short old man with grey moustache, mutton chops, and innumerable wrinkles; and the front row was completed by a chemist. The three immediately behind, Mr. Bosengate did not thoroughly master; but the three at the end of the second row he learned in their order of an oldish man in a grey suit, given to winking; an inanimate person with the mouth of a moustachioed codfish, over whose long bald crown three wisps of damp hair were carefully arranged; and a dried, dapperish, clean-shorn man, whose mouth seemed terrified lest it should be surprised without a smile. Their first and second verdicts were recorded without the necessity for withdrawal, and Mr. Bosengate was already sleepy when the third case was called. The sight of khaki revived his drooping attention. But what a weedy-looking specimen! This prisoner had a truly nerveless, pitiable, dejected air. If he had ever had a military bearing it had

shrunk into him during his confinement. His ill-shaped brown tunic, whose little brass buttons seemed trying to keep smiling, struck Mr. Bosengate as ridiculously short, used though he was to such things. 'Absurd,' he thought—'Lumbago! Just where they ought to be covered!' Then the officer and gentleman stirred in him, and he added to himself: 'Still, there must be some distinction made!' The little soldier's visage had once perhaps been tanned, but was now the colour of dark dough; his large brown eyes with white showing below the iris, as so often in the eyes of very nervous people—wandered from face to face, of judge, counsel, jury, and public. There were hollows in his cheeks, his dark hair looked damp; around his neck he wore a bandage. The commercial traveller on Mr. Bosengate's left turned, and whispered: *"Felo de se! My hat! what a guy!"* Mr. Bosengate pretended not to hear—he could not bear that fellow!—and slowly wrote on a bit of paper: "Owen Lewis." Welsh! Well, he looked it—not at all an English face. Attempted suicide—not at all an English crime! Suicide implied surrender, a putting-up of hands to Fate—to say nothing of the religious aspect of the matter. And suicide in khaki seemed to Mr. Bosengate particularly abhorrent; like turning tail in face of the enemy; almost meriting the fate of a deserter. He looked at the prisoner, trying not to give way to this prejudice. And the prisoner seemed to look at him, though this, perhaps, was fancy.

The counsel for the prosecution, a little, alert, grey, decided man, above military age, began detailing the circumstances of the crime. Mr. Bosengate, though not particularly sensitive to atmosphere, could perceive a sort of current running through the court. It was as if jury and public were thinking rhythmically in obedience to the same unexpressed prejudice of which he himself was conscious. Even the Cæsar-like pale face up there, presiding, seemed in its ironic serenity responding to that current.

"Gentlemen of the jury, before I call my evidence, I direct your attention to the bandage the accused is still wearing. He gave himself this wound with his Army razor, adding, if I may say so, insult to the injury he was inflicting on his country. He pleads not guilty; and before the magistrates he said that absence from his wife was preying on his mind"—the advocate's close lips widened—"Well, gentlemen, if such an excuse is to weigh with us in these days, I'm sure I don't know what's to happen to the Empire."

'No, by George!' thought Mr. Bosengate.

The evidence of the first witness, a room-mate who had caught the prisoner's hand, and of the sergeant, who had at once been summoned, was conclusive, and he began to cherish a hope that they would get through without withdrawing, and he would be home before five. But then a hitch occurred. The regimental doctor failed to respond when his name was called; and the judge having for the first time that day showed himself capable of human emotion, intimated that he would adjourn until the morrow.

Mr. Bosengate received the announcement with equanimity. He would be home even earlier! And gathering up the sheets of paper he had scribbled on, he put them in his pocket and got up. The would-be suicide was being taken out of the court—a shambling drab figure with shoulders hunched. What good were men like that in these days! What good! The prisoner looked up. Mr. Bosengate encountered in full the gaze of those large brown eyes, with the white showing underneath. What a suffering, wretched, pitiful face! A man had no business to give you a look like that! The prisoner passed on down the stairs, and vanished.

Mr. Bosengate went out and across the market-place to the garage of the hotel where he had left his car. The sun shone fiercely and he thought: 'I must do some watering in the garden.' He brought the car out, and was about to start the engine, when some one passing said: "Good evenin'. Seedy-lookin' beggar that last prisoner, ain't he? We don't want men of that stamp." It was his neighbour on the jury, the commercial traveller, in a straw hat, with a little brown bag already in his hand and the froth of an interrupted drink on his moustache. Answering curtly: "Good evening!" and thinking: 'Nor of yours, my friend!' Mr. Bosengate started the car with unnecessary clamour. But as if brought back to life by the commercial traveller's remark, the prisoner's figure seemed to speed along too, turning up at Mr. Bosengate his pitifully unhappy eyes. Want of his wife!—queer excuse that for trying to put it out of his power ever to see her again. Why! Half a loaf, even a slice, was better than no bread. Not many of that neurotic type in the Army—thank Heaven! The lugubrious figure vanished, and Mr. Bosengate pictured instead the form of his own wife bending over her "Gloire de Dijon" roses in the rosery, where she generally worked a little before tea now that they were short of gardeners. He saw her, as often he had seen her raise herself and stand, head to one side, a gloved hand on her slender hip, gazing as it were ironically from under drooped lids at buds which did not come out fast enough. And the word 'Caline,' for he was something of a French scholar, shot through his mind: 'Kathleen—Caline!' If he found her there when he got in, he would steal up on the grass and—ah! but with great care not to crease her dress or disturb her hair! 'If only she weren't quite so self-contained,' he thought. 'It's like a cat you can't get near, not really near!'

The car, returning faster than it had

come down that morning, had already passed the outskirt villas, and was breasting the hill to where, among fields and the old trees, Charmleigh lay apart from commoner life. Turning into his drive, Mr. Bosengate thought with a certain surprise: 'I wonder what she *does* think of! I wonder!' He put his gloves and hat down in the outer hall and went into the lavatory to dip his face in cool water and wash it with sweet-smelling soap—delicious revenge on the unclean atmosphere in which he had been stewing so many hours. He came out again into the hall dazed by soap and the mellowed light, and a voice from half-way up the stairs said: "Daddy! Look!" His little daughter was standing up there with one hand on the banisters. She scrambled on to them and came sliding down, her frock up to her eyes, and her holland knickers to her middle. Mr. Bosengate said mildly:

"Well, that's elegant!"

"Tea's in the summer-house. Mummy's waiting. Come on!"

With her hand in his, Mr. Bosengate went on, through the drawing-room, long and cool, with sunblinds down, through the billiard-room, high and cool, through the conservatory, green and sweet-smelling, out on to the terrace and the upper lawn. He had never felt such sheer exhilarated joy in his home surroundings, so cool, glistening and green under the July sun; and he said:

"Well, Kit, what have you all been doing?"

"I've fed my rabbits and Harry's; and we've been in the attic; Harry got his leg through the skylight."

Mr. Bosengate drew in his breath with a hiss.

"It's all right, Daddy; we got it out again, it's only grazed the skin. And we've been making swabs—I made seventeen—Mummy made thirty-three, and then she went to the hospital. Did you put many men in prison?"

Mr. Bosengate cleared his throat. The question seemed to him untimely.

"Only two."

"What's it like in prison, Daddy?"

Mr. Bosengate, who had no more knowledge than his little daughter, replied in an absent voice:

"Not very nice."

They were passing under a young oak tree, where the path wound round to the rosery and summer-house. Something shot down and clawed Mr. Bosengate's neck. His little daughter began to hop and suffocate with laughter.

"Oh, Daddy! Aren't you caught! I led you on purpose!"

Looking up, Mr. Bosengate saw his small son lying along a low branch above him—like the leopard he was declaring himself to be (for fear of error), and thought blithely: 'What an active little chap it is!'

"Let me drop on your shoulders, Daddy—like they do on the deer."

"Oh, yes! Do be a deer, Daddy!"

Mr. Bosengate did not see being a deer; his hair had just been brushed. But he entered the rosery buoyantly between his offspring. His wife was standing precisely as he had imagined her, in a pale blue frock open at the neck, with a narrow black band round the waist, and little accordion pleats below. She looked her coolest. Her smile, when she turned her head, hardly seemed to take Mr. Bosengate seriously enough. He placed his lips below one of her half-drooped eyelids. She even smelled of roses. His children began to dance round their mother, and Mr. Bosengate, firmly held between them, was also compelled to do this, until she said:

"When you've quite done, let's have tea!"

It was not the greeting he had imagined coming along in the car. Earwigs were plentiful in the summer-house—used perhaps twice a year, but indispensable to every country residence—and Mr. Bosengate was not sorry for the excuse to get out again. Though all was so pleasant, he felt oddly restless, rather suffocated; and lighting his pipe, began to move about among the roses, blowing tobacco at the greenfly; in war-time one was never quite idle! And suddenly he said:

"We're trying a wretched Tommy at the assizes."

His wife looked up from a rose.

"What for?"

"Attempted suicide."

"Why did he?"

"Can't stand the separation from his wife."

She looked at him, gave a low laugh, and said:

"Oh dear!"

Mr. Bosengate was puzzled. Why did she laugh? He looked round, saw that the children were gone, took his pipe from his mouth, and approached her.

"You look very pretty," he said. "Give me a kiss!"

His wife bent her body forward from the waist, and pushed her lips out till they touched his moustache. Mr. Bosengate felt a sensation as if he had arisen from breakfast without having eaten marmalade. He mastered it and said:

"That jury are a rum lot."

His wife's eyelids flickered. "I wish women sat on juries."

"Why?"

"It would be an experience."

Not the first time she had used that curious expression! Yet her life was far from dull, so far as he could see; with the new interests created by the war, and the constant calls on her time made by the perfection of their home life, she had a useful and busy existence. Again the random thought passed through him: 'But she never tells me anything!' And suddenly that lugubrious khaki-clad figure started up among the rose bushes. "We've

got a lot to be thankful for!" he said abruptly. "I must go to work!" His wife, raising one eyebrow, smiled. "And I to weep!" Mr. Bosengate laughed—she had a pretty wit! And stroking his comely moustache where it had been kissed, he moved out into the sunshine. All the evening, throughout his labours, not inconsiderable, for this jury business had put him behind time, he was afflicted by that restless pleasure in his surroundings; would break off in mowing the lower lawn to look at the house through the trees; would leave his study and committee papers to cross into the drawing-room and sniff its dainty fragrance; paid a special good-night visit to the children having supper in the schoolroom; pottered in and out from his dressing-room to admire his wife while she was changing for dinner; dined with his mind perpetually on the next course; talked volubly of the war; and in the billiard-room afterwards, smoking the pipe which had taken the place of his cigar, could not keep still, but roamed about, now in conservatory, now in the drawing-room, where his wife and the governess were still making swabs. It seemed to him that he could not have enough of anything. About eleven o'clock he strolled out—beautiful night, only just dark enough—under the new arrangement with Time—and went down to the little round fountain below the terrace. His wife was playing the piano. Mr. Bosengate looked at the water and the flat dark water-lily leaves which floated there; looked up at the house, where only narrow chinks of light showed, because of the Lighting Order. The dreamy music drifted out; there was a scent of heliotrope. He moved a few steps back, and sat in the children's swing under an old lime tree. Jolly—blissful—in the warm, bloomy dark! Of all hours of the day, this before going to bed was perhaps the pleasantest. He saw the light go up in his wife's bedroom, unscreened for a full minute, and thought: 'Aha! If I did my duty as a special, I should "strafe" her for that.' She came to the window, her figure lighted, hands up to the back of her head, so that her bare arms gleamed. Mr. Bosengate wafted her a kiss, knowing he could not be seen. 'Lucky chap!' he mused; 'she's a great joy!' Up went her arm, down came the blind—the house was dark again. He drew a long breath. 'Another ten minutes,' he thought, 'then I'll go in and shut up. By Jove! The limes are beginning to smell already!' And, the better to take in that acme of his well-being, he tilted the swing, lifted his feet from the ground, and swung himself toward the scented blossoms. He wanted to whelm his senses in their perfume, and closed his eyes. But instead of the domestic vision he expected, the face of the little Welsh soldier, hare-eyed, shadowy, pinched and dark and pitiful, started up with such disturbing vividness that he opened his eyes again at once. Curse! The fellow almost haunted one! Where would he be now—poor little devil! lying in his cell, thinking—thinking of his wife! Feeling suddenly morbid, Mr. Bosengate arrested the swing and stood up. Absurd!— all his well-being and mood of warm anticipation had deserted him! 'A d———d world!' he thought. 'Such a lot of misery! Why should I have to sit in judgment on that poor beggar, and condemn him?' He moved up on to the terrace and walked briskly, to rid himself of this disturbance before going in. 'That commercial traveller chap,' he thought, 'the rest of those fellows—they see nothing!' And, abruptly turning up the three stone steps, he entered the conservatory, locked it, passed into the billiard-room, and drank his barley water. One of the pictures was hanging crooked; he went up to put it straight. Still life. Grapes and apples, and lobsters! They struck him as odd for the first time. Why lobsters? The whole pic-

ture seemed dead and oily. He turned off the light, and went upstairs, passed his wife's door, into his own room, and undressed. Clothed in his pyjamas he opened the door between the rooms. By the light coming from his own he could see her dark head on the pillow. Was she asleep? No—not asleep, certainly. The moment of fruition had come; the crowning of his pride and pleasure in his home. But he continued to stand there. He had suddenly no pride, no pleasure, no desire; nothing but a sort of dull resentment against everything. He turned back, shut the door, and slipping between the heavy curtains and his open window, stood looking out at the night. 'Full of misery!' he thought. 'Full of d———d misery!'

## II

Filing into the jury box next morning, Mr. Bosengate collided slightly with a short juryman, whose square figure and square head of stiff yellow-red hair he had only vaguely noticed the day before. The man looked angry, and Mr. Bosengate thought: 'An ill-bred dog, that!'

He sat down quickly, and, to avoid further recognition of his fellows, gazed in front of him. His appearance on Saturdays was always military, by reason of the route march of his Volunteer Corps in the afternoon. Gentleman Fox, who belonged to the corps too, was also looking square; but that commercial traveller on his other side seemed more *louche*, and as if surprised in immorality, than ever; only the proximity of Gentleman Fox on the other side kept Mr. Bosengate from shrinking. Then he saw the prisoner being brought in, shadowy and dark behind the brightness of his buttons, and he experienced a sort of shock, this figure was so exactly that which had several times started up in his mind. Somehow he had expected a fresh sight of the fellow to

dispel and disprove what had been haunting him, had expected to find him just an
outside phenomenon, not, as it were, a
part of his own life. And he gazed at the
carven immobility of the judge's face, trying to steady himself, as a drunken man
will, by looking at a light. The regimental
doctor, unabashed by the judge's comment on his absence the day before, gave
his evidence like a man who had better
things to do, and the case for the prosecution was forthwith rounded in by a little
speech from counsel. The matter—he
said—was clear as daylight. Those who
wore His Majesty's uniform, charged
with the responsibility and privilege of
defending their country, were no more
entitled to desert their regiments by taking their own lives than they were entitled
to desert in any other way. He asked for a
conviction. Mr. Bosengate felt a sympa-
thetic shuffle passing through all feet; the
judge was speaking:

"Prisoner, you can either go into the
witness box and make your statement on
oath, in which you may be cross-
examined on it; or you can make your
statement there from the dock, in which
case you will not be cross-examined.
Which do you elect to do?"

"From here, my lord."

Seeing him now full face, and, as it
might be, come to life in the effort to
convey his feelings, Mr. Bosengate had
suddenly a quite different impression of
the fellow. It was as if his khaki had
fallen off, and he had stepped out of his
own shadow, a live and quivering creature. His pinched clean-shaven face
seemed to have an irregular, wilder, hair-
ier look, his large nervous brown eyes
darkened and glowed; he jerked his
shoulders, his arms, his whole body, like
a man suddenly freed from cramp or a
suit of armour. He spoke, too, in a quick,
crisp, rather high voice, pinching his con-
sonants a little, sharpening his vowels,
like a true Welshman.

"My lord and misters the jury," he
said: "I was a hairdresser when the call
came on me to join the army. I had a
little home and a wife. I never thought
what it would be like to be away from
them, I surely never did; and I'm
ashamed to be speaking it out like this—
how it can squeeze and squeeze a man,
how it can prey on your mind when
you're nervous like I am. 'Tis not everyone that cares for his home—there's a
lots o' them never wants to see their wives
again. But for me 'tis like being shut up
in a cage, it is!" Mr. Bosengate saw daylight between the skinny fingers of the
man's hand thrown out with a jerk. "I
cannot bear it shut up away from wife
and home like what you are in the army.
So when I took my razor that morning I
was wild—an' I wouldn't be here now but
for that man catching my hand. There
was no reason in it, I'm willing to confess. It was foolish; but wait till you get
feeling like what I was, and see how it
draws you. Misters the jury, don't send
me back to prison; it is worse still there.
If you have wives you will know what it
is like for lots of us; only some is more
nervous than others. I swear to you, sirs,
I could not help it——" Again the little
man flung out his hand, his whole thin
body shook and Mr. Bosengate felt the
same sensation as when he drove his car
over a dog—"Misters the jury, I hope you
may never in your lives feel as I've been
feeling."

The little man ceased, his eyes shrank
back into their sockets, his figure back
into its mask of shadowy brown and
gleaming buttons, and Mr. Bosengate was
conscious that the judge was making a series of remarks; and, very soon, of being
seated at a mahogany table in the jury's
withdrawing room, hearing the voice of
the man with hair like an Irish terrier's
saying: "Didn't he talk through his hat,
that little blighter!" Conscious, too, of the
commercial traveller, still on his left—al-

ways on his left!—mopping his brow, and muttering: "Phew! It's hot in there to-day!" when an effluvium, as of an inside accustomed to whiskey, came from him. Then the man with the underlip and the three plastered wisps of hair said:

"Don't know why we withdrew, Mr. Foreman!"

Mr. Bosengate looked round to where, at the head of the table, Gentleman Fox sat, in defensive gentility and the little white piping to his waistcoat. "I shall be happy to take the sense of the jury," he was saying blandly.

There was a short silence, then the chemist murmured:

"I should say he must have what they call claustrophobia."

"Clauster fiddlesticks! The feller's a shirker, that's all. Missed his wife—pretty excuse! Indecent, I call it!"

The speaker was the little wire-haired man; and emotion, deep and angry, stirred in Mr. Bosengate. That ill-bred little cur! He gripped the edge of the table with both hands.

"I think it's d——d natural!" he muttered. But almost before the words had left his lips he felt dismay. What had he said—he, nearly a colonel of volunteers —endorsing such a want of patriotism! And hearing the commercial traveller murmuring: " 'Ear, 'ear!" he reddened violently.

The wire-headed man said roughly:

"There's too many of these blighted shirkers, and too much pampering of them."

The turmoil in Mr. Bosengate increased; he remarked in an icy voice:

"I agree to no verdict that'll send the man back to prison."

At this a real tremor seemed to go round the table, as if they all saw themselves sitting there through lunch time. Then the large grey-haired man given to winking, said:

"Oh! Come, sir—after what the judge said! Come, sir! What do you say, Mr. Foreman?"

Gentleman Fox—as who should say 'This is excellent value, but I don't wish to press it on you!'—answered:

"We are only concerned with the facts. Did he or did he not try to shorten his life?"

"Of course he did—said so himself," Mr. Bosengate heard the wire-haired man snap out, and from the following murmur of assent he alone abstained. Guilty! Well —yes! There was no way out of admitting that, but his feelings revolted against handing "that poor little beggar" over to the tender mercy of his country's law. His whole soul rose in arms against agreeing with that ill-bred little cur, and the rest of this job-lot. He had an impulse to get up and walk out, saying: "Settle it your own way. Good-morning."

"It seems, sir," Gentleman Fox was saying, "that we're all agreed to guilty, except yourself. If you will allow me, I don't see how you can go behind what the prisoner himself admitted."

Thus brought up to the very guns, Mr. Bosengate, red in the face, thrust his hands deep into the side pockets of his tunic, and, staring straight before him, said:

"Very well; on condition we recommend him to mercy."

"What do you say, gentlemen; shall we recommend him to mercy?"

" 'Ear 'ear!" burst from the commercial traveller, and from the chemist came the murmur:

"No harm in that."

"Well, I think there is. They shoot deserters at the front, and we let this fellow off. I'd hang the cur."

Mr. Bosengate stared at that little wire-haired brute. "Haven't you *any* feeling for others?" he wanted to say. "Can't you see that this poor devil suffers tortures?" But the sheer impossibility of doing this before ten other men brought a slight sweat out on his face and hands; and in agitation he smote the table a blow with his fist. The effect was instantaneous. Everybody looked at the wire-haired man, as if saying: "Yes, you've gone a bit too far there!" The "little brute" stood it for a moment, then muttered surlily:

"Well, commend 'im to mercy if you like; I don't care."

"That's right; they never pay any attention to it," said the grey-haired man, winking heartily. And Mr. Bosengate filed back with the others into court.

But when from the jury box his eyes fell once more on the hare-eyed figure in the dock, he had his worst moment yet. Why should this poor wretch suffer so— for no fault, no fault; while he, and these others, and that snapping counsel, and the Cæsar-like judge up there, went off to their women and their homes, blithe as bees, and probably never thought of him again? And suddenly he was conscious of the judge's voice:

"You will go back to your regiment, and endeavour to serve your country with better spirit. You may thank the jury that you are not sent to prison, and your good fortune that you were not at the front when you tried to commit this cowardly act. You are lucky to be alive."

A policeman pulled the little soldier by the arm; his drab figure, with eyes fixed and lustreless, passed down and away. From his very soul Mr. Bosengate wanted to lean out and say: "Cheer up, cheer up! *I* understand."

It was nearly ten o'clock that evening before he reached home, motoring back from the route march. His physical tiredness was abated, for he had partaken of a snack and a whisky and soda at the hotel but mentally he was in a curious mood. His body felt appeased, his spirit hungry. To-night he had a yearning, not for his wife's kisses, but for her understanding. He wanted to go to her and say: "I've learnt a lot to-day—found out things I never thought of. Life's a wonderful thing, Kate, a thing one can't live all to oneself; a thing one shares with everybody, so that when another suffers, one suffers too. It's come to me that what one *has* doesn't matter a bit—it's what one does, and how one sympathises with other people. It came to me in the most extraordinary vivid way, when I was on that jury watching that poor little rat of a soldier in his trap; it's the first time I've ever felt—the—the spirit of Christ, you know. It's a wonderful thing, Kate— wonderful! We haven't been close—really close, you and I, so that we each understand what the other is feeling. It's all in that, you know; understanding—sympathy—it's priceless. When I saw that poor little devil taken down and sent back to his regiment to begin his sorrows all over again—wanting his wife, thinking and thinking of her just as you know I would be thinking and wanting you, I felt what an awful outside sort of life we lead, never telling each other what we really think and feel, never being really close. I daresay that little chap and his wife keep nothing from each other—live each other's lives. That's what *we* ought to do. Let's get to feeling that what really matters is—understanding and living, and not only just saying it as we all do, those fellows on the jury, and even that poor devil of a judge—what an awful life, judging one's fellow-creatures! When I left that poor little Tommy this morning, and ever since, I've longed to get back here quietly to you and tell you about it, and make a beginning. There's something wonderful in this, and I want you to feel it as I do, because you mean such a lot to me."

This was what he wanted to say to his wife, not touching, or kissing her, just looking into her eyes, watching them soften and glow as they surely must, catching the infection of his new ardour. And he felt unsteady, fearfully unsteady with the desire to say it all as it should be said: swiftly, quietly, with the truth and fervour of his feeling.

The hall was not lit up, for daylight still lingered under the new arrangement. He went towards the drawing-room, but from the very door shied off to his study and stood irresolute under the picture of a "Man catching a flea" (Dutch school), which had come down to him from his father. The governess would be in there with his wife! He must wait. Essential to go straight to Kathleen and pour it all out, or he would never do it. He felt as nervous as an undergraduate going up for his *vivâ voce*. This thing was so big, so astoundingly and unexpectedly important. He was suddenly afraid of his wife, afraid of her coolness and her grace, and that something Japanese about her—of all those attributes he had been accustomed to admire; most afraid, as it were, of her attraction. He felt young to-night, almost boyish; would she see that he was not really fifteen years older than herself, and she not really a part of his collection, of all the admirable appointments of his home; but a companion spirit to one who wanted a companion badly? In this agitation of his soul he could keep still no more than he could last night in the agitation of his senses; and he wandered into the dining-room. A dainty supper was set out there, sandwiches, and cake, whisky and cigarettes—even an early peach. Mr. Bosengate looked at this peach with sorrow rather than disgust. The perfection of it was of a piece with all that had gone before this new and sudden feeling. Its delicious bloom seemed to heighten his perception of the hedge around him, that hedge of the things he so enjoyed, carefully planted and tended these many years. He passed it by uneaten, and went to the window. Out there all was darkening, the fountain, the lime tree, the flower-beds, and the fields below, with the Jersey cows who would come to your call; dark-

ening slowly, losing form, blurring into soft blackness, vanishing, but there none the less—all there—the hedge of his possessions. He heard the door of the drawing-room open, the voices of his wife and the governess in the hall, going up to bed. If only they didn't look in here! If only——! The voices ceased. He was safe now—had but to follow in a few minutes, to make sure of Kathleen alone. He turned round and stared down the length of the dark dining-room, over the rosewood table, to where in the mirror above the sideboard at the far end, his figure bathed, a stain, a mere blurred shadow; he made his way down to it along the table edge, and stood before himself as close as he could get. His throat and the roof of his mouth felt dry with nervousness; he put out his finger and touched his face in the glass. 'You're an ass!' he thought. 'Pull yourself together, and get it over. She will see; of course she will!' He swallowed, smoothed his moustache, and walked out. Going up the stairs, his heart beat painfully; but he was in for it now, and marched straight into her room.

Dressed only in a loose blue wrapper, she was brushing her dark hair before the glass. Mr. Bosengate went up to her and stood there silent, looking down. The words he had thought of were like a swarm of bees buzzing in his head yet not one would fly from between his lips. His wife went on brushing her hair under the light which shone on her polished elbows. She looked up at him from beneath one lifted eyebrow.

"Well, dear—tired?"

With a sort of vehemence the single word "No" passed out. A faint, a quizzical smile flitted over her face; she shrugged her shoulders ever so gently. That gesture—he had seen it before! And in desperate desire to make her understand, he put his hand on her lifted arm.

"Kathleen, stop—listen to me!" His fingers tightened in his agitation and eagerness to make his great discovery known. But before he could get out a word he became conscious of that cool round arm, conscious of her eyes half-closed, sliding round at him, of her half-smiling lips, of her neck under the wrapper. And he stammered:

"I want—I must—Kathleen, I——"

She lifted her shoulders again in that little shrug. "Yes—I know; all right!"

A wave of heat and shame, and of God knows what came over Mr. Bosengate; he fell on his knees and pressed his forehead to her arm; and he was silent, more silent than the grave. Nothing—nothing came from him but two long sighs. Suddenly he felt her hand stroke his cheek—compassionately, it seemed to him. She made a little movement towards him; her lips met his, and he remembered nothing but that. . . .

In his own room Mr. Bosengate sat at his wide-open window, smoking a cigarette; there was no light. Moths went past, the moon was creeping up. He sat very calm, puffing the smoke out into the night air. Curious thing—life! Curious world! Curious forces in it—making one do the opposite of what one wished; always—always making one do the oppo-site, it seemed! The furtive light from the creeping moon was getting hold of things down there, stealing in among the boughs of the trees. 'There's something ironical,' he thought, 'which walks about. Things don't come off as you think they will. I meant, I tried—but one doesn't change like that all of a sudden, it seems. Fact is, life's too big a thing for me! All the same, I'm not the man I was yesterday—not quite!' He closed his eyes, and in one of those flashes of vision which come when the senses are at rest, he saw himself as it were far down below—down on the floor of a street narrow as a grave, high as a mountain, a deep dark slit of a street—walking down there, a black midget of a fellow, among other black midgets—his wife, and the little soldier, the judge, and those jury chaps—*fantoches* straight up on their tiny feet, wandering down there in that dark, infinitely tall, and narrow street. 'Too much for one!' he thought. 'Too high for one—no getting on top of it. We've got to be kind, and help one an-other, and not expect too much, and not think too much. That's—all!' And, squeezing out his cigarette, he took six deep breaths of the night air, and got into bed.

# THE LIFE AND WORKS OF
# JOHN GALSWORTHY

### By DUDLEY BARKER

ON NOVEMBER 10, 1932, a telephone message that he had been awarded the Nobel Prize for Literature was brought to John Galsworthy in the garden of Bury House, his somewhat grand country home at the foot of the Sussex Downs near the southern English coast, where he was playing croquet with his wife Ada. He decided that with the prize money of about £9,000 he would create a Trust Fund for PEN, of which he was founder President. (Galsworthy was not only generous, but rich; he had inherited one fortune and earned a second with his novels and plays.) Then he settled in his study at the top of Bury House to compose the speech with which, the following month, he would receive his honor in Stockholm. He would speak of his life as a writer. "To hale into the field of sight our literary pasts," he began, "that is a task—or, shall we say, a pleasure—from which the modest recoil . . ."

The speech was written, but he was not to deliver it. The day after he had the news of his Nobel Prize, he took a fall from his horse; astonishing, for he was a lifelong, skilled rider. The fall in itself was nothing, but his family fearfully noted it as one more instance of a clumsiness, so untypical of the man, which seemed to have come on him in recent months. His household consisted besides his wife, of a nephew, Rudolf Sauter, and

his wife; the Galsworthys had no children.

He refused to see a doctor. He loathed doctors. To the local man who was brought in he muttered, "You're a *detective*," and went off to finish his Nobel speech. But when it was done, and he tried to rehearse it, he could not. The power of speech was failing him. He could no longer control his hands sufficiently to shave himself. Sadly he told Rudo to telegraph to Stockholm that he was unable to make the journey. Reluctantly he consented to be driven to London for a physical examination. Within a few days he lay on a sickbed in his even grander London house; among the many anxious enquirers for his health were the King and the Prime Minister. Not long afterward, he died of the tumour that had slowly formed on his brain.

In composing the speech he was never to deliver in Stockholm, he had written: "From what point in my past shall I start? From a railway station—a railway bookstall—a voice murmuring, 'You are just the person to write, why don't you?' A startled ear, a startled voice. 'I?' Thus began the career of which you are about to glean the echoes. To me the Gare du Nord in Paris will always be haloed by that soft incitement uttered thirty-seven years ago."

It was certainly the most casual start

for a writer who—whatever the disenchantments of posterity—was to become in his lifetime the acknowledged head of English letters. When that chance remark was made in 1895 by the bookstall in the Gare du Nord, John Galsworthy was already twenty-eight years old, and had given little thought to any career at all, much less to a career of literature. In that radiant period of English prosperity, the latter years of Queen Victoria's reign, the eldest son of a wealthy middle-class family was most likely, unless he chose to take a commission in the Army, to pursue a career of idleness, of rooms in London, the comfortable protection of a St. James's club, and a succession of visits to lavish country houses for field and other sports.

John Galsworthy was such: the elder son (and second child) of a solidly rich lawyer and company director in the City of London, whose portrait was to be drawn almost precisely by his son as Old Jolyon Forsyte. The Forsytes were, of course, the Galsworthys. The Galsworthys, like the Forsytes, had originally been yeomen farmers in the west of England, but had come to London to find a more lucrative use for land—speculative building upon it and property dealing.

Old John Galsworthy had prospered and built up a small country estate on the North Downs, a few miles out of London, where his children spent their childhood; it is the site of Robin Hill, the Forsyte house. Young John went to school at Harrow, where he was an undistinguished scholar but something of a snob, and then to New College at Oxford, where he developed into a dandy, adopted a monocle, and acquired an extensive knowledge of horses and racing form.

To please his father he read law and eventually became a barrister, but with small intention of practicing; the only case in which he is known to have had a brief was settled in court, unbeknown to him, while he happened to be having a conversation with his father in the corridor outside.

He was chiefly busy with London and country-house parties, and with long journeys overseas, to Canada, to Russia, to Australia, New Zealand, and the South Seas, on which his father dispatched him in an effort to disentangle him from a girl who gave singing lessons, with whom he imagined himself indissolubly in love. By a coincidence which no novelist could hope to invent, on the voyage home from the South Seas he became friendly with the sailing clipper's first mate, a Pole named Joseph Conrad, who did not dream of showing young Galsworthy the manuscript of *Almayer's Folly,* which was locked up in his cabin while Conrad pondered whether to send it to a publisher or not.

Back in London, the singing teacher forgotten, Galsworthy fell in love with the unhappy wife of one of his cousins, Arthur Galsworthy, another idle son of the wealthy family. This—though of course he did not then know it—was the most important event in John Galsworthy's life. This is what made him a writer, and gave him the subject of his writing. Without this there would have been no authorship for him, and no Forsytes to fill the bookshelves and eventually the television screens of the world.

Ada Galsworthy, née Cooper, was the only daughter of a Norwich doctor of an eccentric turn of mind; his chief occupation of a Sunday was to sit smoking his pipe in the cemetery, gazing with pleasure at the classical mausoleum he had had built for himself. He was placed within it rather early in life, and his widow set off with her daughter on a tour of the watering places of Europe in search of a rich husband for the orphaned girl. Ada Cooper was slightly built and delicate-looking. Her chief accomplishment was music; she was a pianist of almost concert-platform ability. In 1891 she secured her husband, Arthur Galsworthy, who had no money except an allowance from his father, but had prospects of inheriting a fortune some day; in any event, he had to wait thirty years for it, since his father lived to be ninety. On the strength of his expectations, however, he set up house with his bride in the expensive London borough of Kensington, where most of the Galsworthy clan lived.

Horrific stories of Arthur's brutal treatment of his young wife, and her intense unhappiness, were soon being whispered among the Galsworthy girls. John Galsworthy, always almost too sensitively humane, was filled with indignation and pity when he heard the stories from his sisters. In the warmth of his sympathy, Ada herself began hesitantly to reveal to him the degradation to which, she declared, her husband subjected her. What independent evidence there is suggests, in fact, that Arthur Galsworthy was an ordinary, quiet, undemanding man, and that the brutalities occurred only in his wife's frenzied fancies; throughout her life she was a deep neurotic. But that does not matter. What matters is the effect of the stories, true or false, on Arthur's cousin.

John Galsworthy's indignation turned to rage, and his pity to love. When in 1895 Ada and her mother took a holiday in Monte Carlo, Galsworthy contrived to join them there and confess his love. For prudence they had to separate at Paris on the way home. They parted by the bookstall in the Gare du Nord. He was in despair. He must return to a legal career in which he had no smallest interest, she to a loathed husband to whom she was chained. They could not defy the world and run off together, for he had no money except an allowance from Old John Galsworthy. If only, he lamented, he could find some way of earning independence!

That was when Ada murmured, "You are just the person to write, why don't you?"

Having nothing much else to do when he returned to London, Galsworthy set about writing. He spent the next two years of his life writing ten short stories. Most of them are incompetent and amateur. Only one, in which Galsworthy ventured timidly onto the fringe of the relationship between himself and Ada, gives even a glimpse of a future writer of distinction. Ada continually encouraged him —they were by then privily lovers. But she was alone in her percipience. No publisher would print the stories. So in 1897 John Galsworthy himself paid £100 to have them published as a volume, entitled *From the Four Winds* and signed with the pseudonym John Sinjohn.

The book was scantly noticed and almost nobody bought it. By the very fact of publication, nevertheless, Galsworthy was now an author. He set to work at once on his first novel, *Jocelyn*.

For the next eight years, until his father's death, Galsworthy wrote doggedly and unsuccessfully, and continued his secret love affair with his cousin's wife. The family buzzed with it, of course, but Ada's husband seems for long to have been quite unaware of what was happening; for much of the time he was in South Africa on active service in the Boer War. More importantly still, the secret was kept from old John Galsworthy who, had he learned of the matter, might well have cut off his son's allowance and substantial expectations.

In an essay he wrote thirty years later, Galsworthy admitted that he was not a born writer, but declared that any man sufficiently determined could teach himself to become one, provided he had an independent income while he was learning. Galsworthy had no intention of risking his.

But he was certainly learning. Although, as he once recalled, his first four years of authorship earned him nothing but cost him £100, his first two novels and a further volume of short stories did find publishers who demanded no fee from the author. Moreover, their quality markedly improved as the years of discipline went by, and as Galsworthy dared to move nearer and nearer to the theme that seethed in his brain—protest against the morality of a society that kept a woman such as Ada chained in a loveless marriage, possessed by her husband like a slave.

He started on that path, indeed, in *Jocelyn,* a conventionally melodramatic story of a love affair between an unmarried girl and an unhappily married man; although Galsworthy reversed the sexes of his own predicament, he set much of the story in Monte Carlo, using his own experience of that holiday on which he had told Ada of his love. In his second novel, *Villa Rubein* (1900), he drew for his story upon a match between his sister Lilian and a romantic Austrian artist, Georg Sauter; and began to develop the theme of the impact of art and beauty on the solid, middle-class London men of business of whom his own family was largely composed. In the volume of short stories he next published the Forsytes themselves emerged by name, and the theme was similar—the rejection by a cautious Forsyte of a passionate affair with the daughter of a wild family of Hungarian exiles, and the admission to himself on his deathbed many years later that, in so doing, he had missed life.

This short story, "The Salvation of Swithin Forsyte" (1901), has sometimes been called John Galsworthy's true starting point as a writer. In it he mapped out the Forsyte territory that he was to spend much of his life exploring; Old Jolyon, the portrait of Galsworthy's father, himself makes a first brief appearance; and the protest of the artist against the power

and brutality of wealth is nervously, hesitantly, uncertainly murmured.

This was the story, moreover, that gained for Galsworthy the first genuine respect and interest of a small group of writers and men of letters around Conrad (whose friendship he had retained) and Edward Garnett, the literary critic. Thus encouraged, Galsworthy tried to voice in a play his indignation at Ada's enslavement to her husband. But he had to abandon it, finding himself as yet incapable of writing directly about his relationship with Ada.

He did not, however, abandon the idea of attacking the society in which she was chained. He tried a novel assailing it for its indifference to the desperate poverty of the London slums. To this novel, *The Island Pharisees* (1904), he for the first time signed his own name. It was not well received, nor should it have been. It is a poor novel, although he spent three years on it, rewriting the whole thing twice. In doing so, he at last mastered the technique of his art. As he completed the third writing of *The Island Pharisees,* he was already at work on his next novel, the first in which he dared to deal directly with Ada's marriage as she described it to him, as the moral outrage he deemed it to be. And he set the story firmly in his own family, drawing their portraits with little concealment except for the change of name to Forsyte.

He had written about half of it when his father died, leaving his elder son an immediate legacy of £2,500 and an annual income of £700, to be followed by a large inheritance seven years later. Since the purchasing power of the pound in the first decade of this century was around ten times what it is today, Galsworthy was at last not only independent, but well-to-do. At once he took Ada away to live openly with him in a farmhouse which he partially rented on the edge of Dartmoor in Devon: an invitation to Arthur Galsworthy to take action to divorce her. The case was set down for hearing in March 1905, and was, of course, undefended. Before it came on, Galsworthy took Ada away to Italy.

In 1905 a divorce was no casual matter. A man named in a divorce case had to remove himself from his business or professional associations, resign from his clubs and expect to be outlawed by the society in which he had grown up. All this Galsworthy calmly accepted as preferable to the situation of a woman such as Ada being tied to a loveless marriage. But his rage did not diminish against the society which had first held her inexorably in the depths of degradation (as he believed) and then ostracized her for daring to regain human freedom.

In spite of all the humiliation, the act of freeing her was an immense freedom for him also. It was demonstrated in the novel he was writing. The first two-thirds of what Galsworthy himself called "the most scattered of my manuscripts at the time of my life most poignant" was a confused jumble of scrawled, written and rewritten, over-scrawled notebook pages. The last third, which he wrote in six weeks in northern Italy as the divorce proceeded, was "clean-written with the continuity of a mind at rest." (On the state of this manuscript there is only Galsworthy's own word; some seven years later, in a moment of emotion, he thrust it all into the fire.)

The novel was, of course, *The Man of Property* (1906), in which he paraded the whole company of the Forsytes— "that charming and instructive sight, an upper middle class family in full plumage." In a letter to his sister Lilian, who was deeply distressed that this satirical family group should be made public, Galsworthy made no pretence that the Forsytes were not, essentially, the Galsworthys, or that Irene, the unwilling wife

upon whom Soames Forsyte committed the ultimate act of property, the legal rape, was other than Ada Galsworthy. It has already been noted that the character of Soames was probably unfair to Arthur Galsworthy, and that the theme of the most formidable series of novels of middle-class English life of recent times was almost certainly founded upon a woman's neurosis.

The publication of *The Man of Property* in 1906 established Galsworthy at once among the most notable contemporary novelists, even though critical reviews of the book were not enthusiastic. Moreover, the novel sold well. After writing assiduously for eleven years without making either a reputation or a penny of profit, Galsworthy was suddenly known, accepted, and rewarded—when he no longer needed the money.

In that same year he secured his literary position with the first play he managed to complete, *The Silver Box*. This, too, was an attack upon property and the established order of English society. He wrote it in six weeks in the Devon farmhouse; he and Ada had returned to England, married, and set up house in Kensington, still largely ostracized by the Forsyte society and finding friends only among writers—Conrad of course, Hueffer, the Garnetts, Gilbert Murray, and particularly Barrie.

Galsworthy had deliberately aimed his play at the Court Theatre in Sloane Square, on the Kensington fringe, where Harley Granville-Barker and Bernard Shaw were just setting up the new school of dramatists of reality. They accepted *The Silver Box* within three days of receiving it. When it was performed, it made such an impact that one critic prophesied it would shape the theater of the future. (It is curious to note that, half a century later, John Osborne's play *Look Back in Anger,* accepted in the same manner at the same theater, had much the same impact upon the English stage of our time.)

With his novel and his play in 1906, John Galsworthy was home. He had not got there easily or quickly. He was in his fortieth year.

His literary successes ameliorated the scandal of Ada's divorce. She, indeed, still felt the chill of ostracism deeply and her neuroticism began to turn into predictable physical ailments—asthma, frequent bouts of "the flu," migraine, and such. She was well on the way to semi-invalidism.

But Galsworthy himself was more secure and respected than he had ever been as a young man, and his confidence emerged strongly in his public life, as in his writing. He discovered that he had become a man of authority to whom people turned for leadership in matters of public concern. This began with an attack upon the censorship of plays; Shaw and Granville-Barker were among the playwrights whose plays were forbidden public performance. Galsworthy was urged to organize a protest by the leading writers of the day. He brought in Gilbert Murray and Barrie to aid him, and handled the thing so effectively that the Prime Minister was compelled to receive a deputation, a Parliamentary Committee was conceded, and a private bill was introduced into the Commons.

It is true that the agitation did not succeed. More than half a century was to elapse before the English stage censorship was abolished. But it gave Galsworthy a taste of the power he could exert with his pen in public affairs. He had, he found, as important an influence as any well-known politician or lawyer. This discovery set him on a career, parallel to authorship, of active campaigning to right wrongs and abuses. He fought for the reform of the divorce law (his dearest cause), for the establishment of a minimum wage in sweated industries, for votes for women, for clearance of the slums and for much else—even for a ban on docking horses' tails, another cause dear to him, for all his life he was devoted to horses, as well as to dogs.

He fought always with the dignity that was natural to him, and never expressed an opinion that was not widely respected. His emergence as a publicist of importance probably did more than his success as a writer to erase any memory of the divorce scandal and to reinstate Galsworthy and his wife in respectable society. The Forsytes, whom he had so bitterly attacked, took him back into their midst. For Ada's sake, he did not demur. His next novel, *The Country House* (1907), was again satirical of the well-to-do, but the satire was gentler, and the book was praised everywhere. And although the satire waned still further in each of his two succeeding novels about "the English upper crust," their sales successively improved.

His greatest success, however, came in the theater. That was where his literary status was confirmed in the years before the outbreak of World War I. He wrote two plays that dealt with two of the most controversial public topics of that time. *Strife* (1909) was about the worsening industrial relations between employers and workers. "He has done more than write a play," declared the London *Times*. "He has rendered a public service."

*Justice* (1910), the second play, rendered such service with even greater force. Galsworthy had chanced to visit the grim long-sentence prison on Dartmoor and had been so distressed at what he saw that he rushed into a campaign to abolish the horrors of solitary confinement, then obligatory for all convicts. The play, depicting the agony of a man alone in his cell, was the peak of the campaign. On the first night the audience stayed shouting in the theater until midnight. Winston Churchill, then Home

Secretary, was so moved by the play that he set about exploring the whole question of punishment for crime in England; the reforms he then carried through did not abolish solitary confinement, but reduced it to a maximum of three months instead of nine. It is difficult to think of any other polemical play which achieved so much.

Between 1910 and 1914 Galsworthy wrote four more major plays which were successfully staged in both England and America, where his reputation was by then almost as high. The novel *The Dark Flower* (1915), was a curiosity. In part it told once again the story of his relationship with an unhappily-married woman, but no longer as a protest against society. It had become a straightforward, sensuous account of a passion. He could no longer rage against a world that had received his work so warmly, accorded him a position of respect, and accepted his wife back into the company of honorable women.

That Ada was less reconciled seems probable from her intensifying hypochondria, through which Galsworthy tended her with extraordinary care and devotion. Whatever she wanted he at once supplied. When she was ill, he became sickroom nurse. When the weather turned cold, he dutifully took her to winter in a warmer climate. In the smallest things she must always be placated. When one of his nephews happened to beat her at a game of billiards, Galsworthy at once took him aside to warn him that "in this house Aunty always wins."

The last part of *The Dark Flower,* so largely autobiographical, hints broadly that an artist, such as Galsworthy himself, might sometimes wander into transient love passages with younger women; and probably there was something in it. But it made no difference to his devotion to Ada. Indeed, she made sure it should not. At the least suspicion she headed straight for her sickbed, and Galsworthy was recalled to duty again.

The outbreak of war in 1914 was an immense horror for Galsworthy. So it was, of course, for most people as the fearful slaughter multiplied and the years dragged by. But for him it was a horror from the first moment. He never experienced the jingo excitements. On the first day he wrote in his diary: "The horror of the thing keeps coming over one in waves; and all happiness has gone out of life." He was too old to fight, although a few months before the end of the war in 1918 he was called up, then rejected as totally unfit for military service. The only physical service he managed to perform was to work for a few months in a military hospital in France, massaging the convalescent wounded; Ada went with him and managed the hospital's linen.

At the end of 1917 he was offered, and quickly refused, a knighthood. Between letters and such honors there could be no liaison, he cried. In fact, the honor was gazetted before his refusal had time to arrive, but he insisted it be withdrawn. As Thomas Hardy somewhat maliciously remarked, he had scored both ways; the honor of a knighthood and the honor of having refused a knighthood. The whole thing deeply distressed Galsworthy, who was certainly not seeking publicity, least of all during the grimmest months of his country's agony in war.

The only written thing of significance to emerge from him during the war was a short-story collection, *Five Tales* (1918), and in this book there appeared "Indian Summer of a Forsyte." At the end of *The Man of Property,* in the days of Galsworthy's rage at society over Ada, he had left Irene Forsyte in Soames's house, the tragic wife seemingly doomed to live out her life chained to the husband she loathed.

But that was twelve years earlier. Galsworthy now no longer wished to satirize the society which had taken him and Ada back into its highest favor. So in this short story, which was in effect an epilogue to the novel, Irene left Soames on that same night on which the novel had ended—left him for good, started to cultivate new relationships with the Forsytes, and particularly with Old Jolyon, whose gentle death in the garden of Robin Hill marks the conclusion of the tale. The satire of the novel was thus ingeniously softened into sentiment.

Three days after it was published, Galsworthy realized the implication of this. The short tale, which buried all the former anger, enabled him to go on writing about the Forsytes. The idea came to him on a Sunday afternoon in July 1918, sitting on the lawn of the Devon farmhouse which he still rented. He would make *The Man Of Property* the first volume of a trilogy about the Forsytes. He would call it *The Forsyte Saga* (a title he had first considered for the original novel, then discarded). It would be a work of nearly half a million words—"the most sustained and considerable piece of fiction of our generation at least. . . . But shall I ever bring it off?"

He not only brought off the trilogy of *The Forsyte Saga,* but a second trilogy, *A Modern Comedy* (1929), in which he brought the Forsyte family forward into the post-war years; the two trilogies were then grouped together as *The Forsyte Chronicles.* He wrote these six novels steadily throughout the 1920s wherever he might be—in London, in Devon, at the huge house he later bought in Sussex, on lecture tours in the United States, or on the inevitable winter ramblings in search of sunshine and mild climate for

Ada. He refused to allow her to spend a winter in England, being convinced that her health would not stand the English winter weather, so that some half of every year was for him peripatetic, a mode of life he detested. (After his death, Ada never left England, and she outlived him by twenty-two years.)

He broke off from the novels from time to time to write plays. In six years he wrote seven plays, three of which—*The Skin Game, Loyalties,* and *Escape*—were the greatest theatrical successes of the day in both London and New York. And when, at the end of the second Forsyte trilogy, *A Modern Comedy,* he at last killed off Soames, he started on, and completed just before his own death, a third trilogy about a related family.

Is *The Forsyte Chronicles* one of the great English novels? Was the judgment of the Nobel judges sound?

Forty years after Galsworthy's death it begins to look as though the answer is "yes." For all its faults, the long Forsyte story has the indefinable quality of life. Its characters have stepped out from the books into familiar English use, in the way that, for example, Becky Sharp, or Scrooge, or Sherlock Holmes have, and almost no other fictional characters have during the twentieth century. This was oddly demonstrated in the late 1960s when, after years of copyright difficulties, *The Forsyte Chronicles* was faithfully translated into a television serial. It instantly fascinated many millions of viewers in many countries; so powerfully that, for instance, the hour of Evensong was advanced in some English parishes to allow worshipers to get home in time for the Sunday evening instalment of the Forsytes.

---

Dudley Barker is a British journalist, biographer, and author of *The Man of Principle: A View of John Galsworthy.*

# THE 1932 PRIZE

## By GUNNAR AHLSTRÖM

In 1932 the candidates for the Prize mentioned by the press included such French veterans as Paul Bourget and J.-H. Rosny and, most notably, the French Academy's official candidate, Paul Valéry. Valéry had visited Stockholm in 1931, and his chances now seemed favorable.

Still another candidate had support on a worldwide scale. On January 11, the Swedish Academy received a voluminous petition in favor of the American writer Upton Sinclair. A special committee, headed by some twenty eminent personalities including John Dewey, William McDougall, Albert Einstein, Harold Laski, and Bertrand Russell, had been set up to promote his cause. Its secretariat in New York had done its work well and collected the imposing total of 770 names from fifty-five countries and territories.

This worldwide movement had little chance of success for two reasons: America had only recently had a laureate in the personage of Sinclair Lewis; and the radical opinions of the proposed candidate were not calculated to appeal to the Academy. Little hope could be held out for Maxim Gorki either even though his reputation was solidly established at the time—he was more or less a Soviet showpiece—and his name was put forward by left-wing Swedish writers. When their efforts proved unsuccessful, his partisans organized a demonstration of sympathy as had been done for Tolstoy in 1901.

From the beginning of the year, however, it was assumed that it would be England's turn.

Swinburne, until his death in 1909, had been the official English candidate. He was followed by Thomas Hardy, who was recommended by his fellow countrymen with equal persistence. But, as in the case of Swinburne, the Swedish Academy overlooked this literary giant, and he died in 1928. As the years passed, English-speaking Prizewinners like Yeats and Shaw were considered Irish. So the only Englishman to receive the Prize by 1932 was Kipling (1908). When St. John Ervine, a well-known British writer of the time, visited Stockholm in 1931, he was asked in an interview what he thought of the Nobel Prize. He frankly declared that, since its award to Sinclair Lewis, nobody in English literary circles was particularly disposed to accept it.

While this was certainly an overstatement, Stockholm had to bow to the evidence that the Nobel Prize aroused little interest in England. The Nobel Foundation could pride itself on enjoying enormous prestige in France and Germany but not in England. What was front-page news in Paris and Berlin was, if mentioned at all in London, tucked away at the bottom of a column.

Nevertheless, England had a plethora of suitable candidates who were not only men of considerable literary achievement but had the aging charm and the greying temples that went so well with the Prize. They included G. K. Chesterton, Arnold Bennett, H. G. Wells, John Galsworthy, and E. M. Forster as well as younger figures such as Robert Graves, D. H. Lawrence, Aldous Huxley, and T. S. Eliot who were, as yet, appreciated only by a discriminating few.

Galsworthy was proposed by Professor Henrik Schuck of the Academy. The most formidable rival was H. G. Wells, who was perhaps superior to him both in intellectual vitality and social purpose. What tipped the scales in Galsworthy's favor was the artistic finish of his work and his cultured, gentlemanly demeanor. He had visited Stockholm as chairman of the PEN club and had been their most eminent spokesman. Awarding him the Prize would be a way of paying tribute to the literary internationalism to which he had devoted himself with such impeccable urbanity. And, on November 10, 1932, it was duly decided that he should have it.

The English papers were, as usual, niggardly in their comments. In an interview, Galsworthy expressed his pleasure at the award and stated his intention of going to Stockholm to take part in the ceremony. Unfortunately, illness obliged him to join the large body of Prizewinners *in absentia*. But he was aware, particularly from his wide sales in the Scandinavian countries, of his considerable popularity in that part of the world, and of an admiration much more warmhearted than might be inferred from the grudging appraisal of the citation awarding him the Nobel Prize for 1932 "for his distinguished art of narration, which takes its highest form in *The Forsyte Saga*."

---

Translated by Helga Harrison.